READINGS IN
SCIENCE EDUCATION
FOR THE
ELEMENTARY
SCHOOL

EDWARD VICTOR

Professor of Science Education
Northwestern University

&

MARJORIE S. LERNER

Principal, Donoghue Elementary School
Chicago, Illinois

READINGS IN
SCIENCE EDUCATION
FOR THE
ELEMENTARY
SCHOOL

THE MACMILLAN COMPANY, NEW YORK
COLLIER-MACMILLAN LIMITED, LONDON

First Printing

Library of Congress catalog card number: 67–13603

THE MACMILLAN COMPANY, NEW YORK
COLLIER-MACMILLAN CANADA, LTD., TORONTO, ONTARIO

Printed in the United States of America

PREFACE

This book has been produced with two purposes in mind. First, the current widespread interest and activity in elementary science is rapidly producing new developments in several directions. So much is being written today about issues, problems, practices, current thinking, innovations, and trends in elementary science that it is difficult to read all the literature, digest it, and separate the wheat from the chaff. A book of selected readings makes it possible to include under one cover the key articles that will give a clear picture of what is happening in elementary science today.

Second, it is a common practice for instructors of the methods course in elementary science to distribute reading lists and require outside reading. With today's large enrollments in our colleges and universities, the assignment of articles to be read places a heavy burden on the students and on the already overtaxed library facilities. The demand for the periodicals which contain these articles becomes great, and the students must wait their turn to obtain them. A book of readings eliminates this problem and makes the articles readily accessible to each student.

A book of readings in elementary science has several worthwhile features:

1. It can familiarize the student with the professional journals that are concerned with education and the teaching of science.
2. It can introduce the student to a comprehensive sample of the best thinking in elementary science today.
3. It can acquaint the student with points of view of other persons besides the instructor and the author of the textbook used in the course.

v

4. It can present a number of different positions which have been taken on controversial topics.
5. It can be used either as a basic text or as a supplementary text.
6. It can be especially helpful in late afternoon, evening, Saturday, or summer courses, where the in-service teachers who take the course are hard pressed to find enough time to locate the articles in the campus library and to read them.

This book is concerned not only with current thinking and practices in elementary science, but with innovations and changes as well. Consequently, high priority was given to the selection of recent articles, especially those published since 1960. One or two older articles have been included only because they had something valuable to offer.

The book is organized into sections which correspond closely to the topics that are usually taken up in a methods course in elementary science. The first five sections deal with the role of science in the elementary school, the objectives of elementary science, planning and organizing the science program, methods and innovations in teaching elementary science, evaluation of both science learning and the science program, and the need for adequate materials and facilities for elementary science.

The remaining three sections should be of special interest to both the student and the instructor. Section 6 takes up the pre-service and in-service science training of elementary teachers, and shows how the school administrator, the state, and the federal government can play a leadership role in improving science education in the schools. It describes the need for science supervision and lists the qualifications and functions of the science supervisor. Section 7 presents in detail the thinking of scientists, science educators, and psychologists who are concerned with inquiry and process in the learning of science. Section 8 describes the major experimental curriculum study projects that are currently working on the development of improved elementary science programs.

We wish to express our appreciation and thanks to the authors, publishers, organizations, and institutions who gave us permission to reprint the material that appears in this book.

E. V.
M. S. L.

CONTENTS

READINGS IN
SCIENCE EDUCATION
FOR THE
ELEMENTARY
SCHOOL

THE ROLE OF SCIENCE IN THE
ELEMENTARY SCHOOL

INTRODUCTION

Science is a comparative newcomer to the elementary school curriculum, although its roots can be traced back a hundred years or more. In the latter part of the nineteenth century, children were introduced to object study, where both animate and inanimate objects were observed and described. In the early part of the twentieth century, nature study became very popular in many elementary schools.

However, there is general agreement that elementary science really began around 1930 with the growth of a movement to teach all areas of science in the elementary school and to make science a dynamic and integral part of the elementary school curriculum. This movement grew rather slowly, but steadily, gaining support throughout the country.

In the past ten years two phenomena have taken place which have given the movement tremendous impetus and rapid growth. First, the vast and almost explosive scientific and technological revolution in our midst has produced a fantastic growth of scientific knowledge in all areas of science, and this wealth of knowledge is now exerting an effect on all of science education. Second, the impact of the satellite Sputnik succeeded in arousing the concern of scientists, science educators, teachers, administrators, the public in general, and the government in the kind and amount of science being taught and learned in our schools. As a result, there is widespread interest and activity in elementary (as well as secondary) science today. There is also unanimous agreement on a strong K-12 science sequence in our schools, and on a well-developed science program in the elementary school as part of this sequence.

An effective science program can play an important role in the elementary school. It can add to the child's store of knowledge about himself, his environment, and his world. It can give the child an insight into the structure of science, enabling the child to learn key concepts, conceptual schemes, and their relationships to each other.

1

It can help the child live successfully in a changing world by showing that our universe is based upon change. Learning about change in science, and how to cope with change, will help the child react more intelligently to the changes he may expect in his future.

Elementary science can play an important role in helping the child learn the nature of scientific inquiry and the key operations, or processes, of science and of the scientist. A program based on inquiry and process will encourage real learning to take place, not the memorization of facts. The child will be encouraged to think critically and to develop scientific attitudes and skills.

The very nature of an effective science program makes it possible to offer a wide variety of learning activities and experiences which can provide for the individual differences in ability, interest, and need that all children have. The science program lends itself very well to individual learning, making it possible for each child to develop to the limit of his capacity.

Finally, the science program can be correlated very effectively with other programs in the elementary school curriculum. Learning is always more effective when all phases of the curriculum are integrated. There are many opportunities in the elementary school to correlate science with mathematics, language arts, social studies, and the creative arts.

SCIENCE AS A WAY OF LIFE*

Ellsworth S. Obourn

Ellsworth S. Obourn expresses concern that adults today are surrounded by all that science and technology bring to human life, yet so many of these adults remain scientifically illiterate. He decries the fact that too few of us use science as a way of life; too few use its attitudes, its modes of thought, its philosophy, its strategy, and its tactics as determinants of human behavior. The product and the process of science must not be separated if science is to serve each individual in our culture.

D ID YOU read the paper this morning or listen to a newscast? It would be uncommon not to encounter news about science: a new discovery or a new application of an earlier discovery; further research into water pollution, water fluoridation, air safety, radioactive fallout; the latest advances in rocketry or in other fields that, a mere ten years ago, may have been of little concern or even unknown.

This year, 1961, is in the Atom-Space Age. Many things that were science fiction only yesterday are becoming realities today. Back in the lifetime of millions of adults, this earth was plodding along in the horse-and-buggy era. In one average life-span, we have been moved rapidly through the ages of the airplane and the jet; from the age of creative chemistry into the age of synthetics and beyond to the age of atomic fission and nuclear fusion. Today we stand on the threshold of the age of space.

Terrestrial time and space have been conquered and the shackles of gravitation have been loosened. Wake up, Americans! Open your eyes! Look about you! Have you taken full note of science? Interwoven with technology, science surrounds you. It confronts you every hour. It permeates almost everything you do. You find its products wherever your pathway leads. It clothes you, feeds you, shelters you, transports you, and enables you to communicate your thoughts to others. It has lengthened your life-span and has mitigated and lessened your illnesses and sufferings. It has extended your intellectual frontiers to include space both near and far.

But science must never be regarded merely as the control of nature. Science is a subtle thing: It is part product and part process, part control and part

---

* REPRINTED FROM *Science as a Way of Life*, U.S. Office of Education, Document OE-29023, 1961, pp. 1–16. Dr. Obourn has been Specialist for Science at the U.S. Office of Education.

understanding. And these two entities are bound inextricably together in the true image of science.

It has been said that the opportunity to understand things of fundamental and permanent importance is what makes the pursuit of science fascinating and worthwhile. As noted earlier, science and technology are interdependent. The only way to make significant advances in technology, whether in engineering, medicine, agriculture, or other applied science, is first to understand the basic principles of pure science. Technology without science is incomplete and science without technology is inconclusive.

Science and technology have given America the Midas touch—we live virtually in a wonderland they have created, where almost any material thing that anyone could desire can be produced.

As technology advances in the wake of new scientific discoveries, it produces new jobs and makes some older ones obsolete. It provides new ways whereby we may enjoy the added leisure hours resulting from the reduced hours of labor that it brings. Over the years science and technology have brought us the automobile, the record player, the radio, the motion picture, and the television set—to name only a few of the many things they have provided for our hours of relaxation.

And there is more to come. Scientists predict that we are only on the threshold of undreamed things to come. They say that the human life-span may be longer in the future and that man may live more than a hundred years. They envision the day when the waters of the earth may possibly provide us with a supply of energy that will be practically inexhaustible and will be used to make the deserts bloom and produce food.

Perhaps the day may dawn when man will really explore the distant bodies in space. If he is able to overcome outer space, it will be the fulfillment of a dream of the ages and will be possible only because of science and technology.

THE OLD ORDER CHANGETH

Despite the rapidity with which science has advanced, its achievements have engulfed our lives so gradually that millions of people are almost totally unaware of the new world—the new culture—in which we live, a culture based on science. We have drifted along with the stream of change. Almost without realizing it we adapted ourselves to the moving picture, and again we did so when radio, and then television appeared. Vaguely conscious of change, we have moved from the horse and buggy to the jet. Many of us are still groping about as though under the spell of some magic drug, but all the while science is constantly altering our lives.

FOR WHAT? HOW WELL? HOW LONG?

It is easy to accept benefits coming to us from new advances in science. These make our work hours easier, dispel our suffering, and provide more leisure time—but for what? *Do we really live* in this scientific world of ours? How well do we live? Is it possible that what we think of as full and abundant living is only a mirage and that perhaps we do little more than just flounder in a vast sea of scientific gadgets surrounded by ignorance and scientific illiteracy? How may we determine just how far up we can reach—how nearly have we achieved the fullest realization of living with the abundance that science and technology have given to us? Do we take them for granted? Do we understand all that science can do for us? How many adults use *science as a way of life*? That is, how many use its attitudes, its modes of thought, its appreciations, its philosophy, its strategy, and its tactics as determinants of behavior?

The Challenges of Today

Among the deepest aspirations of man is his longing to know, as far as possible, the real meaning of life: its purposes, its greatness, its splendors. Today perhaps more than ever, man desires to acquire real knowledge of himself, his world, and his relationship to the vast universe of which he is so small a part. He wishes to attain the intellectual levels necessary for understanding life's problems. He wants to secure the technical and scientific knowledge that will enable him to make the fullest use of his opportunities; and finally he yearns to achieve, in this new milieu of science, a satisfying success.

During this era of vast intellectual activity and achievement in science, we are evaluating the past in the light of the present and interpreting it anew in an effort to extend our thinking into an unpredictable and uncertain future. Great changes are taking place in human thought and society. New movements are being organized and put into operation. Our Nation and others are struggling to survive. Never was the life of man more serious, more precarious, or more challenging. The entire world is having its knowledge, its way of life, its power, and its resources tested. In every nation the wisdom of the common man as well as that of the intellectual leader is challenged to solve day-to-day problems.

These are the inevitable and inescapable challenges that present themselves to the people of America and the people of the world in this Era of Science.

The New Frontier

Ever since the mists of antiquity dissolved and early man emerged with a little mastery over some aspects of his environment, by means of the axe, the spear, the lever, and the wheel, he has been an inventor and a producer of things. Today we live our lives surrounded by the gadgets and gimmicks that are the products of science. In many ways it is to these that we are indebted for our modern standards of living. But these are only a part of what science can give us.

Science is a strange and baffling complex: it is part intellectual and part practical. Both are elements of a single whole. The new knowledge and inventions coming from science are the result of the processes of the human intellect. They have been conceived first in the mind of a scientist or inventor. If science is to yield its maximum potentials to each individual in the culture which it has produced, these two aspects—the product and the process—must not be separated.

But since the earliest days, man has exploited the wheel and the lever, the axe and the spear in the worship of the material products of science. Mostly, however, man has neglected to seek and fully cultivate its processes, its modes of thought, its attitudes, its philosophy. These are the elements which could emancipate the mind and make man the true master rather than the servant of the giant which he has created.

To see the evidences of this gap between product and process, we have only to look at the lag that has existed through the ages. From the earliest times, man has been beset by fear and superstition. His life has been insecure and he has been the prey of charlatans and practitioners of cults of magic. These we are prone to associate with more ancient times when man was frightened by lightning and thunder, and comet and eclipse.

We would like to think that modern man has progressed far beyond those days when ignorance of natural phenomena made him attempt to solve the problems arising from that ignorance by consulting fortune tellers, sorcerers, and medicine men, and imploring the help of multitudinous gods.

Coming up to the present, what can be said about the ordinary ways in which the average man thinks? What of his attitudes and appreciations? Does he pursue the processes of science? Does he use its tactics and strategy to fullest advantage in the more enlightened scientific culture in which he lives? These are the questions to be answered in an adequate evaluation of how much science education contributes to solving man's day-to-day problems.

The place of science in the lives of people has been summed up eloquently in the following words:

Science is a human enterprise. It directly involves multitudes of extremely worthwhile people, from scientists through physicist, engineer, teacher, and writer. But no less directly are all people involved in science. They eat, wear clothes, and travel in and communicate through the products of science (and technology). Their judgments and beliefs are conditioned by what they learn of science and the scientific process. There is scarcely an issue, whether it be a political, social, or economic one, that does not in some way involve science.

The behavior of people is marked by the process of science. It influences the extent to which they are self-directing and self-reliant—and the extent to which they seek and arrive at rational decisions to issues and effective solutions to problems. This science-influence behavior applies to society and also to individuals. While not necessarily being creative in the more profound sense, all individuals can profit by using the methods and attitudes of science in finding needed information and in seeking solutions to life's multitude of problems. In this sense, every man could be his own scientist—his own problem solver. He could use the process and the product of the scientific enterprise to be a more competent individual and a more responsible citizen, to live life more abundantly, and to understand better his own place in time and in space, in life and in thought.

To assure advances in basic science, to maintain our standard of living, and to safeguard the national security, a scientifically literate citizen is indispensable. Because of the place of science in the culture of our times and its impact on the personal lives of people it becomes imperative that science have a prominent place in every level of education.[1]

A Closer View

For a moment, let us place the organism we call "Mr. Average American" under the microscope and try to examine in an objective way some aspects of his behavior. Perhaps one of the most sensitive barometers registering his cultural or intellectual interests is commercial television. Here the programs are largely matched to the interests of the viewing public.

Among too many people superstition, fear, and unfounded belief are commonplace. Almost no American city is free from practitioners of such occult trades as palmistry, phrenology, and numerology. Many thousand copies are sold every month of magazines devoted to astrology, and many otherwise sophisticated newspapers continue to print a daily horoscope. Dream books, charms, ouija boards, and other gadgets of modern sorcery are sold to many gullible individuals.

Millions of our people are preyed upon by unscrupulous charlatans who dispense fads and cure-alls. More than a billion dollars are wasted annually in the pursuit of health from poorly trained practitioners and through products of questionable value.

Many more examples could be cited to document the point that in some ways the behavior patterns of many people are not so scientific as we'd like to believe. In this world that depends so much upon science and technology, our literacy in those fields may be lower than it should be. The time to ponder this situation and to remedy it is not tomorrow, but today.

Science Education: A Hope and an Imperative

A generation ago Alfred North Whitehead of Harvard University made a prophetic statement. He said:

In the conditions of modern life, the rule is absolute, the race which does not value trained intelligence is doomed. Not all your heroism, not all your social charm, not all your wit, not all your victories on land or at sea, can move back the finger of fate. Today we maintain ourselves. Tomorrow science will have moved

[1] National Science Teachers Association, *Planning for Quality in High School Science* (Committee Report). Washington: The Association, 1961.

forward yet one more step and there will be no appeal from the judgment which will then be pronounced on the uneducated.[2]

These words were prophetic because they brought into clear focus a problem which has faced education in general, and science education in particular, for more than two hundred years. The problem is: What, exactly, constitutes an education that is adequate to meet the challenges of the modern scientific culture? What must be done to make certain that our schools will produce more and better trained young men and women to become the scientists of tomorrow—trained and inspired to make the breakthroughs that can help secure both the economic and military leadership of America for the decades ahead? What must every school district in America face up to if its schools are to turn out young men and women having the necessary level of scientific literacy to cope with the new culture? These are the questions which should have been faced when Dr. Whitehead made his prophetic statement. Today, more than thirty years farther down the road, the prophecy has come true and still we have not faced the problems squarely. Today we stand at the cross roads—the alternative routes are clear. Our schools must teach science so that it becomes a *way of life* for all pupils, or these pupils, when they get out into the world, will be unable to cope with the problems which that world will thrust upon them.

For more than a century, education in America has proceeded to an unfortunate degree on the assumption that a mind crammed with facts about science is an educated mind. Most of our methods and our materials of instruction have been predicated upon this assumption and have been guided by the mistaken magic in the phrase "knowledge is power."

In pursuit of this knowledge goal, the profession of science education has done a most commendable job. In every list of objectives prepared for science you will find a knowledge goal. The basic conceptual understandings of science have been identified, analyzed, and organized into discrete learning elements. Some progress has been made, also, toward assigning these elements to specific levels of the educative process.

Effective techniques for teaching and learning these concepts have been developed. Textbooks have been written and teaching aids, in infinite numbers and varieties, have been invented. Perhaps in the years ahead some phases of the teaching-learning process may be accomplished with the help of machines. For the most part, education in science has kept pace with the advancing frontiers of knowledge as new concepts related to space, atomic energy, earth science, and other areas have been introduced into existing courses.

It is conceivable that this country's high level of achievement in making available the material products of science has been due, at least in part, to

2 Whitehead, Alfred N. *The Aims of Education and Other Essays.* New York: The Macmillan Company, 1929.

the high degree of devotion which we have given to mastering science and technology. For over two centuries there has been little basic change in our goal and only incidental changes have occurred in our methods for attaining the goal.

Even though we have achieved much in this respect we still have not reached perfection, especially with the average product of our schools. The average pupil, it seems, has failed to gain a sufficient level of scientific understanding to make science a way of life for him.

Undoubtedly, we need some new and fresh approaches toward the subject matter of science for understanding. We need much more imaginative thinking than heretofore—more creative techniques for penetrating pupils' minds. Only thus will pupils truly master the facts, principles, and concepts of science to become fully operative in their lives.

Whitehead [3] implied another meaning by his use of the term "uneducated" in science. In our great concern to disseminate the knowledge or content component of science, we have neglected to teach its philosophy, its strategy, and its tactics. These aspects of science are the ones which the schools must also teach if science is to become a way of life with all people.

The fabric of science is woven from a warp that is knowledge and a woof that is process. No hypothesis or theory was ever created and no fact, principle, or concept of science was ever established apart from the intellectual processes of some scientist. This is a fundamental tenet and must be attended to by those who prepare teachers of science if changes in our young people are to be effected. Everyone who stands before a class as a teacher of science must be guided by this principle, even as those in the medical profession are guided by the ancient Hippocratic oath. In the teaching-learning relationship *science product* may not be separated from *science process* lest the fabric be weakened.

A mind filled only with the facts, principles, and concepts of science is void of the richness of attitudes, modes of thought, appreciations, and deep abiding interests which make up in part the process discovering the facts, principles, and concepts. As we go forward into the Age of Science with its new and pervasive culture, it is essential that our teachers be trained to teach the processes of science along with its product. Process goals can be analyzed into elements in much the same manner that the concepts have been analyzed. First, we need to know what constitutes such abilities as defining a problem, hypothesizing, interpreting, generalizing, and applying. We need to know too more exactly what it is that constitutes a scientific attitude or appreciation: how the scientist weighs and evaluates evidence and how he arrives at the strategy or tactic that enables him to solve a problem.

These matters are complex ones; they should engage the research and attention of our most competent scholars. We need prolonged classroom research to develop expert methods for teaching the process of science.

[3] *Ibid.*

If our future citizens are to achieve full competence in using the processes of science, they must be confronted in the classroom, day after day, with appropriate preplanned learning situations. These situations must be planned and presented as rigorously as those for the mastery of facts, concepts, and principles. How does one learn to identify problems, to observe with discrimination, to hypothesize, to distinguish good from questionable evidence, to sort fact from assumption, to make reasonable interpretations from evidence, and to generalize? Only by continuous practice in actual situations.

Perhaps one reason that adults do not generally use the conceptual understandings of science in their day-to-day living is because they have acquired the concepts apart from the processes by means of which the concepts were established. Mastery of the facts and principles of science is essential to learning its processes: they are the tools of thought and the key which unlocks and opens the doors that lead to the attainment of intellectual richness. No one can have an attitude except toward *something specific*. A science problem must be defined about *some specific fact* or principle of science. Evidence is made up of facts. When interpretations of data are made it is again the facts and principles of science that are being interpreted. Thus, science content that is learned along with the processes becomes much more meaningful and important than content mastered only as an end in itself. Knowledge of science becomes the *sine qua non* for learning science processes.

In this matter of science as hope and imperative for the future of America, it is not only the voices of the educator and the philosopher that are being heard, but also the voice of the industrialist. And their three voices are as one, giving the same message. Thus, not long ago, one great American industrialist said the following words:

Carefully planned training in how to think critically and how to develop desirable attitudes, appreciations, and judgments of value should prove invaluable to the student himself and to society as a whole. To the student because his later success may depend largely upon his ability to solve the problems confronting him in his daily life and occupation. To society because, directly or indirectly, it benefits from the ability of human beings to think clearly and to distinguish truth from error. One of the most valuable skills any person can possess is the ability to reason successfully and thus discover truth. That more and more people should possess this ability, leading as it does to the advancement of civilization, has been, and doubtless will continue to be, one of the paramount needs of the world.

The kind of reasoning and critical thought which has done most to advance human knowledge is that kind employed by research in the sciences. The scientific achievements of the past several centuries clearly demonstrate these methods to be the most reliable now known. In today's fierce competition among Nations, a competition possibly deciding our survival, that Nation will probably be best prepared to endure which can muster from its citizens the greatest number who can think critically and solve new problems as they arise.

Training young people in the intellectual skills of problem solving is absolutely imperative. The solution of the problems of this and the next generation, our progress—indeed, the very survival of our way of life—could well depend upon the ability of our citizens to think coherently and to find truth. Let us not conceive of education only in terms of its duty to transmit to our children the cultural heritage achieved by mankind throughout past ages; let us conceive of it also in terms of its equal duty to equip our children to go forward from where the past generation has left off.

And finally, I say, education must pass on the heritage, but that heritage becomes more meaningful when in addition it has the intellectual basis for going on.

THE TASK AHEAD

Science and science education have come in for a great deal of criticism in recent years. Many believe that the present emphasis on science and mathematics is creating a distortion and imbalance in the school program. It is, of course, extremely important that we keep balance in the education of our young people. Certainly science should receive only its fair share of talented pupils graduating from our high schools. We do need humanists, artists, musicians, poets, writers, and lawyers. We need them desperately, but they can exist only if our way of life is kept intact. If this is threatened or taken from us because of lack of emphasis on science and technology then we have lost everything.

Moreover, today the artist, the musician, the poet, the writer, and the lawyer have no alternative but to live in a world dominated by the concepts and applied principles of science. To move and vote and eat and sleep—in short, just to exist in that world means that each individual must be scientifically literate. This seems to demand that every citizen have a basic and functional understanding of the products of science—the concepts, the principles and the facts; and be able to understand and use the process of science—the modes of thought, the attitudes of mind, the tactics and strategy, and the appreciations. With regard to appreciations, Dr. C. P. Snow recently said:

Anyone who has ever worked in any science knows how much esthetic joy he has obtained. That is, in the actual *activity* of science, in the process of making a discovery, however humble it is, one can't help feeling an awareness of beauty. The subjective experience, the esthetic satisfaction, seems exactly the same as the satisfaction one gets from writing a poem or a novel, or composing a piece of music. I don't think anyone has succeeded in distinguishing between them. The literature of scientific discovery is full of this esthetic joy. These are prime requisites for effective living in the world of today. Science must become, as it were, *a way of life* with every citizen.[4]

This goal can be achieved through the schools in every hamlet and city across the Nation. It can be realized, however, only as it is initiated by local effort and grows up from the grass roots. It must have the support of every

[4] Snow, Charles P. "Appreciations in Science." *Science.* 133: 256–259. January 27, 1961.

citizen in every local community. It will require a concerted and organized effort, but these costs are low when weighed against the realization that this kind of education in science may be basic to our survival.

THE LIBERAL EDUCATION
VALUES OF SCIENCE *

Morris Kline

In this article Morris Kline describes how science contributes to the liberal education of the child. Three key components make up this liberal education: knowledge, a rational spirit, and an appreciation of esthetic and emotional values. The author also makes a strong plea for teaching the cultural values of science. In his discussion science is described as encompassing pure science, technology, and mathematics. He finds strong unity in these three fields, even though their immediate goals may be different.

A LIBERAL education imparts the knowledge, beliefs, law, customs, and mores which our civilization possesses. However, it is not the purely factual knowledge but the significance of that knowledge that matters. The goal is wisdom. A liberal education also produces a state of mind. It trains the intellect by inculcating a critical attitude, independence of mind, open-mindedness or a mind open to change, a reasoned approach to problems, a willingness to look at facts either as a test of beliefs or as support for beliefs, and a sympathy for strange ideas. It imparts the ability to rise above one's age and to examine critically the presuppositions of one's age. I shall use the word rationalism to stand for all these qualities. Thus, in brief, a liberal education teaches rationalism. The third factor in a liberal education is an appreciation of the creations that satisfy emotional and esthetic needs. Art, music, religion, and literature are among the creations that cater to these needs. In discussing the liberal education values of science, I shall concentrate on those which can be taught to young people.

---

* REPRINTED FROM *The Science Teacher*, Vol. 32, No. 8, November 1965, pp. 22–24. Copyright, 1965, by the National Science Teachers Association, Washington, D.C. Reprinted by permission of the author and the publisher. Dr. Kline is Professor of Mathematics at New York University.

There is a unity of mathematics, science, and technology which is sufficiently strong that, for the purposes of this discussion, I shall use the word science to embrace all three fields. I am not recommending that we confuse the three. Their immediate goals are different; funds for basic research must be distinguished from funds for development; the individual temperament must play a role in the individual's choice of his own specialty.

Pure science to satisfy intellectual curiosity is not enough. Science is to be used, not for the narrow purpose of making money, but in behalf of mankind. Science is a river with two sources, the practical and the esthetic, and neither is nobler nor more fruitful than the other. If anything, technology is the fruit of science.

SCIENCE PROPER IS PART OF A LIBERAL EDUCATION

The knowledge which science offers is as much a part of our culture as literature and painting. That the two have become separated and that we speak of science and culture as though they were fields apart are the result of historic factors which I cannot take up here. But we should not allow ourselves to be confused or influenced by current misconceptions.

The knowledge that science offers is weighty and interesting knowledge. Our astronomy tells us the scheme by which we make sense of the grandest spectacle in nature. The phenomena of light and sound are with us almost at every moment, and surely we should like to know about such prevalent and necessary phenomena. Biology gives us knowledge of the structure of our bodies; and psychology, of our own drives, fears, anxieties, memory, and emotions. Science answers basic questions man raises about a world which is more immediate to him than foreign countries, ancient history, and even the government in Washington.

Science makes available practical knowledge. Science is man's weapon to cope with nature and the weaknesses in his own body. Science helps us to use the minerals of the earth, to improve agriculture and the husbandry of animals, and to fight diseases of the body. More generally put, science is the organization of our knowledge which enables us to command nature and the potential in nature.

But scientific knowledge *per se* is not by any means the be-all and end-all of the educational role of science—in fact, the values of science which transcend mere knowledge are more significant than the factual information.

A liberal education develops a state of mind which for brevity I have tried to describe by the word rational but which encompasses a critical outlook, a skeptical attitude, a willingness to face facts, the insistence on evidence to back up beliefs or assertions, an ability to rise above the prejudices of the herd and idols of the tribe, a reliance upon the mind, independence of thought, open-mindedness, weighing of evidence and other qualities I mentioned earlier. If I were to single out the greatest contribution of science to culture I would emphasize the inculcation of this rational spirit.

Each of these elements of the rational spirit can be learned through science education; for example:

Science teaches us how to think. There are various methodologies of thinking in science. The experimental method teaches how to look for a cause-and-effect sequence by isolating the cause and effect. Numerous possible causes of a given effect may be present, and these must be considered and eliminated. The classificatory method of the biological sciences does institute order in thousands of varieties of plant and animal life and permits inferences to be made about them. For example, if oxygen is necessary to sustain life in animals, fish must secure oxygen; and we are directed to look for and into that mechanism. The mathematical sciences have been extolled for teaching deductive thinking, and there is justice in that claim. Even the obvious fact that several verifications of a general statement do not prove it, has to be learned and is taught by mathematics. The importance of quantitative knowledge in resolving many problems is one of the greatest methodologies of science.

The Substantive Implications of Science

The values of science extend far beyond the purely factual content of science. Rationalism is one value. There are also those which I shall call substantive implications of science—implications for nonscientific knowledge and values.

Science teaches us that the universe is accessible to man's reason and that its functioning can be described by laws. This very knowledge is of immense value. For example: Fears, dread, and superstitions have been eliminated by just the knowledge that the heavenly bodies follow laws and that these bodies will repeat the past behavior invariably. Man is now the proud possessor of knowledge which enables him to view nature calmly and objectively. We breathe freely because we know that nature is not willful or capricious.

Science gives us factual knowledge about the physical world and man's body. But more important than these are the answers to the questions of why is man born, what is his role in life, and what is his destiny? Since the Sixteenth Century, science has dealt blow after blow to the egotism of man, who is no longer the central figure in the universe as he was thought to be under the geocentric theory of heavenly motions. Many of the implications of science as to the role and destiny of man are not comforting. Nevertheless, it is helpful to learn the facts. Education demands that we exchange an infantile mentality for a mature one and live with this knowledge. Man's knowledge of himself is very much dependent on his knowledge of the physical world.

The theories of science determine our philosophical outlooks. The role of science here is enormous. For example, the laws of Newtonian mechanics established the existence of a completely determined universe obeying uniform, invariable, and inexorable laws. Thus arose the philosophy of determinism, which states that the world functions according to a fixed, unalterable plan.

The doctrine of determinism, or at least some aspects of it, have been altered by recent developments in quantum mechanics, particularly the uncertainty principle. It was also challenged by what is called the statistical view of nature, a view itself due to the creation of statistical mechanics in the late Nineteenth Century. But the point I am making is still valid, namely, that philosophical doctrines are now determined by scientific developments. Should not students know these implications of the theories of science?

Another example of the substantive implications of science is one which affects almost all domains of knowledge, the matter of truth. Science does not claim to offer truths but it does come close, closer and closer some believe, to truth. Science offers theories, not creeds; it offers policies, not dogmas. This is an attitude toward knowledge which is worthy of inculcation.

In the search for truth the sciences offer another value, and here I would emphasize the word search. The scientist is constantly willing to reexamine his theories. He takes literally the word re-search.

An education in science prepares for citizenship in the very civilization which science has fashioned. Our government is heavily involved with science in defense, communications, transportation, health, and numerous other activities. The future citizen may be called upon even as a nonscientist to take a hand in these affairs. The citizen will have to vote on issues which involve science, and the citizen should know also what governments can do to support science. Many leaders are quite ignorant of what basic research is and how it leads to benefits for society. In particular they do not know the long road from pure science to technology.

Contributions to Esthetics

The third area with which a liberal education is necessarily concerned is the appreciation of the esthetic and emotional values. Science contributes much here, too. Many of these values are accessible only to the professional scientist who undergoes the experiences and acquires the maturity to appreciate them. But one value which I believe can be imparted to young people is the opportunity to create and the pleasures of that act. Probably, young people will not be creating but re-creating with the help of a teacher, but they can begin to feel the emotional satisfactions even from their own little contribution to thought if they are allowed to contribute to building up the knowledge.

For young people I would emphasize the esthetic values that might appeal to the nonprofessional. And there are many of these. Most people are not aware that the greatest period in Western painting, the Renaissance, was fashioned by mathematics. In poetry, science enters into intellectual content. To understand the poetry of an age and appreciate just what the poets were celebrating or deploring, one must know what world-views science had created in that age. The appreciation of poetry on a significant level calls for a knowledge of science.

Teaching the Cultural Values of Science

We must teach the cultural values in our science courses. Not to teach the larger cultural significance of science while teaching science is like asking students to swallow food but not letting them digest it.

Another reason for teaching these cultural values in science concerns motivation. Despite the fact that the sciences deal with as real and as significant a world as painting, and poetry, it is much harder to interest students in science and especially mathematics than in literature. First teach the importance and significance of an idea and then examine it in detail. Without the significance, much of mathematics and science appears to be gibberish. Technological applications are a means of arousing interest; use them.

We must teach the broader cultural values in our science courses for still another reason. Knowledge is a whole. Life is not segregated into mathematics, physics, chemistry, and the like, and into distinct values which these subjects offer.

Finally we must not turn out stunted scientists. Too many mathematicians today are just mathematicians and too many scientists are just scientists. We must develop people who are prepared to live in a world which will make many and varied demands on them and which also offers numerous roads to enjoyments and satisfactions.

SCIENCE AND COMMON SENSE *

Morris H. Shamos

This probing discussion by Morris H. Shamos questions the interpretation of the concept of what is science as it is presented in today's curriculum. Although acknowledging the importance of natural history and technology in the science curriculum, Shamos believes we should resist the tendency to present them under the guise of science. He believes that the purpose of science is to discover the order in nature, not simply to classify it or to put

* REPRINTED FROM *The Science Teacher*, Vol. 29, No. 5, September 1962, pp. 7–11. Copyright, 1962, by the National Science Teachers Association, Washington, D.C. Reprinted by permission of the author and the publisher. Dr. Shamos is Chairman of the Department of Physics at New York University.

it to use. According to the author, the intellectual values of science must be stressed instead of the technological values.

T HE PAST two decades have seen marked changes in the influence of science on our society. When historians look back upon this period it will surely be recorded as an age of science, not necessarily because the public understanding of science is greater now than ever before but because the products of science have influenced so profoundly the affairs of men. It is now reasonably clear that in science, and particularly in technology, what is past is truly prologue. The developments of the past half century, remarkable as they have been, will appear trivial compared with what will occur in the future.

And the trend probably is irreversible. Once shown the practical fruits of science in such dramatic fashion as H-bombs and space flight it is inconceivable that governments, who now look to science as the chief instrument of national growth as well as survival, and the people, who look to it chiefly for the material conveniences it provides and for the prolongation of life, can ever again turn their backs on science. All are irrevocably committed to a scientific society and against such a background the responsibilities of science education take on important and new dimensions.

As a result of the growing national interest in scientific affairs, there has been in the past decade a substantial increase in efforts to improve the scientific literacy of both students and the public. These efforts take many forms, but most noteworthy are the revised courses of study in secondary school science and mathematics that are now under way on a nationwide basis, plus indications that this trend will soon carry down into the elementary grades. In the light of these activities, one might "pause to re-think the basic philosophy of science education," as pointed out perceptively in the editorial of the November 1961 issue of *The Science Teacher*. The warning is appropriate for it comes at a time when misjudgment in this area can seriously affect the future development of science in America.

It might be expected that with all this interest in science the task of the science educator would be greatly simplified. Yet this has not been the result. If anything, the problems of science education have been magnified by the sudden "respectability" of science, by the impatience of some educational reformers, and by the realization that those who teach it now share a greater responsibility, and that these teachers are faced with the growing complexity of science itself.

THE COMPLEXITY OF SCIENCE

The complexity of science is, in many ways, the heart of the problem. There is a basic difference, unfortunately, between science and other forms of human knowledge. However much one might deplore the mutual antagonism of

C. P. Snow's [1] "two cultures," that they are different can not be denied. The difference lies chiefly in the fact that science and mathematics—and the kind of reasoning that is characteristic of science—are remote from one's everyday experience. By this is not meant the products of science or the outward appearance of nature, for with these one does have a direct kinship. Rather, it means that the basic concepts in terms of which the scientist tries to account for the over-all aspects of nature do not accord with *common sense* understanding.

In fairness one could not say that there ever was a time in the development of science when public understanding of it, or of its purpose, was very good; yet in the present century the difficulty of interpreting science has become pronounced. As Herbert Dingle (University College, London, England) points out, for a civilization so proficient in the practice of science we are astonishingly backward in our understanding of it. The reasons, not difficult to find, are connected with what is usually known as "common sense," or rather with the absence of it.

Toward the end of the nineteenth century, when the universe was still described as a well-behaved, deterministic mechanism of moving "billiard balls," it was possible to talk of it in common-sense terms; at least one was not required to stretch his imagination beyond reasonable limits. Now the picture has changed. The basic concepts today, upon which in the final analysis all of science is built, have become so abstract as to defy common-sense understanding. To make matters worse, from the point of view of the general public, determinism has been replaced with probabilism and the universe is now viewed as a cosmic game of chance.

The tenacity with which man tends to cling to common-sense ideas is readily apparent in our everyday activities, as it has been throughout history. What David Hume (1740) called "natural instinct" and Thomas Reid (1764) later termed "common sense" is, in fact, the guiding principle for most of our thoughts and actions. It is well known that in practical life philosophical doubts readily give way to common sense or "natural instinct," and this is what frequently stands in the way of teaching modern science to the average individual. The point was well illustrated by A. S. Eddington some thirty-five years ago in the first of his series of Gifford Lectures at the University of Edinburgh, Scotland.

Eddington spoke of the "two tables" before which he stood and before which science teachers find themselves in the classroom. One is the familiar, commonplace object of the "real" world, the one which can be described in common-sense terms; that is, in terms which evoke meaningful images. It has dimension; it has color; it has substance and some degree of permanence. In short, it is a *real thing*, a common-sense object because by this description one can evoke recognition and understanding among all civilized people. It is

---

[1] C. P. Snow. *The Two Cultures and the Scientific Revolution.* Cambridge University Press, New York. 1959.

unlike space, or time, or temperature, about which reasonable men can form totally inconsistent views.

So much for the "real" table. The other is our scientific table, one which is a total stranger to the real world. It consists mostly of empty space, but with enormous numbers of electric charges (electrons) moving randomly about with great speeds; yet their combined bulk (volume) amounts to much less than one-billionth the bulk of the table itself. Despite this strange construction the table performs "real" functions. It supports things lying on it because the electric charges in it keep colliding (electrically) with similar electric charges in the objects on the table and prevent them from "falling through" the empty spaces. And if one strikes his hand on the table it does not pass through, again because of the electric charges.

But why does this scientific table not fall apart? Again we call upon the electric charges, this time to hold one another in some semblance of order so as to provide the over-all structure of the table. And as Eddington pointed out, the only time the scientific table shows to advantage over the real table is when one sets it on fire and it goes up in smoke. Then what happens to it can be accounted for, while the fate of the real table remains a mystery.

Thus without pursuing this point further, consider how unreal the scientific table must seem to a common-sense individual without going into the complexities of spinning electrons, wave-particle dualism, uncertainty principles, etc. However convincing the scientific table may be to the scientist, it is clear that it will never be easy to persuade the average person to think *primarily* in terms of this kind of abstraction. The fact is that the science teacher finds it difficult to divorce completely his own thinking from the real table that can be seen and felt.

The entire trend of modern science, whether it be physics or chemistry or molecular biology, is to find a common basis for all of our experience. Scientific inquiry generally begins in the real or common-sense world with observation and in the end it returns to that world in the form of technology or medical advances. The beginning and end are easily understood by the layman but the "in between,"—truly the essence of science—is where he tends to become lost.

There are no common-sense counterparts for molecules, electrons, genes, or electric fields. Yet the student demands *concrete* explanations of the things discussed in science. The molecular theory of matter, the kinetic theory of heat, the gene theory of heredity; all relate to concepts not directly accessible to the senses. The lack of a meaningful model is a great disadvantage, of course, particularly when one attempts to teach science to students who are bound by common-sense experiences and who quite naturally tend to reason by analogy with these experiences as a basis.

This is a problem which confronts all science teachers today, and which might be perhaps their greatest challenge; how to guide students through the illusory world of modern science in such a fashion as to leave them with a reasonable understanding of this enterprise called "science." While not entirely impossible it is clearly not a simple task, and grows more difficult the later one begins.

Having seen that modern science is incompatible with what is generally called common-sense understanding, the other side of the coin should now be examined. While on the one hand a scientist may not use common-sense descriptions when talking about scientific theories, he is nevertheless expected to exercise common-sense judgments when talking about educational theories or about the role of science in our general culture. It is in this area that we have not always brought to bear the same degree of logical reasoning demanded in science. This point is perhaps well illustrated by the perennial debate on the question of general education in science.

A COMMON LITERACY IN SCIENCE?

Science teachers are convinced that science and science education are important, and that a common literacy in science should be promoted among all segments of the educated public. Yet as reasonable as this may seem today, and was to many of our predecessors—to Thomas Huxley almost a century ago, to Albert Einstein and George Sarton in more recent times, and even to John Dewey—it is evident that there is no general agreement on this point among nonscientists; and even in the scientific community considerable differences of opinion on what constitutes a good science curriculum exist.

What then is the basis for believing that science should be part of a liberal education, without specifying for the time being what is meant by "science"? Why should science educators encourage a wider understanding of the nature of science? Should we not be content with educating only those few who are destined to become scientists or engineers, and perhaps to increase this number somewhat in accordance with the needs of our society?

The answer, unfortunately, does not always stand the test of reason. The present era is one in which many of the national and international issues have what may be considered a scientific base; bomb testing, missiles, space exploration, polio vaccines, fluoridation of water, etc. The intelligent citizen, so this line of reasoning goes, must be prepared to judge these issues and therefore should have some training in science. Think how unrealistic this argument is. What about foreign affairs, social problems, political science, economics, and other similar fields. Must the intelligent person be expert in all these areas in order to be a responsible citizen? The answer obviously is in the negative, however attractive such an educational utopia may seem.

Surely it is clear that the amount of scientific training one can reasonably expect the average person to have would not equip him to exercise intelligent judgment on the scientific merits of issues such as these. Professional scientists, in fact, generally do not have the specialized knowledge in scientific fields other than theirs to evaluate such matters independently—and it is well known, even in one's special field, that while there may be general agreement on questions of scientific interpretation, the interplay between science and society frequently finds scientists at swords' points with one another. The mark of an intelligent person is not necessarily how much he knows, but rather how well he is able to exercise sound judgments with what little he knows. With involved scientific issues, as in all others, this means assessing wisely the opinions of those who are more expert in the field.

An apparent weakness exists, therefore, when one takes as the argument for general education in science, the utilitarian view that it helps to prepare the student in some *direct* fashion for his role in the community. If this were its primary purpose one could certainly make a stronger case against science education than for it.

Another argument one often hears is that as the products of science play an ever-increasing role in our society more youngsters must be directed in science and related fields so as to assure a steady flow of specialists into these areas to fill our future needs. And the way to accomplish this is to expose *all* students to science in the hope that sufficient numbers will be won over.

One must have uneasy feelings about this argument for general education in science, for it does not appear to stand the test of a democratic society. Moreover, if society needs more scientists and engineers surely this demand could be filled in other, more selective ways than through a "shotgun" technique such as this.

This leaves as the major argument for general education in science the one that generates least enthusiasm among the general public, among legislators, and among many educators; yet it is the one which in the final analysis offers the greatest potential. The development of science is, after all, one of man's major intellectual achievements, a product of the mind which can be enjoyed not for its fruits alone but rather for the sense of order it provides of our environment. The mental stimulation and the satisfaction of learning should be reasons enough for the study of science, just as they are for the study of any other discipline. While this may suggest an ivory-tower approach, it is the only one, in my opinion, which can stand firmly on its merits. When trying to rationalize science education on purely utilitarian grounds, the result is to drive the wedge deeper between this and other forms of human knowledge. The intellectual values of science must be stressed with the practical values as secondary benefits, rather than the reverse, as is now done.

The Science Curriculum

Assuming that science should be part of the educational experience of all students, of what then should the curriculum consist? This is the same as asking what the average person should know of science. Should he know that the earth is nearly round; that it spins on an axis and rotates about the sun? Should he know that warm air rises, that oxygen is needed to support combustion, how living things function? Of course he should and more! He should know these facts of nature just as he knows various facts of history and geography. They are a part of his natural environment—of his total being.

But this is not science; it is natural history, and here lies the crux of our problem. *How* does one know that the earth is nearly round and spins on an axis? *Why* does warm air rise? *Why* is oxygen needed to support combustion? It is the "how" and "why" of things that constitute science—not the facts alone. The purpose of science is to discover the order in nature, not simply to classify it or to put it to use.

Knowledge of the natural world falls into three broad categories: natural history, science, and technology. Together these constitute the scientific enterprise, but elementary science education consists mainly of the first and last of these categories, with little or no science. The results have not been encouraging as far as public understanding of the nature of the scientific enterprise is concerned, but the reasons why it has generally been taught this way are not difficult to find.

They stem from efforts to relate science *primarily* to everyday experience and thus to stress its practical aspects. Among our earliest impressions are the natural phenomena of our environment, the kind that are seemingly simple and can be presented in purely descriptive fashion. Hence the emphasis on natural history; it is the obvious starting point in a science curriculum, but should not be the end-point as well.

As for the emphasis on technology, this too is easily understood. Our everyday contact with science is through its end products, through the technology that turns on its discoveries. In highly developed countries such as ours, one is literally surrounded by the material products of science. Our habits, our mode of life, our health, perhaps even our freedom to enjoy the arts—all are conditioned by advances in technology. These advances, moreover, result generally from specific needs of society rather than the creative spirit of man. Against such a background it is not surprising that control of nature; *i.e.*, technology, is so frequently confused with man's intellectual desire to understand it, which is the main goal of science.

This has been the general pattern of introductory science education in the past and it is pertinent to ask whether continuing the same practice on a broader scale can ever achieve the goal of a scientifically literate public. The answer must clearly be negative. Even the most casual observer of the educational scene cannot help but conclude that the views of science held by the average adult, and which are derived mainly from just this sort of exposure to science, are at best badly distorted. It is equally evident that somehow our young children, who are fascinated by most experiences with science while in the primary grades, are later repelled by it. Why this aversion to one of man's major intellectual accomplishments?

CONCLUSION

The answer must lie at least partly in the way it is taught. It must be recognized that to achieve our goal requires a major change in the structure of science education. *Science* will have to be taught as well as the usual natural history and technology, and when teaching the latter it is important that they be properly labeled. There can be no reasonable objection to natural history and technology in the science curriculum; on the contrary they are obviously essential. But it is imperative to resist the tendency to present these under the guise of science, especially when it is the only formal introduction the student may have with the world of nature. To give the impression that science consists solely of observation and application is of no great value or service to the students, and certainly not to the cause of science.

TOWARD A THEORY OF SCIENCE EDUCATION CONSISTENT WITH MODERN SCIENCE*

Paul DeH. Hurd

This statement of issues and suggestions by Paul DeH. Hurd provides for the formulation of acceptable purposes in science education and gives some needed insight into the basis for curriculum development. Seven challenging issues of science teaching are presented, together with seven equally challenging viewpoints which offer suggestions for the advancement of science teaching as related to these issues. A logical plan is presented for science teaching that is consistent with the structure of science.

INTRODUCTION

The purpose of this paper is twofold—to describe issues and to make suggestions for the advancement of science teaching. It provides a basis for discussion and debate; it does not pretend to supply answers to all questions that may be raised.

Science curriculum developments are influenced both by changes in society as well as by new developments in science. This means that the curriculum

* REPRINTED FROM *Theory into Action . . . in Science Curriculum Development*, National Science Teachers Association Document, Stock No. 471-14282, 1964, pp. 5–15. Copyright, 1964, by the National Science Teachers Association, Washington, D.C. Reprinted by permission of the author and the publisher. Dr. Hurd is Professor of Education at Stanford University.

specialist in science needs to examine the writings and research in a wide range of fields: economics, sociology, public policy and manpower, as well as the current status of science. Each of these areas has relevance for the teaching of science.

The development of a literate citizenry in science does not result from the teaching in a single grade nor is it the product of any one course. It can be achieved with a carefully planned kindergarten through grade 12 (K-12) program in which there is a vertical as well as a grade-level coherence within the science curriculum. Curriculum improvement in science then, should be viewed from kindergarten through grade 12 and perhaps through the undergraduate years of college.

To begin a curriculum reform without first establishing at least a tentative basis for decisions is wasteful of time and effort and seldom produces significant improvements. A major problem in science education in American schools has been the lack of a viable theory of science teaching which could serve as a base for decision making. Consequently the schools can make no answer to their critics. The value of theory in education is that it frees the teacher and the researcher from the constraints of tradition and makes the development of new ideas more likely. It gives perspective to curriculum and instructional issues and provides a basis for making decisions.

Local action groups can make the best use of this document by first comparing it, issue by issue, with their own views on science teaching, noting what they can or cannot accept. Second, they should prepare a clear-cut formulation of acceptable purposes for an education in science, using this as a basis to assess the need and directions in curriculum reform. It should be expected that working groups will wish to change their viewpoints as progress is made in curriculum design and communication between members of the curriculum committee becomes clearer.

In formulating this statement, advantage has been taken of the ideas expressed in the modern science curriculum studies developed over the past decade. At the secondary school level, the works of the Biological Sciences Curriculum Study, the Chemical Bond Approach Project, the Chemical Education Material Study, the Earth Science Curriculum Project, the Junior High School Science Project (Princeton University), and the Physical Sciences Study Committee have been particularly enlightening. At the elementary school level, curriculum studies developed by the American Association for the Advancement of Science, the Educational Services Incorporated, the University of California, the University of Illinois, the Minne Math Science Project, the School Mathematics Study Group, and the United States Office of Education have provided new insights into science teaching.

SCIENCE TEACHING AND CULTURAL CHANGE

A rapidly changing society stimulated by advances in science demands an educational program designed to meet the challenge of change.

Schools exist to help young people know about and participate in the life of their time. In the past when cultural change and progress in science were slow, instruction in science could lag fifty years or more with little ill consequence for the individual or the nation. At the turn of the century, however, America began to move from an agrarian society to a scientific-technological society. Adjustments made in the science curricula reflected new technological developments but generally failed to reflect the advent of modern science. The impact of science on man's thinking, on social conditions, on economic development and on political action escaped widespread attention, even among highly educated nonscientists. In many ways the influence of science in shaping modern America is the unwritten history of the Twentieth Century.

By the close of World War II it was evident to nearly everyone that America had changed from an agrarian to a scientific-technological society, from rural to metropolitan communities, and that in a thousand related ways our pattern of life and philosophic values had changed. The demand for men and women trained for scientific and technological vocations more than doubled in a decade. But the science curriculum remained static, largely oriented to a culture that no longer existed, and taught from a content that had lost its scientific significance.

Point of View

To escape the threat of obsolescence, education in the sciences must be based upon the kind of information that has survival value and upon strategies of inquiry that facilitate the adaptation of knowledge to new demands.

American schools need a science curriculum suited to recent advances in science and to a changing society. They require courses to prepare young people for change and progress and to help them meet the problems they will face during their lifetimes. A rapidly changing society stimulated by advances in science demands an educational program designed to meet the challenge of change.

Because our culture is characterized by change and progress, the greatest threat to either the individual or national security is obsolescence. This means that an education in the sciences must be based upon the kind of information that has survival value and upon strategies of inquiry that facilitate the adaptation of knowledge to new demands. This education must go beyond the immediate and include the future. What is more important, it should provide young people with the background and intellectual talents for shaping the future in a manner that assures the welfare of human beings and sustains progress. Progress is found not so much in tools and material resources as in the extension of intellectual capabilities of people and the viability of their knowledge. This suggests an education in the sciences that is oriented to lifelong learning, rational and independent thinking, and the acquisition of productive knowledge. A curriculum is needed that is oriented toward a period not yet lived, influenced by discoveries not yet made and beset with social problems not yet predicted. The need is for an education designed to meet change, to appreciate the processes of change, and to influence the direction of change.

The influence of science on national policy, on the thought of our times, on economic, social and political problems, and on the life of each person means that everyone needs an understanding of science. Men and women who do not have this background will be excluded from the intellectual life of the times and blindly buffeted by the forces that give direction and meaning to modern living. Without a grasp of science they will not be prepared to partake fully of the culture in which they are living.

GOALS OF SCIENCE TEACHING

Science teaching must result in scientifically literate citizens.

Goals of education tend to be an expression of American values. They describe what the ideal American citizen should be like. As such they remain fairly stable over long periods of time. Our conception of the ideal does not change very rapidly. What changes are our ideas of how to achieve the ideals expressed through the goals. Unfortunately the connection between goals and the methods employed to reach them seldom is clear. We encounter very diverse kinds of curricula, all directed toward essentially the same ends. But we possess no satisfactory method for connecting the curriculum to abstract goals.

Point of View

To state the goals of science education is to describe the cognitive skills expected in the student rather than the knowledge assumed essential to attaining these skills.

Goals generally are stated in terms which are much too abstract to be useful as a guide in building a curriculum. It would be more to the point to break general goals down into smaller component steps that could be attained one after the other. Thus, for example, the general goal of producing independent inquirers might be achieved by first discovering what support skills should be learned and which ones should be learned first. Thus, the operative goals for a course would consist of precise statements of specific cognitive skills to be attained each year in science.

Talking about goals is a little like talking about building a bridge. We may know the concept of "bridge" just as we know the concept of "inquiry" but that, by itself, will not suffice to build a satisfactory bridge. We need to know where and for what purpose the bridge will be constructed. Similarly we need to examine the goal of "inquiry" to find out what kind of inquiry and the purposes for which we intend to use the inquiry skills. Once these general questions are answered, criteria or standards for curriculum design, teaching methods, and evaluative procedures may be established.

A statement of goals should describe what we mean by a scientifically literate person living in the last half of the Twentieth Century. A person literate in science knows something of the role of science in society and appreciates the cultural conditions under which science thrives. He also understands its conceptual inventions and its investigative procedures.

LEARNING SCIENCE

The strategies of learning must be related to the conditions that will lead to an understanding of the conceptual structures of science and of the modes of scientific inquiry.

It is difficult at any time to formulate a satisfactory definition of learning, and it is particularly difficult if we wish to apply this definition specifically to the learning of science. Learning is sometimes defined as the relatively permanent behavior changes which result from experience. The goals of science teaching describe the desired behaviors. We can assume that some teaching procedures and learning materials are better than others for motivating inquiry and for developing an understanding of science concepts.

Point of View

The educational setting and the choice of instructional materials are closely related to achieving the goals of science teaching.

We must assume that the educational setting for attaining the goals of science teaching can be facilitated and that some instructional materials are more efficient than others for achieving goals. In the paragraphs that follow, a few learning principles relevant to science teaching will be identified and their significance for curriculum development and instruction will be illustrated.

One of the first tasks in teaching science is to teach the inquiry processes of science. Inquiry skills provide the learner with tools for independent learning. By means of extensive experience in inquiry the student learns to place objects and events in categories or classes. He discovers the utility of coding systems and becomes aware that systems of classification are not inherent in nature but are man-made. He establishes a conceptual framework. This conceptual framework, in turn, focuses his attention on other phenomena and helps him build new categories which are more comprehensive or more abstract. The conceptual structure ties past experience to the present and serves as a guide for the comprehension and assimilation of new facts and concepts. It serves as a basis for prediction of what will happen in a new problem or situation.

While the significant facts in science change at a bewildering rate, the conceptual structures are more stable. However, we need to recognize that conceptual frameworks also change. The problem is to produce learners with the concepts and modes of inquiry that will permit them to understand these changes.

The ability to form science concepts depends upon the learner's own background and the conditions under which he is taught. To insure in some measure the likelihood that a concept will be acquired, it must be presented and used in different contexts. In a well-organized course of study, concepts formed early in the year are used to develop new concepts that occur later. Concepts are most easily acquired when familiar and concrete perceptual materials are used. To enlarge the understanding of a concept requires that it be taught many times at different levels of abstraction.

Words facilitate the development of concepts only when the ideas they represent are understood. Verbalization without understanding is likely to hinder the learning of concepts. This is the danger of attempting to teach science concepts through definitions and names. The ability to verbalize a concept is not a guarantee that the learner can apply or relate the concept. Nevertheless, there is an interdependence of concept and language. It is difficult to form a concept without a language rich enough to express it.

How shall we teach the investigatory process that characterizes a researcher and marks the skilled learner? Research provides some suggestions. It is wasteful to teach facts divorced from a meaningful concept. When facts, which have meaning for the learner, are tied into a logically related conceptual pattern, retention is improved and insight is more likely to occur. After learning one pattern, a student tends to respond more systematically to the alternatives in a new situation. An understanding of conceptual structure and training in inquiry help him select what is pertinent in a new situation. The test of learning is the extent to which a student is able to use a conceptual pattern and associated inquiry skills in new contexts.

In any given situation, more than one explanation may seem to apply. There may be no good basis for choosing among alternatives until rather late in the decision-making or problem-solving process. Uncertainties exist during the interval in which the learner actively seeks and processes more data, examines other possible solutions, and finally makes a choice. Children have to be taught to consider alternatives and to recognize that answers must be sought in the environment of the problem, not primarily in the activities of the teacher. That is, they need to learn a pattern of delaying responses and of tolerating uncertainty until sufficient data are collected and alternative hypotheses are evaluated.

These procedures imply that the concepts which form the core of a course must be something more than questions for which students seek answers. Problem-solving is only one small part of scientific inquiry. We are seeking to develop a range of inquiry skills within the structure of a discipline which permits the student to increase his own efficiency in knowing.

The investigative strategies in science and the organization of scientific knowledge suggest valid and desirable principles of teaching. Stressing these procedures has the effect of minimizing authoritarian teaching and encouraging independent learning.

SELECTING THE CONTENT OF THE CURRICULUM

Because science and the cultural scene are in a continuous process of change, the content of science courses must be constantly re-evaluated and, if necessary, revised to reflect major shifts in thinking and new interpretations of phenomena.

Science is a systematic and connected arrangement of knowledge within a logical structure of theory. Science is also a *process* of forming such a structure. Much of the effort in science is directed toward seeking new knowledge. There is also a certain lack of durability in this knowledge and scientists are dedicated to keeping this so. The significance of facts and concepts is constantly shifting within the scientific discipline. New ideas and theories cause the meaning of present knowledge to change. Correction and refinement are always operating to modify scientific information. And in science there is always more to be discovered and new relationships to be described.

Although the information phase of science is tenuous and overwhelming in amount, there are a small number of theories, laws, principles, and inquiry processes which provide the basis for interpreting a great variety of phenomena.

Point of View

To develop a comprehensive science program that will achieve the goals of science teaching, the curriculum maker must extract the essence of scientific knowledge and define the significant concepts in terms of their usefulness for understanding the structure of science.

Criteria for the selection of curriculum materials should be consistent with the purposes of science teaching and consistent with the structure of science. The task of the curriculum-maker is to extract the essence of scientific knowledge and define the significant concepts in terms of their usefulness for understanding the structure of science. This is a process that begins with the "big picture" of science, not with bits of information, bodies of facts, or concepts in isolation. Thus it is the conceptual schemes and the inquiry processes that provide the framework for curriculum design and for developing courses at each grade level. By this approach we can reasonably expect to develop a comprehensive science program that presents a valid image of a science and will achieve the goals of science teaching.

Criteria for the selection of curriculum materials should be consistent with the purposes of teaching science and consistent with the structure of science. 1. The knowledge must be familiar to the scholar in the discipline and useful in advancing the learner's understanding of science. 2. The content should serve the future as well as the present; therefore the selection of content should focus on the conceptual aspects of knowledge. 3. Every field of science has a basis in experimental and investigative processes. To know science is to know its methods of inquiry. 4. There are connections between the sciences themselves and between the sciences and other subjects. The content for courses needs to be selected to take full advantage of these relationships and to provide wherever possible a logical integration of knowledge. Transdisciplinary skills, intra- and interdisciplinary understanding should rank high as instructional aims. 5. Only a small fraction of the basic knowledge of science can be selected for teaching in a K-12 program; consequently special attention should be given to including those concepts that are most likely to promote the welfare of mankind as well as the advancement of science. This must also include the knowledge that will enable individuals to participate in the intellectual and cultural life of a scientific age.

ORGANIZING THE SCIENCE CURRICULUM FOR LEARNING

Organization of the science curriculum demands a dominant cognitive pattern.

A science curriculum is a systematic organization of instructional materials designed to achieve the purposes of science teaching with maximum efficiency. The science curriculum developer begins his task by considering the nature of the knowledge he is to work with and what is involved in learning this field of knowledge. Because we are interested in how the pupil gains knowledge and understanding, the implication of cognitive processes for curriculum development must be considered. There are other aspects to curriculum planning, but these are the major considerations.

Point of View

To assure that at every point there will be a readiness for more advanced learning, the curriculum continuum needs to be planned to provide for increasingly complex inquiry skills as well as for growth in the meaning of the conceptual schemes.

The patterning and integrating of information is essential for developing knowledge, suggesting that the logical schematization peculiar to the nature of science should be used in organizing the science curriculum. The materials chosen to form the curriculum should be organized in a manner that requires the learner continually to reorganize, synthesize, and use his knowledge.

A comprehensive curriculum should have unity resulting from a coherent structure and continuity. This suggests that learning should take place in a context which relates to previous knowledge and supplies a foundation for what is to come. The curriculum continuum needs to be planned to provide for increasingly complex inquiry skills as well as for growth in the meaning of significant concepts. This helps to assure that at every point there will be a readiness for more advanced learning. Good curriculum organization establishes its own continuity by making the next steps in learning seem reasonable.

Construction of a science curriculum should not be done in isolation from other parts of the school curriculum. In addition to modes of thought which can be useful in other subjects, there are transcurricular skills such as measuring, coding, observing, and inferring. These skills, rather than information, are the most fertile connections between subjects.

The organizational basis for designing a science curriculum is derived from the nature of science and from the intellectual development of the learner. Conceptual schemes and inquiry processes provide the integrative basis which serves to give both coherence and continuity to the curriculum. Within this framework it is then possible to select information that represents the current status of the discipline and will be most likely to move the learner toward the goals of science teaching.

THE TEACHING OF SCIENCE

A newly conceived curriculum prescribes a style of teaching consistent with the goals of instruction and with the nature of the discipline.

The success of a new curriculum greatly depends upon how it will be taught. A curriculum reform is as much a matter of improving instruction as it is a re-evaluation of course content. A newly conceived curriculum prescribes a style of teaching consistent with the goals of instruction and the nature of the discipline.

Point of View

To encourage independent learning in science, teaching practices should be related to the inquiry aspects of science, to its investigative strategies, and to the structure of scientific knowledge.

A theory of instruction that is particularly suited to the teaching of science is crucial to modern curriculum development. This theory needs to have a broad base and should include the following aspects of instruction: 1. *The nature of science*: its structure, its processes of inquiry and its conceptual schemes. 2. *The nature of the learner*: his motives, cognitive style, emotional background, and intellectual potential. 3. *The nature of the teacher*: his cognitive style, ability to communicate, control pattern, educational philosophy, and understanding of science. 4. *The nature of learning*: its processes, contexts, conditions, and purposes. 5. *The nature of the curriculum*: its organization, its sequence, and its substantive, attitudinal, and procedural dimensions. 6. *The nature of the social structure*: social and cultural forces with their demands and incentives.

Instruction links curriculum with teaching goals. While we have recognized instruction as the role of the teacher, we have not fully recognized it as a function of the student. What the pupil does, determines in some measure what the teacher does, for both pupil and teacher are influenced by the texture of the teaching and learning environment. There is also an interplay between instructional activities and the materials of instruction and both of these in turn are influenced by the discipline.

LABORATORY WORK IN SCIENCE TEACHING

Laboratory and field work are central to the teaching of science.

Learning from work in the laboratory and field is central to the teaching of science. It is here that the student relates concepts, theories, experiments, and observations as a means of exploring ideas. While technical skill and precision are important outcomes of the laboratory, it is the meaning they have for the interpretation of data that is more significant.

Point of View

To achieve its greatest educational value, work in the laboratory must provide opportunities for the student to interpret observations and data.

The laboratory is a place to explore ideas, test theories, and raise questions. Here, meaning is given to observations and data. The data from an experiment remain inert facts until rational thinking makes something more of them. It is at this point that work in the laboratory has its greatest educational value.

Experiments, at whatever grade level, should have a dimension in the investigative aspects of science and provide a variety of experiences with scientific inquiry. Experiments solely for the purpose of gathering data, even though the data are carefully described and summarized, represent merely a preliminary step for understanding science. To collect experimental data is not enough. The student must learn to formulate statements based on data and to test these statements against theory. The conclusion to an experiment is found in the interpretation of data, and it is this interpretation that generates new questions, stimulates further inquiry, helps to solve problems, and leads to the refinement of theories.

A few of the elements of scientific inquiry that need to be systematically introduced throughout science laboratory work are: 1. The variety, characteristics, and limitations of experimental designs. 2. The relationship between experimental options and the nature of the data obtained. 3. The relationships between observed data, experimental results, and the inferences based on the data and results. 4. The tools of measurement and their influence on experimental accuracy. 5. The use of data in generating hypotheses and defining questions and, conversely, the use of hypotheses to guide data collection. 6. The use of theories and models in interpreting data and in making predictions. 7. The analyzing, ordering, and displaying of data in precise and valid ways.

Laboratory work should be seen as a means of relating science concepts, inquiry processes, observation, and experimentation. The child's first experiences with science, even in the primary school, should involve aspects of experimental inquiry. He should learn how to observe with all of his senses, how to measure, classify, use numbers, communicate, and practice similar subdisciplinary skills. As he progresses through school he should have opportunities to use these knowledge skills to further his understanding of science concepts.

Laboratory experiences need to be planned in both horizontal and vertical sequences, thus providing for progressive learning within as well as across problems. A good laboratory program at any grade level is not a series of "one shot" activities. Some laboratory experiences form substructures for others. The proper sequencing of experiments makes it possible for the pupil to use earlier learning to attack increasingly complex problems.

There are other factors associated with making the best use of laboratory procedures in schools. These include communicating the results of experiments, pacing inquiry skills in science with those in mathematics, and providing for a wider use of mental experiments. We need to recognize that the value of an experiment lies more in the means it presents for exploring the unknown than in the verification of the known.

CONCLUDING REMARKS

It would be rash to suggest that a new curriculum in science has been developed, but it is clear that new viewpoints have emerged. The purpose of this section of "Theory Into Action" has been to present a logical plan for science teaching that is consistent with the structure of science and a modern view of science education.

Not all phases of science teaching have been discussed. There is need for more research and experimentation on some of the proposals. For others, the answers must emerge from one's own rational analysis of the problems. The need for a new approach to science teaching is no longer a matter for debate; it is the nature of the new curriculum that is not clear. The issues and viewpoints presented here are intended to focus discussion and provide a pivot for local action.

HISTORICAL BACKGROUND OF
ELEMENTARY SCIENCE *

Herbert A. Smith

The following is a portion of an article by Herbert A. Smith entitled "Educational Research Related to Science Instruction for the Elementary and Junior High School: A Review and Commentary." Dr. Smith traces the history of

* REPRINTED FROM *Journal of Research in Science Teaching*, Vol. 1, Issue 3, 1963, pp. 200–205, 223, by permission of the author and the editor. Dr. Smith is Professor of Education at Colorado State University, Fort Collins.

elementary science education, beginning with its roots in Britain and Germany. He describes the influence of object teaching, the National Education Association Committee of Ten, the nature study movement, and the works of Harris, Hall, Strait, Jackman, Parker, Pierce, James, and Dewey. Two historical landmarks are discussed—namely, the published thesis of Gerald S. Craig in 1927, and the Thirty-First Yearbook of the National Society for the Study of Education in 1932.

THE roots of the modern American elementary school science program can be traced through their development of more than 100 years. Two definite influences can be identified as early as the decade of the 1850's. One of these was the didactic literature brought into this country largely from Britain and adapted and then reprinted by American publishers. This instructional literature reflected its origins in an aristocratic conception of education and was designed for use by private tutors or by parents teaching the children at home. It was within the financial reach of only the upper classes. Most of this material was directed to children's observation and to study of natural phenomena. Underhill has traced the didactic literature to the influence of such men as Francis Bacon, John Locke, and other writers who at that time were stimulating democratic thought in Europe as well as in America.[1] When the National Education Association was organized in 1857, it helped to stimulate the task of adapting some of this literature for use in school classrooms.

The second influential factor during the late 1850's rose from the "Pestalozzian object teaching" movement. This method of teaching was very widespread and was an international educational development. The applications made of the method varied greatly from one country to another. In Germany it developed into *Heimatkunde*,[2] or "community study." In England and in the United States object teaching evolved into, and was later supplanted by, nature study. However, the American and English versions of nature study varied greatly in spite of their common origin in object teaching.

The best known American adaptation of the Pestalozzian method was developed at Oswego, New York. Due to the influence of the National Education Association which supported it, the "Oswego method"[3] was given nearly universal acceptance in this country. The new method aroused interest in the revision of content and in the method of study in the rapidly growing elementary schools.

The methodology of object teaching had a highly formal structure which tended to obscure the legitimate purposes of science instruction; it did not contribute effectively to a sense of sequence and direction. Men like Franklin and Jefferson had encouraged the development of science in elementary education hoping for and working for programs that had merit due to their continuity and practicality. Object teaching destroyed whatever gains had been made in this direction because the emphasis tended to shift to mere description of animate and inanimate objects and to neglect the interpretation and understanding of events and phenomena. The content was further fragmented by the organization of information concerning the particular object of study into formal separate sciences, thus imposing a mature scientist's view on children. Profound meanings tended to be neglected in favor of mere obvious descriptions.

The old method of object teaching tended to be supported by the principles of faculty psychology.[4] The emphasis on observation and memorization for very young children was based on the assumption of the sequential development of capacities. It was falsely assumed that young children were able only to observe and identify objects but were unable to reason or to interpret phenomena. In addition, the specialized methodology of object teaching, together with the exclusion of the use of books, made heavy demands upon the ability and knowledge of the teacher. It appeared to be particularly ill-suited to the purposes and needs of teachers and pupils in a rapidly developing industrial society.

Some insight into the nature of the ideas underlying the "object study" movement may be gained from the following selected excerpts. The method was:

to place objects before them [children] in which they are interested, and which tend to cultivate their perceptive faculties; and, at the same time, lead them to name the object, to describe its parts, and to state the relation of these parts. Thus language also is cultivated; and, from the observation of a single object, the pupil is led to compare it with others, and the first steps in classification are taken.

. . . These lessons are designed specially to cultivate the perceptive faculty; and hence, in any true system of education, they must be considered as fundamental— not only in their relation to the faculties, but as giving the first ideas, or laying the foundation of all branches of knowledge. Object Lessons in form lead directly to Drawing, Writing, and Geometry; in sound and form, to Language, including Reading, Speaking, and Spelling; in place, to Geography; and in animals, plants, minerals, etc., to Natural History. . .

This method commences with an examination of objects and facts, then institutes comparisons by which resemblances, differences, and relations are observed; and with the results so obtained, repeats the process until the remotest relations are known and the highest generalizations reached. This process may, with propriety, be called the Objective Method or Objective Teaching.

Objective Teaching, in this enlarged sense, includes Object Lessons, and a great deal more. It comprehends the unfolding of the faculties in the order of their growth and use, and the presentation of the several branches of instruction in their natural order. Its great aims are mental growth and the acquisition of knowledge.[5]

The decade of 1870 witnessed the culmination of a number of developing trends. The writings of such men as Herbert Spencer [6] in his essay, "What Knowledge is of Most Worth," and the rising importance of science and technology had forced the consideration of science as a field of study upon the public. It was during this decade that colleges and universities first came to accept science subjects as satisfactory prerequisites for admission to colleges.

The depression of 1873 spurred a critical examination of the program of the public schools; and the elementary schools, particularly, were the object of a veritable storm of abusive criticism. Tax-conscious citizens were demanding clarification of the aims and purposes of education. Most of the educational journals joined the hue and cry for more science in the public school programs. There were accompanying changes in the social and economic patterns of the time. Old patterns of teaching and learning were seen to be ill-adapted to the changing times and not fully in accord with characteristics of the learning process.

Near the end of the 19th century, the National Education Association sponsored an extensive study at the secondary school level that was to influence the entire educational system. This was the work of the National Education Association Committee of Ten. The results of this Committee's study tended to stabilize science offerings and led to the discontinuance of a large number of short-term specialized science courses taught in the secondary school. The report put emphasis on laboratory and other direct experiences and on the need for special training for science teachers. Its influence was effective primarily on textbooks, syllabi and other instructional material. These changes at the secondary level were reflected rather quickly in the elementary schools. It was only after the report of the Committee of Ten that materials for pupil use and teacher planning appeared in any appreciable volume.

A number of men rose to prominence in the field of elementary school science around the turn of the century. Of these, William F. Harris [4] first translated philosophy and educational theory into a specific and extensively detailed elementary science curriculum which provided help to teachers in the field. G. Stanley Hall [7] and Colonel Francis W. Parker [8] contributed general philosophies of education supporting nature study. These philosophies opened the way for others to experiment and to work out detailed elementary programs, especially in elementary science. Much of this work was done by Henry H. Strait and Wilbur S. Jackman at the Practice School of the Cook County Normal School, later the Chicago Institute, and now the School of Education at the University of Chicago.[1] Parker strongly supported the work of Strait and Jackman in Chicago, influencing the use of science as a unifying principle in elementary school curricula. Jackman's writings represent a connecting link between early writers of children's literature and modern elementary science. His positive, dynamic view of children and science is in close accord with modern ideas. Jackman's contributions to elementary science were obscured for a time by the extended development of a nature study movement.

Liberty Hyde Bailey and associates at Cornell University were prime movers of the nature study movement. They were motivated by the need to improve agriculture and to halt the increasing migration of young people from farms to cities where they would add to already swollen city relief rolls.[9] One of the important publications to come out of Cornell was the *Handbook of Nature Study* by Mrs. Anna Botsford Comstock which ran through many editions after 1911. This book, along with the Cornell rural school leaflets was, and still is, widely distributed to schools. These and other publications by the Cornell group rank among the most comprehensive efforts in teacher education ever undertaken in the field of science education. Like object study, nature study was based on the principles of faculty psychology and on the alleged serial development of traits. The child was considered in terms of his limitations rather than in terms of his capabilities. Nature study had been developed by specialists in science who lacked the perception and understanding of men like Jackman who were specialists in science as well as experienced teachers of children.

By the 1920's the enthusiasm for nature study was beginning to wane. The influence of the new designs in curricula for science was beginning to be felt. In addition, new thinking in other fields was again beginning to make an impact on all of education and was particularly relevant to science instruction. Men of the stature of Charles Sanders Peirce,[10] William James [11] and John Dewey [12] were having tremendous influence on education. William James and Charles Sanders Peirce had contributed a theory of pragmatism which meant in essence that the meaning of a conception is to be found in the working out of its implications. The link between concept and experience was seen as fundamental. Peirce's thinking was basic to the development of the operational theory of meaning which was closely associated with the development of pragmatism. Dewey's contributions were numerous; but, perhaps, the most significant for the developing field of elementary science was his contention that the methodology of science is at least of equal—or perhaps of greater—significance than the actual knowledge accumulated. The present emphasis on "science as inquiry" would seem to be a reaffirmation of a position which Dewey took nearly half a century ago. It was apparent by the middle of the 1920's that nature study was no longer a satisfactory vehicle for a modern science program. Its whole rationale was no longer consistent with the psychology, philosophy and methodology of the time. It was inconsistent with the existing social and economic realities. With the benefit of historical perspective it is patently obvious that a substantial change in the science program for the elementary school was in order.

It is probably no exaggeration to say that Columbia University was, at that time, the colossus of American education as a training institution for public school administration and for other general leadership positions in the educational field. In 1927 a thesis was written at Columbia which came at a time when the situation was ripe for change. It represented the then most prestigious institution in professional education and was to have, perhaps, the most far-reaching influence on the development of elementary science of any single event in the history of the field. The study was entitled *Certain*

Techniques Used in Developing a Course of Study in Science for the Horace Mann Elementary School.[13] It represented the culmination of three years of work by Gerald S. Craig at the famous laboratory school and profoundly affected subsequent developments in elementary school science. Craig turned his back resolutely on the nature study movement and, in so doing, took note of the great chaos of educational goals to which lip service was then being paid. These goals included various esthetic, ethical, spiritual, intellectual, and civil-training goals without adequate indication as to how such aims were to be achieved. Parenthetically, it is perhaps worth noting at this point that the question of purposes is one which is still not fully resolved, although it is certain that there is far more unanimity as to the purposes and ends to be served today than there was at the time that Craig was doing his original study. Some of the present arguments and debates in the profession represent confusion among the disputing parties as to the real purposes to be served by the elementary science program. Craig saw the function of science in the elementary school to be significant in terms of general education, pointing out that the laws, generalizations, and principles of science have vital meanings to individuals regarding numerous questions which confront them. He also saw the utilitarian aspect as it is related to health, safety, and the economy. He was aware, moreover, of more than the cognitive aspects of science instruction and emphasized also the affective dimensions: attitudes, appreciations, and interests. Clearly, Craig's thesis has been one of the landmarks in elementary science and is basic to much of the later writings in the field including his own.

Another important step forward was taken when the Thirty-first Yearbook [14] of the National Society for the Study of Education was published in 1932. This Yearbook presented a plan for an integrated program of science teaching. This marked the beginning of a trend which has continued to be more and more emphasized down to the present time. Problems involving sequence and articulation of science instruction between the various grades and school units have continued as vexing difficulties. The National Science Teachers Association has had a committee at work for several years on the K-12 science program. Others are equally concerned with problems of articulation between high schools and colleges. The design of an appropriate sequential series of science experiences which shall extend from elementary school through college is a problem which has occupied the thinking of many persons. This problem has stimulated study of such diverse questions as content and placement, when track programs should be instituted, when non-science and non-college bound students should terminate their study of science, when advanced placement programs should be used, and how elementary teachers should be educated. These questions are obviously inter-twined with conceptions of the ultimate purposes and goals of education and no universal agreement has been attained as to what these should be. Perhaps no such agreement is possible or even desirable; but an understanding of the problems and their complexities would at least reduce the confusion.

The Thirty-first Yearbook also placed an emphasis on the major generalizations of science as objectives of instruction. This emphasis had profound effects on course syllabi and textbooks, and a generation of these documents tended to emphasize the understandings and applications of the principles of science. One other obvious example of the Yearbook's influence was the great amount of research devoted to identifying the major principles of science which were of significance to general education. In fact, a great body of the research that was subsequently done in science education was a reflection of the influence of this famous Yearbook. The Yearbook was clear and definite in its support of elementary science rather than nature study and, as a result, it contributed to the rapid advancement of science at the elementary school level. The report advocated basing the selection of science content on personal and social criteria; thus, probably, both conforming to and augmenting the educational thinking that was then developing in this direction.

The Society also devoted its Forty-sixth Yearbook, published in 1947, to problems of science education. The increasing impact which science was obviously having upon the social, cultural, and economic affairs of men continued to be very much in evidence in the thinking revealed in this Yearbook. The following quotation is illustrative of this fact.

Instruction in science must take cognizance of the social impact of developments produced by science. It is not enough that they be understood in a technical or scientific sense; it is most important that their effects on attitudes and relationships of people be studied and understood. Science instruction has not only a great potential contribution to make but also a responsibility to help develop in our youth the qualities of mind and the attitudes that will be of greatest usefulness to them in meeting the pressing social and economic problems that face the world.[15]

There is a marked sensitivity to some of the "affective" objectives of science instruction in this Yearbook. There is also a more obvious reflection of sensitivity to the responsibility which educators have to prescribe the precise way in which statements of intangible and illusive objectives can be translated into practical programs and to determine how the effectiveness of instruction can be measured.

The most recent document prepared by the National Society for the Study of Education of primary concern to science education was the Fifty-ninth Yearbook which was published in 1960. This Yearbook takes cognizance of the increasing dependence of society on science. The implications for the scientific training of citizens of such a society are clearly considered to be of fundamental importance. The Yearbook goes further than preceding reports of the Society in stressing that characteristic of science which is known as "process" or "inquiry." It is perhaps significant to quote the Yearbook with respect to this latter observation.

One function of the elementary school has always been to help children learn a part of what they need to know from the world's storehouse of knowledge. In recent years this function has embraced more and more science. Scientific methods of investigation, by which knowledge may be acquired and tested, are now very much a part of our culture. The elementary school should help children become acquainted with these methods.[16]

One may summarize the historical overview by pointing out that the past century has been a century of unprecedented social, economic, scientific, and technological change. The elementary schools are to a very large degree a mirror of the ambient culture, and they are probably more sensitive to social change than any other educational level. They are always, to a degree, consonant with the prevailing philosophies and state of knowledge in existence at any particular time. Fundamental changes in philosophy, in theories of child rearing and educability, in the need for universal and extended educational training for all children and adolescents of our society with capacity to learn, have been accepted within this century. Science, itself, has progressed from the dilettantism of the leisured intellectual to a basic and fundamental activity of a substantial percentage of mankind. No human being of any civilized nation can remain untouched by these multifarious developments. In such a milieu it is not surprising that elementary science instruction has been beset by numerous perplexing problems.

REFERENCES

1. Underhill, Orra E., *The Origin and Development of Elementary School Science*, Scott, Foresman and Company, Chicago, 1941.
2. Shoemaker, Lois Meier, *Natural Science Education in the German Elementary Schools*, Bureau of Publications, Teachers College, Columbia University, Contributions to Education, No. 445, New York, 1930.
3. Lammers, Theresa J., "The Thirty-first Yearbook and 20 Years of Elementary Science," *Science Education*, **39**, 39–40 (February, 1955).
4. Craig, Gerald S., "Elementary School Science in the Past Century," *Science Teacher*, **24**, 4, 11–14 (February, 1957).
5. Krusi, Hermann, *Pestalozzi: His Life, Work and Influence*, Wilson, Hinkle and Co., Cincinnati, 1875, pp. 162–164.
6. Spencer, Herbert, "What Knowledge Is of Most Worth?" in *Education*, Appleton, New York, 1926 (Reprinted from 1860 edition).
7. Hall, G. Stanley, *Aspects of Child Life and Education*, Appleton, New York, 1921.
8. Parker, Francis W., *Talks on Pedagogics*, Kellogg, New York, 1894.
9. Comstock, Anna Botsford, *The Comstocks of Cornell: John Henry and Anna Botsford Comstock, an Autobiography by Anna Botsford Comstock*, Comstock Publishing Associates, New York, 1953.
10. Peirce, Charles Sanders, *Philosophical Writings of Peirce*, Dover, New York, 1955.
11. James, William, *The Principles of Psychology*, Holt, New York, 1890.
12. Dewey, John, *Democracy and Education*, Macmillan, New York, 1916.
13. Craig, Gerald S., *Certain Techniques Used in Developing a Course of Study in Science for the Horace Mann Elementary School*, Bureau of Publica-

tions, Teachers College, Columbia University, Contributions to Education, No. 276, New York, 1927.

14. National Society for the Study of Education, *A Program for Teaching Science*, Thirty-first Yearbook, Part I, Public School Publishing Company, Bloomington, Illinois, 1932.
15. National Society for the Study of Education, *Science Education in American Schools*, Forty-sixth Yearbook, Part I, The University of Chicago Press, Chicago, Illinois, 1947, pp. 1, 145–147.
16. National Society for the Study of Education, *Rethinking Science Education*, Fifty-ninth Yearbook, Part I, The University of Chicago Press, Chicago, Illinois, 1960, pp. 112–113.

SCIENCE IN THE ELEMENTARY SCHOOL*

Paul E. Blackwood

Paul E. Blackwood reports on a study of the status of elementary science education in the United States today. This survey of practices encompasses objectives, extent of science teaching, teaching patterns, departmentalization, consultant services, curriculum sources, time allocations for science teaching, equipment, expenditures for elementary science, science clubs, and some barriers to effective science teaching. The study reveals many inadequacies in the science program of elementary schools. Dr. Blackwood makes five recommendations for the improvement of elementary science teaching based upon the findings of his study.

NEARLY ALL public elementary schools in the United States teach science at some time during the school year. This statement, though true, covers wide variations. Schools treat science as a separate subject or as incidental to another subject. They give several hours a week to science teaching or only minutes. A few schools have special teachers, but most rely on the classroom teacher, with or without the help of a specialist, to teach science. Budget allowances for science equipment and material are ample and scant—and every degree between.

These facts and others have come to light in a recent study completed by the Office of Education on science teaching in the elementary schools of the United States in school year 1961–62. A full report on the study will be

* REPRINTED FROM *School Life*, Vol. 47, No. 2, November 1964, pp. 13–15, 27–28. Dr. Blackwood is Specialist for Elementary Science at the U.S. Office of Education.

issued in an Office publication (*Science Teaching in the Elementary School: A Survey of Practices, 1961–62*) now in press. This article is a report on some of the highlights of the findings of the study.

Information for the study was obtained from a questionnaire sent to a representative sample of the Nation's more than 87,000 public elementary schools. Schools in every State were included, but the study does not report the status of science teaching by region or by State. Questionnaires were sent to individual, general purpose elementary schools rather than to school systems, and they were completed by principals with the help of teachers.

Replies to the questionnaire have been broken down by enrollment for schools and administrative units (districts). The breakdowns by schools are *800 and over, 400 to 799, 50 to 399,* and *49 and under; by districts, 25,000 or over, 6,000 to 24,999, 3,000 to 5,999, 600 to 2,999,* and *599 and under.*

OBJECTIVES

The questionnaire began by asking schools to rate as *very important, of some importance,* and *of little or no importance* 10 commonly accepted objectives of science teaching. The respondents rated nearly all of the objectives as *very important* or *of some importance.* Only one—to develop scientists—was not considered *very important* by at least 40 percent of the schools. See table 1.

EXTENT OF SCIENCE TEACHING

Only a very small percent of all schools did not teach science at all. Three-fourths or more taught science at every grade level except kindergarten for at least one-half the year; 4.5 percent did not teach science in kindergarten, and 4.4 percent did not teach it in the first grade.

TABLE 1

The Importance of 10 Objectives of Science Teaching as Rated by Public Elementary Schools (Ranked by Percent of Response to Very Important)

OBJECTIVE	VERY IMPOR- TANT	OF SOME IMPOR- TANCE	LITTLE OR NO IM- PORTANCE
1. To help pupils develop curiosity	87.0	12.0	1.0
2. To help pupils learn to think critically	85.2	14.3	0.5
3. To introduce pupils to typical science topics— weather, electricity, plant and animal life	84.3	14.9	.8
4. To help pupils acquire knowledge of their environment	84.2	15.5	.4
5. To help pupils develop an appreciation of their environment	82.4	17.1	.5

TABLE 1—CONTINUED

OBJECTIVE	VERY IMPOR-TANT	OF SOME IMPOR-TANCE	LITTLE OR NO IM-PORTANCE
6. To develop problem-solving skills	73.9	24.2	1.9
7. To develop in pupils a sense of responsibility for the proper use of science	69.3	27.7	3.0
8. To prepare pupils for high school science	42.8	45.2	12.1
9. To develop hobbies and leisure-time activities	40.9	50.4	8.7
10. To develop scientists	17.6	51.8	30.6

The percent of schools teaching science more than half a year varied by grade and size. More large schools than small taught science more than half a year in almost every grade. In the third grade, for instance, the percent ranged from 70 in the *49 and under* schools to 90 in schools enrolling *800 and over*. Figure 1 gives the percent of public elementary schools teaching science more than half a year by grade.

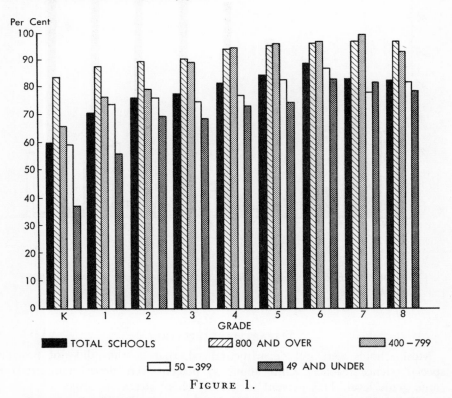

FIGURE 1.

Percent of public elementary schools that teach science more than half a year, by grade.

TEACHING PATTERNS

Schools were asked to indicate which of these five titles most aptly described the science teaching pattern they followed:

(1) *Taught as a separate subject,* (2) *integrated with other subjects,* (3) *incidental,* (4) *separate subject and incidental,* and (5) *integrated and incidental.* The replies indicate that the grade level made a difference. In the upper grades schools most often followed the pattern *separate subject and incidental;* in the lower grades, *integrated with other subjects.* In other words, the percent of schools teaching science as a separate subject increased by grade. In the *400 to 700* group of schools, for example, the range was from 13 percent in kindergarten to 89 percent in the eighth grade. See figure 2.

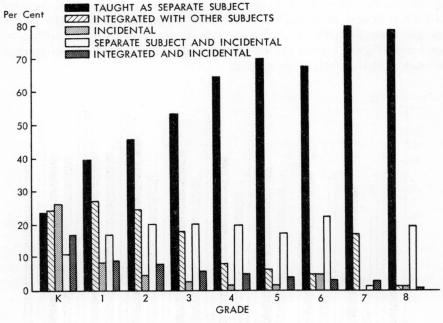

FIGURE 2.

Percent of public elementary schools that teach science by various patterns, by grade.

DEPARTMENTALIZATION

Most schools were not departmentalized, that is, they did not provide special science teachers. Only about 15 percent were departmentalized at some grade level. This percent varied by school size as follows:

ENROLLMENT:	PERCENT OF DEPARTMENTALIZATION
800 and over	36.5
400–799	21.8
50–399	18.5
49 and under	.08

THE TEACHERS

The study found that the classroom teacher was the person most frequently teaching science in all grades in all schools. But the percent of schools in which science was taught only by a classroom teacher decreased progressively from the first grade (86.5 percent) to the seventh (72.9).[1] About 8 percent of the schools provided special assistance to the classroom teacher through a specialist in the central office. Although a large percent of the smaller schools did not have special science teachers, schools in every enrollment group had specialists available, particularly the *800 and over* group. About 30 percent of the schools in this group reported that a special science teacher from a central office was available to help classroom teachers in kindergarten through grade six.

A small percent of the schools reported that television was the primary source of science teaching. Though the percent was small, it may be significant in view of the widespread interest in educational television. The practice was most common in the large schools; none in the *49 and under* group reported using television.

See table 2 for the findings on the source of science teaching in the elementary school.

CONSULTANT SERVICES

About 42 percent of the schools had some type of consultant help in science available to teachers. Of these, nearly 40 percent depended on general elementary supervisors. About 15 percent had elementary science consultants, although the percent ranged from 39.5 percent in the *800 and over* schools to 5.6 percent in the *49 and under*. High school science teachers were available for consultation in 27 percent of all schools having help, particularly in schools in small administrative units.

The questionnaire asked schools which had consultant service to indicate by grade level whether teachers used this help *very often* (at least once a week), *occasionally* (once a month), or *rarely or never* (less than once a month), and to indicate on a list of nine the ways they used consultants.

[1] The grades 7 and 8 represented in this report are in schools organized by grade levels, kindergarten through 8. It does not report on conditions in grades 7 and 8 in junior high schools, where the percent of special science teachers is higher.

TABLE 2

Source of Science Teaching in Public Elementary Schools: Percentage by Grade

SOURCE	GRADES—ALL SCHOOLS								
	K	1	2	3	4	5	6	7	8
Classroom teacher only	84.0	86.5	86.6	84.4	82.6	80.4	77.0	72.9	72.9
Classroom teacher with help from science specialists attached to school staff	5.5	5.0	4.8	6.2	6.8	6.2	6.4	4.4	4.6
Classroom teacher with help of science specialist from the central office staff	10.1	7.5	7.5	7.6	7.6	7.6	7.6	1.5	2.5
Special science teacher on the school staff	.0	.1	.3	.3	.9	2.2	3.4	15.7	15.8
Special science teacher on central office staff	.0	.0	.0	.1	.1	.1	.1	.1	.0
Classroom teacher with special competence in science in lieu of regular classroom teacher	.0	.6	.6	.8	1.0	1.6	3.3	4.6	4.0
Television	.4	.3	.3	.7	1.1	1.8	2.1	1.0	.1

Roughly 50 percent of the schools used consultants *very often* or *occasionally* in kindergarten through grade 3 and about 60 percent used them *very often* or *occasionally* in the upper grades. The responses to the list of ways consultants are used show considerable variation from one enrollment group to another, but all groups indicated that consultants were used most often to provide materials and to plan and consult with teachers. See figure 3.

CURRICULUM SOURCES

The questionnaire asked schools to indicate the frequency of use (*very often, occasionally,* or *rarely or never*) by grade of (1) State guides for courses of study, (2) administrative unit guides, (3) local school guides, (4) textbooks, and (5) teacher's own ideas. Over one-third of the schools said they used guides provided by the State *very often* in grades 7 and 8 and over one-fourth in grades 1, 2, and 3. Over 50 percent of the *800 and under* said they used State guides *rarely or never*. But about 50 percent of the *49 and under* schools used State guides *very often*. All in all, schools in the small administrative units tended to use State guides more often than schools in other units.

LOCAL SCHOOL GUIDES. A higher percent of the larger schools used local guides *very often* than did the smaller schools, at every grade level. But a

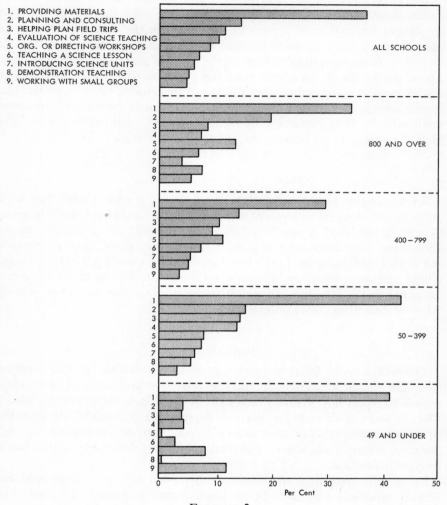

1. PROVIDING MATERIALS
2. PLANNING AND CONSULTING
3. HELPING PLAN FIELD TRIPS
4. EVALUATION OF SCIENCE TEACHING
5. ORG. OR DIRECTING WORKSHOPS
6. TEACHING A SCIENCE LESSON
7. INTRODUCING SCIENCE UNITS
8. DEMONSTRATION TEACHING
9. WORKING WITH SMALL GROUPS

ALL SCHOOLS

800 AND OVER

400 – 799

50 – 399

49 AND UNDER

Per Cent

FIGURE 3.

Nine ways consultants are used in teaching science, ranked within school enrollment groups.

relatively high percent of schools *rarely or never* used local school guides, probably because they were not available.

TEXTBOOKS. A high percent of the schools, 78.1 to 90, reported that they used textbooks *very often*, except in kindergarten (where textbooks are rarely used at any time). The percent of schools using textbooks *very often* increased from the lower grades to the upper grades in every administrative unit enrollment group.

ADMINISTRATIVE UNIT MATERIAL. The percent of schools using science guides developed by the administrative unit rose with the size of the unit enrollment. More than 50 percent of the schools in the largest administrative unit group, at every grade level, used an administrative unit science guide *very often* in contrast to 10 percent in the *500 and under* administrative unit. About one-fourth of the schools used the guides *rarely or never* in the large school systems, compared to three-fourths of the smaller school systems. The largest schools also tended to use administrative unit guides far more than small schools. It is important to realize, however, that schools may have marked *rarely or never* because no guides were available.

TIME GIVEN TO TEACHING

Schools usually taught science two, three, or five periods a week. But what do these periods mean in terms of minutes, a better measure of the time given to science teaching? A small but significant percent of all schools taught science less than 20 minutes a week at almost every grade level, particularly the *49 and under* schools. In the lower grades only a small percent of schools taught science as much as 200 minutes a week (an average of 40 minutes a day), but in the fifth through eighth grades a substantial percent of schools taught it more than 200 minutes a week.

EQUIPMENT

The questionnaire listed 42 selected items used in science teaching, ranging from the simple and common, to the expensive and unusual, and asked schools to report how many of each item were available for use in the school. The list was not all inclusive, nor was it presented as a model list since the equipment requirements of a school depend on its curriculum. It did, however, contain items which curriculum guides and elementary science books frequently mention.

For almost every item the mode number (that is, the number most frequently reported) was *zero*. In no instance was it greater than *one*. The schools in the *800 and over* group fared best. But even in this group, though many schools had enough equipment for a demonstration type program, they did not have enough for a program of individual investigation. The *50 to 399* and the *49 and under* schools reported an extreme dearth of items by actual count.

As to the availability of equipment, the difference among enrollment groups was most striking. The smaller the school, the less available and the less adequate the equipment and supplies. Over one-fourth (26 percent) of the *49 and under* schools compared to less than 1 percent of the *800 and over* schools, for example, reported that equipment and supplies were completely lacking. Eight percent of all schools said that equipment and supplies were *very plentiful*; 46 percent, *generally adequate*; and 46 percent, in the two categories, *far from adequate and completely lacking.*

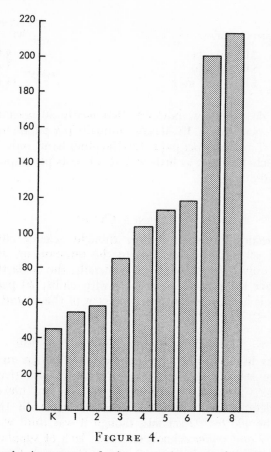

FIGURE 4.

The number of minutes a week given to science teaching in schools in the 400 to 700 group.

EXPENDITURE FOR SCIENCE

The mean expenditure by school enrollment was from 44 cents to 60 cents a pupil. The mode number, however, indicates that the largest percent of schools spent from 11 to 14 cents per pupil. The *49 and under* schools spent as much per pupil as the larger schools, but the amount spent by these schools was inadequate to support good programs. The percentages of all schools in each of several expenditure categories were these:

AMOUNT SPENT PER PUPIL:	PERCENT OF SCHOOLS
0–20 cents	40.1
21–40 cents	9.4
41–60 cents	11.7
61–80 cents	10.6
81 cents–$1	4.6

AMOUNT SPENT PER PUPIL:	PERCENT OF SCHOOLS
$1.01–$1.24	4.6
$1.25–$1.50	3.4
$1.51 and over	15.6

These figures do not show, however, that nearly 50 percent of the *49 and under* schools spent from 0 to 20 cents annually per pupil and that 21 percent spent over $1.51 annually per pupil. On the other hand, only 4.3 percent of the *800 and over* schools spent as little as 0 to 20 cents per pupil, and 9.2 percent spent $1.51 and over.

SCIENCE CLUBS

On the question of whether they thought science clubs desirable, 75 percent of all schools said yes. But to the question on whether they had science clubs, only 7 percent said yes. Generally, the larger the administrative unit, the higher the percent of schools with clubs: 20 percent of the *800 and over* schools had clubs, but only 5 percent of the *49 and under*.

BARRIERS TO EFFECTIVE TEACHING

Of 13 items listed by the questionnaire as "barriers to effective science teaching," the schools indicated that "lack of consultive service" is the greatest barrier. There were differences of opinion, however, among the groups. "Inadequate room facilities" ranked first with the *800 and over* schools and the *400 to 799* schools, though it was third with the other two groups. The *49 and under* schools checked "lack of supplies," "lack of consultant help," "not enough money," and "not enough time for instruction" as the greatest barriers. See table 3.

RECOMMENDATIONS

The data obtained by this study seems to point to inadequacies in the science programs of some elementary schools. Many changes will be necessary before these schools can eliminate them. The findings of the study point to these recommendations:

• Schools should determine whether the time they give to science teaching is enough to provide sound and adequate instruction.

• Schools teaching science incidentally should reassess the advantages and disadvantages of this method in comparison with programs based on systematically planned curriculums.

• Schools with inadequate supplies should acquire more materials and equipment. Small schools and small administrative units, particularly, need to put more effort into obtaining and using science equipment and supplies.

• Schools need to develop and take part in inservice programs for teachers to help them update knowledge and acquire better methods.

• Schools need to identify additional consultant resources, particularly for the classroom teacher who most often teaches science in elementary schools.

TABLE 3

Barriers to Effective Science Teaching in Public Elementary Schools Ranked by Replies from All Schools and by Enrollment Groups

		RANKING BY SCHOOL ENROLLMENT GROUPS			
BARRIER	ALL SCHOOLS	800 AND OVER	400 TO 799	50 TO 399	49 AND UNDER
Lack of consultant services	1	4	3	1	2
Lack of supplies	2	7	5	2	1
Inadequate room facilities	3	1	1	13	8
Insufficient funds	4	6	6	3	3
Teachers lack sufficient knowledge of science	5	2	2	4	7
Insufficient inservice opportunities	6	10	8	7	5
Teachers lack ability to improvise	7	5	7	6	10
Teachers do not know methods	8	3	4	5	9
Not enough time given to science teaching	9	8	10	8	4
No community support	10	12	11	9	6
Teachers lack interest	11	9	9	10	13
No definite curriculum	12	13	12	11	12
Other subjects considered more important	13	11	13	12	11

ORGANIZING AND PLANNING FOR TEACHING ELEMENTARY SCIENCE

INTRODUCTION

The science program in the elementary school should be planned and structured, just as is done in the other areas of the elementary school curriculum. All too often elementary science programs have been either non-existent or else very loosely planned and structured. In such cases the elementary science textbook would usually serve both as science program and curriculum guide for the teachers. Sometimes a school system would list the science topics and concepts to be learned for each grade and include a number of suggested activities for teaching these topics and concepts.

In recent years there has been a steadily increasing trend to planned, structured programs, developed cooperatively by the teachers with the help of administrators and science supervisors, educators, and specialists. When planning such programs the first step invariably consists of identifying and clearly delineating the objectives, or goals, of science teaching.

The objectives of science education have changed very little in the past twenty-five years. The same objectives apply to both the secondary and the elementary school, the only difference being one of depth and degree of attainment. Although the literature lists a wide variety of objectives, they all fall into two categories: those that pertain to the structure of science and those that pertain to the process of science.

The structure of science refers to science content. An effective science program aims for the acquisition of concepts and principles. There is no rote memorization of facts or laws, but the learning through appropriate techniques of concepts which lead to an understanding of conceptual schemes.

The process of science is a comparatively recent term in science education and is extremely popular. However, its frame of reference

53

is not new. It refers to the key operations, or processes, of science and the scientist. In earlier years such terms as "ways of the scientist" and "desirable behaviors" have been used in the same context as process. They all refer to the methods of science that make it possible for children to learn science. These include all those abilities, skills, and attitudes that make critical thinking and problem-solving possible. In an effective science program great emphasis is placed upon process, because process is the means whereby real learning of the structure, or content, of science takes place in the classroom.

The elementary science program should be organized and structured so that it has adequate scope. The science topics that make up the program should be chosen with quality in mind, rather than quantity. The program should have balance, so that the child is given the opportunity to explore in the area of biological, physical, and earth science.

The program should have a well-developed sequence. The sequence should be such that the same science topics will be taken up not at successive grade levels but at alternate grade levels. This creates a spiral of fewer topics per grade, but allows the topics to be taken up in much greater depth than would be possible if a large number of topics were assigned to each grade.

Existing research on the mental, physical, and emotional behavior of children should be used as a guide in the development and grade placement of science units. Consideration should be given to the children's intellectual capacity, their ability to think abstractly, their curiosity, their aptitude for originality and creativity, and their span of attention and persistence.

A well-planned and well-organized science program should make proper provision for needed supplies, equipment, and reference materials. Also, an adequate amount of time per day should be allocated for the teaching of science. All too often the science lesson is the first to be dropped when other classroom activities run overly long. Finally, the science program should be in a process of continual evaluation if it is to retain its effectiveness.

SCIENCE EDUCATION FOR
CHANGING TIMES*

National Society for the Study of Education

The following two articles are excerpts from Chapters Two and Three, respectively, of the Fifty-ninth Yearbook, Part I, of the National Society for the Study of Education, Rethinking Science Education. *They show how little the objectives of science education have changed since they were stated in the Society's Forty-sixth Yearbook. These objectives included the development of such learning outcomes as (1) functional information, concepts, and principles; (2) instrumental and problem-solving skills; (3) attitudes; (4) appreciations; and (5) interests. In the Fifty-ninth Yearbook, such terms as "critical thinking," "scientific process," and "inquiry" are introduced, and greater emphasis is placed upon those aspects of science that deal with these terms. Members of the committee who wrote Chapter Two include Paul DeH. Hurd, Vernon E. Anderson, J. W. Buchta, John H. Fisher, Eric M. Rogers, Guy Suits, and Ralph W. Tyler. Those who wrote Chapter Three include Paul L. Dressel, Mary A. Burmeister, John M. Mason, and Clarence H. Nelson.*

THE OBJECTIVES of science-teaching as they appear in educational literature have changed little in the past twenty-five years. On the other hand, there have been changes in the nature of the science taught; for example, the sciences have become more unified and have gained an important position in world affairs. These factors suggest the need to re-think the purposes of teaching science in schools.

Recently there has been much criticism of science-teaching. Some scientists have been concerned that science was not being taught either as understanding or as enterprise. They have thought that science-teaching should reflect the nature of science, and it should harmonize with the scientific point of view. The lack of social orientation in science-teaching and the failure to teach modern science have concerned other groups.

The objectives of the teaching of science are essentially the same from the elementary through the high school. The degree of attainment and the level

---

* REPRINTED FROM *Rethinking Science Education,* 59th Yearbook of the National Society for the Study of Education, Part I (Chicago: University of Chicago Press, 1960), pp. 33–37, by permission of the publisher.

of competency vary according to the development, interest, and abilities of young people. We cannot expect that every objective will be achieved by all students, that the rate of achievement will be uniform, or that everyone will reach the same level of understanding. This suggests that the objectives of the student who is oriented to a science career and those of the college-bound student will be different from those of other pupils.

Many criticisms directed toward the objectives of science-teaching are actually a censure of classroom procedures which fail to realize those objectives; for example, methods which demand too many facts, too little conceptualizing, too much memorizing, and too little thinking.

The following list of objectives provides a model by which the teacher may orient his thinking in developing his own purposes for teaching science.

UNDERSTANDING SCIENCE

There are two major aspects of science-teaching: one is knowledge, and the other is enterprise. From science courses, pupils should acquire a useful command of science concepts and principles. Science is more than a collection of isolated and assorted facts; to be meaningful and valuable, they must be woven into generalized concepts. A student should learn something about the character of scientific knowledge, how it has been developed, and how it is used. He must see that knowledge has a certain dynamic quality and that it is quite likely to shift in meaning and status with time.

The pupil needs at each grade level to acquire a background of ordered knowledge, to develop an adequate vocabulary in science for effective communication, and to learn some facts because they are important in everyday living, such as knowledge that is useful in maintaining health, promoting safety, and interpreting the immediate environment.

Recent theories and new knowledge should have priority in science-teaching when they are significant and can be made understandable at a specified grade level. The generalized concepts selected for teaching should be those which tend to explain or involve many science facts.

PROBLEM-SOLVING

Science is a process in which observations and their interpretations are used to develop new concepts, to extend our understanding of the world, to suggest new areas for exploration, and to provide some predictions about the future. It is focused upon inquiry and subsequent action.

Methods for solving problems in science are numerous. There is no one scientific method; in fact, there are almost as many methods as there are scientists and problems to be solved. Inevitably the details of scientific investigation are seldom the same for any two problems. What is done is highly flexible and quite personal. Incentive, intuition, the play of imagination, fertility of ideas, and creativeness in testing hypotheses are important parts of the process. The methods of science are something more than measurement, laboratory techniques, and data processing followed by logical deductions. Sometimes they are not very logical, but the search for truth is always present. Presenting problem-solving as a series of logically ordered steps is simply a technique to isolate the critical skills and abilities and to give them special attention in teaching.

A process of inquiry involves careful observing, seeking the most reliable data, and then using rational processes to give order to the data and to suggest possible conclusions or further research. At higher levels of achievement the student should be able to establish relationships from his findings, and in turn to make predictions about future observations.

THE SOCIAL ASPECTS OF SCIENCE

Young people need to understand the dependence of our society upon scientific and technological achievement and to realize that science is a basic part of modern living. The scientific process and the knowledge produced cannot be assumed to be ends in themselves except for the classical scientist. For him the pursuit of new knowledge is a professional effort, and any lack of social concern on his part may be accepted. But a liberal education has a wider orientation, particularly at precollege levels. A student should understand the relation of basic research to applied research, and the interplay of technological innovations and human affairs. More of technology than science will be involved in social decisions; both are important in public policy.

APPRECIATIONS

A student with a liberal education in science should be able to appreciate:

1. The importance of science for understanding the modern world.
2. The methods and procedures of science for their value in discovering new knowledge and extending the meaning of previously developed ideas.
3. The men who add to the storehouse of knowledge.
4. The intellectual satisfaction to be gained from the pursuit of science either as a scientist or as a layman.

ATTITUDES

The knowledge and methods of science are of little importance if there is no disposition to use them appropriately. Open-mindedness, a desire for accurate knowledge, confidence in the procedures for seeking knowledge and the expectation that the solution of problems will come through the use of verified knowledge, these are among the "scientific attitudes."

To understand the scientist is also to understand some of his attitudes, such as the desire to know and to discover, a curiosity about the world, the excitement of discovery, and the desire to be creative.

CAREERS

Science instruction should acquaint students with career possibilities in technical fields and in science-teaching. A continuous effort should be made to identify and motivate those who develop special interests. They should be given opportunities for some direct experience of a professional nature and a perspective of the fields of science.

ABILITIES

Science as a field of study is characterized by a moving frontier and an ever increasing amount of knowledge. Young people need to acquire those skills and abilities which will enable them to assume responsibility for expanding their own learning. Some of these skills and abilities are:

1. Reading and interpreting science writings.
2. Locating authoritative sources of science information.
3. Performing suitable experiments for testing ideas.
4. Using the tools and techniques of science.
5. Recognizing the pertinency and adequacy of data.
6. Making valid inferences and predictions from data.
7. Recognizing and evaluating assumptions underlying techniques and processes used in solving problems.
8. Expressing ideas qualitatively and quantitatively.
9. Using the knowledge of science for responsible social action.
10. Seeking new relationships and ideas from known facts and concepts.

THE OBJECTIVES OF SCIENCE TEACHING *

National Society for the Study of Education

IMPORTANT among the objectives of science teaching are the learning of concepts, generalizations or principles, and scientific methods and attitudes.

THE DEVELOPMENT OF SCIENTIFIC CONCEPTS

Northrop interprets "concepts" as words that have been given concise meanings; accordingly, he defines science as the discipline which conveys the techniques for giving precise meanings to significant words. To some persons a concept is simply a thought or an idea. In any case, the clarity and completeness of one's concepts are measures of success in learning.[1] Russell believes that concepts do not really, by themselves, solve any problems, but he argues that they are necessary for thought and for communication.[2]

Concepts are abstractions which organize the world of objects and events into a smaller number of categories. These, in turn, can be organized into hierarchical systems, thus extending organized knowledge. Although the term *concept* is often restricted to ideas descriptive of classes of objects or events, such as "tree" or "motion," generalizations and principles may also be treated as concepts. A generalization or principle differs from a simple concept in that it states some kind of relationship between two or more abstractions, objects, or events. The statement that "for every action there is an equal and opposite reaction" is an example of a generalization involving relationship among three concepts, "action," "equal," and "opposite."

Scientific concepts include mathematical concepts, concepts of space, time, and weight, as well as concepts specific to the various areas of science. Concepts of measurement are dependent upon concepts of number and the development of measuring procedures. Since science depends to a large extent upon measurement, scientific concepts develop rather slowly.

[1] F. S. C. Northrup, "The Problem of Integrating Knowledge and the Method of Its Solution," *The Nature of Concepts: Their Interrelation and Role in Social Structure*, p. 25. Proceedings of the Stillwater Conference conducted by the Foundation for Integrated Education, Inc., and co-sponsored by Oklahoma A. & M. College. Stillwater, Oklahoma: Oklahoma A. & M. College, 1950.

[2] David H. Russell, *Children's Thinking*. New York: Ginn & Co., 1956.

* REPRINTED FROM *Rethinking Science Education*, 59th Yearbook of the National Society for the Study of Education, Part I (Chicago: University of Chicago Press, 1960), pp. 39–46, by permission of the publisher.

In addition, the learning and understanding of science is complicated by the introduction of concepts of objects which are postulated or imagined. Such ideas as the gene, the atom, and the electron, which were invented to explain observations, create difficulties for the beginning student who often has trouble distinguishing between concepts derived from perception such as "egg" and an imagined concept such as "gene." Similarly, it is difficult to distinguish generalizations which are concerned with concepts derived from perception, such as "Elements unite chemically in a definite proportion by weight," from theoretical statements, such as "All elements are composed of atoms."

Again, difficulty in the mastery of scientific concepts may arise from common-sense meanings, which are often quite different from precise, scientific meanings. The term "force" is one example. The scientific concept is more restricted than the common sense one.

One of the problems which confronts the teacher is that of ascertaining whether or not a student has grasped a concept instead of a generalization. There are two different methods of measuring the level of concept attainment. One involves defining the word or stating the generalization; the other involves the identification of objects or events by members of the class. The results of these two methods do not agree.[3] A student may be able to define force without being able to give an example, or he may memorize the relationship but be unable to use it. On the other hand, another student, though lacking in knowledge of the precise formula, may manifest some understanding of the general relationship. Deductions from vaguely defined or imprecise generalizations are entirely possible. Some of our teaching practices seem to assume that rote memory and recall of a definition or generalization demonstrate mastery of the concept, but unless the concept is seen by the individual as a unifying element in many different experiences, it is doubtful that a meaningful concept could have been acquired. Harlow[4] points out that broad concepts or principles do not arise from learning or over-learning a specific problem; breadth rather than intensity appears to be the key to concept formation.

What, then, is the best method of acquiring concepts? There is some evidence to indicate that for relatively easy material the inductive method of deriving the concept out of many specific examples is adequate. For difficult material, or when the possibility of error in concept formation is great, it appears that a deductive approach in which the presentation of the concept is followed by extensive application is preferable. A combination of the two methods appears to be superior to either method alone. However, these conclusions are tentative and require more research.

Since concepts and generalizations may be formed in various ways, such

[3] Donald M. Johnson, *The Psychology of Thought and Judgment*. New York: Harper & Bros., 1955.

[4] W. F. Harlow, "Thinking," in *Theoretical Foundations and Psychology*. Edited by H. Nelson. New York: D. Van Nostrand Co., 1951.

as from perceptions, from communicating with other people, from inference or content, or from problem-solving situations, it is not surprising that there are many sources of error in concept formation. According to Russell, the causes of errors in concept formation are:

1. Errors in the percepts from which the concepts emerge.
2. Confusion between images and memories aroused during recall.
3. Lack of experience to check or validate the generalizations reached.
4. Set or suggestibility caused by certain features of the environment being more influential than others equally important.
5. Overconfidence in the results of one's observations and conceptual thinking.[5]

Concepts arising from perceptions are apparently more easily formulated than abstract concepts. Likewise, undifferentiated and discrete concepts are more readily grasped than differentiated and organized concepts. The order of acquisition of concepts seems to be related to the level of abstraction of the idea. For example, such an order of acquisition as concrete object, spatial form, and mathematical relationship is found in the atomic molecular theory.[6] The concept of the atom as a unit of matter is acquired with relative ease; the idea of molecular structure is somewhat more difficult; while the actual deduction of various atomic weights from the atomic theory is an extremely difficult operation for most students.

Since concepts which arise from perceptions are formed more readily than more abstract concepts, the actual manipulation of materials should facilitate conceptualization. Davidson [7] checked this inference experimentally and suggested that grouping materials aids in the fixing of concepts. Any arrangement of materials which emphasizes the common characteristics and minimizes the irrelevant characteristics apparently helps in concept formation. Numerical concepts are made easier by illustrating them in spatial or graphic form. If they can be illustrated by use of visual models, this further facilitates the ease of conceptualization.

LEARNING CRITICAL THINKING

The wide usage of a word often clouds its meaning and leads to the addition of qualifying phrases or to the use of alternative terms. *Thinking* is such a word. *Critical, reflective, productive,* and *creative* are such qualifiers. *Problem-solving, judgment,* and *scientific method* are much used alternatives, each having presumably different but unclear shades of meaning. Lacking adequate research, the interrelationships of critical (considered as a synonym

---

[5] David H. Russell, *op. cit.*

[6] Donald M. Johnson, *op. cit.*

[7] B. S. Davidson, "The Effect of Symbols, Shift, and Manipulation upon the Number of Concepts Obtained," *Journal of Experimental Psychology,* XX (1952), 285–296.

of careful) thinking, creative thinking, judgment, and scientific method can only be examined on rational grounds.

The Nature of Critical Thinking

Critical thinking is commonly analyzed into steps which suggest the nature of the process and which must not be regarded as discrete and sequential. They include:

1. Recognizing and defining a problem.
2. Clarifying the problem by making appropriate definitions, distinguishing between facts and assumptions, and collecting and organizing relevant information.
3. Formulating possible explanations or solutions (hypotheses).
4. Selecting one or more promising hypotheses for testing and verification.
5. Stating tentative conclusions.

Implied in these steps are certain attitudes, such as doubt or a degree of skepticism of too quick or authoritarian explanations, a curiosity as to the why of things, intellectual honesty, suspended judgment, and belief that phenomena are subject to explanation.

Discussions of the scientific method [8] have repeatedly led to steps almost identical with those just enumerated, and attempts to elaborate the scientific attitude have resulted in statements of qualities similar to those mentioned. Science proceeds through making careful observations, by using relevant knowledge to make hypotheses and inferences and, finally, by seeking corroborative evidence. Critical thinking and the scientific method are apparently closely related; many persons see them as simply different names for the same intellectual activity.

The common use of "steps" and of "method" referring to intellectual activity may seem to rule out creativity, for creativity implies insight and originality which transcend methodical plodding through a series of steps. Yet every really significant thought process contains a creative element. The formulation of a hypothesis, the making of an inference, or the venturing of a new theory are essentially creative tasks. Observation is a creative act for the individual who perceives something not previously noted by himself or by others. Creativity, even in the arts, is often largely trial and error, although a brilliant rationale may be presented later. So, too, the "steps" of the scientific method are easier to find in retrospect. Creative thinking, like critical thinking, involves attitudes. The creative individual must have some skepticism of existing ideas or even a disdain for them; he must escape the social pressures toward conformity.

[8] Oreon Keeslar, "A Survey of Research Studies Dealing with the Elements of Scientific Method as Objectives of Instruction in Science," *Science Education*, XXIX (October, 1945), 212–216.

Situations and Methods Which Evoke Critical Thinking

There are various ways to study critical thinking. In one method, the observed product of thought implies stimulation of mental processes. Others have explored their own thoughts by introspection or retrospection. Logicians see the rules of logic as descriptive of systematic thinking, although these rules are more useful in presenting results of thinking than in experiencing the process.

The first two of these approaches to critical thinking—the inferring of mental process and the exploring of the process from original thinking to its product—have not yielded definite conclusions as to how the mind works. This leads to doubt that critical thinking is directly teachable. Rather, the task is to develop a favorable attitude and to provide examples and experiences which permit and encourage critical thinking. In contrast, those favoring an approach through logic would have the student learn the principles and techniques of logic and develop the habit of applying them. Pupil discovery of these principles is sometimes emphasized. This conception of critical thinking provides an effective pattern for analyzing the thinking of others, but it makes no allowance for the creative element of planning and hypothesis formulation required in original thinking. Moreover, the logical organization of the process and its results is often literally an afterthought.

It is not surprising that no simple prescription for teaching critical thinking exists. This lack, coupled with reverence for the mastery of information, leads to disregard of the ability as a formal goal of teaching. Yet there are some definite principles for encouraging critical thinking. Critical thinking must start with a problem which holds some interest, which is within the ability of the students, and for which the students do not know the answer. Such problems may arise fortuitously out of student experiences in or out of the classroom or they may be "planted." Failure to find appropriate problems is usually an indication of preoccupation with giving answers.

Relatively simple problems for which explanations are easily found must be followed by more difficult ones wherein the student learns that even errors and false leads may be productive if only they are viewed in the proper light. Such student projects as those described by Woodburn illustrate some of these possibilities.[9] Reading about the projects of practicing scientists, such as the attempt to explain Crater Lake or the search for a new refrigerant, will also give the student some insight into how scientists work. Brief, readable reports of these and other investigations are available for this purpose.[10] Such reports give a far different impression of science than do most textbooks which concentrate on presenting the ultimate findings. In a way, too, such

[9] John H. Woodburn, *Encouraging Future Scientists: Student Projects.* National Science Teachers Association, Future Scientists of America Bulletin. Washington: National Education Association, 1958.

[10] *If You Want To Do a Science Project.* National Science Teachers Association, Future Scientists of America Bulletin. Washington: National Education Association, 1955.

reports provide models which encourage and guide the student in thinking about his own projects.

Can Critical Thinking Be Taught?

The effect of emphasis on critical thinking or the scientific method in particular courses has been studied, and the results in many cases have been positive in that improvement in classes planned around the objective has been demonstrated to be greater than in classes taught with more traditional emphases. Usually the increase in knowledge is equal to or greater than that found in classes taught with content emphasis. The extent to which the increased ability is more broadly applicable to problems in other courses and in life is less certain, for no example of concentrated attention to the objective throughout an entire curriculum over several years has been reported. Nevertheless, the conclusion that students can learn to think more critically if appropriate instruction is provided seems to be justified.

LEARNING SCIENTIFIC ATTITUDES AND METHODS

Views as to the Nature of Scientific Attitudes and Methods

In the present century scientific methods and attitudes have been emphasized, particularly by Dewey, as objectives of formal education.[11] Many articles and investigations on the nature of scientific method have been published since Dewey's analysis. An inspection of this literature leads one to assume that such phrases as "scientific methods," "methods of science," "scientific thinking," "problem-solving," and "critical thinking" mean much the same and may be used interchangeably without undue confusion.

There developed through the years an interpretation that there was one scientific method with definite steps to be followed in a sequential order. Conant[12] and others have pointed out that this is not an acceptable interpretation. At present, most writers on this subject feel that there are many ways to solve problems scientifically and that no one way is necessarily typical of scientific thinking. It is also to be noted that the methods of science do not necessarily produce a successful solution to every problem.

Some writers on scientific method emphasize the inductive process; others the deductive process. However, it seems reasonable to infer that both processes are involved, at least in certain kinds of problems. It has been argued as to whether scientific methods are largely empirical or largely theoretical. There appear to be learning activities that are mainly empirical and descriptive, others that are highly conceptual, and still others in which theory and trial and error are both employed.

[11] John Dewey, How We Think. Boston: D. C. Heath & Co., 1933 (revised).
[12] James B. Conant, On Understanding Science. New Haven, Connecticut: Yale University Press, 1947.

CURRICULUM DESIGN IN SCIENCE *

Fletcher G. Watson

Fletcher G. Watson, reflecting upon the complex problems of curricular design, pleads for specificity and clarity in any statement of objectives. He believes that objectives must be stated operationally for at least four reasons: (1) The several individuals working on a curriculum need to agree on their targets so they can work together effectively. (2) Explicit objectives in terms of pupil behavior must be used to appraise the effectiveness of materials. (3) School administrators and parents should be provided with explicit statements of the purposes of the instruction proposed for their children. (4) Teachers need to know what is expected, or otherwise they may unintentionally distort the intent of the instruction as initially planned. Dr. Watson also discusses five necessary dimensions of planning.

THE REDESIGN of science courses and curricula is an important and continuous operation. Yet in many instances, this important task is approached within an overly limited framework that fails to consider many of the dimensions that must be met. Any group, whether local, state, or national, that undertakes curricular reforms must assume responsibility for all aspects of such procedures.

Time in the classroom is precious. Each pupil may experience about 180 sessions in a year; whatever he takes away at the end of the year depends upon what happens during those brief and fleeting sessions. Perhaps the teacher can "learn through experience" year after year, but the pupil has only one chance. Therefore much effort is desirable to ensure that even the first time a new curriculum or course is used it accomplishes the purposes for which it was intended.

Reflecting upon the complex problem of curricular changes, the following comments are given to stimulate discussion, to emphasize the range of factors that must be considered, and to plead for great attention for specificity and clarity in the statement of objectives. As an ultimate criterion of a successful plan, it could be sent through the mail to a distant (and competent) teacher who would agree that his instruction from this material paralleled that of the maker to the extent that they could properly use the same examination.

---

* REPRINTED FROM *The Science Teacher*, Vol. 30, No. 4, March 1963, pp. 13–16. Copyright, 1963, by the National Science Teachers Association, Washington, D.C. Reprinted by permission of the author and the publisher. Dr. Watson is Professor of Education at Harvard University.

LEARNING BEHAVIOR

Since the several courses of study or the over-all curricula are blueprints or guidebooks to possible teaching, their effectiveness depends upon what they communicate to the teacher. The teacher receives the blueprint, considers it, interprets it, (and perhaps distorts it). Then he performs some operations in the classroom. There, in its starkest simplicity, X "teaches Y" to Z. The term "teaches Y" comprises the actual curriculum to which the pupil, Z, is exposed.

But a persistent problem faces the teacher: what has each pupil learned, and how can the teacher become aware of this learning? As it is impossible to see the brain cells "turn from blue to pink," the learnings *are inferred* from our observations of the changes in pupils' behaviors. Thus, from the start, clear statements of anticipated behaviors (hopefully new and socially significant ones) must be of central concern to all curriculum planners. French (1) * and Kearney (2) pointed out the importance of stating teaching objectives in behavioral terms, but unfortunately this approach has usually been neglected.

Fundamentally, the planning of instruction involves the design of a predictive system relating the input of experience through pupil and teacher behavior to the output of changed behavior by the pupil (and possibly also by the teacher). For the essential moment-to-moment and day-to-day modification of classroom efforts, the teacher needs clear and immediate feedback evidence of the pupils' learning. That is, he must have specific expectations of how *these* pupils will react to *this* setting. The difference between the teacher's expectations and his classroom observations of pupils' actions comprises the error-signal which the teacher uses to modify his subsequent behavior during the lesson. Those designing curricula and courses of study assume the responsibility for making clear their expectations of the resulting pupil behavior—the criteria for evaluating the effectiveness of a particular teaching procedure with particular experiences by particular pupils.

Over the past years greater clarity in objectives has been attained by shifting from such topical headings as: parallel circuits, or the liver, to such form as understanding that: (followed by a complete statement) (3). Yet we naively proceed on the assumption that learning is an all-or-nothing operation; either the pupil "understands" or he does not. All teachers know that understanding grows slowly and is never complete. Help must be given the teacher to estimate the degree to which the pupil understands. To aid in sharpening these objectives, propose that they be stated in terms of "virile verbs" such as: plan, predict, make, compute, read, demonstrate, seek, criticize, argue, hypothesize, test, etc. Probably such pupil actions occur to the teachers as they are planning curricula and lessons, yet rarely do they get stated sharply as the basis for evaluating the proposed instruction. Instead, evaluation often takes the traumatic form of a test made (often hurriedly)

* See references.

after the instruction, rather than planned from the start as an integral and continuous part of the instruction.

The changed behaviors that may result are legion; some are desirable while some are undesirable. Some depend upon what is taught, and some depend upon how it is taught. But not "everything" can be taught, and not all behaviors can be developed simultaneously. Therefore, selection and pacing are necessary. Thus, the curriculum is seen as planned input of experience with chosen procedures intended to produce a developing series of behavioral changes in the particular pupils enrolled in a course.

In the past, teachers have been laboring under disadvantages because syllabuses and textbooks have failed to specify the anticipated pupil behaviors. Busy teachers with their individual backgrounds and images of what was proper have been obliged to infer what was desired, or desirable. Too often the teacher's behavior was reduced to "talk and chalk," and the pupils' to responses on certain examinations which sample only a limited and often minor portion of the pupils' capabilities. Teachers, professors, parents, and employers expect more than the competencies exhibited on tests. The larger goals must be planned into the instruction and continuously evaluated during the act of teaching by planned and careful observations of the pupils' behaviors in specific programs.

OBJECTIVES

Objectives must be stated operationally for at least four reasons: (1) The several individuals working on a curriculum need to agree on their targets so that they can work together effectively; (2) During any tryouts of draft materials, explicit objectives in terms of pupil behavior must be used to appraise the effectiveness of the materials. Lacking this, no one knows whether what happened was what was intended to happen; (3) School administrators and parents should be provided with explicit statements of the purposes of the instruction proposed for their children; (4) Teachers need to know what is expected or otherwise they may unintentionally distort the intent of the instruction as initially planned.

The dimensions of planning are many. At least five, of which each is necessary but not sufficient, can be recognized. These are: (1) The large and small concepts which constitute the structure of the particular subject; (2) The many procedures which give vitality, continuity, and commonality to the efforts of scientists (process goals); (3) The peculiar characteristics of the learner: his age, sex, and the cultural attributes of his community; (4) The intellectual behaviors of classifying, transforming, and formalizing (among others) through which each individual appraises and organizes his experience into significant conceptions; and (5) The appropriate tactics and strategy of teaching through which the teacher evokes in the learner the particular responses desired from the instructional setting.

1. Most groups begin their planning with the conceptual structure of a

science: the ideas, explanations, or the theories which constitute the discipline of a science. Presumably a relatively small number of general scientific conclusions would serve as the framework for a long-term curriculum. Small blocks of instruction would be concerned with numerous specific concepts which contribute toward developing in the pupils a growing awareness of the grander concepts. As an example, consider the six major generalizations which Brandwein recently proposed (4).

a. Under ordinary conditions, matter can be changed but not annihilated or created.
b. Under ordinary conditions, energy can be changed or exchanged but not annihilated or created.
c. There is an interchange of materials and energy between living things and their environment.
d. The organism is a product of its heredity and environment.
e. The universe, and its component bodies, are constantly changing.
f. Living things have changed over the years.

While Brandwein spelled out the possibilities of these generalizations, they are used here only to suggest the kind that would give continuity and structure to a long-term curriculum.

2. Practice with the processes by which scientists go about their tasks individually and collectively comprises another type of objective. These are called "process objectives, or themes." Consider the following examples:

a. Man extends his limited sensory capability by the use of various instruments; the invention of novel instruments has opened up large new fields for scientific investigation.
b. Various forms of models and analogues, including working replicas, verbal statements, as well as mathematical formulations, are frequently used to simplify and organize experience.
c. Through journals, meetings, and letters, scientists report and discuss their work with those of similar interests in many countries.
d. Scientific studies are concerned with describing phenomena in parsimonious terms; technology is concerned with practical applications.
e. Since scientists are conscious of the limitations of their generalizations and of the many shortcomings which can occur in generalizing from limited experience, they expend considerable effort upon the testing of generalizations to establish the conditions under which they apply and do not apply, especially the latter.

While lists of such objectives have been published (5), almost surely any curricular group would wish to make its own phrasing and condensation of the important aspects of scientific work which are inherent in the particulars being studied.

3. Inasmuch as the total effort of the school is to bring about changed

behavior in the child, the design of curricula without careful consideration of the pupils may be unrealistic. Teachers and educators must be concerned with the learner as a social individual of a given age having a unique and limited background of relevant experiences. The sex of the learner seems to be important, if not in cognitive abilities, at least in the motivation to interpret and structure the phenomena observed. In addition, each learner exists in a subculture of his family with its peculiarities and in a larger culture of the community with its unique attributes depending upon the geographical locations, the particular group of individuals that have settled there, their financial status, their religious beliefs, and their interest in academic learning. Here groups planning curricula (or textbooks) for use nationwide may encounter difficulties.

4. Another attribute of the individual learner, as described through the investigation of Piaget and Inhelder (6)(7), Bruner, *et al.*, (9), Vygotsky (10), and many others deals with his ability to organize his experience in various ways. While it is not yet clear to what extent these abilities are "age-bound," at least they appear to occur in a sequence. In discussing such developments, the psychologists refer to the child's ability to classify objects and experiences into various category systems, to perform various transformations by rearranging the entities presented to him, to utilize symbols for objects (initially words and later more abstract mathematical symbols), and ultimately to organize his experience formally in terms of "might be's" and then check the natural or contrived phenomena to see what actually does occur. Apparently most of the operations are acquired gradually and naturally by the typical child by the age of 12 to perhaps 14. Therefore their consideration in the planning of science instruction for young children would be particularly significant. There is no guarantee however that older children or adults have actually become competent in each of the operations and the strategy decisions that are necessary in the selection and application of appropriate operations.

5. This fifth objective is concerned with clarifying the act of teaching. In the classroom, the teacher's image of what is important, and his manipulation of what educators call the "classroom climate" has a significant influence upon the ultimate yield of the instructional materials. The way in which the instruction is approached and the clarity to the teacher of what is important to gain through the lesson reminds us that teachers can have widely differing initial views of what might and could be done with the materials. As self-protection against misinterpretation each curricular group should communicate to the teacher point by point the major intent of the instruction with suggestions for classroom procedure expected to evoke the desired pupil behavior quickly and efficiently. Thus the method of teaching—the teacher's classroom behavior—is deducible from the particular objectives of the lesson (aspects 1 and 2 above), from the environmental factors (aspect 3), and from the competencies of the pupils (aspect 4).

CONCLUSION

Any effective approach to curriculum planning must include consideration of at least five distinct aspects of which each is necessary, but not sufficient. The entire process is clarified and made operational by a central concern for the changes sought in pupil behavior, for these guide the teacher in the classroom and provide continuous criteria for appraising the effectiveness of the instruction.

REFERENCES

1. Will French, et al. Behavioral Goals of General Education in High School. Russell Sage Foundation, New York. 1957.
2. Nolan Charles Kearney. Elementary School Objectives. Russell Sage Foundation, New York. 1953.
3. Paul Brandwein, F. G. Watson, and Paul Blackwood. Teaching High School Science: A Book of Methods. Harcourt, Brace and World Company, Inc., New York. 1958.
4. Joseph Schwab and Paul Brandwein. The Teaching of Science. Harvard University Press, Cambridge, Massachusetts. 1962.
5. Glen Heathers. "A Process-Centered Elementary Science Sequence." Science Education, 45:201. April 1961.
6. Bärbel Inhelder and Jean Piaget. The Growth of Thinking from Childhood to Adolescence. Basic Books, Inc., New York. 1958.
7. Jean Piaget. Logic and Psychology. Basic Books, Inc., New York. 1957.
8. William Kessen and Clementina Kuhlman. Thought in the Young Child. Monograph 83. Society for Research in Child Development, Inc., Purdue University, Lafayette, Indiana. 1962.
9. Jerome Bruner, Jacqueline J. Goodnow, and George A. Austin. A Study of Thinking. John Wiley and Sons, Inc., New York. 1956.
10. Lev Semenovich Vygotsky. Thought and Language. Massachusetts Institute of Technology Press, Cambridge, Massachusetts. 1962.

THE DEVELOPMENT OF SCIENTIFIC
ATTITUDES *

Richard E. Haney

Although considerable emphasis has been placed recently on the teaching of inquiry skills, manipulative skills, and science knowledge, Richard E. Haney sees the need to re-focus attention on the learning of scientific attitudes. He discusses the following attitudes which directly govern the intellectual behavior of scientists and science students: curiosity, rationality, suspended judgment, open-mindedness, critical-mindedness, objectivity, honesty, and humility. These attitudes must be planned for and not simply accepted as concomitants to cognitive outcomes. Eight steps are suggested that teachers can take to facilitate the learning of attitudes.

IN THE last few years considerable emphasis has been placed on the teaching of inquiry skills as well as on useful knowledge and manipulative skills. Some mention has been made of scientific attitudes, to be sure, but these still remain inconsistently defined in the literature and obscure in teaching plans. Daily lessons tend to center around some conceptual theme, a major principle, or some other form of cognitive learning outcome while affective learnings at best are considered peripheral to this central idea.

The habits of thought associated with scientific thinking deserve more careful consideration. Problem-solving skills are essentially amoral. Knowledge and intellectual prowess divorced from the controlling influence of desirable attitudes toward man and nature contribute to the phenomenon which Robert Cohen termed the "frustration of humane living inherent in science of the twentieth century." (2) Science supposedly molds the character of its practitioners. To be scientific means that one has such attitudes as curiosity, rationality, suspended judgment, open-mindedness, critical-mindedness, objectivity, honesty, and humility.

Science lessons present many opportunities for teachers to help pupils develop these attitudes, which also have value outside the classroom and in other areas of human experience. Let us then consider the nature of attitudes,

---

* REPRINTED FROM *The Science Teacher*, Vol. 31, No. 8, December 1964, pp. 33–35. Copyright, 1964, by the National Science Teachers Association, Washington, D.C. Reprinted by permission of the author and the publisher. Dr. Haney is Associate Professor of Education at the University of Wisconsin, Milwaukee.

examine these eight attitudes and the overt behavior governed by them, and suggest appropriate learning experiences.

One of the most frequently quoted definitions of attitudes is the statement by Allport in which an attitude is described as a "mental and neural state of readiness, organized through experience, exerting a directive or dynamic influence upon the individual's response to all objects and situations with which it is related." (1) Sells and Trites point out that such mental and neural states cannot be observed directly in students. "An attitude is a psychological construct, or latent variable, inferred from observable responses to stimuli, which is assumed to mediate consistency and covariation among these responses." (6) Attitudes regulate behavior that is directed toward or away from some object or situation or group of objects or situations. Attitudes have emotional content and vary in intensity and generality according to the range of objects or situations over which they apply. For the most part, attitudes are learned and are difficult to distinguish from such affective attributes of personality as interests, appreciations, likes, dislikes, opinions, values, ideals, and character traits.

GUIDES TO SCIENTIFIC BEHAVIOR

A recent attempt to analyze the process through which attitudes are acquired appears in the *Taxonomy of Educational Objectives, Handbook II: Affective Domain*. Attitudes are said to emerge first at the level of "willingness to respond" and become increasingly internalized in the learner through the stages of "satisfaction in response," "acceptance of a value," "preference for a value," "commitment," and "conceptualization of a value." At this last stage the learner is able to "see how the value relates to those that he already holds or to new ones that he is coming to hold." (4)

The first attitude to be considered is *curiosity*. This is the desire for understanding on the part of the student when confronted by a novel situation which he cannot explain in terms of his existing knowledge. A curious person asks questions, reads to find information, and readily initiates and carries out investigations. Curiosity is a stimulus to inquiry, and it is a desirable outcome of instruction as well. Each discovery raises new questions and suggests new undertakings. Pupils should leave science courses with greater curiosity than they had at the outset. But, who are the most curious? Usually they are the younger children. Somehow our pupils manage to lose the spirit of inquiry with advancing age. Each teacher must ask himself how he can teach for heightened curiosity. Curiosity is learned. It can be learned or repressed in the classroom. Problematic situations in which answers and explanations are not immediately available help to stimulate curiosity. The solutions of problems should raise new problems.

While curiosity stimulates inquiry, the attitude of *rationality* guides the scientist's behavior throughout his investigation. This is the habit of looking for natural causes for natural events. The rational person is not superstitious.

The prescientific period in our history was marked by numerous examples of mythological explanations. This tradition still abounds in our folklore and in the everyday thinking of many persons. To help them develop the attitude of rationality, pupils can be confronted with situations in which careful reasoning proves superior to explanations of a superstitious nature.

Willingness to suspend judgment is another attribute of personality fundamental to scientific behavior. Persons with this attitude accumulate sufficient evidence before making judgments or drawing conclusions. They recognize the tentative nature of hypotheses and the revisionary character of our knowledge. To learn the attitude of suspended judgment, our students should be confronted with situations in which this behavior is rewarded or in some way leads to success while formation of conclusions without evidence leads to failure. Pupils should examine explicitly the consequences of jumping to conclusions.

Science teachers ought to examine closely the common practice of asking students to formulate a conclusion at the end of every five-minute demonstration or forty-minute experiment. These activities concern but a limited sample of all the phenomena governed by the principle under consideration. At the end of these experiences students should have the opportunity to choose among formulating a generalization with various qualifications, stating that they have only learned something about the particular operation at hand, or stating that they could make no sense of the data.

ACCEPTANCE OF NEW IDEAS

Open-mindedness is closely akin to suspended judgment. To comprehend science as the human enterprise that it is, our future citizens must learn from experience that our ideas of what is true may change. They must be able to revise their opinions or conclusions in the light of new evidence. Experiences that foster open-mindedness include those in which pupils are confronted with the need to revise a belief as the result of having acquired new information on the subject.

The willingness to consider novel hypotheses and explanations and to attempt unorthodox procedures is a form of open-mindedness toward creative ideas which amounts to the "no holds barred" attitude of the scientist. The scientific method is not simply the application of routine and predetermined procedures to new problems. The study of new areas of knowledge often requires the invention of new methods of inquiry. Popular conceptions and explanations may fail to fit new bits of evidence. The history of science contains the stories of men who broke with traditions and saw nature in a new light. To foster this creative spirit in the classroom, teachers can provide experiences in which pupils have the opportunity to design their own investigations and invent and evaluate their own explanations for natural phenomena.

New ideas are not accepted in science simply because they are new or different. To be scientific also means to be *critically minded*. A person with this attitude looks for evidence and arguments that support other persons' assertions. He challenges authority with the questions "How do you know?" and "Why do we believe?" He is concerned about the sources of his knowledge. One of the greatest temptations confronting the science teacher is that of giving direct answers to children's questions and of offering glib explanations. Teachers need to be careful of answers that include the word "because." Most explanations are not as simple as they might possibly appear at first.

How must teachers behave if their students are to learn the attitude of critical-mindedness? How often do they encourage their students to ask in class "How do you know?" To foster the learning of this attitude, teachers should provide evidence to support the generalizations in the lessons. Pupils should be taught to look for arguments and evidence supporting important propositions, and they should be taught to provide these in their own communications. The reading of historical and biographical accounts of investigations are also valuable experiences from which pupils can learn of the sources of our current knowledge.

The scientist must also be *objective* in gathering and interpreting his data and intellectually *honest* in communicating his findings. To learn the attitude of objectivity, students may be confronted by situations in which the temptation to permit personal feelings to interfere with the recording of an observation or the interpretation of data must be successfully resisted in order to achieve a correct or accurate solution of a problem. Complete objectivity is difficult to achieve because an observer's perceptions are governed by his previous experiences and his expectations.

Intellectual honesty, on the other hand, is concerned with the conscious act of truthfully reporting observations. Teachers have to ask themselves how they reward honesty in their classrooms. In the laboratory, for instance, do the pupils know the *right* answers to report regardless of their actual sense data? The value of open-ended experiences for instructional purposes is that they are more like those of the scientist at the frontier of knowledge where the answers are not yet known. Science could not be the cumulative enterprise that it is if it were not for the objectivity and honesty of its practitioners.

PERSONAL VIEW OF WORLD

The foregoing attitudes directly govern the intellectual behavior of scientists and science students. To be "scientific" means to have these personality traits. In our classrooms, however, children learn more than the content and processes of science. They incorporate these bits of knowledge and skills along with those gained in other subjects and extracurricular experiences into their personal views of the world and their places in it. Each student gradually builds his own philosophy of life.

Humility is a desirable ingredient of the mature personality. It can be learned, at least in part, as a result of science instruction. Science can teach children to recognize their own limitations as well as the limitations of science itself. This is the attitude that underlies the conservation movement. It is the humble person who uses natural resources wisely, for the common good, even though he might have to forego immediate gains that could accrue from their exploitation.

Relationship to Nature

On the other hand, man's relationship to nature is more than a matter of "wise use." He shares this world with other beings whose "rights" deserve to be recognized. The history of science and also of religion is a story of man's struggle with his own egocentricism. The message that Rachel Carson gave us in *Silent Spring* relates a current episode in that story. Albert Schweitzer has expressed the attitude of humility in terms of "reverence for life" which identifies the moral principle that the good consists in the preservation, enhancement, and exaltation of life, and that destruction, injury, and retardation of life are evil. The world presents a spectacle of "will-to-live" contending against itself. One organism asserts itself at the expense of another. Man can only preserve his own life at the cost of taking lives. One who holds to the ethic of reverence for life injures or destroys only out of necessity. Never does such a person kill other beings from thoughtlessness. (5) There is a curious similarity in the messages of Rachel Carson, the scientist, and Albert Schweitzer, the theologian.

What sort of humility or reverence for life is taught in our biology classes? The trend, at present, is to increase the amount of experimentation with living materials in order to make the work of the student more like that of the scientist. But, perhaps, we have in "reverence for life" a limitation to the discovery method of teaching. What attitudes do the students learn if animals are dissected merely to show that the chart on the wall or the plastic model on the demonstration table is correct? What concern for other lives is taught if an anesthetized rat is cut open so that the students can experiment with the heart of a dying animal? Such activities are likely to reaffirm the attitude that all of creation belongs to man to be plucked, manipulated, harvested, or controlled at his will for purposes *he* considers essential. To teach the attitude of reverence for life, it may be that vicarious experiences will have to be employed to a great extent, even though to do so would be to compromise the principle of making learning experiences as much like those of the scientist as possible.

To Foster Attitude Building

The attitudes which have been explored are attributes of intellectually and emotionally mature individuals, persons who not only behave outwardly in desirable ways but who understand why they act as they do. If these and other attitudes are to be fostered, they must be planned for and not simply accepted as concomitants to cognitive outcomes. Klausmeier suggests eight steps that teachers can take to facilitate the learning of attitudes. (3) These may be interpreted in terms of the problems of science teaching in the following manner:

1. The attitude to be taught must be identified. Examples of attitudes related to science have been identified in this article.
2. The meanings of the vocabulary used to describe attitudes or the behaviors related to them must be clarified for the learner.
3. Informative experience about the attitude "object" should be provided. In the case of scientific attitudes these "objects" are usually the various situations that occur in the problem-solving process. Typical of these are (a) the sensing of the problem in a perplexing situation, (b) clarifying and defining the problem, (c) formulating of hypotheses, (d) reasoning out the consequences of the hypotheses and the designing of investigations, (e) gathering of data, (f) treating and interpreting of data, (g) generalizing or drawing conclusions, and (h) communicating the results of the investigation to others. Students need to be instructed in the performance of each of these steps and in their relationships to the various attitudes that characterize the scientifically minded person. It is hoped, of course, that pupils will exhibit these attitudes in appropriate situations outside the classroom. To help them generalize these attitudes, teachers can point out the general nature of the attitude object by showing similarities between scientific problem-solving procedures and the treatment of problematic situations in daily affairs.
4. Desirable identifying figures for the learner should be provided. These models, whether they be teachers, parents, peers, or historical figures, provide the learner with ready-made behaviors which he can use as his first attempts at the desired behavior.
5. Pleasant emotional experiences should accompany the learning of the attitudes. Pupils need freedom to attempt their own patterns of exploration and sufficient time to pursue an investigation to the point where they experience the satisfaction that accompanies inquiry and discovery.
6. Appropriate contexts for practice and confirmation should be arranged. Learning experiences must be selected on the basis of knowledge, skills, and attitudes to be learned. At times the central theme of a lesson might have to be a particular attitude with other learnings playing secondary roles.
7. Group techniques should be used to facilitate understanding and acceptance. The varied activities possible in well-equipped science rooms permit students to learn as individuals on some occasions and as members of groups of varying sizes on others. Group decision making that occurs in the planning and carrying out of investigations and the evaluation of results permits a sharing of emotional commitment which can enhance the learning of an attitude.
8. Deliberate cultivation of the desired attitude should also be encouraged.

Pupils need to be aware of the behaviors that accompany an attitude and to practice them. Sometimes this requires the difficult task of breaking old habits or of improving poorly learned ones. The teacher must be able to provide guidance for this learning.

There are implications in what has been said for the education of teachers as well as for the instruction of schoolchildren. It has often been said that "you can't teach something you don't know." A corollary to this generalization might be this: "Pupils cannot learn attitudes that their teachers don't have." It may very well be that the first step in meeting this challenge to science education will consist of an inward look upon our own knowledge and value systems. Science teachers have a responsibility. It is to them that the public turns for an understanding of science, not just the facts of science, or the skills, but also for a perspective that relates science to all other areas of human experience

REFERENCES

1. Gordon Allport. "Attitudes." Chapter 17 in *Handbook of Social Psychology*, C. Murchison, Editor. Clark University Press, 1935. p. 806. Quoted in *Children's Thinking* by David Russell. Ginn and Company, Boston, Massachusetts. 1956. p. 170.
2. Robert S. Cohen. "Individuality and Common Purpose: The Philosophy of Science." *The Science Teacher*, 31:27–33. May 1964, p. 31.
3. Herbert Klausmeier. *Learning and Human Abilities: Educational Psychology.* Harper & Row, Publishers, New York. 1961. p. 267.
4. David Krathwohl et al. *Taxonomy of Educational Objectives, Handbook II: Affective Domain.* David McKay Company, Inc., New York. 1964. p. 36.
5. Albert Schweitzer. *The Philosophy of Civilization*, translated by C. T. Campion. The Macmillan Company, New York. 1959. pp. 307–329.
6. Saul Sells and David Trites. "Attitudes" in *Encyclopedia of Educational Research*, Chester Harris, Editor. The Macmillan Company, New York. 1960. p. 103.

PREREQUISITES OF AN EFFECTIVE
ELEMENTARY SCIENCE PROGRAM *

Edward Victor

The following is a portion from Chapter 3, "The Elementary Science Pro-gram," of Science for the Elementary School. *Edward Victor cites with pre-cision the necessary prerequisites for an effective elementary science program. The program must be planned and structured. It should be a coordinated part of an overall K–12 science program, and correlated with the rest of the elementary curriculum. It should have scope and sequence, and a balance of content from all the sciences. The emphasis should be on concept develop-ment rather than technology. There must be a variety of activities, provision for necessary materials, sufficient time, and help and encouragement for the teacher. Finally, the program must be evaluated continuously if it is to be an effective one.*

IN RECENT YEARS a large number of science programs for the elementary school have been emerging. These programs are the result of cooperative efforts of classroom teachers, supervisors, administrators, and science specialists.

There is a tremendous contrast between these newer science programs and the earlier programs. Sometimes the older programs were nothing more than skeletal courses of study, consisting usually of an outline of the chapter titles of the elementary science textbooks being used at the time. The more ambitious of the earlier programs listed the science topics and sub-topics to be taken up in each grade, and then included a number of suggested activities or references that the teacher or children could use when studying these topics in class.

Usually, however, science programs did not exist in elementary schools, and each teacher taught science as she wished. Materials and equipment were often unavailable. There was no one the teacher could turn to for help.

Although the teachers were urged to teach science, no time was allocated in the daily program for science. When science was taught, usually the same popular topics such as air, weather, magnets, and plants were taken up in

* REPRINTED FROM *Science for the Elementary School* (New York: The Macmillan Company, 1965), pp. 31–40, by permission of the publisher. Dr. Victor is Professor of Edu-cation at Northwestern University.

grade after grade so that the material became highly repetitious, boring, and distasteful to the children.

In contrast, the newer programs are rich in science content, providing a wealth of basic science information related to the children's environment. An abundance of learning activities are included in the program. These activities are directed specifically at giving the children an opportunity to investigate and explore so that effective learning of basic science information takes place. Desirable behaviors that may emerge from the learning activities are often listed. Provision is made for all kinds of learners: slow, average, and fast. Teachers are supplied with source materials and with equipment. Competent supervisors or specialists are available for assistance.

Science programs may vary somewhat in the scope and sequence of their science content, in the learning activities they include, and in the teaching format they use. However, all programs should meet the following prerequisites, if they are to be effective and successful.

PLANNING

A science program should be planned. When science was first taught in the elementary school, and for some time thereafter, there was no such thing as a planned science program. Science learning was organized around incidents that occurred in the classroom. If a child brought a magnet, whistle, unusual-looking rock, queer insect, or pretty leaf into class, a lesson or unit in science was developed around the incident. Often the lesson was quite brief and ended the same day. Usually this kind of lesson tended to stress identification, nomenclature, and the learning of facts rather than major science concepts. If there were no incidents, there were often no lessons in science.

There is no question that incidents arising in the classroom can be a tremendous motivating experience for the children. Under the direction of experienced and skillful teachers with a good science background, such incidents can be used to produce excellent teaching and learning. However, incidents alone are not sufficient to ensure an adequate science program for the elementary school. Nor would the teachers even think of teaching other areas in the elementary curriculum solely on this basis.

One of the most significant forward trends in science education today is the general agreement that the science program should be planned and structured, just as the programs in the other areas of the elementary school curriculum are planned and structured. A planned program not only provides a steady progression of science learning in all grades, but also gives the teacher a definite background and framework of basic science information with which to work in the classroom.

A properly organized program will not discourage incidents that occur, but rather will welcome them as an additional means for producing more effective learning in the classroom. In fact, a planned program now makes it possible for the teacher to create deliberately the kinds of incidents that will instill in the children a desire for exploration and investigation. And when unusual or important incidents do arise, such as sending a satellite or astronaut into space, the planned program can be flexible enough to provide time for these incidents to be taken up in detail.

A planned program should provide for and be guided by the interests of the children. An effective program takes into consideration the children's interests and uses them to motivate learning in science. At the same time it permits the children to help plan and carry out the daily and long-range work in science.

The planned program, when properly organized and administered, cannot restrict or limit the elementary teacher's initiative and freedom of operation in the classroom, even if the program is structured in great detail, with a comprehensive course of study or curriculum guide, and with well-defined teaching units. In fact, it is a common axiom that the more intensive and detailed the planning is, the greater opportunity there will be for the children to conduct true scientific investigations and explorations.

When planning a program there is freedom for grade placement of science topics between schools. A science topic assignment to a third grade in one school can be allocated to a fourth grade in another school, if the teachers so desire. All teachers can have a choice in the selection of the learning activities they may use to teach for the basic science information to be learned. Teachers may also delve deeper into a unit, if they so prefer. There is ample opportunity to provide for individual differences within the classroom. There can even be allowance for variation in the time of the year when the science topics are taken up. Some teachers prefer to study plants in the spring whereas others prefer to study plants in the fall when the leaves are turning color. Many programs even provide some free time within the school year so that teachers and pupils can work or study on some science projects of their own choice.

A Coordinated Part of a K–12 Science Program

Science in the elementary school should be planned and coordinated so that it is part of an overall K-12 science program. In this way haphazard teaching, unnecessary repetition, overlap, and flagrant omissions are eliminated. Instead, a steady progression of learning takes place at each grade level, building upon knowledge from previous grades and leading to further knowledge in the following grades. The basic science information to be learned will proceed steadily from the very simple to the abstract, as the children grow in maturity. In addition, the children will have an opportunity to grow steadily in the development of desirable behaviors and to acquire gradually experience in solving problems, thinking critically, and utilizing effective methods of working.

Correlation with the Elementary Curriculum

The correlation of the science program with the rest of the elementary curriculum has already been discussed in detail in Chapter 1, under the broad goals for the elementary science program, as well as earlier in this chapter, when possible guides to be used in selecting science content for the science program were suggested. Care should be taken, however, when correlating science with the rest of the curriculum, that the learning of science is not lost in the process. Real science learning cannot take place in a combined social studies–science unit on "Communications," when teachers take up the social aspects in great detail and merely talk about the science portion. Moreover, although it is good educational practice to correlate science when possible with the rest of the curriculum, it is also impractical and unwise to insist that all science be integrated with other areas. There are many phases of science that are learned best alone. Also, there are times where it is more logical to integrate the other areas with science rather than integrate science with the other areas.

Scope and Sequence

The science program should have scope and sequence. *Scope* refers to the content in the program, and *sequence* refers to the grade level or levels where the content will be allocated. The science program should be broad in scope so that the children will have ample opportunity to learn major concepts and basic principles that affect all the principal aspects of their environment. These broad understandings should be drawn from all areas of science, and their introduction should begin as early as kindergarten, then developed and expanded through the elementary grades. This will help enable the children to acquire a greater understanding of their environment, of how man strives to use and control his environment, of how living things adapt and adjust to their environment, and of how living things are or may be interdependent and interrelated.

There is increasing agreement about the scope of the science content to be taught in the elementary school, as demonstrated by an examination of current elementary science textbooks and science programs. However, this agreement is not true of sequence. Both textbooks and science programs vary widely and consistently in their grade placement of science topics. Some research is being conducted to determine the age levels or grades where selected science topics or understandings can be taught successfully. The findings generally tend to show that children at any grade level can learn something about all areas of science, provided the concepts are simplified or are within the children's level of maturity and comprehension.

It is becoming more obvious that any attempt to develop one universal science program, with a rigid or fixed grade-placed sequence, is virtually impossible. Children can and do differ widely in ability between schools in the same community and also between schools of different communities. It is not uncommon for a teacher to find that the children differ in ability from year to year even in the same grade. Moreover, the growing conviction that elementary school children can learn more science than was hitherto believed possible has resulted in increasing the science content being introduced into the science program.

Yet it is equally obvious that some kind of sequence is necessary. In every science topic the concepts range from the very simple to the more complex. Some topics involve concepts that are more abstract than others. Whatever topics are assigned to a lower grade level will contain concepts that cannot be developed fully, regardless of the children's ability. Further development of these concepts will be needed at a higher grade level to ensure complete comprehension and learning.

Earlier science programs attempted to solve the problem of sequence by requiring the same topics to be taught each year, with provision for a steady spiral of concepts to be developed in each grade, progressing from the easily understandable to the more difficult. When the topics were narrow and unrelated, such as magnets, static electricity, soil, sound, and so forth, the science programs proved to be highly unsatisfactory for everyone.

To get as wide a scope as possible, so many of these narrow, unrelated topics had to be included in each grade that the teacher could not find enough time to teach satisfactorily all the science that was required for the grade. This would lead to gaps in the children's science learning. Often it was difficult to find enough concepts on a single narrow topic for the program so that some could be distributed for each grade. It would be difficult and perhaps futile, for example, to collect enough concepts on the topic of magnets so that a satisfactory number could be allocated in each grade from kindergarten through grade 6. This would necessarily make the treatment of magnets in each grade highly superficial. No sooner would the teacher initiate a unit on magnets than she would have to stop because she had taken up all the concepts that were assigned to her grade level. If the teacher did succumb to the interest and pleas of the children to learn more about magnets, this procedure would create a hardship upon teachers in succeeding grade levels.

Most science programs today have either bypassed or abandoned this tight, grade by grade, spiral of narrow topics and have adopted a much looser spiral pattern. This has been accomplished by incorporating the individual topics under broader, related content areas. In this way, although a major area is taken up each year, an individual topic—such as sound or magnets—is taken up only periodically.

As a result, the grade placement of science topics in these programs varies, depending upon the basic philosophy of the different schools or school systems and upon the number of broad content areas that make up the program. Some schools organize their science content so that a topic is taken up three times during the kindergarten through grade 6 period: the sequence is as follows: once in grades K–2, a second time in grades 3–4, and a third time in grades 5–6. Other schools take up a science topic just twice: in grades K–3 and again in grades 4–6. Still other schools have no regular pattern, but will take up a topic two, three, or even four times, depending upon the amount of science content entailed in the topic.

Some schools assign specific science units to the kindergarten. Others suggest only that the kindergarten teacher scrutinize her daily program of activities closely for science implications, then plan accordingly for experiences in science. Still others provide for both planned science units and incidental activities arising from the questions that the children will ask.

Regardless of which grade-placement plan a program uses, in all cases individual topics are now taken up periodically from kindergarten through grade 6. This plan enables each topic to be explored in greater depth and more satisfying detail. As a result, not only is there a greater opportunity for more major understandings to emerge each time, but also relationships between these understandings can now develop more easily, in a number of ways and from more than one direction. Programs such as these make possible a real spiral of learning. When a topic recurs in a spiral, new and more difficult concepts are built upon previously learned concepts. In each case previous knowledge about the topic is reviewed briefly, and then this knowledge is extended further. Repetition thus serves to associate the old concepts with the new.

Exact grade placement of basic science information in the science program can and should be an individual concern, left to the decision of those working with the program. The grade placement may vary from school to school within the same community, or from community to community. Most concepts allocated for a specific grade level can be learned with equal success in one grade level immediately above or below the specified grade. However, difficulties are more likely to arise when the difference in allocation of concepts involves two or more grade levels.

The following suggestions may be helpful in organizing the sequence of topics and concepts for a science program. To begin, many individual topics can be related and incorporated to form broader content areas. Magnetism, static electricity, and current electricity, for example, can be combined to constitute one content area. Similarly, machines can be combined with friction, heat with fire and fuels, water with weather and climate, soil with rocks and minerals, and air with planes and space travel.

Some science topics might be placed in the same grade because they are all concerned with a common concept or theory. For example, an understanding of the theory of molecular motion will explain many of the phenomena of heat, sound, magnets, and physical states of matter. If the molecular theory is allocated to a certain grade level, the placement of these topics in the same grade level may save needless repetition and at the same time ensure a greater understanding of the theory because it was approached from different directions. Also, when the atomic theory is allocated to a certain grade, static and current electricity could also be profitably placed in the same grade.

Allocation of topics and concepts will also depend upon the children's growth in ability to understand cause-and-effect relationships, to recall and rationalize, and to grasp abstract ideas. In some programs the science for kindergarten through grade 2 is primarily devoted to making the children aware of science phenomena in their environment. Science in grades 3–4 is directed toward promoting the understanding of simple cause-and-effect relationships. In grades 5–6 the more complex or abstract concepts involved in the cause-and-effect relationships are developed. For example, in the first spiral the children may learn that water can disappear or go into the air, where it becomes an invisible gas called water vapor. In the second spiral the children will explore the factors that affect evaporation, such as heat, wind, surface area, and so on. In the third spiral the children will learn the molecular theory and how evaporation and the factors affecting evaporation can be explained according to the molecular theory. Thus the children develop awareness in the first spiral, deal more with the effects in the second spiral, and devote more time to the causes in the third spiral.

One should keep in mind the facts that there is no sharp delineation in function or intent between spirals and that it is not obligatory to always have the same number of spirals for each content area. The difficulty of the concepts will be a deciding factor. Thus it may be feasible in some cases to teach for the development of an awareness of science phenomena in the second or even the third spiral. By the same token, causes of some phenomena can be learned in the first spiral. In all cases the science program should attempt to have the children learn key concepts and major understandings as early as possible.

Finally, the science program should evaluate its sequence continuously, not periodically. Only if the effects of a particular sequence on learning in the classroom are carefully observed, and the sequence constantly reshuffled whenever the grade placement appears to be unsuited, can a well-organized and effectively structured science program emerge.

BALANCE

The science program should have balance. A well-balanced program should provide opportunities for the children to explore regularly in each of the three major areas, which include the earth and the universe, living things, and matter and energy. Equal emphasis should be given to the physical and the biological sciences in the overall program. A balance in the length of units might be desirable so that some would be long and others would be shorter. There should also be balance in the number of units taught each year. The present trend is toward the adoption of a relatively small number of units per year, however, with provision for greater depth in science content.

EMPHASIS ON CONCEPTS

The science program should be concerned with more than technology. Too many science programs place undue emphasis upon how science helps us in our daily life, and not enough emphasis upon the underlying science concepts. The result is that the children, our future adult citizens, acquire a distorted image of science. They tend to view science primarily as an agent for developing useful gadgets and appliances, and thus making their lives more pleasant and comfortable. They never learn, or else lose sight of, the fact that science is a way of life—an exciting open-ended process that man uses to explain the natural phenomena of the world in which he lives.

VARIETY OF ACTIVITIES

The children should have ample opportunity to use a large number of diversified activities when learning science. They should have a chance to do experiments and demonstrations, read, give reports, participate in discussion, take field trips, listen to resource persons, use audiovisual aids, do research, and work on projects. There should also be activities that reinforce learning for the slow learner, and activities that challenge and extend the knowledge of the fast learner. At the same time, opportunities should be provided for children to investigate incidents or problems that arise and are not part of the planned program.

PROVISION FOR NECESSARY MATERIALS

It is useless for a science program to include "doing" learning activities unless the necessary supplies and equipment are made available. Thus an annual budget must be allotted to the elementary school for science materials so that the science program can function successfully. Moreover, each classroom should have its own science library, and the school library should have an adequate selection of science books. Provision must also be made for easy accessibility to films, filmstrips, and television programs.

HELP AND ENCOURAGEMENT FOR THE TEACHER

In a planned science program the elementary teacher must be familiar with the basic science information in the five major fields of astronomy, biology, chemistry, geology, and physics. This knowledge requires a larger science background than most elementary teachers receive in their pre-service training. It is also an accepted fact that many teachers are reluctant to teach science because their science background is so limited. These teachers need help, if the science program is to be effective.

This assistance can be furnished in many ways. Professional books, sourcebooks, and curriculum materials can be made available. In-service education in science itself, in the form of courses or workshops, can be provided. Many of the larger school systems are beginning to employ science consultants. These persons, proficient both in science and in working with children, can do much to strengthen the science program and the morale of the teachers. They can plan with the teachers, suggest additional learning activities, frequently do demonstration teaching, locate and order equipment, and conduct local workshops.

Some school systems employ full-time science consultants or supervisors. They are given either a limited teaching schedule or none at all so that they can spend most of their time working on the program or with those teachers who need help. Other school systems may have a consultant on a part-time basis. Sometimes school systems use a competent junior high school teacher, who is given only a half-time teaching load so that the rest of the time can be devoted to the elementary teachers. Sometimes they use a science-minded elementary school teacher, letting someone else take over her class part of the time while she works with the other teachers in her building. Some school systems have a science educator come periodically to furnish advice and assistance to the teachers. Planned science programs in the elementary school are still comparatively new, and the position of elementary science consultant or supervisor is even newer. The trend, however, seems to be quite definitely toward the increased use of full-time consultants.

SUFFICIENT TIME

There is definite agreement that science should be a regular part of the daily program, and have adequate time within the program. Both interest and learning are lost if science is scheduled only once or twice a week. Opinions vary, however, as to how much time should be allotted to science, daily or weekly. The general feeling is that more time should be devoted to science in grades 4–6 than in K–3. Some schools require that a definite amount of time be devoted daily to science. One recommended time allotment is 20–30 minutes per day for K–3 and 30–40 minutes per day for grades 4–6. Some schools set aside three days a week for science, with an average of 40–60 minutes per day. Other schools merely stipulate a definite amount of time per week, usually 120–180 minutes, and let the teacher allocate the time as needed throughout the week. Still other schools require that science be taught, but leave the time allotment to the discretion of the individual teacher.

CONTINUOUS EVALUATION

To be effective the science program should be evaluated continually, with everyone involved in the program participating in the evaluation. The scope and basic science information can be examined for corrections, additions, or deletions. The sequence must be evaluated to ensure optimum grade placement. Activities should be scrutinized critically to see if they are achieving maximum learning. Newer, more productive activities should be substituted as they appear in text, reference, and resource books. Initiating activities may be evaluated for greatest possible motivating and problem-raising potential. Even the evaluation techniques themselves should be examined regularly to see if learning is taking place in the classroom.

THE ELEMENTARY SCIENCE PROGRAM *

National Society for the Study of Education

The following is an excerpt from Chapter 7, "Developing Science Programs in the Elementary School," of the Fifty-ninth NSSE Yearbook, Part I, Rethinking Science Education. Members of the committee who wrote this chapter include Glenn O. Blough, Paul E. Blackwood, Katherine E. Hill, and Julius Schwartz. The committee describes how successful programs have their origins in a variety of sources: (a) the child, (b) the environment, (c) the sciences, and (d) the total school program. All these sources must be considered when planning the program. Also, the properly organized program should have structure and sequence.

How the Selection of Subject Matter Is Made

Experience in the teaching of science in the elementary school has demonstrated that the most successful programs have their origin in a variety of sources: (a) the *child,* with his emotional, intellectual, and physical needs; (b) the *environment,* both natural and man-made, in which the child lives; (c) the *sciences,* especially biology, chemistry, physics, and astronomy; and (d) the *total school program,* as it relates to the needs of *society* for informed citizens, capable of participating in social living.

Curriculum-planning has sometimes drawn heavily upon one of these sources without due regard to the others. Thus, in some localities, science has been made an adjunct to social studies, whereas in others the science program has leaned heavily on selected features of the local environment. In some instances, the science program of the elementary school has been designed as a "simplification" of junior and senior high school science. This

---

* reprinted from *Rethinking Science Education,* 59th Yearbook of the National Society for the Study of Education, Part I (Chicago: University of Chicago Press, 1960), pp. 119–125, 128–129, by permission of the publisher.

"watered-down" approach, while generally rejected at this time, crops up sporadically in some "crash" programs which attempt to "scale down" upper-school apparatus, experiments, and ideas to "fit" young people.

Science programs drawn chiefly from one source are sometimes helpful in demonstrating the limitations of such programs. Today, however, there seems to be widespread agreement that the most vital programs are those based on the needs of the child in his environment, programs which are in harmony with the total school program and mindful of the needs of society and which utilize the materials, concepts, and methods unique to science. The process of curriculum development involves the exploration of *all* these sources to find in them the content and the methods for the science program. Curriculum projects as designed are generally prepared by teams of classroom teachers, supervisors, curriculum specialists, and personnel from teacher-training institutions and community organizations.

Owing to recent developments such as those noted, elementary school science is now for the first time achieving full and independent status; it is no longer to be found on the periphery of other subjects in the elementary-school program; nor is it regarded as a downward extension of upper-grade science. Elementary science is now beginning to develop its own structure. It is discovering its own setting and its own problems as it develops programs drawn from each of the four enumerated sources. Let us explore individually these sources.

THE CHILD.   The curriculum in science is based on the nature and needs of children: on their delight in sensory experiences, their sense of humor, their curiosity, their concerns, their ability to generalize and to apply principles, and their urge to create. It recognizes that children are different —varying in rate of growth, in manual dexterity, in kinds of experience they have had, in the depths of their interests, and in their capacity for learning.

Children respond with enthusiasm and understanding when they are provided with wire, batteries, switches, and electrical devices like bells, lights, and toy motors and are encouraged to experiment with these materials.

Children get deep satisfaction from firsthand experiences with the forces of nature. They sense the spirit of science when their curiosity is rewarded with discovery.

As teachers, we get clues to science content when we listen intently to children's questions. We get other clues from our observations of toys they play with, the way they spend their afternoons, the television programs they watch, the books they select for reading, the sports and hobbies they engage in, the responsibilities they accept at home, and the pets they take care of.

The science program should encourage creativity and originality in the activities of children. These traits may be fostered by providing materials and situations which permit children to investigate problems and practices which are new to them, and which encourage creative expression reflecting their individual talents and capacities.

THE ENVIRONMENT. As has been indicated earlier, one of the important values of science in the elementary school is that it contributes to the child's understanding of his immediate environment at a time when he is most curious about it and most ready to explore it. The typical questions asked by children illustrate this breadth of curiosity.

It follows that each school should build into its curriculum the peculiar features of its own environment. The nearby river, the "empty" lot, the park, the brook, the swamp, the tree on the street, the vegetable market, the bakery, the flower shop, the large gas tanks, the school bus, all these are resources that can be utilized.

THE SCIENCES. We have observed how elementary science stems from the needs of children and how it flourishes when it is rooted in their environment. However, the uniqueness of elementary science is derived from the content of organized knowledge and the methods of discovery inherent in the formal sciences.

In designing the elementary-science curriculum we look to the basic sciences for both answers and questions. We look to biology, physics, chemistry, geology, and astronomy for answers to questions arising out of the total life of the child; we seek answers that furnish facts, concepts, principles, techniques and materials, approaches and methods. We look to these sciences also for key questions which will lead children into the structure of organized science. Science gives information; it furnishes concepts and principles; it suggests techniques and materials; and it provides approaches to problems and methods of thinking. Science asks questions. While rejecting the idea that elementary science is a watered-down version of the science of higher levels, we should not disregard the opportunities which present themselves for using guidelines which may help lead young people into the formal sciences. When, for example, we encourage children to discover that shape has something to do with buoyancy, we are starting them on the way to an understanding of the principle of flotation. When children are led to uncover, layer by layer, the disintegrating leaves of a forest floor, they are on the road to understanding the cycles which make life on earth possible. When they experiment to find out how to make their electromagnets more powerful, they are acquiring concepts which will be useful when they study electromagnets in advanced courses.

We find the clues to problems like these by looking for them in the structure and history of the various sciences, in their methods of discovery, and in the important concepts and principles which run through them. Incidentally, the study of the history of science is especially fruitful in suggesting many experiments which represent great triumphs of scientists, yet which children of today can perform and understand.

The search for these guidelines to the sciences is facilitated when curriculum teams include individuals who have had training in the various sciences. For example, personnel from high school and college should be included; perhaps doctors, engineers, geologists, and chemists of the community may help; so, too, may representatives of scientific, technical, and business institutions. From the use of teams of such diversified membership a broader understanding of the problems at all levels may result.

In the last decade there has been a strengthening of the sequence for science from Kindergarten through Grade XII. Articulation between the various levels is being advanced as the elementary schools look more intently at the science content of the upper grades and expect to include these observations in their planning. Articulation is also strengthened as the philosophy of the junior and senior high school embraces more of the educational values which the elementary schools have found so invigorating in the last three or four decades.

THE TOTAL SCHOOL PROGRAM.   A basic premise underlying the science program is that it should be in harmony with the total program of education. This implies that elementary science is an integral part of the fabric which includes social studies, language arts, music, mathematics, art, and health education. Science brings new strength to the elementary schools. Its methods, its approach to problem-solving, and its informational content enrich the whole program and give it new scope and depth.

Social studies, which in Kindergarten through Grade VI includes geography, history, and civics, is, of all subjects, the one most closely allied to elementary-school science. Its concern with problems of living and working together in the home, school, neighborhood, community, or country makes social studies a good background for many science activities. Communication, transportation, food, clothing, shelter, water supply, are topics which are shared by social studies and science.

"If in the social studies, for example, a class is studying the buildings and building construction in their neighborhood, questions with science implications will undoubtedly arise. The children will want to know about some of the materials used—wood, rock, iron, glass, bricks, sand, cement—their origin, their preparation for use, their qualities. . . . They may be interested in some of the machines—wheels, levers, gears—that move things. They may explore the ways in which buildings are protected from the weather. As they watch men at work connecting utilities to the building, they learn about water, sewage, electricity, and telephones." [1]

But supplying information is only one of the contributions that science makes. Science vitalizes units by encouraging children to raise questions and to find ways of answering them. When children are permitted to experiment with materials and to find out, for example, why steel bridges and iron fences are painted, how concrete is made and used, why a lever makes some kinds of work easier, why water rises in the pipes of a tall building, or why electric wires are insulated, they are doing more than talking about science; they are living it.

[1] *Science, Grades K–6.* Curriculum Bulletin #3, 1958–59 Series. New York City Board of Education.

Science is allied to mathematics because of its emphasis on measurement, accuracy, and numerical relationships and because it suggests many uses for mathematics in real life situations. Using instruments such as the thermometer and the rain gauge and making calculations required in planning models for a planetarium are illustrations of the use of mathematics in science.

Science makes use of language arts and art skills. Reading, writing, listening, speaking, painting, and sketching are essential tools in elementary science. Here again, the necessary skills are developed by the science program as the child needs them.

The foregoing observations do not mean that science serves only to enrich other areas. Science is the center for many units of planned, co-ordinated experiences, organized around central scientific themes and problems. These science-centered units draw on skills and knowledge from the other curriculum areas as need indicates; but their over-all focus is on science.

ORGANIZING THE PROGRAM

THE STRUCTURE. The National Society's Forty-sixth Yearbook pointed the way to the organization of the elementary-science program, stressing the importance of acquainting pupils with the broader areas of the physical and biological environment by introducing such subjects as the universe, the conditions necessary to life, living things, physical and chemical phenomena, and man's attempts to control his environment.[2]

During the last decade, elementary-school science has succeeded in developing many vital experiences for children within these broad areas and in suggesting sequences of unifying concepts from the kindergarten through the sixth grade. A wealth of content in science is emerging as a result of the efforts of classroom teachers, science specialists, curriculum workers, college teachers, and writers of children's books. Although science programs vary markedly from place to place, content areas such as the following appear in many curriculums: living things, earth in space, communication, transportation, resources of the earth, magnetism and electricity, weather, machines, changes in the earth, and health.

These areas—or similar ones—are broad enough to serve as centers for organizing many experiences and activities to meet the needs and interests of children and, at the same time, are rich enough in science content to provide for sequential mastery of science concepts and principles.

Different schools and school systems allocate content to individual grades in different ways, depending on various factors, such as basic philosophy or the nature of the experience of their teachers. Some have divided the content to provide specific teaching materials for each of the grades, Kindergarten through Grade VI. Other schools or school systems have organized the

---

[2] "Organization of the Curriculum in Science," *Science Education in American Schools*, pp. 75–76. Forty-sixth Yearbook of the National Society for the Study of Education, Part I. Chicago: Distributed by the University of Chicago Press, 1947.

content for groups consisting of two or more grades, as for example, Kindergarten–II, III–IV, and V–VI. This broader grouping permits great flexibility in developing science instruction while providing for a measure of continuity.

ADVANTAGES OF STRUCTURED PROGRAM.   Those who advocate an unstructured program in elementary science argue that teachers should be guided solely by the interests of the children. They regard a course of study as stultifying and unnecessary. There is no question but that some excellent teaching has been done without a structured program in a number of small school systems, particularly in those in which science consultants were available or in which the teachers have had an unusual background in science. However, the claims for a structured program are more compelling.

(a)   A structured program provides a framework of science principles which can help teachers unify their own experiences and give them confidence in meeting difficult classroom situations that arise. The answer suggested a decade ago to children's questions—"I don't know, but let's find out together"—is not sufficient for all of today's needs.

(b)   A structured program does not have to be a rigid one. Within the broad content areas, there are many choices which permit the teacher to adapt the program to the needs of the class. Both the unit approach and the provision of a variety of materials and situations which foster children's creativity and originality are possible within a structured program.

(c)   The freshness engendered by the use of unanticipated incidents is not lost in a structured program. Indeed, the incident becomes more significant because the teacher sees it as part of the whole and thus may be able to convey its importance to the pupil. A structured program helps the teacher anticipate, identify, and incorporate into the program the many incidents which arise during the school year.

(d)   While it is true that children come to school with many interests, it is also true that interest can be aroused and cultivated by what takes place in school.

(e)   A structured program makes it easier for children to acquire the science concepts essential for their understanding of the complex world they live in.

(f)   A structured program is a democratic one: many can share in building it and in changing it. It provides a common framework for testing and evaluation by the children as well as by the teachers.

THE SEQUENCE.   Elementary science can serve the general purposes of elementary education, as well as its own unique purposes, if its content provides for children's growth in their understanding of science concepts and principles. Studies of children's development provide clues to the order of complexity of science concepts. Some of the following generalizations have been found helpful in guiding the organization of sequence:

(a) The child's view of the world begins with the here and now and extends to the far away and long ago.
(b) The child grows in ability to reason, to generalize, to apply principles, to see cause-and-effect relationships.
(c) As the child develops physically he is able to participate in activities requiring greater strength and dexterity.
(d) The child's increasing capacity for comprehending such dimensions as time, distance, size, speed, direction, or weight may influence sequence.
(e) Strong motivation provided by current interests and the special character of the local environment may sometimes outweigh other considerations in the determination of sequence.
(f) Sequence will be influenced by the desirability of taking into account the science to come in the upper grades.

Sequence is something that must be tested and judged in the setting of the entire program. Continuous experimentation and careful observation are fundamental to growth in knowledge about what is most appropriate at a specific level.

THE TEACHING OF ELEMENTARY SCIENCE

INTRODUCTION

Planning is essential for successful teaching and learning in the classroom. This may not be readily apparent when one is observing an experienced and skillful teacher at work, because so often the science lesson seems to have developed quite extemporaneously. However, as the lesson progresses, it becomes quite evident that learning is taking place in a logical, well-ordered manner. Problems are raised. The teacher and children together discuss and decide how to solve these problems. Appropriate learning activities are selected and performed. The supplies and equipment needed for these activities appear or are available at just the right time and in just the right place. The reading materials necessary for finding information or for checking conclusions are either present or easily accessible. All this happens because of careful planning and preparation. This makes it possible for the teacher to guide and direct the children's learning of science into profitable channels.

When helping children to learn science, the teacher should always keep in mind that there is no one best method of teaching science. No single method is superior to any other, and one method should not be used constantly in preference to others. A variety of methods is desirable because some methods lend themselves better to a learning situation than others.

Science teaching and learning are always more effective when the learning begins with a problem that arouses the curiosity and interest of the children. The problem may come from a number of different sources. It may come from the teacher, the curriculum guide, the textbook, a current event, or even the children themselves. Planning ways and means of solving this problem will help determine the appropriate method to be used and will also help decide the selection of suitable learning activities.

Provision should be made for the use of a wide variety of learning activities. The children should be given the opportunity to do experiments, to read, to give reports, to participate in discussions, to take field trips, to consult resource persons, to use audio-visual aids, to do research, and to work on projects. All these activities are the means whereby the children are given the opportunity to perform the key operations of the scientist, and in the process learn science concepts.

Provision must also be made for individual differences. For the slow learner there should be additional activities that will either ensure or reinforce his learning. For the fast learner there should be activities that will challenge his intellectual ability and extend his knowledge. With increasing attention being focused today on the problem of teaching the culturally deprived child, specially designed science learning activities may be both necessary and desirable.

When teaching elementary science, care should be taken that the planning does not become rigid. Planning is necessary, but it should be flexible enough so that as new or unexpected problems arise, they can be easily incorporated into the lesson. In this way the children's investigation can digress at any point, if necessary, without disorganizing the general pattern of learning.

As innovations in education appear, they are quickly adapted wherever possible for use in the teaching of elementary science. The three most widely publicized teaching innovations in recent years are educational television, team teaching, and programed instruction. Of these, television and team teaching are already being widely used to teach elementary science. Although programed instruction has been introduced with some success in the secondary school, adaptations for its use in the elementary school have been very slow.

TEACHING SCIENCE IN THE
ELEMENTARY SCHOOL *

National Society for the Study of Education

Certain principles are observed wherever there is good science teaching. These principles are in accord with what we know about children and learning. This article discusses the principles involved in the teaching process, the teaching-learning situation, the characteristics of good science-learning activities, and adequate planning for science teaching. This discussion is an excerpt from Chapter 8, "Teaching and Evaluating Science in the Elementary School," of the Fifty-ninth Yearbook of the National Society for the Study of Education, Part I, Rethinking Science Education. Members of the committee who wrote this chapter include Glenn O. Blough, Katherine E. Hill, Willard J. Jacobson, and Albert Piltz.

O BVIOUSLY there is no *one* best method for teaching science in the elementary school any more than there is *one* best way to teach any other subject. We shall, however, attempt in this chapter to set forth some principles that, if observed, will raise the level of science instruction. They are practiced wherever there is good science-teaching. They are in accord with what we know about children and learning.

THE TEACHING PROCESS

Problem-Solving

Greater effectiveness in science-teaching is almost sure to result if the learning begins with a perplexing problem—one for which the learner is motivated to seek a solution, either because he has generated his own perplexity or because his teacher has stimulated him to wonder. The problem, then, becomes the motivating factor, and curriculum activities are performed only to solve the problem. The purpose gives focus to the method. It makes selection of the activities clearer; it makes evaluation easier.

Problems to be solved may come from a variety of sources. They may be

* REPRINTED FROM *Rethinking Science Education*, 59th Yearbook of the National Society for the Study of Education, Part I (Chicago: University of Chicago Press, 1960), pp. 136–144, by permission of the publisher.

presented by the pupils; they may be suggested by a current happening; they may come from the teacher, from the textbook, or from a prescribed course of study. Whatever the source, learning will be more effective if pupils become genuinely interested. As has been indicated elsewhere in this yearbook, these problems should constitute a developmental program as the pupils progress through the school.

The Activities

Faced with a problem, the solution of which appears important, pupils are motivated to respond to the question, "How shall we find the answer?" And, if pupils are really to grow in ability to solve problems, they must be encouraged to experiment, observe, read, discuss, look at pictures, inquire, and make use of all available resources for learning. Such activities as these are now performed in order to solve a problem.

Pupils may begin to search for experiments that will shed light on the problems. They may originate experiments for the same purpose. Each experiment is performed so that data may be gathered to apply toward the solution of the problem. Pupils will soon see that it is not possible to learn everything from experimenting. Relying entirely upon experimentation would necessitate jumping to conclusions. They must consult authorities. They must check their findings against what others have discovered. This constitutes the real reason for using the text and supplementary materials.

When it becomes necessary for pupils to study objects or processes not present in their environment, they may use slides, motion pictures, and other visual aids that will help verify or disprove their findings. The method of science constantly cautions the learner to hold conclusions tentative, collect more data, and verify the findings. The method of teaching then becomes a scientific method, simulating on a small scale the method used by scientists.

Many avenues of learning are necessary if the method of instruction is to lead pupils toward the goals of instruction. Science teaching cannot be a reading course and achieve the objectives assigned to it as part of the total curriculum. Neither can it be confused with useless construction of models and painting of murals. Each activity must have focus: the attainment of the objectives.

The Sequence of Learning

Effective science-teaching must be actively concerned with helping pupils develop a logical sequence of ideas as they proceed through the elementary school. The teaching method must make it possible for pupils to build on their previously acquired knowledge, to put together their learning experiences, and to make increasingly complex generalizations.

The method of instruction should be so designed that pupils are challenged at each new level of their program. As their ability to see relationships increases, so should the expectation of instruction. Unless pupils are challenged to extend themselves as they proceed, it is unlikely that they will achieve the objectives of the science programs.

In the elementary school we need continually to remind ourselves that good methods of instruction in science are similar to good methods of instruction in other areas of the curriculum.

THE TEACHING-LEARNING SITUATION

The Teacher

Any discussion of a good classroom teaching-learning situation may logically begin with an appraisal of the teacher and of his role. There is scarcely anything wrong with the science education in our schools today that some skillful science-teaching cannot cure. The improvement begins with the assignment of a teacher who has a good science background, has a knowledge of the objectives for teaching science, is interested in teaching, knows how children learn, and *wants* to be a good teacher. The teacher, then, is the key to the learning situation. His enthusiasm carries to the learner. His interests often become theirs. His concern for them is reflected in his success as a teacher.

The good teacher is a guide; but he is more than that. Because of his experience and understanding he not only guides but also directs the learning into profitable channels. He keeps learning from being a narrow experience by broadening the interests of the learner and by opening up new avenues of learning.

CHARACTERISTICS OF GOOD SCIENCE-LEARNING ACTIVITY

The impact of the activity movement in education is now legend. The movement is described in considerable detail in an earlier yearbook.[1] Science activity begins at birth when the child first interacts with his physical environment. In his early development his behavior is that of orientation to his surroundings. His inquisitiveness leads him to test his world in a variety of ways.

The elements which comprise a good science-learning activity are not unlike the elements of a good learning activity in other areas. However, there are some aspects of a science activity which are peculiar to science. Just as science, as a tool of learning, has a unique contribution to make to the educative process, so do science activities make a contribution toward helping children gain in power and in maturity. As has been indicated, problem-solving is essential to effective learning in science; the activity is the vehicle which provides the means for the solution to the problem.

[1] *The Activity Movement.* Thirty-third Yearbook of the National Society for the Study of Education, Part II. Chicago: Distributed by University of Chicago Press, 1934.

Variety of Activities

In a learning situation, the child carries on activities which help him internalize experience and gain basic understandings commensurate with his needs, abilities, and interests. Certain situations may require different types of activity. Some activities are more effective than others for individuals of different needs and interests. A wide variety of activities should be planned in order to adequately take into account the differences among individuals. Since interest and need are inextricably tied up with children's day-to-day experiences, it is important that activities have both meaning and significance to them if they are to achieve the goals that are sought through problems and developmental tasks.

Variety in the plan of organization of activities is also desirable. In some instances children may, with profit, work together in a certain general area but, within that area, may also pursue their individual interest. For example, if the main area of concern is the International Geophysical Year, interests in rocketry, satellites, orbits, oceans, and Antarctica would naturally arise, and appropriate activities would follow accordingly. Some youngsters might engage in an activity in a related area such as "weather at the South Pole" and remain within the broad organizational plan. Activities may, of course, be of varying length and importance.

Activities and Direct Experience

Whenever possible, children should be given opportunity to gain knowledge of the world about them through direct experience. When children engage in activity in which they gain firsthand knowledge for a purpose, clear understanding and intelligent interpretation of the environment are likely. When activities are related to the life experience of boys and girls, it is more likely that the learning will have greater application to daily living.

Adequate Planning for Science-Teaching

As has been pointed out, the objectives in science can be achieved in many different settings. The structural organization of science education, science as a separate subject or combined with other areas of learning, is significant but not nearly as important as what the teacher and his pupils do daily in the classroom.

Teacher-Pupil Planning

Teacher-pupil planning cannot be structured in advance. The planning and selection of activities should take into account the composition of the group, the competence of the teacher, and the nature of the learning that is in progress. Encouraging pupil participation in decision-making, planning, and evaluation will make the activity more purposeful and the attainment of desired goals more probable. The teacher guides and directs the pupils in the joint planning session.

The extent to which science is taught in the classroom is related in great measure to the degree to which science experience is valued by the teachers and the pupils. The amount taught tends to be large when the significance of science in our culture and its role in education are generally understood.

SOME WAYS OF HELPING CHILDREN
TO LEARN SCIENCE *

Beatrice Hurley

Beatrice Hurley discusses some of the kinds of activities which can serve as channels through which children may learn science. This discussion includes such activities as direct observation, field trips, reading, experimenting, and using audio-visual aids. It is intended as a guide for those who seek ways of helping each child learn how to go on learning science for the rest of his life. This article is a portion of a larger article, "What Is Science?" which appears in an Association for Childhood Education International service bulletin entitled Science for the Eights-to-Twelves.

CHILDREN learn science in a wide variety of ways. Obviously, there is no one blueprint which should be followed by all teachers. The activities selected for and by children should take several factors into account. Greater effectiveness in the teaching-learning process is almost always achieved when there is a challenging problem to be solved—one that children feel is worth solving. At times, the problem to be solved comes from a child's proposal; at others, the selection of the problem is the teacher's. And at still other times children and teacher jointly select it. Who makes the selection matters little, if all involved accept the problem as one worthy of solution.

When the solution of a problem is accepted as genuinely important

* REPRINTED FROM *Science for the Eights-to-Twelves,* Copyright, 1964, Bulletin No. 13A of the Association for Childhood Education International, 3615 Wisconsin Avenue, N. W., Washington, D. C., pp. 23–32, by permission of the author and the publisher. Dr. Hurley is Professor of Education at New York University.

enough to work on, planning must be done and accurate information gathered from many sources. There must be a period of exploration, time for proposals as to how and when the work shall get done and by whom. Shall the entire group be involved in each step, or shall small groups or individuals take responsibility for portions of the work and report their findings to the large group? Well-guided discussions are essential throughout the entire planning and working times. For example, let us suppose that a group of children are finding answers to the question, "What do plants need in order to grow?" This general topic might well be broken up into smaller segments:

What does soil have to do with plants' growing?
What does water have to do with plants' growing?
What does temperature have to do with plant growth?
What does light have to do with the growth of plants?

Children working in small groups or individually could work effectively upon one or another of these questions. One group might suggest experiments which would yield evidence concerning the needs of plants for growth. Another might suggest going to books to find out. Another might suggest a trip to a greenhouse, a farm, a botanical garden to talk to persons involved in successfully growing many kinds of plants.

Children should carry on activities within the large problem area which they are able to tackle with a reasonable expectation of success. Provision for individual differences in interest and maturity should be carefully assessed as decisions of work assignments are made.

It is desirable to use a variety of procedures for finding out. Not all individuals learn equally well, nor do they take the same things from any one experience.

DIRECT OBSERVATION

Whenever possible, and within the bounds of safety, children should be given opportunity to learn about their world through direct observation of it. What a learner learns through seeing, feeling, smelling, tasting and hearing gives him much firsthand knowledge of the nature of things in the local environment. With the use of certain instruments such as a telescope, observations of more distant phenomena can be made.

Young children learn much of what they know through keen use of their senses. Older children should be encouraged to continue to learn in this manner. Skill in observation is perhaps one of the most useful tools a person can acquire. Teachers can enrich the lives of boys and girls by helping them learn how to see and interpret their environment. Children who know where the first crocuses are to be found, when the spring migration of warblers takes place, what stream is best to fish to catch the biggest trout, which kinds of clouds bring clear weather are usually children who have learned to be keen observers of what goes on around them.

Learning is made more vivid and pleasurable through numerous direct observational experiences. The goal worth striving for is growth in accuracy of one's observations and in reporting them to others. The ability to observe accurately is a part of all other activities in science. Without it, experiments are of no value. Excursions benefit children more when blinders have been removed from eyes and children are helped to see what spore cases look like on the underside of fern leaves; how a robin's flight habits differ from those of a hawk; what the buds on a tree look like in midwinter; how a mullein leaf differs from a plantain leaf in the way it feels in your hand.

TAKING FIELD TRIPS

Some of the most valuable learning situations occur outside the classroom. The distance covered from school to the place to be visited is not the measuring stick for the value of an excursion. Every local environment holds numerous possibilities for fruitful observational experiences. There are inexhaustible resources for teaching science in any community, even in one that at first may appear to hold few possibilities for direct learning through trips.

Within the school building itself investigations could be made that might include:

How our school is heated
How electricity comes to our building
Where the fuse box is
How the intercommunication system works
How food is prepared in the cafeteria
How garbage is disposed of

A study of the schoolyard has much of value for learners. Suggested investigations are:

Places where soil is being eroded or where grass grows best.
Do animals live on the schoolground? If so, what do these animals find to eat? Where do they make their homes?
What kinds of trees and other plants are there that can be studied throughout the four seasons?
What machines are used in play equipment on the playground?

Exploration of these things helps bring science into the lives of children.

Moving away from the school and schoolground, there is the community to explore—persons, places and things. Trips to fields, farms, bogs, a vacant lot, a zoo, a park, a stream, an excavation or an abandoned quarry can acquaint children with a great variety of living and nonliving things and give them knowledge of how these living and nonliving things are interrelated. Return visits to places help children realize the changes that occur as seasons pass. Likewise, trips to processing and manufacturing plants, a telephone exchange, newspaper printing plant, TV station or water purification plant can reveal much of man's use of technological advances.

Almost any community has resource persons who can offer enrichment to the school curriculum. A teacher's source file of such persons will help children to benefit from the talents of special people in the community. There may be an amateur astronomer, a naturalist, a conservationist, a geologist, a photographer with color film and slides, a tropical fish keeper, a physician or a world traveler, who would be glad to share knowledge and experiences with boys and girls.

Trips into the community should be carefully planned ahead of time. Children should know the object of taking the trip, what they wish to find out while there. They should keep records on the spot, make sketches or take pictures if these activities are appropriate. One of the goals the teacher should hold in mind is to make more careful observers of children. Also, children should learn to check their observations of natural phenomena with reliable sources, a necessary operation which requires the use of books.

READING

Through reading children learn about the ideas of others. Books are useful tools for learning science. It is important to recognize that factual textbooks and trade books should be used to add information to a topic under consideration and should be consulted when unanswered questions are hanging fire. Under these conditions, children go directly to that part of the book dealing with their specific concerns. The learner may have any of several reasons to consult a book. He may wish to check his own conclusions; to get added information; to learn how to do an experiment; or to answer a question.

Using factual books in this manner helps children learn to use books effectively and efficiently. Skill in using encyclopedias is not quickly learned, but teachers who guide children in using their science textbooks and single-volume factual books as research tools build basic skills for using encyclopedias and other complex reference books.

Many teachers have in the classroom library factual books and other reading matter relating to science topics, chosen with concern for the varying reading abilities of a group of children. Assignments of topics can then be made for the individual child, using books neither too hard nor too easy. Developing skill in reading and learning science can go hand in hand if the teacher guides children well in their selection of books and other reading matter.

Thoughtful, deliberate reading of science material often sparks discussions that further enhance children's understanding of a given topic and of new topics as well. Varying points of view of authorities may cause children to question authoritative sources. Lack of agreement may also help children sense the tentative nature of much that is now known and thought to be fact. This, in itself, is a valuable experience. A healthy skepticism is a wholesome attribute.

From the foregoing, it must be evident that books and reading have an important role to play in the science program. It must also be clear that "Open the book to page 34 and read to page 39" is an undesirable kind of assignment.

Sometimes an interest catches fire in the classroom that leads children to search for new information not readily found in textbooks.

Such a search engaged the energies of a group of sixth-graders. As an offshoot of a study centering around the concept that "we are caretakers of the environment," these children learned that some animals once numerous are now extinct and that others are on the way to becoming so.

Committees set to work to find out which animals had already died out and why; which ones were threatened with extinction; and what was happening to correct the situation. This search led children to magazines, bulletins, daily papers, movies, TV programs and books for information about whooping cranes, the condor of California, the bald eagle now scarce in this country, and other scarce animals throughout the world. The children were stunned to learn that giraffes are still being slaughtered, not for food, but for their tails which are marketed as flyswatters; and that the rhinoceros are killed for their horns which are ground into a powder that is an aphrodisiac.

The New York Times of December 22, 1963, carried a story of the killing of 351 rare, gray seal calves on an island in the North Sea by marksmen from the Ministry of Agriculture, Fisheries, and Food. Fishermen had complained that the calves were damaging their nets and eating their fish. The children were puzzled at the wanton destruction of seal calves by a body of men engaged in the conservation of wildlife. Was this not a shortsighted act on the part of these men? "Aren't there wiser ways to keep nature in balance?," they asked. Many more questions were asked.

But the children's faith in human nature was somewhat restored as they learned of the exciting wildlife survival centers being set up in many zoological parks for breeding stock of endangered species. Children's letters to persons planning these centers brought replies with many details concerning which animals were to be protected.

If it is true that concepts govern actions, this vital science enterprise may well have conditioned the behavior of these sixth-graders in matters pertaining to the responsibility of each as a "caretaker of his environment."

Among the concepts that the teacher sought to advance in this experience were the following:

Countless species of plants and animals that once lived on Earth are nowhere to be found today.

Once a species has died out, it is never likely to develop on Earth again.

Thoughtless acts may cause great damage.

Sometimes men have helped to cause the extinction of some living things.

Sometimes men have helped to save species of living things from extinction.

Boys and girls not only need to learn about the living things in their environment, but they also need to learn the importance of their actions in bringing about change.

Part of this understanding about the importance of individual acts can be gained by studying some of the changes which have occurred in the past.

Each individual is responsible to some degree for the care of his environment.

Concepts of such magnitude clearly illustrated that this teacher was not concerned with pouring in a mass of small facts. To be sure, a great number of facts were uncovered and utilized, but it was not the memorizing of small content that guided the teacher as she worked with the boys and girls. Her goals were changes in behavior, deepening of understanding, appreciation of the vital role of each individual in enjoying and protecting the environment. The teaching of science that aims at changes in behavior is quite different from that which is set out to be learned, such as covering the book and passing the test.

Experimenting

An experiment is an activity intended to supply information in solving, or helping to solve, a problem. It is a means to an end rather than an end in itself. Experimentation is conducted primarily for learning something that the experimenter does not already know.

Let us suppose a fourth-grade child asks, "Where is the attraction of a magnet strongest?" He asks because he doesn't know the answer. This is the moment for the teacher to suggest that he go to the storage cupboard, get a magnet and experiment to find the answer he seeks.

Equipment for most experiments done in elementary school should be simple. A paper bag can be used as successfully as a bicycle pump and tire to show that compressed air can do work. Occasionally, the use of simple materials stimulates children to improvise equipment from materials at hand; often such improvisation is ingenious and quite creative.

In guiding experiments done by children, the teacher needs to bear in mind that the factor of *control* is very important; that is, all conditions must be the same except for the experimental one, called the *variable*.

For example, a child might set about to find out "what would happen to green plants if there were no more sunlight." One way to find out is to plan an experiment. Since the answer is not known, the situation is truly experimental.

The child decides to use two potted green plants. He chooses the same kind of plant, in the same-sized pots, growing well in the same kind of soil; that is, he attempts to get plants as nearly alike as possible.

He allows one plant to continue to grow under ordinary conditions just as it has been doing. This is his control. He places the other plant in a completely dark place. Otherwise, he keeps conditions as identical as possible. The factor of light is the variable.

Periodically, he examines both plants. He notes and keeps a careful record of any changes that take place. At the end of ten days, dramatic differences have developed. Since all other aspects of the experiment are the same, the experimenter concludes that the differences may be ascribed to the difference in the amount of light available to the two plants. This is the answer to his question, "What would happen to green plants if there were no more sunlight?"

But this answer must be considered tentative only. It may not be the final answer. There is always the possibility that the results obtained were only accidental. Perhaps another plant kept in darkness would not react in the same manner.

He might try more than two plants—perhaps ten—keeping five in darkness and the rest in the light. He repeats the steps used earlier. At the end of ten days, he finds that the plants in the dark reacted in a similar manner to the one used in the first experiment.

If this happens, he has a sounder basis for his conclusion. Even so, he should check his conclusions with an authoritative source.[1]

Not all situations call for experimentation. Many answers are to be found by direct observation of phenomena, by asking others, by reading books. Doing experiments when the answer is already known, not only by the teacher but by the students as well, is a dull and unproductive use of time.

AUDIOVISUAL AIDS

Although personal, firsthand experiences furnish the richest ways for acquiring correct concepts in science, they are not always possible. Glaciers and geysers can seldom be visited. Hence the teacher seeks another source to help children learn about glaciers and geysers.

Often visual or auditory aids can be profitably used, such as colored photographs, slides, filmstrips, movies and recordings. Many schools now budget for the purchase or rental of such materials. Catalogs of major distributors of audiovisual materials should be available to teachers. Often the school librarian is custodian of the audiovisual aids, which are kept in the library and checked out as books are loaned.

Museums sometimes have dioramas and mounted exhibits to loan to neighborhood schools. Many commercial and industrial plants have exhibits that can be had for the charge of mailing them back to their owners. Models, such as a model of the human body, can be profitably used.

---

[1] Gerald S. Craig and John Urban, Teachers Manual for *Science Today and Tomorrow: Facing Tomorrow with Science* (Boston: Ginn and Company, 1958), p. 12.

For example, in discussing geometrical shapes, children in a fourth grade had become interested in Pythagoras and the introduction of geometry into Greece. The name of Socrates was mentioned in answer to the question, "What other famous men lived in Ancient Greece?" Then it was brought out by the teacher that a favorite saying of Socrates was "Know thyself."

The children pondered on what "Know thyself" really meant. Someone suggested that it was important to know what is in our bodies, and this launched the class on a study of the human body.

Through much research in encyclopedias, trade books and many texts, children found that the smallest part of a healthy body is a cell. After initial total class discussion, individual and small groups of children worked on their own to delve into this study, under the guidance of the teacher. Various activities included:

> taking apart the large model of the human body (and putting it together again)
>
> learning about the bony framework, joints, and organs
>
> writing reports and drawing figures.

As well as "knowing themselves," children developed vocabulary and research skills in their study of the human body.[2]

Perhaps one of the most exciting innovations now being used in schools is the tape recorder. There is no end to the possibilities for enriching classroom living through carefully prepared tapes. Recordings of talks by specialists in any number of areas can be made and re-used. Discussions of children concerning scientific matters are frequently worth taping and re-using, often as an evaluative device wherein children examine their own ability, or lack of it, to think critically. Recordings of bird songs, of sounds at a pond, of porpoises communicating in a tank, of animals when in danger are among other uses of tapes.

Needless to say, the same careful planning for using auditory and visual aids that characterizes uses of other materials is essential for the best results.

There are, then, many types of activities which can serve as channels through which boys and girls may learn science. The choice of the particular activity, or activities, depends upon the goals to be achieved. Whatever is chosen, that activity should promote understanding, interest and appreciation in science. It should make science concepts and principles more vivid, more clearly understood. As was said earlier in this bulletin, science experiences should help children construct a comprehensible and orderly system of explanations for natural phenomena and build a basis for intelligent control and utilization of the natural world.

[2] Highview School, Hartsdale, N. Y., Fourth Grade.

THE UNIT *

Edward Victor

Edward Victor presents a comprehensive discussion of the key components of a planned and structured elementary science unit. These components include the overview, teacher's objectives, initiating activities, pupil objectives, learning activities, materials, bibliography, vocabulary, culminating activities, evaluation, and work sheets. Dr. Victor describes the purpose of each component, and shows in detail how the components may be developed and incorporated into the unit. This excerpt on the unit is taken from Chapter 5, "Planning for Science in the Classroom," of Science for the Elementary School.

CONCOMITANT with the need for planning is the need for organizing the elements of good planning into a suitable framework, through which the teaching-learning situation in the classroom has scope and sequence. A highly effective means of organizing such a framework is the unit.

The unit is a logical division of class work or activity. When constructed, the unit becomes an *anticipated* plan for using a wide variety of activities and materials so that learning can take place. The objectives of the unit are to help the children learn basic science information and develop desirable behaviors. As stated before, the term *basic science information* is used broadly to include science facts, understandings, generalizations, principles, laws, concepts, and conceptual schemes. And the term *desirable behaviors* includes abilities and skills (both functional and mental), scientific attitudes, appreciations, and interests. Thus, the unit presents a plan for providing learning activities that will achieve the objectives of the unit.

When planning and constructing the unit, the teacher selects the objectives, develops the means for arousing pupil interest and problems, anticipates a logical sequence of learning activities, provides for the necessary laboratory and reference materials, and even gives consideration to the possibilities for evaluating both the learning and the desirable behaviors that the children will gain. The teacher strives at all times to give the unit suitable scope and sequence.

---

* REPRINTED FROM *Science for the Elementary School* (New York: The Macmillan Company, 1965), pp. 112–127, by permission of the publisher. Dr. Victor is Professor of Education at Northwestern University.

Although the unit is developed in a logical sequence, it should not be rigid. It must be flexible enough to permit digression at any point, if necessary, without interrupting the broad pattern of learning anticipated by the unit. It is necessary to plan the day's work in advance, but the plan should be pliable enough to include and incorporate new situations and questions as they arise.

What to include in a unit is always a matter of discussion. Proponents of the various types of units differ somewhat about content and organization. However, it is generally agreed that a unit should contain most—if not all—of the following:

1. Overview.
2. Teacher's objectives.
3. Initiating activities.
4. Pupil objectives.
5. Learning activities.
6. Materials.
7. Bibliography.
8. New science vocabulary.
9. Culminating activities.
10. Evaluation.
11. Work sheets.

A detailed discussion of each of these components of a unit follows.

OVERVIEW

The purpose of the overview is to describe the nature and scope of the unit. Some teachers or school systems, when constructing units, omit the overview. However, the overview can serve a definite purpose. When a school system sets up a science course of study and constructs units, it is likely that a science committee or workshop group is given the responsibility of preparing the units for the rest of the teachers in the school system. This preparation will result whenever a school system is large and has so many elementary school teachers that it becomes impossible to involve all the teachers in constructing every unit for each grade level. Furthermore, with the consistent rapid turnover of elementary school teachers, there will always be new teachers or beginning teachers who have started teaching after the units have been constructed. In such cases, whenever units are presented to the teachers who have had no part in constructing them, it is always helpful to provide an overview with a brief description of the nature and scope of the unit. Even when the teacher makes her own unit, an overview can be of real service when shown to administrators, parents, or other teachers who visit her class and need a quick briefing on what is going on.

Overviews may be written in two or three different ways. One of the techniques is to make a list of the key subtopics that make up the general science topic being studied. These subtopics are usually given in the form of statements or understandings. They may even occur in the form of questions or problems as the children might visualize them.

For example, when studying the science topic of "Leaves" in the fourth or fifth grade, such an overview might be as follows:

1. What kinds of leaves are there and how do they differ?
2. What are the parts of a leaf?
3. What do leaves do for the rest of the plant?
4. Why and how do leaves change color in the fall?

A more elaborate but highly effective way of presenting on overview is to give it in written form, consisting of two or three paragraphs. The overview might begin by describing the importance of the science topic in our daily lives, for both child and adult. Then it might list the subtopics, and conclude by giving some general values and key desirable behaviors that the children will derive from the unit.

An example of this kind of overview, on the same topic of "Leaves," is as follows:

Leaves are important to the daily life of both children and adults because they are one of the primary sources of food for all living things. Leaves and grass contain chlorophyll and can manufacture food, and from green leaves and grass we get all our food—either directly or indirectly. Hence, the study of leaves can be basic to the understanding of life and how it exists on earth. In addition, leaves give us one of the several signs of the change of seasons in many parts of the country.

This unit hopes to teach (1) the kinds of leaves and how they differ from one another, (2) the parts of the leaf, including its external and internal structure, (3) the function of the leaf, with special emphasis on photosynthesis, and (4) the change in color of leaves in the fall.

From the learning activities in this unit the children may gain a better understanding of leaves and their function, and an appreciation of the beauty and the way leaves are constructed. The children will develop further their ability to observe carefully and accurately, to listen intelligently, and to read science books for information. They will be asked to draw conclusions from what they have learned, and to apply these conclusions to life situations. Finally, they will learn how to express themselves more effectively, to participate more ably in class discussion, and to work democratically with their peers.

TEACHER'S OBJECTIVES

In general, the teacher has two main objectives: (1) to help the children learn basic science information, and (2) to develop desirable behaviors in the process. Both objectives are vital, and one is meaningless without the other. Consequently, definite provision must be made to incorporate both objectives into the unit. Otherwise the unit will fail to accomplish its purpose.

Some school systems develop only a scope and sequence chart, leaving the construction of units to the individual teacher. Other school systems appoint a science curriculum committee, which, under the guidance of a science supervisor or consultant, constructs a comprehensive set of units for all the teachers. An analysis of science units, which have proven to be highly successful and which have enabled the teacher to achieve effective learning in the classroom, shows that they all have one factor in common. In all cases, the units contain an outline or list of the basic science information that the children are expected to learn while the units are in progress. And it seems that the more detailed the outline or list, the more successful are the units.

The preparation of an outline or list of concepts for inclusion in the unit helps the teacher in two ways. First, regardless of whether the unit is constructed by the teacher or by a committee, such an outline can be of great help as a guide when the learning activities are selected for the unit. Second, the outline serves as a check to make sure that the teacher will have the necessary science background for the topic being studied.

Giving the elementary teacher as much help as possible in acquiring the necessary science background is an important facet of any planned science program. An examination of current elementary science textbooks shows that approximately 33 percent of the content is in the area of biology, 33 percent is in the area of physics, 20 percent is in the area of geology, 8 percent is in the area of astronomy, and 6 percent is in the area of chemistry. (Meteorology is incorporated into the area of geology.) Thus to teach science effectively in the elementary school, the teacher should have a certain measure of knowledge and proficiency in these five areas. Unfortunately, this situation is not prevalent. It is generally agreed, and is verified by the findings of research, that most elementary school teachers have inadequate science backgrounds. Consequently, many of these teachers are reluctant to teach science.

Therefore, if teachers with an inadequate science background are given units that do not contain the basic science information, the teachers will be reluctant to use the units. This situation is easily understandable because all teachers realize that, unless they are at least moderately qualified to teach any subject, they may eventually be put into the embarrassing position of appearing inept before the children. A teacher does not mind saying "I don't know" occasionally to the children. But when she has to say "I don't know" repeatedly, she soon stops teaching the particular topic or subject that places her in this awkward position. The teacher prefers to teach subjects in which she feels competent, comfortable, and secure.

If one of the objectives of science is to help the children understand and learn key concepts and conceptual schemes, it is imperative that the teacher be well informed about the science topics being studied. Otherwise the teacher will not be able to guide the children's learning profitably.

For the children to learn about the methods of heat travel, the teacher herself must be thoroughly familiar with the theory of molecular motion, the concept of heat, and the differences between conduction, convection, and radiation. She must know how these methods of heat travel are used in our daily lives and how they apply to the various phenomena in the children's environment.

When teaching about machines, the teacher must be familiar with the concepts of force, work, mechanical advantage, and energy. She must know what machines are, how they help us, and their limitations. She must be aware that there are just six simple machines, and that all machines are made up of one or more of these simple machines. She must know the parts of each of these simple machines and their function. And she must have a working knowledge of the law of conservation of energy.

It seems fairly obvious, then, that a unit that spells out the science content to be learned can be of real value to the teacher. Yet many units fail to include a sufficiently detailed outline or list of the basic science information. This lack often exists in units that have been prepared by a curriculum committee for all the elementary teachers in a school system. This situation is unfortunate because any resulting reluctance or failure of the teachers to use the units will weaken or destroy the effectiveness of the planned science program.

Of course, many seemingly valid reasons can be offered for not including the basic science information in a unit. Perhaps a committee may feel that the teachers are already familiar with the science content. If the findings of research are to be believed, however, this assumption is usually not true. Perhaps the committee may feel that the teachers can obtain the information quickly and easily from the elementary science textbooks. Unfortunately, however, most textbooks distribute the science content over several grades, so that it is cumbersome for a teacher to locate all the concepts and put them together to achieve an overall view. Besides, most well-constructed units usually contain more science content and learning activities than can be found in the current elementary science textbooks.

Perhaps the units do not include the basic science information to discourage any tendency of the teachers to make learning of the "subject matter" the most important part of the unit. The term "teaching subject matter" has fallen into disrepute, especially in science, because science learning has too often consisted mainly of reading the textbook and then memorizing a mass of facts. As a result, there has been little or no development of desirable behaviors. This situation should not occur with a properly constructed unit. A good unit provides effective learning activities, which help the children learn worthwhile "subject matter" and at the same time develop the desirable behaviors. Thus, learning "subject matter" does not take place without the acquisition of desirable behaviors, and vice versa.

This condition is as it should be. For a long time, in an effort to dissuade teachers from just "teaching subject matter," the teachers were often admonished to remember that "We are not teaching science (or arithmetic or social studies, and so forth), but rather we are teaching children." Actually, the statement should be, "We are teaching *science* to *children*; we are teaching *social studies* to *children*," and so forth. In this way we have equal emphasis upon both the learning of "subject matter" and the development of desirable behaviors by the children.

Another reason why an outline or list of basic science information is not included in units may be the feeling that such an outline or list will tend to make the unit too rigid. In fact, some persons do object to detailed structuring of a unit because they feel this structuring deters exploration, investigation, and creativity from taking place freely in the classroom. The consensus, however, is that structuring helps rather than hinders. Only by careful planning and structuring by the teacher—and this factor is true especially for both the beginning teacher and the teacher with an inadequate science background—can effective ongoing investigation, exploration, and learning take place in the classroom. Perhaps the objecting persons lose sight of the fact that the highly structured planning is primarily for the teacher, not for the children.

When a science curriculum committee constructs units for all the teachers in the school system, the members of the committee are usually competent in science. They have no difficulty in deciding which concepts are pertinent to the science topic and in organizing these concepts into a logical learning sequence. However, what about the teacher who is required to construct her own units? How can she select and organize the concepts, especially if she is unfamiliar with the science topic and if the elementary science textbook does not contain enough science content for her needs?

One solution, found to be surprisingly effective, is for the teacher to consult a good junior high school textbook. Here she will find a complete presentation of the basic science information dealing with the topic she wishes to take up in class, expressed simply and clearly and arranged in a logical sequence. She can acquire the science background she needs and at the same time select those understandings she would like her pupils to learn. Naturally, consulting a high school textbook, or even a college textbook, would be still better. However, when teachers have little or no science background, they are rather shy about using or reading books on more advanced levels. They also encounter increasing difficulty in selecting appropriate science understandings and adjusting them to the desired grade level. The junior high school textbook is usually adequate, and the science content is quite easy for the teacher to comprehend. Another source of help is the increasing number of reference books dealing with individual science topics at the elementary school level. These books present the basic science information simply and clearly, and they suggest many appropriate experiments and other learning activities.

After the teacher becomes familiar with the science content, the next step is the selection of science understandings that will be suitable for her grade level. If the teacher's school system has a planned science program, with scope and sequence, she will have some indication of what understandings to include. If there is no such program, the solution will have to be left to the judgment of the teacher. In either case she simplifies the wording of these understandings (without losing their scientific accuracy) to meet the vocabulary level of her class, and organizes them into what she thinks will be a logical sequence of learning. The latter is very important because one set of understandings will lead easily into another set of understandings, and in this way learning can take place quickly and efficiently.

When studying fire, for example, the children can begin one possible sequence by learning what fire is, then proceed to the factors necessary to produce fire, the concept of flame and smoke, the factors necessary to put out fires, different kinds of fire extinguishers, and finally appropriate safety rules for preventing or controlling fire.

The learning of basic science information by the children, then, is one of the teacher's two major objectives. The second major objective is the development of desirable behaviors. These behaviors include abilities and skills, scientific attitudes, appreciations, and interests. They also involve learning how to think critically and to solve problems. Such behaviors emerge from the learning activities that are conducted while the unit is in progress. The behaviors that emerge may be either immediate or long-range behaviors. Examples of these behaviors have already been described in Chapter 2, "Objectives of Elementary Science."

Although the basic science information is selected before the unit is written, it is difficult to select the desirable behaviors in advance. If the behaviors are selected first, the teacher is usually pressed to find the proper learning activity that will develop these behaviors. Learning activities call for specific behaviors. An oral report tends to develop the ability to speak effectively whereas a written report does not. An experiment helps to develop close and accurate observation much better than does reading. Each learning activity, as a rule, will call for the emergence of certain behaviors that are logical outcomes of the learning activity. The key to success is for the teacher to be fully aware of all the potentially desirable behaviors, and then to examine each learning activity closely, and to work for the development of those behaviors associated with that activity. If the teacher regularly uses the unit method of teaching and employs a wide variety of learning activities in her units, eventually she will have ample opportunity to develop any or all of the desirable behaviors she wants.

When constructing the unit, the teacher should be aware that, although there are many abilities and skills, there are much less scientific attitudes, and even fewer worthwhile appreciations and interests. Consequently, it would seem advisable to look for and select only those behaviors that would logically emerge from the learning activities. Otherwise they will seem farfetched and unrelated, and give the effect of padding the unit.

Finally, the behaviors should be worded clearly and specifically, and in terms that lend themselves to evaluation. Vague and indefinite behaviors are both meaningless and valueless because there is no possible way of evaluating them to see if they really did develop. It is also helpful if the behaviors are expressed in a consistent form. Some teachers prefer to express the behaviors in the form of questions. "Did the children go to reliable sources for evidence?" "Do they realize the need for a control experiment?" "Are they relating acquired facts into a meaningful whole?" "Are they able to apply what they have learned to a new situation?" Questions such as these lend themselves quite easily to evaluation by the teacher.

INITIATING ACTIVITIES

The purpose of initiating activities is to involve the children in the unit; these activities are the means whereby pupil interest and curiosity are aroused. In the process, questions and problems are raised that, when answered or solved, will help achieve the teacher's objectives. The main purpose of initiating activities is to raise questions or problems, the answers to which the children do not know but will find out as they proceed with the learning activities in the unit. Because the children do not know the answers, their curiosity is piqued and their interest in finding out the answers is aroused. Consequently, when the children participate in the learning activities for the unit, they learn basic science information that enables them to answer their questions or problems, and at the same time to develop desirable behaviors.

Usually a general or overall initiating activity is used to introduce or "initiate" the entire unit to the children. There are several ways of initiating the entire unit. Sometimes a previous unit will lead the children quite naturally into a new unit. If the class has just finished a study of magnets, for example, it will require very little effort to motivate the children for the study of electromagnets. Units can also be initiated by books and stories. Sometimes, merely the announcement of the next topic or problem may be sufficient to arouse pupil interest and problems.

Another way to initiate a unit is to set the stage for the unit. A good example is an attractive bulletin-board display, accompanied by thought-provoking questions. To initiate a unit on "Evaporation and Condensation," a teacher may plan to put on the bulletin board a series of pictures showing evaporation and condensation taking place. This display can include pictures of a puddle of water on a concrete sidewalk under the warm sun, sheets or towels drying on the clothesline, droplets of water on a bottle of soda pop or on the sides of a pitcher of lemonade, fogged-up windows, a person's breath visible on a cold, wintry day, and so on. Under the pictures can be questions such as—"How does the water get into the air?" "How does water come out of the air?" "How can we make water go into or come out of the air more quickly or more slowly?"

Another way to set the stage for a unit is to have a display of materials on a table with accompanying questions. Materials for display can include pictures, books, models, or specimens. When initiating a unit on leaves, it will be natural to have a variety of leaves on display, especially in the fall. Typical questions that can be asked would be—"Are these leaves alike?" "How are they different?" "How many parts does each leaf have?" "What do leaves do?" "Why do leaves change color in the fall?"

A thought-provoking experiment or demonstration is an excellent way to initiate a unit. A teacher can initiate a unit on "Methods of Heat Travel" by simply placing a spoon in a cup of hot water. Pupil interest and curiosity will be raised about why the part of the spoon that is out of the water also becomes hot.

Even a thought-provoking discussion can initiate a unit. In temperate climates most children are quite familiar with the effects caused by static electricity, especially on a cold, dry day. The teacher can initiate a unit on such a day by first asking the children to describe personal experiences with static electricity and then leading into an on-going discussion about the characteristics of and reasons for this phenomenon.

It may well be mentioned again that the initiating activity should raise questions and problems that the children cannot answer immediately but will be able to answer later, after they have performed or participated in the learning activities that will supply the information to answer the questions or problems. If the initiating activity selected does not raise questions or problems, it should be discarded and a new one substituted.

There are many who believe that one good general or overall initiating activity is sufficient to sustain pupil interest and motivation for the entire unit. They feel that the one activity will raise enough questions and problems to ensure the learning of all the science understandings in the unit. On the other hand, there are others who think that additional initiating activities are necessary as the unit progresses. These additional activities may be necessary, especially when a unit extends over two, three, or even more weeks. Interest and motivation may flag over a period of time for even the most enthusiastic children.

Also, when teachers organize the basic science information into outline form for easier use in the unit, the science understandings in the outline seem to arrange themselves into groups of related understandings that make natural headings or subtopics for the main science topic. Although these headings or subtopics are all part of the main topic, they differ in science content sufficiently among themselves to warrant having their own initiating activities. Thus, a unit may need enough initiating activities to raise pupil questions or problems involving all the science understandings in the outline of basic science information. Usually one initiating activity is needed for each group of related science understandings that constitutes a heading or subtopic in the outline of basic science information. Thus each initiating activity leads to learning activities from which the children will learn a group of related understandings.

The need for subsequent initiating activities while the unit is in progress

can be illustrated by the topic "Magnets." The understandings in an outline of basic science information may easily fall into headings or subtopics
such as: (1) "What Magnets Are and What They Do," (2) "The Law of
Magnetic Attraction," (3) "What Materials the Force of a Magnet Will Pass
Through," (4) "How Magnets Are Made," and so forth. A good general
initiating activity should prepare the children for study of magnets in general.
The same general initiating activity may even be used to initiate learning
activities for the first heading or subtopic, "What Magnets Are and What
They Do." However, it seems obvious that a new initiating activity is needed
for the second heading, and for the third and fourth headings as well.

Thus, additional initiating activities—other than the general or overall
initiating activity—may be used at various intervals as the unit progresses.
The most effective activities are thought-provoking experiments and demonstrations, questions or series of questions, and discussions. Occasionally, one
or more frames of a filmstrip can be used as an initiating activity. Often the
general or overall activity can also be used as the initiating activity for the
first heading or subtopic of the outline of basic science information.

Films, field trips, and speakers should rarely be used as initiating activities.
The purpose of initiating activities is to raise questions or problems, the
answers to which the children do not know, which then necessitates special
learning activities to find the answers. Films, field trips, and speakers as a
rule not only raise questions, but also usually provide the answers to the
questions immediately afterward. This procedure defeats the purpose of the
initiating activity.

Similarly, because the initiating activity raises questions instead of giving
answers, the initiating activity is almost never used as the first learning
activity. The purpose of the learning activity is to find out information
whereas the initiating activity is designed only to raise questions. However,
the initiating activity can be used to advantage as an evaluative technique
later in the unit. If the children have really learned the science understandings
in the subsequent learning activities, they should now be able to answer the
questions or solve the problems raised by the initiating activity.

The selection of good initiating activities is perhaps the most difficult
phase of unit construction. Very often, many pupils are able to explain what
were intended to be thought-provoking experiments or demonstrations. Thus,
the initiating activities have not fulfilled their purpose and are valueless.
The teacher should not become discouraged, but she must discard the unsuccessful initiating activities and continue her search for new and better
ones.

Pupil Objectives

Units often include pupil objectives. These objectives are the anticipated
pupil questions or problems that will emerge from the initiating activities.
The questions and problems are stated as the children might raise them in the

children's own vocabulary. Pupil objectives thus also remind us that the children's aims may be quite different from those of the teacher. The teacher may want the children to learn about heat expansion. The children, however, will want to know why cracks are intentionally put into concrete sidewalks. The teacher is interested in electrical circuits; the children want to learn how to connect a dry cell, wires, and a porcelain socket containing a bulb so that the bulb will light up. The teacher is interested in the laws governing vibrating strings; the children want to know what can be done to make the musical note from a violin or guitar higher or lower. The teacher is primarily concerned with the learning of basic science information and the development of desirable behaviors. The children want to know "why," "what," "how," "when," "what will happen if," and so forth.

If the initiating activities are properly selected, the pupil objectives will emerge easily. However, because the pupil questions and problems in the planned unit are anticipated, if the children should fail to raise them, the teacher may ask them instead. Actually, the children often raise better or more questions and problems than those anticipated by the teacher. The wise teacher incorporates these questions and problems into the unit.

LEARNING ACTIVITIES

Learning activities are the means by which the children learn basic science information and develop desirable behaviors. In the process, the children acquire understandings that enable them to answer the questions or problems raised by the initiating activities. The teacher uses a wide variety of learning activities in the unit to accomplish this purpose. All the techniques and activities suggested in Chapter 4, "Methods of Teaching Science," are utilized. These include experiments, demonstrations, observation, reading and study, discussion, oral and written reports, films, filmstrips, speakers, models, charts, posters, individual and group planning, and so forth.

Many teachers have a tendency to use many more learning activities than are necessary to ensure satisfactory learning. This overpreparation tends to prolong the unit unnecessarily, slow down learning, and dull pupil interest. The experienced teacher employs her learning activities wisely and economically, especially when teaching for science understandings. She realizes that sometimes one activity is enough for an understanding to be learned. Occasionally one good learning activity will suffice to produce the learning of more than one understanding, especially if the understandings are simple or are related to each other. Other times, when an understanding is difficult or abstract, more than one activity may be necessary to obtain adequate learning. Slow learners usually learn better when more than one activity is used.

The grade level may also influence the number of learning activities needed. In the lower grades, where the children's attention span is small and their ability to think abstractly is not well developed, more than one activity is often necessary to obtain satisfactory learning of an understanding. However, in the upper grades one well-chosen activity is usually sufficient.

In all cases the best procedure is for the teacher to use as many—but *only* as many—activities as are necessary to ensure satisfactory learning. And if the teacher finds that there is a surplus of activities, they can always be used as additional activities for slow and fast learners.

MATERIALS, BIBLIOGRAPHY, NEW SCIENCE VOCABULARY

When planning a unit, the teacher should list all the materials that will be needed for the learning activities. This list includes supplies, equipment, textbooks, reference materials, films, and filmstrips. In this way the teacher can begin to accumulate the necessary materials and have them ready and available as the activities require them.

Most units contain a bibliography of the textbooks and other reference materials that will be used during the unit. This bibliography includes materials for both the children and the teacher. The pupil list contains those references that the children will use to answer questions, solve problems, learn how to do an experiment, check conclusions, and find additional information for reports, and so forth. Where possible, it is wise to include duplicate references on the same topic, but on different grade (reading) levels. Thus, there will be available reading materials for slow and rapid learners. The teacher list should contain either those references that describe in detail an experiment or demonstration that she plans to use or those that give her additional information about the topic.

For clarity, the pupil and teacher references should be listed separately. Each reference should include the title, author(s), publisher, place and date of publication, and grade level (if it is part of an elementary science textbook series). Films and filmstrips should be included in the bibliography, usually under a separate listing. Besides listing the title and the producer, it may be helpful to add such information as the running time, whether it is in black or white or color, and so forth.

With the development of ideas and understandings, the children regularly will encounter new words and terms. This new vocabulary must be thoroughly explained and understood for maximum learning to take place. Many teachers find it expedient to include a vocabulary list of the new science terms that will be learned and used during the unit; this list reminds the teacher to give full attention to the learning of the terms when they appear for the first time.

CULMINATING ACTIVITIES

A culminating activity is an activity that concludes the unit. It should be a logical part of the unit and a natural outgrowth of the work in the unit. It should appear when the objectives of the unit have been achieved. The culminating activity helps summarize the learnings and brings the high points of the unit into focus.

Culminating activities can be many things. They can be films, filmstrips, field trips, or speakers. They can be exhibits, science fairs, newsletters, or reports. They can even be discussions, programs, assemblies, or dramatizations. However, the teacher should always keep in mind that culminating activities are primarily for the benefit of the children, even though others may profit from them as well.

Certain precautions should be noted about the use of culminating activities. They should not try to summarize every science understanding in the unit because this procedure would make the activity much too long, with the resulting loss of interest and educational value. Not every unit needs a culminating activity. Some units do not lend themselves well to such activity, and to have one arbitrarily would make the activity highly contrived and artificial. Also, sometimes a culminating activity can actually hinder the children from continuing quite naturally to another unit. Finally, tests and other evaluative techniques are not culminating activities and should not be used as such.

EVALUATION

It seems natural that the teacher should plan evaluation when constructing the unit. It is much easier to think about how to evaluate pupil progress and growth while every phase of the unit is fresh in the teacher's mind. Evaluation should be continuous while the unit is in progress. The teacher must determine how well the children have learned the basic science information. Evaluation must be made for the development of desirable behaviors. The children themselves can—and should—participate in much of the evaluation. They can evaluate their work, their daily progress, and their learnings and behaviors as well. The various techniques for evaluation that can be used by both teacher and children are described in Chapter 8, "Evaluation of Science Learning in the Classroom."

WORK SHEETS

When constructing the unit, the teacher must give much consideration to how the work in the unit will proceed. Once the unit is in progress all the components of the unit must be coordinated and utilized to achieve maximum learning. Thus, the basic science information, the initiating activities, the pupil objectives, the learning activities, and the materials should be combined into functional learning situations. At the same time provision must be made for evaluation of the work that is being done. Consequently, the working period is the vital part of the unit and, as such, must be thoroughly integrated. For in the working period lies the success—or failure—of the unit.

There are several forms in which the working period can be presented. Of these forms, two are most commonly used, both using work sheets. One form describes the working period in outline form, giving an on-going description of how the learning will be developed. The other form, which seems to be more popular, uses parallel columns. The number of columns as well as the order in which the columns are listed may vary. Each column contains a phase of the working period. For example, one column may contain the teacher's objectives; a second column, the pupil objectives; a third column, the learning activities; a fourth column, the materials needed; and a fifth column, provision for evaluation. The advantage of arranging the working period by columns is that everything can be laid out so that the teacher can immediately see the direction in which the work is going and the progress that is being made. By using adequate spacing, the teacher's objectives can be placed beside corresponding pupil objectives, learning activities, materials, and evaluation techniques. Thus, the teacher has a horizontal row of related components, all clearly delineated. To set up the work in columns may involve a little more time and effort, but the result is certainly worthwhile.

PROGRAMED LEARNING—A USEFUL TOOL FOR THE SCIENCE EDUCATOR *

William B. Reiner

Programed learning is one of the newer techniques being offered as a means of more effective science instruction. Because of the interest and extensive experimentation in this technique, this article is intended to offer some guidance in understanding and evaluating the various aspects of programed learning. William B. Reiner defines programed learning as the arrangement of the materials to be learned, in graded steps of difficulty, in such sequence and in such manner of presentation that will result in the efficient rate of understanding and retention.

RECENT developments in psychology, communication theory, and technology have advanced the science and art of programed learning and teaching to unexpected levels of efficiency. Much study and new developments

* REPRINTED FROM *The Science Teacher*, Vol. 29, No. 6, October 1962, pp. 26–33. Copyright, 1962, by the National Science Teachers Association, Washington, D.C. Reprinted by permission of the author and the publisher. Dr. Reiner is Professor of Education at Hunter College, New York.

are being invested in programed learning; much more remains to be done. Despite the exaggerated claims by salesmen of teaching machines, there is sound reason for optimism in the future of programed learning and teaching. The heart of automated teaching or programed learning *is the program.* Some of the psychological and educational principles employed in constructing the programs which are used in "teaching machines" will be discussed in the sections which follow. Sections of programs concerned with teaching science will be used to illustrate the "how" and "why" of programed learning. Included also is a purchaser's guide to science programs.

At this point certain terms should be defined for the guidance of the reader. A *Program* is the subject matter to be learned by the pupil. *Programed Learning* is the arrangement of the materials to be learned, in graded steps of difficulty, in such sequence, and in such manner of presentation that it will result in the most efficient rate of understanding and retention.

Programing is the process of arranging materials to be learned by the student into a series of steps carefully plotted for logical or psychological sequence and meaning, from the concrete to the abstract, from the familiar to the new, and from fact to concepts. Competent teachers have long followed the principles implied in the above definitions. They have planned instruction and have implemented their teaching by asking questions and reacting to pupils' answers.

What, then, makes programed learning different? The answer is that it consists of a system which makes it possible to accomplish the important critical functions of teaching without the presence of a "live" teacher. A learner, a program, and a device to present the program (not necessarily a machine or gadget, special books or cards will serve, too) constitute a basic programed learning system.

Although machines are useful, and in some types of systems even necessary, the program *is* the heart of the matter of programed learning. While the machine or "hardware" is an auxiliary device, the glamour of automation and technology has given the headlines to gadgetry, consigning to the back pages top-level psychological research which has advanced programed learning, sometimes called automated learning, to its present levels of acceptance.

The principle of immediate reinforcement is the psychological basis upon which programed teaching rests. Reinforcement, in terms of the classroom, is getting the right answer or praise from the teacher, or a good grade, or the approval of classmates, and other satisfactions. In terms of programed learning or the teaching machine, it means getting the correct answer to the question presented to the pupil by the program. The guidance, satisfaction, and assurance of knowing immediately how well he has done enables the pupil, in general, to learn faster and retain better. There is no doubt as to the scientific soundness of the principle of reinforcement, though there may be about the teaching value of some of the programs based on the principle. Countless experiments with animals and human beings have proved the principle. F. Curtis and G. Woods in their paper "A Study of the Relative Teaching Values of Four Common Practices in Correcting Examination

Papers" in the *School Review* of October 1929 showed that pupils who obtained their test results immediately achieved better in science classes or courses.

BRIEF VIEW OF TEACHING MACHINES

A teaching machine is a device that presents a program and requires the pupils to respond to the questions. The difference between a teaching machine and an ordinary audio-visual device is that the teaching machine requires an answer and usually the pupil writes or speaks it into the machine. A sound film or tape player is not classified as a teaching machine because normally the pupils are not required to give answers to the materials it presents.

A teaching machine has several recognized functions. The following are listed by Finn and Perrin [1] as basic:

1. Used for individual instruction.
2. Contains and presents program content in steps.
3. Provides a means whereby the student may respond to the program.
4. Provides the student with immediate information of some kind concerning his response that can act as a psychological reinforcer.
5. Presents the frames of the program individually.
6. Presents the program in a predetermined sequence.
7. Is cheat-proof.

The following are listed as additional functions:

8. Discriminates correctness of response.
9. Automatically advances program.
10. Provides random access to program frames allowing for branching.
11. Memory function holds out frames on which error has been made for further presentation.
12. Records results.
13. Selects program items based on evaluation of previous responses.
14. Permits two-way communication between student and machine (typewriter —computer).
15. Stores complete programs and responses.

With allowance for physical refinements and variations such as sound, film, electric power, etc., a machine works as follows:

1. It exposes a single frame on which is presented a single step or problem for the pupil to study. It also has a question, a problem, or an exercise for the pupil to answer. In brief, a frame is a question-answer segment of a program.

[1] J. D. Finn and D. G. Perrin. *Teaching Machines and Programed Learning, 1962: A Survey of the Industry.* Occasional Paper No. 3. Technological Development Project, National Education Association, Washington, D. C. 1962. p. 18.

2. The pupil indicates his answer to the problem on the space provided. Some machines are adapted to allow a limited time for the pupil's response.
3. The machine lets the pupil know whether or not his response is correct. If he is wrong, he usually can make another try.
4. Most machines record the number of correct answers or errors, and some distinguish the types of errors made.
5. The teacher need not be present while the student is working out his program. This allows greater flexibility for the teachers and pupils.

PROGRAMING TECHNIQUES

S. L. Pressey, B. F. Skinner, and N. A. Crowder are prominent names among the pioneers and developers of program techniques. The philosophy of each in regard to programed instruction is briefly presented below.

Pressey considered teaching programs to be a supplement to textbooks not a substitute. Teaching machines were quiz devices, adjuncts to testing which helped consolidate materials previously learned in textbooks, lectures, or a laboratory. Pressey's devices employed principles which most psychologists agree are essential to achieve effective learning; namely, the continuous active state of the pupil in answering questions, the reinforcement when the pupil is immediately informed as to the correctness of his response, and the progress of the pupil individually and at his own rate. Pressey employed the multiple-choice type of question. If an incorrect answer were given, a student could be referred to a correct source of information and could return later to answer the question. This type of program is called "branching" because the pupil's activity branches out from questions to learning materials (to get the correct answer) and back to questions. This is a sharp contrast to "linear" programing which employs an unbroken sequence of questions and answers.

Skinner believed that "reinforcement" was the primary basis of programed learning. The main objective was to bring pupil behavior under control of a variety of stimuli. By developing the subject matter in very small steps in each frame, the success of the pupil reinforces him. Frequently the information asked of the pupil in the frame is merely verification of some simple information he has learned. As he progresses, he is rewarded by his correct responses and as a result is highly motivated. Skinner's technique is in closer accord to the concept of programed learning because of the tight, unvarying, carefully constructed sequence of questions and answers in each frame. This is called the linear type of program.

Schematically, the sequence of items in a linear program appears as follows:

$$\boxed{1} \longrightarrow \boxed{2} \longrightarrow \boxed{3} \longrightarrow \boxed{4}$$

Item 2 with its information would have to follow 1.

In a branching type of program there would be diversion and intermediate steps if the student had to look up information before he could go from

Step 1 to 2 and from 2 to 3. Conceivably, he might have to back track from 3 to 2 to make sure he knew what he was doing.

Crowder is closely associated with intrinsic programing in which multiple choice items are employed. The errors made by the pupil in answering questions are used to build knowledge and skill. The pupil is referred to correct sources of information so he can eliminate the mistake and proceed. This branching procedure resembles the blind alley in a maze, except that the learner is given a specific direction to help him find his way when he meets an obstacle. Intrinsic programing requires a clear anticipation of how pupils think. (Every experienced teacher uses this approach in classroom teaching!) Although the format of questions and answers in the frame can be quite flexible, two requirements must be followed. The items must be two or more choices to be answered and the incorrect answer should result in directing the pupil to materials or information which will correct him and guide him back to the correct program sequence.

Branching is a teaching technique that is familiar to teachers who have elicited answers from pupils by cogent reasoning and well-conceived questions. For example, in a laboratory experience, a pupil unable to explain why sugar changes to porous carbon after being treated with concentrated sulfuric acid is guided by a series of questions and helpful hints until the correct response has been developed. It takes a masterful teacher to anticipate the errors and strengths of pupils to do this on a face-to-face basis. To program this teaching process on paper, so that a pupil can experience similar learning, requires great insight and verbal artistry. In short, good programing ability is a highly developed skill. Space limitations preclude the inclusion of a sample of a branching program.

A linear program which develops some facts and concepts about measuring temperature is given below. It is part of a program developed by the staff of the New York Institute of Technology, New York City, under Alexander Schure. Each information segment, question, and answer constitute a frame of a section, "The Weatherman's Measurements." Note the economy of learning which Figure 1 contributes to the development of the idea. Information as well as simple skills in reading a thermometer is developed.[2]

One of the most important measurements that the weather forecaster must know is the temperature of the air. As you know from observations made in your own home, temperature is measured by an instrument called a ....
(*thermometer*) A thermometer is a glass tube with a bulb at one end filled with

---

[2] *The Wonders of Science.* "A Learning Program." Educational Aids Publishing Company, Carle Place, New York, 1962.

TABLE 1

Skinner's High School Physics Program Reconstructed According to the Ruleg System

CLASS	SENTENCE TO BE COMPLETED	WORDS TO BE SUPPLIED
ru+$\widetilde{\text{eg}}$	1. To "emit" light means to "send out" light. For example, the sun, a fluorescent tube, and a bonfire have in common that they all send out or .... light.	(*emit*)
$\widetilde{\text{eg}}$	2. A firefly and an electric light bulb are alike in that they both send out or .... light.	(*emit*)
ru+$\widetilde{\text{eg}}$	3. Any object which gives off light because it is hot is called an incandescent light source. Thus a candle flame and the sun are alike in that they both are .... sources of light.	(*incandescent*)
$\widetilde{\text{eg}}$	4. When a blacksmith heats a bar of iron until it glows and emits light, the iron bar has become a(n) .... source of light.	(*incandescent*)
$\overline{\text{eg}}$	5. A neon tube emits light but remains cool. Unlike the ordinary electric light bulb, then, it is not an .... of light.	(*incandescent source*)
$\widetilde{\text{ru}}$	6. An object is called incandescent when	(*it emits light because it is hot*)
ru+$\widetilde{\text{ru}}$	7. It has been found that an object, an iron bar, for example, will emit light if its temperature is raised above 800 degrees Celsius. Therefore we say that above ...., (temperature) objects will become	(*800° Celsius*) (*incandescent*)

A. A. Lumsdaine and R. Glaser. *Teaching Machines and Programed Learning: A Sourcebook.* Department of Audio-Visual Instruction, National Education Association, Washington, D. C. 1960. p. 491.

a ...., such as mercury or alcohol. (*liquid*) As the temperature changes the length of the column of the liquid in the tube rises or falls. As the temperature goes up, the liquid in the tube .... (*rises*)
You read the temperature from a scale marked right on the tube or alongside it. Temperature is marked in degrees Fahrenheit. When you say, on a hot summer day, that it is 90 degrees in the sun, you mean that the temperature is 90 degrees .... (*Fahrenheit*)
The temperature would be abbreviated 90° F. A thermometer with several important markings is illustrated. Note that the present temperature as read by the thermometer is .... (*90° F*)
From the marking on the scale it is clear that normal room temperature is much .... on the scale than 90° F. (*lower*)

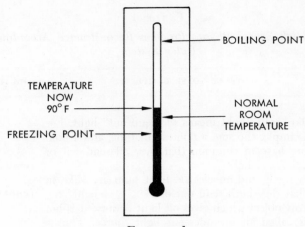

FIGURE 1.

The above diagram may be repeated in each subsequent frame of the illustrated linear program designed to develop certain concepts.

For scientific purposes, normal room temperature is taken to be 68° F. On a normal day at sea level, water freezes at 32° F. We say that the freezing point of water under these conditions is 32° F. The point is abbreviated as .... in the diagram. (*FP*)

At the opposite end of the scale we see the letters "BP." Water boils at 212° F. Thus the abbreviation BP must represent .... (*boiling point*)

A widely accepted type of program is known as Ruleg (combined from the words "rule" and "example"). This program consists primarily of rules and examples which the pupil is asked to match. For example, a rule is given and then the pupil must fill in an example which illustrates it. In Table 1 some illustrations are given of various types of problems. The abbreviation "ru" is for rule, "eg" for example. A tilde (~) over the symbol means incomplete, a bar (—) means negative. The column "Class" indicates varieties of combinations of questions based on rules and examples. The answers are given in the right-hand column.

PROGRAM PURCHASER'S GUIDE

Programs in science are becoming available in greater quantities. What program(s) shall a school or department buy is a frequent question. Several guiding questions for purchasers are given in the October 1961 issue of *Programed Instruction*.[3] The questions are similar to those needed to decide to buy textbooks or equipment.

[3] *Programed Instruction*. The Center for Programed Instruction, Inc., 365 West End Avenue, New York 24, N. Y.

1. Is the content (material) appropriate?
2. Is the content well programed?
3. What have the students learned from the program?
4. What are the characteristics of the student population(s) involved in the trial run?

In 1961, the American Educational Research Association, the American Psychological Association, and the department of Audio-Visual Instruction of the National Education Association issued a series of guide lines for users of automated teaching devices.[4] The guide lines point out that just any set of question and answer materials does not make an acceptable program. There should be appropriate goals and content and good question development carefully planned.

[4] "Keeping Abreast in Education." *Phi Delta Kappan*, 11:145. December 1961.

TEAM TEACHING IN THE ELEMENTARY SCHOOL: IMPLICATIONS FOR RESEARCH IN SCIENCE INSTRUCTION *

Abraham S. Fischler

and Peter B. Shoresman

In this article seven basic assumptions about the efficacy of the self-contained classroom are challenged by the team-teaching approach to instruction of children. The authors define team teaching as an effort to improve instruction by the re-organization of teacher personnel, involving the assignment of two or more teachers to a group of pupils. This reorganization forces new roles for teachers, ranging from specialist to observer. Two models of team teaching are described, and the impact of the team teaching approach on curriculum organization and sequence and on grouping for instruction is discussed.

* REPRINTED FROM *Science Education*, Vol. 46, No. 5, December 1962, pp. 406–415, by permission of the authors and the publisher. Dr. Fischler is Dean of the Education Center and Professor of Science Education at Nova University of Advanced Technology and Research, Fort Lauderdale, Florida. Dr. Shoresman is Assistant Professor of Education at the University of Illinois.

For many school systems team teaching has become more than an enticing phrase: many communities have now initiated the utilization of new personnel patterns to which the label "team teaching" might be applied. Generally, the organization of these various teams has consisted of a group of two or more teachers working together, within or without a formal hierarchy, to plan for, initiate, accomplish, and evaluate the instruction of the same group of children.

Before introducing two models of team teaching and some of the problems which need to be researched, the structure of the self-contained class will be examined. It is hoped that this review will help clarify some of the assumptions which new personnel organizations are now challenging.

Self-Contained Classroom Organization

In the self-contained classroom organization, the elementary school principal assigns twenty to forty students to a class, either homogeneously or heterogeneously grouped. If homogeneous, the assignment is usually on the basis of I.Q. and/or reading ability. The principal is also responsible for the supervision of all the teachers in the building and for curriculum coordination, pupil discipline, and public relations.

The elementary school class itself is usually under the direction of one teacher who provides instruction in the four basic areas of the elementary school curriculum: language arts, social studies, mathematics, and science. Teachers are expected to have knowledge and skills in all of the major areas and, furthermore, to be equally enthusiastic and competent in their presentation of each subject. They are expected to provide for a wide range of individual differences; this is usually accomplished by dividing the class into three groups: "high, average, and low." The teacher is also responsible for many non-teaching duties such as lunchroom supervision, bus duty, collecting milk money, and other tasks of a similar nature. The beginning teacher, just out of college, assumes *full* responsibility for her class; she assumes as much responsibility for instruction as teachers who have been teaching for twenty years. There is little chance during the school day for communication between this beginning teacher and teachers with many years of experience. The only time for extended communication is during the noon hour or before and after school.

Within the structure of this organization there is no career pattern for the young teacher who aspires to increased responsibility, increased prestige, and increased salary. Since all teachers are on the same salary schedule, which calls for increments on the basis of education and longevity of service, there is usually no provision made for higher salary based on increased responsibility. In this situation there seems to be no career pattern within the teaching profession for those who wish to remain in the classroom. If a teacher is seeking increased prestige or more responsibility, he usually moves into the field of administration. This removes him from actual teaching which, hopefully, is the reason he initially entered the profession.

ASSUMPTIONS CHALLENGED

The following are seven basic assumptions which are being challenged by the team teaching model:

1. That all teachers are approximately of the same quality, with the result that the superior teacher never moves (as teacher) to a position of greater influence over a larger number of learners.
2. That each teacher should enjoy individual instructional autonomy; that is, that he has a right to be an absolute "king of his classroom."
3. That the assignment of differential reward and status leads to poor morale and lower productivity.
4. That the employment of part-time and/or sub-professional personnel will somehow have undesirable effects.
5. That the ideal class size approximates thirty.
6. That pupils can relate to only one teacher.
7. That values accrue from having one teacher teach all subjects.

DEFINITION OF TEAM TEACHING

Team teaching, as we envision it, is an effort to improve instruction by the reorganization of teaching personnel. It involves the assigning of two or more teachers to a group of pupils. This involves different schedules for teachers as well as changed allocations of time and space for instruction. It eliminates the rigid grouping based on one or two criteria and allows for variations in student grouping depending upon the outcomes being sought. It allows for teachers to observe other teachers teach the same group of learners. It *forces* teachers to communicate in planning for the same group of learners. It allows for a variety of period lengths, sub-groups, and part-time teachers with special competencies, as well as for programmed instruction. Evaluation of students is based upon the common observations of several teachers. Team teaching, furthermore, encourages teachers to become specialists in one or more areas. The particular model which we are researching provides for a hierarchy of positions which are based on expertness and responsibility. It allows for increased salary and prestige accompanying greater knowledge and responsibility. The model also provides for the use of non-professional help as well as for the use of part-time professional help, lay readers, and other individuals who might aid in the learning process.

DIFFERENT ORGANIZATIONAL PATTERNS

There are several types of organizational structures built on different value systems. We shall discuss two of them.

1. Two "master" teachers (at increased salary) plus one teacher-aide are assigned to a group of seventy-five pupils. In order to keep the cost stationary the teacher-aide is employed instead of a third regular teacher. In the self-contained class structure, the ratio of teacher to pupil is approximately one to twenty-five, the same as above. Thus, by rearranging the budget, we are able to pay additional salary to the two teachers and still have funds with which to pay the salary of the aide. Implied in the value structure of this organization is that the cost will not be greater to operate a team teaching school than it was to operate a traditional school.

Among the duties of the teacher-aide is the assistance of pupils as they work individually. A variety of lessons are taped, programmed or individualized, so that pupils can work with a minimum of verbal teacher direction. The teacher-aide, a semi-professional person, circulates among the pupils to answer questions and offer any necessary help. In addition, she helps with such details as typing worksheets, collecting milk money, and supervising the playground.

2. A second organizational structure necessitates a higher budget. This model assigns six teachers and one teacher-aide to approximately one hundred and fifty children. The team is organized on a hierarchical basis. At the top is the Team Leader who receives $1,000 to $1,500 more than the regular teacher. This additional salary is given for increased responsibility as well as greater competency in an area of instruction.

On this same team there might be one or more Senior Teachers who receive from $500 to $1,000 more. These individuals have acquired competency in one or more subject fields. Usually both Team Leader and Senior Teacher have had three to five years of teaching experience in the elementary school.

The regular teachers on the team are trained elementary school people capable of teaching the normal elementary school curriculum. They usually teach in all of the subject areas, but begin to specialize in one or two if they aspire to become Senior Teachers.

The teacher-aide has the same type of responsibilities mentioned in the previous organization.

In the ideal situation, the Team Leader and Senior Teachers would complement each other by having competencies in different areas. In addition, these people should be capable of curriculum development in their particular strengths; of giving in-service education to members of their team; of supervising classroom interaction between teacher and pupil; and of aiding in the articulation of their subject area with others. Thus we have a small "school of education" built into the team.

The total school program is coordinated by the principal who heads two cabinets: an *administrative* cabinet composed of the Team Leaders which is responsible for policy decisions; and an *instructional* cabinet composed of the Team Leaders, Senior Teachers, and other specialists in the school, which coordinates and integrates the total school curriculum.

Insight and Implications

During the past two years, the authors have been engaged as science consultants and research personnel to work with the staff of a Lexington, Massachusetts, team teaching elementary school organized along the lines mentioned in pattern 2. Although it is felt that our short experience with team teaching does not, and cannot, entitle us to make any definitive statements as to what can and cannot be done, how certain tasks should be performed, or how specific problems should be solved, it has provided us with a number of problems and questions necessitating serious soul-searching on the parts of both ourselves and the teachers involved. Comparisons are still being made between this school and a control school in the same town, but evaluation is far from complete with so many problem areas still to be resolved.

While we have encountered many problems in our work so far, many seemingly inherent in a personnel structure where it is both *necessary* and *desirable* for a number of teachers to work closely together, the problem areas outlined below are unquestionably crucial ones for the instruction of science within the team teaching organization.

Curriculum Organization and Sequence

1. *Does the teaching of science within the context of team teaching require a reorganization of the traditional "content-topic" oriented curriculum?*

It has been our experience that the pattern of team teaching cannot find its most effective expression unless the curriculum utilized is modified or reorganized in the light of the unique aspects of flexibility which are afforded by this personnel structure. The following aspects seem especially worthy of mention:

1. The possibility of utilizing groups of different sizes, from large groups where two hundred children are taught by one teacher to small discussion, laboratory, and project groups where an almost one-to-one tutorial type of instruction can be offered.
2. The associated possibility of deploying and redeploying a number of teachers according to the nature and size of the pupil groups formed.

   Given the two preceding attributes inherent in the team teaching model, the limitations imposed upon the experimental and discovery approaches in the self-contained classroom because of lack of adequate supervision need no longer comprise obstacles to an exciting and creative science program for elementary school children.

The preparation and presentation of extremely worthwhile demonstrations and experiments is now economically feasible time-wise, since not only will the senior teacher in science be allotted adequate time to prepare such presentations, but also since it will be necessary to offer these presentations only once—via the medium of the large group lesson. The structure, wherein many teachers must plan together to develop a science curriculum, also necessitates that the "incidental science" curriculum so typical of many elementary school classrooms be replaced to a large extent by a *planned* and *sequential program* of science experiences. Perhaps, the team teaching pattern will provide conditions conducive to releasing the elementary school's current preoccupation with the "products and things" of science and raising to its proper position of emphasis, and to a more appropriate balance with the former, the consideration and practice of the "process" of science and "sciencing."

2. How can the coordination of the science curriculum of an entire teaching team be reconciled with the flexibility of instruction necessary for individual groups?

The team teaching structure provides opportunities for the following: the utilization of large group instruction, the periodic regrouping of students as the situation and their own individual needs indicate, the deployment and redeployment of teaching staff as necessary, the administration of cooperatively developed, team-wide instruments of evaluation, and many more important adjuncts to the learning process. If, however, the flexibility of team teaching is to be utilized to a maximum degree, it then becomes imperative that the efforts of every teacher teaching science within the team be coordinated to a considerable extent. This coordination is further necessitated by scheduling considerations which often require that all science (and this is true for other subjects as well) within a specific team be taught during the same time interval in the course of the school day. This procedure is necessary to facilitate pupil regrouping and the presentation of large group lessons.

However, it is quite important that individual teachers be provided with the degree of freedom necessary to plan, or modify, within the context of the team's science program, content and activities which are appropriate for the pupils within their own group. Despite the apparent contradiction which the terms may connote, it does seem possible to provide for "coordination" on the one hand, and "flexibility" on the other, without subordinating either one to the other. For example, let us suppose that a particular topic may most suitably be presented through the medium of a large group lesson. It is necessary that the room required for this lesson (for example, the cafetorium) be scheduled in advance because of the program demands for this space which might also be made by the other teams operating within the same building. If it is to be anticipated that most of the pupils in the team are to be present at this large group lesson, it is necessary to agree upon the goals to serve as a foundation for this lesson. If agreement has been reached a week or so in advance of the lesson, it would seem that each individual teacher should attempt to guide her own pupils toward some realistic goal which would provide them with the degree of readiness necessary to make the large group lesson as meaningful as possible. It is certainly quite un-realistic to expect that all children in a team should be approaching the same goal at the same time; however, if given sufficient time and adequate planning, by teachers, it is *not* unreasonable to expect that some commonality of general goal attainment be achieved by a certain time. This requirement places heavy responsibility upon the shoulders of individual teachers, for they must not only carefully assess the readiness of the students in their own group and devise the most appropriate program to bring them to a certain general level in the curriculum by a certain time, but they must also plan considerably further ahead than they are accustomed to do. For some teach-ers this may mean carefully selecting key points of content upon which to concentrate exclusively; for other teachers it may mean developing a wide variety of enrichment activities to occupy profitably the time of those stu-dents who have completed the essential core of science material to be studied by each group.

3. What is the proper place of teaching machines and other programmed materials in science instruction within the team teaching structure?

Within most classrooms utilization of teaching machines and other pro-grammed materials (such as programmed textbooks) has considerable prom-ise for providing greater opportunities for individualizing instruction in the various subject matter areas. The evidence available in the literature suggests that programmed instruction can be used to good advantage for certain spe-cific learning tasks. If we accept the fact (upon which much additional research must be done in relation to the specific applications of this tech-nique) that programmed instruction supplies another possible approach to learning by children, while also providing for greater economy of time in learning—both in regard to actual classroom time required and to the as-signment of professional teaching personnel, then it would seem that for specific purposes this economy would find maximum expression and reali-zation in the large groups possible within the structure of team teaching. Most likely, what can be taught by programmed materials in a group of thirty children could be taught just as effectively in a group of two hundred chil-dren.

In the field of science, programmed materials might be utilized for pur-poses of review and evaluation, drill and practice, and for learning subject matter which required rote memorization (such as science vocabulary words or formulas) or the learning of the steps in the tight logical development of a concept or of the procedures involved in a technological process (such as the extraction of various metals from their ores). However, before we plunge into programming various aspects of elementary school science, it is neces-sary that serious consideration be given to specifying those behaviors which we expect pupils to acquire as a result of utilizing our programs.

It should be stressed, however, that the possible contribution of pro-grammed instruction to science teaching is only one complementing the contributions of a myriad of other approaches. It is the feeling of the authors that this approach may be somewhat limited in its application. This is especially true if the current philosophies of elementary school science education, based upon providing opportunities for children to seek answers about natural phenomena by having actual manipulative experiences with these same phenomena, are not to be lost.

4. What implications does team teaching have for the development and utilization of various teaching "technologies"?

It is to be hoped that serious thought related to the goals of elementary school science education and to the concepts which we wish to develop will improve the various teaching "technologies" which have been traditionally used in the small group of the self-contained classroom. It is also hoped that new and appropriate instructional aids will be developed. However, the possibility of large group instruction which is afforded by team teaching makes it imperative that considerable effort be expended in transforming the instructional aids designed for use in the small classroom to a form which will be appropriate for their utilization in a very large group. Two criteria, at least, must be satisfied for materials which are to be used with large groups:

1. The materials must be easily seen from all locations in the room where the lesson is to be held; where large rooms and very large numbers of children are involved, the materials—models, projected images, and so on—must be LARGE. We have experienced considerable success utilizing the overhead projector as a "chalkboard substitute" as a light source for a shadow-graph effect, for projecting the images of various semitransparent, translucent and opaque objects (such as marbles, iron filings, colored solutions in Petri dishes, etc.), and for projecting both commercially-made and teacher-made multi-overlay transparencies.
2. The materials should possess certain "dynamic and dramatic" qualities such as moving parts, unexpected behavior and appropriate contrasting coloration.

Many more qualities have been shown through experience to be necessary ingredients but lack of space prohibits their mention here.

5. What is the proper place of the science textbook within the team teaching model?

As has been intimated in preceding sections, team teaching allows for an unprecedented flexibility and wealth of different science activities. These, in turn, should obviate the former reliance which has been placed in the elementary school science curriculum on the information-dispensing properties of one or two commercial textbooks or trade books. Within the model proposed above, teachers qualified to teach science will be available for the purpose of guiding learning in the area of science as will be sufficient professional staff to supervise experimentation and other activities by students. It is hoped that the textbook in this situation will assume its proper function as another adjunct to learning and will not continue to be the sole dispenser of information about science so common in too many elementary school classrooms. Within team teaching it is possible for the textbook to find its proper niche as a resource or reference to which the children should have ample opportunity to turn when their own investigations or classroom discussions indicate that specific or general information available from this source is necessary.

GROUPING FOR INSTRUCTION IN SCIENCE

1. If greater flexibility in inter-class and intra-class grouping is one of the main attributes of team teaching, what rationale, criteria, or predictors should be utilized to determine the formation of groups of appropriate composition and size for various diverse purposes?

In approaching this question, we should explore the possibility that certain subject matter, and the activities suitable for the presentation of such subject matter, indicate the means by which the total team should be broken down to form the most appropriate "instructional units." For example, does Subject Matter A (e.g., the study of heat phenomena) with appropriate Activities A′ (e.g., the laboratory investigation of the expansion of different solids, liquids, and gases) indicate that the team be broken down into small sub-groups of approximate Size X (e.g., manipulative ability)? (e.g., 3 to 4 children per sub-group on the basis of criterion M). Or perhaps, the grouping criterion might more suitably be I.Q., manifested pupil interest, reading ability, or previous knowledge of the area being studied.

We might also ask the question whether small groups which are homogeneous with respect to a specific criterion are more suitable for certain activities than are small groups of heterogeneous composition which have been formed purely for the advantages accruing from their small size. So far our experience has not provided us with any criterion which we have found highly successful for grouping in science, although we have tried random heterogeneous groups and groups whose composition has been determined by the results of an experimental science vocabulary test which was administered to all the children in one team late last fall.

2. What factors should govern the time and method of regrouping for instruction in science?

This problem is related to the preceding one. It is obvious that usable criteria must also be found for regrouping as well as for the initial formation of instructional sub-groups. These criteria might very well be the same. One generalization which has arisen from our experience is that the composition and size of initially established groups must be flexible and that appropriate regrouping should occur periodically according to the needs of the teaching-learning situation and of the students themselves. Perhaps, regrouping may be accomplished by merely transferring a single child from one group to a more appropriate one after evaluation of the total situation by the teachers concerned. On the other hand, it may be discovered that the underlying rationale for the initial organization of the various science groups of a team has been faulty; in this case, an over-all reorganization of all of the instructional units of the team may be necessary.

3. For what purposes and to what ends can large group instruction best be utilized?

In viewing the optimum utilization of large group instruction, a wide variety of possibilities confronts us. For example, can large group instruction (involving groups of approximately two hundred pupils) best be utilized for the purpose of (1) introducing a unit of study, (2) motivating pupils toward the study of a specific sub-topic of a unit, (3) presenting a teacher or pupil demonstration, (4) hearing a guest lecturer, (5) viewing a particularly outstanding visual aid, (6) raising additional problems for consideration, (7) clarifying a particularly difficult concept which most of the teachers of the team cannot explain adequately, or (8) summarizing a unit or sub-unit at the end of a topic? Perhaps, it is possible that one type of unit, for example, one in astronomy and space travel, might be completely or almost entirely taught in large groups, whereas this approach would not be appropriate for the study of a unit dealing with rocks and minerals. Perhaps (and we do not have experimental evidence to refute this contention) it is possible that *most* science at certain grade levels (for example, the intermediate level) may be taught in large groups of approximately sixty pupils per group regardless of the subject matter being considered.

Another question which must be considered under this sub-problem is whether large group instruction in science is more appropriate and applicable to certain ability levels than to others. Perhaps the bright, independent child will be stimulated by the presentation of subject matter in large groups and by the relative individual freedom accruing to him from the nature of the group size, whereas the slower child, needing both to receive considerable individual attention from the teacher and to proceed through the curriculum at a slower pace, will not be able to progress as rapidly with this method of instruction as he might in a smaller instructional unit. As a matter of fact, subjective evaluation by one of the authors seems to have confirmed the statement of the situation presented in the preceding sentence: The slower children become very restless in large group lessons and do not seem to derive much benefit from what does occur within these groups. In discussion groups immediately following the large group lessons, these children are often unable to recall even the general nature of what has occurred during the preceding period.

We must also ask ourselves, and obtain an answer to, the following important question: "Where do the great majority of school children—those who fall within the range of 'average' academic ability—fare better (for a particular objective), in the large group or in a group of smaller numerical size?"

It is also necessary to ask how large group instruction may most profitably be articulated with the total instruction pattern which has been established for science. How should children in the various individual science classrooms be prepared for a large group lesson? How should the content of a large group lesson be followed up? Should all children attend every large group lesson regardless of their needs, abilities, and interests? Several points have bcome increasingly evident during the course of our experience with team teaching: (1) Large group lessons must be planned well in advance. This is necessary so that the teacher presenting the lessons can either meet with, or distribute a summary sheet to, the other teachers in the team so that they, in turn, are aware of and can prepare their students for the content to be considered therein. (2) In many instances, if follow-up of the large group lesson is advisable or imperative, the teachers who are to lead subsequent small discussion or laboratory groups must take the responsibility either to attend the large group lesson themselves or to discuss the lesson with the teacher who presented it. Too often the maximum effectiveness of stimulating and provocative large group lessons has been lost because the other teachers who teach science did not know what had transpired during the lesson and, therefore, could not develop appropriate follow-up experiences. (3) It has become quite obvious that a single large group lesson cannot be all things for all children. The bright children may have already discussed and mastered the material considered. The slower children may not be ready to consider the concepts being developed or may not be capable of understanding what is being presented at the level at which it is being presented. A possible alternative to requiring all children in all groups to attend a certain large group lesson would be to provide one-to-several "splinter" groups— for example, one for the bright children for whom the lesson would be just a review and another for the slower children who would not benefit greatly because of their current lack of readiness. Teachers "released" by the teaching of the large group could be assigned to these splinter groups, where activities more appropriate to the needs and interests of certain children could be offered.

Utilization of Teaching Members of the Team

1. *Under what patterns of teacher deployment and redeployment within the team teaching model can the objectives of science instruction best be served?*

There are many questions which relate to the many possible ways in which teachers might be deployed and redeployed to yield optimum learning conditions in science. Careful consideration and research might be directed to the following questions: (1) Can one teacher successfully teach a total group lesson to sixty youngsters at one time? If so, for what purposes and under what circumstances? (2) What criteria might be utilized to enable us to select the most appropriate teacher for a particular group of children? (3) For certain activities, can the flexibility provided by the team organization be utilized to good advantage? For example, if laboratory or individual project work requiring close supervision is indicated at a particular point in a unit of study, would it be possible and appropriate to break a group of sixty children down into smaller units, each supervised by a separate teacher who, for that particular class and activity, has been especially redeployed to this classroom? The students of the redeployed teachers might in turn, be regrouped and assigned to one teacher who would supervise a lesson of programmed study.

For the most part, in the school where we have worked, one teacher has been assigned to twenty-five or thirty pupils for laboratory and discussion sessions. For most teachers, this method of assignment has not proved very satisfactory. Although considerable use has been made of the intra-class "buzz group" discussion technique, adequate supervision has still been lacking for an active experiment and project oriented science program. Collaborative teaching by two and three teachers with groups of thirty to sixty has proved much more successful. The added supervision made available by this technique has provided opportunities for extensive and intensive laboratory work and teacher-guidance involving a great majority of the children in the groups concerned.

2. How can time be made available to the senior teacher science specialist of the team so that he has an opportunity to discharge the functions inherent in his role?

If, according to the model presented above, the team's specialist in science is to have responsibilities related to the initiation, development, coordination, evaluation, and supervision of the program in science, he must have time during which to perform these functions. It was mentioned in the first part of this paper that the specialist should be released from the responsibility of teaching at least one subject matter area. Thus, some time is made available in the course of the school day for the discharging of his responsibilities related to science. However, it also seems necessary to release the science specialist from the teaching of a regularly scheduled science class at times so that he may observe the other members of the team teach science, so that he may participate in collaborative teaching with various of the team members, and so that he may provide special guidance, supervision, and instruction for special pupil groups (for example, those working on a special project, those setting up a school science display, etc.). Some serious thought must then be given to appropriate scheduling to permit this flexibility. Only two alternatives were utilized this past year in regard to this problem: (1) One of the authors assumed responsibility for the specialist's class several times while he was engaged in classroom visitations within the team; and (2) the members of the specialist's science class were divided equally among the other five science classes for the period. This latter approach has not proved to be desirable or effective for several reasons; especially contributory to this outcome is the fact that very intelligent, highly verbal students were necessarily placed in classes consisting of considerably less gifted students.

EVALUATION

It is evident that the problem of adequate evaluation is not unique or peculiar to the team teaching pattern. However, the entire process of evaluation, especially certain mechanical aspects, is made considerably more difficult because it must be developed in a situation where a number of teachers must work together cooperatively to determine what approaches are to be utilized. The following questions, then, which are undoubtedly applicable to many types of personnel organization found in the elementary school, are especially pertinent to the team teaching structure.

1. What should be the main emphasis in the evaluation of science instruction within the team teaching model?

We have mentioned in an earlier section of this article that it is rather unrealistic to expect all of the children in a team to have acquired a certain amount of science knowledge or to have attained a certain level of science sophistication by a certain point in time. Within the team structure, where individual science groups may be proceeding through only limited portions of the science curriculum via different methods of approach, is it educationally desirable for us to evaluate all youngsters by a method which assumes that they have considered the same subject matter in the same way? Perhaps not. Let us only say at this point that it is very necessary for us to review the major goals for which we are teaching science in the elementary school and then to determine the outcomes which we wish to have assessed by our instruments of evaluation. In any case, an understanding of the process or methods of science should undoubtedly serve as a more prominent target for evaluation than in the past, while the current emphasis solely on retention of scientific fact should be moderated accordingly.

2. What are some of the characteristics of an adequate testing program in science within the structure of team teaching?

The characteristics of an adequate testing program in science within the model proposed above should not be very much unlike those of an adequate testing program in any good elementary school, regardless of the personnel structure. There are many obstacles standing in the way of good testing programs in elementary school science, in general. The most important and significant of these obstacles is serious lack of availability of a variety of different kinds of standardized tests for the various elementary grades. A survey of current elementary school science tests does not provide a very impressive list of up-to-date and carefully devised instruments designed to evaluate the child's science interests, his understanding of science as a process, the nature of the scientific enterprise and of the scientists, and his factual knowledge in various specific content areas. Some adequate tests designed to evaluate the scientific reasoning of children are available, however. It is evident that appropriate tests designed to evaluate the areas mentioned immediately above are urgently needed.

It is also important for teachers within the team pattern, as well as elsewhere, to learn to devise effective teacher-made tests. Generally, the science test questions asked by many elementary school teachers of their students are of a purely factual nature or are worded in an exceedingly ambiguous and frustrating (for the children) manner.

Perhaps within the team structure, where several teachers might be deployed to a single classroom, evaluation procedures other than those utilizing paper and pencil tests might be employed. For example, the responses of individuals or of small groups of children to an original problem depending for its solution upon an experimental approach might provide carefully observing teachers with important information of an evaluative nature.

3. How might evaluation procedures best be developed within the team structure?

As has been mentioned, evaluation, within the team structure, of both the students involved and of the total effectiveness of the science program, is a cooperative and collaborative endeavor. Although individual teachers might find it desirable at times to develop evaluation instruments for use within their own classes, valuable ideas are to be gained by consultation with the science specialist and with fellow team-mates. Unit-end and year-end evaluation of all the students in a team necessitates the cooperation of all those teachers involved in teaching science within the team. The experience of the teachers of individual science classes must be pooled in order to develop an instrument which will be as valid as possible for all children of the team. A paper and pencil test might consist of a series of "difficulty ranked" items some of which could be answered by the members of even the "lowest" science group. The group of items as a whole should represent, in an equitable fashion, all of the major goals and objectives for which science is being taught. In any case, it has been found fairly effective to ask individual teachers to submit a series of questions which they would consider appropriate for their own class to a sub-team assigned to construct the evaluation instrument. These questions are then "hashed over" and refined in subsequent meetings of the sub-team. The questions are then resubmitted to all the teachers involved in teaching science within the team. After a final discussion and revision of all of the items by the former group, the finished instrument is then produced by the sub-team.

Periodic and end-of-the-school-year evaluations of the total science program of a team should incorporate the efforts of all team members. These evaluations might consider the appropriateness and effectiveness of content, methods utilized, staff utilization, and pupil evaluation. It seems that only in this way can a science program be restructured and developed in a direction which is consistent with both the philosophies of the majority of the team members and with the facts gleaned from the evaluation instruments administered. Hopefully, a cooperative evaluation program of this nature will eventuate in the provision of better conditions for learning and more appropriate and stimulating experiences in the area of science instruction.

TEACHING BY TELEVISION—
THE PICTURE IN PERSPECTIVE *

Ford Foundation and
Fund for the Advancement of Education

The search for new and better ways of educating our nation's youth has led to experimentation with the use of television. Today every area in the elementary school curriculum is being taught directly or enriched through television instruction somewhere in the country. Television offers two unique advantages. First, it can vastly extend the reach of the nation's best teachers. Second, it can bring to children experiences beyond the potential of conventional means of instruction. As with all new approaches, the role of the classroom teacher in television instruction needs to be clarified. The following is an excerpt from Teaching by Television, *a joint publication of the Ford Foundation and the Fund for the Advancement of Education.*

A DISTINGUISHED professor once remarked that it took about fifty years for a new idea to gain general acceptance in American education. A few years ago not many educators would have quarreled with that assertion. During the past four or five years, however, there has been a restless stirring in the nation's schools and colleges. This ferment has taken the form of a questioning of accepted practices, a challenging of long-held concepts, and a search for new and better ways of going about the job of providing a better education for the nation's young people.

---

* REPRINTED FROM *Teaching by Television*, Ford Foundation, Office of Reports, New York, January 1961, pp. 1–18. Reprinted by permission of the publisher.

In part, this ferment has been stimulated by the unprecedented increase in the number of boys and girls to be educated. Since the end of World War II, the number of births has risen more than fifty per cent, and each year for the past five years it has hovered around the four-million mark, which is one and one-half times the level of the depression decade of the thirties. Enrollments have risen steadily at all levels of education, and as wave upon wave of new students have swept upward through the grades, educators have come to realize that this is not a temporary phenomenon, but a problem—and a challenge—that will be with us for the foreseeable future.

Coupled with the rapid rise in enrollments has been an acute shortage of able teachers. Since the end of the war, the number of new college graduates entering teaching has not kept pace with the number of teachers leaving the profession, and the number of poorly qualified teachers hired each year has remained distressingly high. This shortage of well-qualified teachers has now edged its way up to the college level, where the number of new faculty members with a Ph.D. is declining steadily while the number of new faculty members with less than a master's degree is rising at a corresponding rate.

The combination of a growing number of students and a shortage of able teachers has spurred many thoughtful educators to seek new ways of multiplying the effectiveness of the *good* teachers that are available at the school and college level lest a whole generation of young Americans be shortchanged in their education and, in turn, shortchange future generations when they themselves become teachers.

Two other factors that have helped to bring about a search for new approaches in education have been a dramatic increase in the range of knowledge today's students will have to acquire in order to live intelligently in the space age, and a similar increase in the complexity of the new things to be learned.

Some observers would argue that the greatest spur for improvement in American education came in the fall of 1957 when Soviet scientists launched, in quick succession, the first man-made satellite and the first passenger-carrying satellite. But actually the ferment was already under way. Sputnik and Laika merely accelerated the trend.

The past few years have brought a wave of bold and imaginative experimentation—in new ways of attracting a higher proportion of top-quality people into teaching, upgrading the teachers already on the job, extending the reach of superior teachers, making more effective use of time and space, challenging able students, and arranging the curriculum so as to put greater stress upon the new body of knowledge.

One of the most promising tools for attacking many of these problems has been television, the most powerful medium of communication yet devised by man. Commercial television burst upon the American scene shortly after the end of the war, and its growth since then has been nothing less than phenomenal. Ten years ago, there were only a few thousand receiving sets in American homes. Today there are more than fifty million. Commercial television has done more to influence American culture in the past decade than any other medium of communication. For better or for worse, it has also had a tremendous impact on the education of American children.

The direct educational value of the new medium was recognized early, and the Federal Communications Commission set aside some 250 channels for educational purposes. The Fund for Adult Education, established by the Ford Foundation in 1951, immediately took steps to help local communities establish educational stations. Through a series of matching grants, it was instrumental in the activation of about thirty of these stations. It also made possible the establishment of the Joint Council on Educational Television and the National Educational Television and Radio Center. (Since 1956 the Center has been supported by grants of more than $11.6 million from the Ford Foundation.)

Now only about eight years old (the first station, KUHT at Houston, began operations on May 25, 1953), educational television has grown almost as fast as commercial television. As of this writing, there are fifty-two educational stations in operation and nineteen more under construction. In addition, the Joint Council on Educational Television reports that there are more than 150 closed-circuit installations in schools and colleges throughout the country.

Educational television has two broad categories: cultural and informational programs broadcast principally over community-owned stations for an adult audience, and programs that are part of a school or college curriculum. The latter are also broadcast over educational stations but, in addition, use closed-circuit systems. This report is concerned with the latter category—*direct instruction by television*. Specifically, this means the use of television by schools and colleges to teach courses for credit.

Pioneers in the use of television as a medium of instruction were a few Midwestern universities, including Western Reserve and Iowa State, which first began to offer televised courses for credit about seven or eight years ago. The armed services also realized the potential of the new medium, and began to use it extensively for instruction and training purposes. Medical and dental schools in several universities soon discovered that television could provide every student a "front-row seat" in observing complicated surgical and dental operations and quickly adopted the new medium as a teaching tool. One of the earliest experiments at the school level took place in New Jersey in the spring of 1954, when fifth-grade students in the Red Bank and Long Branch public schools viewed a two-week series of televised lessons in American history that had been prepared by six teachers under the supervision of researchers at Montclair State College.

Today, practically every course in the school and college curriculum, from first-grade arithmetic to college zoology, is being taught somewhere over television.

Television's unique advantages as a medium of instruction are: first, it can vastly extend the reach of the nation's best teachers; and second, it can bring to students educational experiences that are quite beyond the potential of conventional means of instruction. In 1958, for example, fifth-graders in the Pittsburgh public and parochial schools had an opportunity to see and hear Robert Frost read some of his poems over television. The experience these youngsters had was quite different from the experience they might have had in a conventional poetry class. They were not reading Robert Frost's poems from a book, nor were they listening to their teacher read them. They were seeing and hearing the poet himself. This difference in experience might not show up on a standardized achievement test, which is designed to measure the subject-matter content mastered by a student in a given course, but it was nevertheless real.

When television first began to be used for direct classroom instruction, many questions were raised about its role in education. There were some who took a dim view of its potential. It was argued, for example, that television was essentially a one-way medium of communication and that its use for instruction would deprive the student of valuable contact with the teacher. As one critic put it, "an electronic tube cannot understand a child." It was also argued that learning would be reduced to a passive experience in which the student merely soaked up what was presented by way of a flickering image on a screen. Finally, of course, it was argued that "television will never replace the teacher."

What most of these arguments overlooked was that television is not a teacher, but merely a conveyer of teaching, and that a good teacher on television can be much more effective in stimulating *learning* than a mediocre teacher in the intimate environment of a classroom.

As teachers became more familiar with television as a medium of instruction, much of the early opposition evaporated. It soon became evident that television, far from being a threat to the status and prestige of the classroom teacher, was actually a powerful new tool for enhancing the art and prestige of teaching and for bringing to the student richer, broader, and deeper learning experiences.

The Fund for the Advancement of Education took an early interest in the possibilities of the medium for helping to meet important educational problems, and particularly the problem posed by the growing number of students and the continuing shortage of able teachers. During the past six years, the Fund and the Ford Foundation have provided financial support amounting to $20 million for a variety of experiments at the school and college level involving the use of television as a medium of instruction. Each of these experiments has been aimed at exploring the potential role of television as an instrument for improving the quality of education.

The primary focus of these experiments has been on multiplying the effectiveness of able teachers. Following are a few illustrative examples:

At Pennsylvania State University and at Miami University, in Oxford, Ohio, closed-circuit television is being used successfully in the required freshman and sophomore courses, which traditionally enroll the largest number of students. At both institutions, it has been found that this method of handling large classes is not only educationally sound but also economically feasible.

At Chicago City Junior College, open-circuit television is being used to bring the major portion of the freshman and sophomore curricula to students off campus.

In Oregon, four colleges and universities have been linked in an inter-institutional television network, and outstanding teachers from each campus have been made available to the students at all four institutions.

At the University of Minnesota, closed-circuit television is being used to enable student teachers, without being physically present, to observe teaching and learning situations in a classroom.

In Texas, the facilities of a state-wide network of commercial stations were made available to the state department of education for reaching beginning teachers with a series of lecture-demonstrations designed to start them on the road to permanent certification.

In Nebraska and Oklahoma, open-circuit television is being used to bring to students in small rural high schools college preparatory courses that otherwise would not be available to them because of the lack of qualified teachers.

In Alabama, an educational-television network is being used to bring high-quality instruction to more than 300,000 students in 600 elementary and secondary schools throughout the state.

In southwestern Indiana, sixteen school systems around Evansville have banded together to form an educational-television council, which is financed out of a common treasury. The council makes available to students in each member school system, and in a group of neighboring schools, the combined teaching resources of all.

In Washington County, Maryland, a closed-circuit television network that eventually will link up all fifty schools in the county is being used to bring daily instruction in thirty-one courses—at all grade levels—to nearly 16,500 students.

In more than a dozen large cities throughout the country, television is being used as a major resource in the teaching of classes several times the size of conventional classes.

In New York City, closed-circuit television is being used in a low-income housing project to bring the school and the community closer together and to help overcome the language barrier between English-speaking and Spanish-speaking children.

Over the nationwide network of the National Broadcasting Company, outstanding teachers have taught courses in modern physics and chemistry. The program is continuing this year with a course in modern mathematics and a re-run of the chemistry course. Well over 400,000 high-school teachers, school and college students, engineers, housewives, and others have been regular viewers of the program. Since it presents full college courses offered for credit by institutions throughout the country, the program is appropriately called "Continental Classroom."

Although it is too early to draw any final conclusions about television's ultimate role in education, the results of the experimentation to date have been very encouraging. These results show, among other things, that students at both the school and college level learn as much—and in some cases significantly more—from televised instruction as from conventional instruction. The usual finding from most of the experiments has been that there is no significant difference in achievement between students in television classes and comparable students in regular classes. This finding is in itself remarkable, in view of the newness of television as a medium of instruction, the relative inexperience of those who have been using it, and the fact that existing school and college classrooms as well as existing television equipment were not designed for televised instruction.

Interim results from two of the most extensive school experiments indicate that superior teaching over television stimulates much better learning on the part of the student than ordinary teaching in the classroom. This has been particularly true when the team approach to teaching has been employed— when studio teachers and classroom teachers have pooled their skills and each has undertaken that particular part of the total teaching job to which the individual teacher is best suited by interest, ability, and temperament.

The two experiments where this method of teaching is producing results superior to conventional methods are the Washington County, Maryland, project, involving some 16,500 students, and the National Program in the Use of Television in the Public Schools, a nationwide project that in 1959–60 involved nearly 200,000 students in some 200 public school systems throughout the country.

Preliminary test results concerning the achievement of Washington County students in classes taught by television have been compared with the achievement scores of students in conventional classes, as well as with previous records. The results show an impressive gain by students who received televised instruction.

Altogether 251 different comparisons were made. In 1957–58, they included 14,326 television students and 12,666 control students of equal ability; and in 1958–59, they included 43,105 television students and 26,092 control students. Of the 251 comparisons made during the two-year period, 165 favored the television students and eighty-six favored the control students. In ninety cases, there was a statistically significant difference in the achievement of students in the two groups—that is, a difference that could not reasonably be attributed to chance. Of these statistically significant differences, sixty-nine were in favor of the television classes and twenty-one were in favor of the control groups.

Other encouraging results have emerged from the experimentation. For example, it has been found that televised instruction requires the student to accept more responsibility for his own learning than is the case with conventional methods of instruction. Also, students in television classes at the elementary and secondary level make more extensive use of the school library than students in regular classes.

In addition, experience to date has shown that the team approach to teaching, particularly at the elementary and secondary levels, opens up exciting new possibilities for capitalizing on the varying teaching skills among teachers in any given school system. Televised courses have been much more carefully planned and organized than conventional courses, and the combination of the skills of the studio teacher and of the classroom teacher has made possible a cooperative teaching effort far better than either teacher could achieve alone. At the elementary and secondary levels, for example, the usual practice has been for the studio teacher to "meet" only one class a day, generally for twenty or thirty minutes. The teacher then has the rest of the day to plan tomorrow's lesson. This opportunity to plan carefully, combined with the unique possibilities that television affords in the presentation of visual materials that reinforce learning, has stimulated the studio teachers to do a much better job of teaching than they had done in their conventional classes. In the meantime, the classroom teachers, relieved of the burden of planning and presenting the principal material in several different subjects during the course of a day, are free to concentrate on other important aspects of teaching—such as eliciting student participation, answering questions, leading discussions, reinforcing when necessary the main concepts presented in the telecast, providing individual help where needed, and stimulating the students to do something with what they have learned. Studio teachers and classroom teachers who have mastered the techniques of the team approach say they greatly prefer it to the conventional method of teaching.

One other important result of the experimentation to date has been a more effective use of teaching time and classroom space. This has been especially true in the elementary and secondary schools, where the shortage of teachers and classrooms is most acute. Several school systems, notably those of Dade County, Florida, and Washington County, Maryland, have found that the use of television in teaching large classes has enabled them to serve more students with the able teachers already on their staffs and to get along with fewer new teachers than they otherwise might need. This means that they can be much more selective in hiring new teachers. The use of auditoriums, cafeterias, and other large rooms for certain television courses also has meant a substantial saving in classroom space.

Several other school systems have used the teacher time saved by the use of television in large classes to establish much smaller classes than usual for slow learners and for rapid learners, and to provide overworked classroom teachers with one or more free periods during the school day.

Finally, the use of superior teachers on television has proved an important means of upgrading the quality of other teachers, particularly beginning teachers. Several superintendents have reported that television has brought a system-wide improvement in teaching, and that even some of their best teachers have learned new techniques by observing the studio teachers.

There also have been problems with teaching by television.

One of the biggest single problems at the elementary and secondary levels has been that today's school buildings were not designed for instruction by television, especially in large classes. (A study of building and space designs for the use of television in education was published in 1960 by Educational Facilities Laboratories, an independent organization established by the Ford Foundation. The study, *Design for ETV*, is available upon request to Educational Facilities Laboratories, 477 Madison Avenue, New York, N. Y.)

Aside from the problem of learning how to house the new teaching patterns evolving from television, these patterns themselves—for example, the large class and the team approach—have yet to be fully mastered. In large-class situations, further exploration is needed on how to deal effectively with differences among individual students, especially at the elementary and secondary levels. And although some teaching teams are functioning skillfully, the respective roles of the studio teacher and the classroom teacher remain to be fully defined.

Another problem at the elementary and secondary level—particularly in those school systems using open-circuit telecasts originating from educational-television stations—has been the matter of scheduling. This has taken two principal forms. First, there has been the difficulty of timing the telecasts to fit the schedules of as many schools as possible. (For example, fifth-grade arithmetic is not usually taught in all elementary schools of a given school system at the same hour each day.) The second aspect of the scheduling problem has been how to fit a thirty-minute telecast into class periods of varying length. (Observers agree that thirty minutes is not necessarily the optimum length of the telecast part of the lesson in every subject every day, but educational-television stations, like their commercial counterparts, traditionally operate in terms of thirty-minute blocks of time.)

A technological problem that currently limits the use of television as a medium of instruction has to do with transmission of the signal. Open-circuit broadcasting, in which the signal is sent out from a transmitter, has the advantage of being able to cover a wide area, and thus it can reach many school systems. It has the disadvantage of being limited to one program or lesson at a time. This means, for example, that in the course of a six-hour school day only twelve thirty-minute lessons can be broadcast—the equivalent of only one for each grade level. Closed-circuit broadcasting, in which the signal is carried by coaxial cable, has the advantage of being able to transmit several lessons simultaneously (six in the case of Hagerstown), but it has the disadvantage of not being able to cover a wide geographic area except by the use of microwave relays or long-line telephone wires, both of which are relatively expensive.

Preparation for a novel open-circuit television experiment designed to make courses available to schools and colleges within a 150-to-200-mile radius of the transmitting point has been under way during the past year under the direction of the Midwest Council on Airborne Television Instruction, which is composed of educational and civic leaders from the six states involved—Indiana, Illinois, Kentucky, Michigan, Ohio, and Wisconsin. Videotaped courses will be broadcast from an aircraft flying at 23,000 feet over east-central Indiana. Demonstration courses will begin early in 1961, and a full school year of broadcasting will start in September, 1961. Two standard-band UHF channels will carry courses ranging from the elementary-school level through college six hours a day, four days a week during the 1961–62 academic year. Meanwhile, the Council will experiment with the application of narrow-band UHF channels, which could double available UHF transmission space.

The Council's main headquarters are located at Purdue University. It has developed an initial curriculum and screened and selected a corps of television teachers to prepare courses and supplementary materials and to videotape lessons at various production centers. The Council has also established centers at colleges and universities where area committees of educators, technical experts, and lay leaders counsel interested schools and conduct workshops for classroom teachers. To help finance these activities, the purchase of aircraft, transmitting and other equipment, the Ford Foundation has granted $4.5 million. Business and industrial firms are also supporting the experiment.

Potentially, the experiment could transmit simultaneously over six channels and thus telecast a total of seventy-two expertly taught lessons a day to schools and colleges over an area that includes five million students. In particular, airborne television provides a new resource to small rural schools presently out of reach of educational-television stations.

Videotape, which is being used in the airborne-television experiment, is a technological development that is helping to surmount many of the technical and administrative problems impeding the adoption of television for teaching. Recorded on magnetic tape rather than film, lessons can be more readily reproduced for later showing than with kinescopes. The visual quality is equal to that of a live telecast. This method of recording broadcasts has brought a new dimension of flexibility to educational television. First, lessons can be recorded in the studio at a time convenient to the television teacher, instead of being limited to broadcasting times. Second, once on tape, they can be shown at alternate times, thus making it easier to accommodate them to different academic schedules. Third, because an unlimited number of copies can be made from a single tape, their possible distribution is greatly multiplied. Finally, lessons can be stored for use in subsequent semesters and revised or updated as teaching experience or course content may require. The advantages of videotape are being provided to many communities through grants by the Ford Foundation to the National Educational Television and Radio Center for the purchase of recording equipment by its affiliated stations.

To sum up, television has already demonstrated that it can be a powerful tool for helping to raise the quality of education in the face of rising numbers of students and a shortage of able teachers. It also has demonstrated its potential for attacking other important educational problems, such as challenging able students to their full potential and bridging the gap between school and college; bringing top-quality teaching to students in small rural high schools; upgrading the quality of teachers already on the job; and finally, making more effective use of the physical and financial resources available to schools and colleges.

Much has been learned in the past six or seven years about television's potential as an important educational resource; much more remains to be learned. On the basis of the experimentation to date, it appears that when schools and colleges have learned to capitalize on the full potential of the medium, students at all levels will receive a far broader, deeper, and richer education than has been possible heretofore.

CHALLENGING THE MORE ABLE STUDENT *

Theodore W. Munch

Every classroom has its share of exceptional children. Meeting the needs of all of these students presents many organizational and planning problems to the classroom teacher. Theodore W. Munch presents one way of challenging the more able student—namely, the use of simple unstructured experiments. Six specific scientific skills should come into play as the more able child works through the unstructured experiment. Dr. Munch describes a recent unstructured experiment that evolved in a sixth grade class.

ONE WAY of challenging the more able student in your classroom is to help him work through a simple, unstructured experiment. Essentially, an unstructured experiment is a question or a statement of a problem, the answer to which cannot be found in a text or an encyclopedia—at least not easily so. Unstructured experiments differ from the average science experi-

* REPRINTED FROM *Elementary School Science Bulletin*, Issue No. 74, December 1962, pp. 1–3. Copyright, 1962, by the National Science Teachers Association, Washington, D.C. Reprinted by permission of the author and the publisher. Dr. Munch is Professor of Science Education and Physics at Arizona State University, Tempe.

ence in that the former do not have a fixed number of things to do, and the results cannot be determined in advance. Such experiments are research in the true sense of the word, not cookbook type experiences.

Working on unstructured experiments involves a number of skills:

1. Isolating and defining problems concisely.
2. Discovering what other people (scientists, engineers, and technicians) know about the problem. This involves reading, talking to, and sometimes writing to people to obtain information. Reading often contributes ideas about how to approach experiments.
3. Hypothesizing, that is, getting ideas about possible solutions to the problem.
4. Assembling equipment or inventing simple apparatus to test hypothesis.
5. Collecting and recording facts discovered while testing hypotheses.
6. Drawing conclusions from the facts and information he has gathered.

Doing unstructured experimentation is not as involved as the description would imply, and children find it stimulating. Here is a recent unstructured experiment which evolved in a local sixth grade class.

In a study of chemistry, the class learned about acids and bases. They found that acids taste sour, and that bases were often bitter and slippery to the touch. They also learned that acids and bases could be harmful to the human body. In the course of their work they discovered that there was a safe way of telling whether things were an acid or base. (This is done by using certain chemicals which chemists call indicators.) These are substances which have one color in acids and another in bases. The teacher obtained some red and blue litmus paper from a high school chemistry teacher. The class found that in acids, blue litmus turned red; and in bases, red litmus turned blue. The supply of litmus paper was limited, so the teacher wondered aloud if other substances found about the home could be used as indicators. He wondered particularly about the juice from red cabbage. Several volunteers brought some cabbage juice to class the next day. The juice was made by boiling cabbage and filtering the water through a paper towel placed in a funnel. Cabbage juice was found to turn red in acids and bright green in bases.

Indicators

The first unstructured experiment suggested itself: "What plant extracts make good indicators?" In less than a week, the class had extracted and tested the coloring from twelve different flowers and several vegetables. Red cabbage juice still seemed to be the best indicator. During the week, the students discovered through reading and class work the meaning of pH (a way of measuring the amount of "acidness" or "baseness" of solutions). They also discovered that acids and bases could neutralize each other to form a salt and water, and that certain indicators would react only within a narrow acid or base range.

The teacher suggested another unstructured experiment that the class could carry out now that there was a good indicator at hand, "Which common household things are acid and which are base?" The students made solutions in distilled water of aspirin, vitamins, seasonings, and many other items brought from home. Each was tested using the cabbage juice as the indicator. Each item was carefully classified under the heading of "acid," "base," or "neutral," as tested with red cabbage juice.

Here are some additional ideas which can be used as points of departure for simple, unstructured experimentation.

—How does light, filtered through various colors of cellophane, affect the growth of plants?
—Is dry yeast or wet yeast best for baking bread?
—Is there any relationship between the number of turns of wire on an electromagnet and the number of tacks the magnet will attract?
—How much weight will sprouting bean seeds lift?

While conducting your unstructured experimentation, here are some points to keep in mind:

—Start by using the combined talents of the class or group. Later, when routines are established, individuals may explore on their own.
—Keep the experimentation within the limits of time, talents, and easily available apparatus. Explore these limitations *before* suggesting problems.
—Be alert to the open-endedness of this type of experimentation. Frequently, questions will arise such as "Suppose we varied the experiment in *this* way, what will happen?"
—Do not assume that even the gifted child will continue to have a sustained interest in a problem. You must continually check on progress.

A second method of challenging the more able learner in science is to include as many quantitative aspects as possible into the units. In addition to answering "how" or "what," help the child to find out "how much" or "what relationships exist between?" Being quantitative involves combining mathematics with science. Let us explore a problem in which the quantitative aspects are stressed.

Have the children plant 15 grass seeds in each of four different flower pots, all having identical soil. Cover the grass seed with a different color cellophane, red, yellow, or blue. Keep one pot in sunlight as a control. Allow the grass to grow for two–three weeks. Now have the students measure the height of each blade of grass to the nearest millimeter (or to the nearest 1/16 of an inch). This would be an excellent opportunity to compare the metric and English system of measuring length. Have several students measure each blade of grass and determine an average height for their particular pot. This is done to help eliminate individual errors of measurement. Now find the average height for *all* of the blades in that pot by getting a total of all blade measurements and dividing by the number of blades measured. The chart of your data might look like Table 1. (This is imaginary data and will not necessarily resemble data the class gathers.)

TABLE 1

Heights of Grass Seedlings
Grown Under Blue, Yellow, and Red Cellophane
All Heights Are in Centimeters

SEEDLING	BLUE	RED	YELLOW	COLORLESS (CONTROL)
1	10.2	11.5	7.3	13.1
2	10.0	11.2	7.2	13.0
3	11.0	12.3	7.5	13.2
4	10.5	12.6	7.7	11.0
5	10.6	10.8	8.0	13.3
6	9.8	10.7	7.1	13.5
7	10.3	11.5	7.0	13.7
8	10.4	11.6	6.5	13.8
9	10.0	11.7	6.3	13.6
10	9.7	12.0	7.4	13.9
11	8.8	10.0	7.7	12.1
12	10.6	11.3	7.8	12.0
13	10.8	11.8	7.9	13.3
14	10.4	11.9	7.6	13.5
15	10.3	11.7	7.3	13.7
AVERAGE HEIGHT	10.2 cm.	11.5 cm.	7.4 cm.	13.1 cm.

How can you express the facts found in this experiment in a more concise fashion? Here are several suggestions:

—Place the average heights in a column:

Yellow	7.4 cm.
Blue	10.2 cm.
Red	11.5 cm.
Colorless (control)	13.1 cm.

—By such a simple arrangement, you have brought the data into a neat column which is easier to read and interpret.
—Discover and record, in a column, the *range* of heights in each pot. The range is merely the height of the smallest plant and the height of the largest.

Range of Growth of Grass Seedlings Under
Various Colors of Cellophane

	LOW	HIGH
Yellow	6.3 cm.	8.0 cm.
Blue	8.8 cm.	11.0 cm.
Red	10.0 cm.	12.6 cm.
Colorless (control)	11.0 cm.	13.9 cm.

Notice that with this arrangement, you can tell at a glance which pot had the shortest plants and which had the longest. These ideas will help you decide which color of light most stimulated or retarded growth. If the ranges overlap to a great degree, you cannot say that any particular color of light affects growth more than any other. If the ranges are widely separated, you may suggest that certain colors affect plant growth more than others.

—You may also want to assemble data in the form of a bar graph. (Table 2 shows a bar graph of the range of plant heights.)

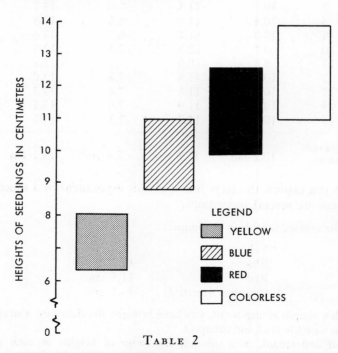

TABLE 2

Bar Graph Showing Range in Heights of Seedlings
Grown Under Blue, Yellow, Red Cellophane

By treating your data in this fashion, you have gone far beyond just looking at the grass and "guesstimating" about the effects of light. You have accounted for more subtle differences which may not be noticeable in a cursory, qualitative examination. Most important, you have started the students in the way scientists work at assembling and interpreting the data they receive from experimenting.

THE CULTURALLY DEPRIVED CHILD AND SCIENCE *

Samuel Malkin

The teaching of children who are termed "culturally deprived" is one of the major problems in education today. The past five years have seen a surge of much-needed experimental approaches to the teaching of this exceptional child. Science education can play a great role in assisting these children who generally have extremely limited experiential opportunities. No other area of the curriculum offers quite the same opportunity for meaningful experiences as does the science program. Samuel Malkin discusses how the science program should be used in approaching instruction with this disadvantaged child.

EDUCATORS have always had the problem of adapting the curriculum to the needs of children with special problems. Today teachers throughout the country, particularly in urban areas, are being confronted in ever-increasing numbers by the special problem of the culturally deprived or disadvantaged child. In New York City, it is estimated that 225,000 out of 573,000 elementary school children and 75,000 out of 186,000 junior high school pupils are in that category. Coupled with the disadvantaged or culturally deprived child is the non-English speaking child. About 11.5 percent of the

---

* REPRINTED FROM *Science and Children*, Vol. 1, No. 7, April 1964, pp. 5–7. Copyright, 1964, by the National Science Teachers Association, Washington, D.C. Reprinted by permission of the author and the publisher. Dr. Malkin is Supervisor of Audio-Visual Instruction, New York City Board of Education.

entire elementary school population of New York City speak English halt-
ingly or not at all.[1]

What are some characteristics of these children? In working with them,
one quickly becomes aware of their general lack of achievement in the basic
academic skills of reading, writing, and arithmetic; their general low self-
image; and their lack of interest. Then one becomes aware of their limited
experiences. What we tend to take for granted in youngsters—that they are
familiar with gardens, pets, automobiles, trains, bicycles, elevators, and the
country—is not necessarily true for these children. Indeed, many have never
strayed from their own neighborhood or block, even though they may live
in a city with many places to go and things to do.

What are some of the conditions that cause cultural deprivation? Although
poverty may not in itself be a cause, most culturally deprived children come
from poor areas. Many come from broken homes or from families with de-
teriorated social standards; many come from areas where there is conflict
between their own existing subculture and the standard American middle-
class culture. Then, too, these areas may contain a constantly changing population with families moving in, staying awhile, and moving away again. The
youngsters may have no roots, no feelings of loyalty, or no sense of responsibility to the community.

Teachers need orientation to work with these children since the children's
expectations contrast sharply with the teaching and therapeutic processes
which the teacher is normally trained to use. For example, these children
desire authority and direction rather than training in self-direction; they desire action rather than introspection; they desire structure and organization
rather than a permissive situation; they desire simple, more concrete, scientifically demonstrable explanations rather than symbolic, circuitous interpretations; and they desire informal, sympathetic, nonpatronizing relationships
rather than intensive ones.[2]

These desires and expectations of the disadvantaged child are positive elements upon which a functional and developmental curriculum can be built.
Frank Riessman, in his book *The Culturally Deprived Child*,[3] strongly advocates such an approach. His observations identify other elements which
have a direct bearing on the development of curriculum for these children.
These are: ability in abstract thinking, but at a slower rate than middle-class
children; skill in nonverbal communication; greater achievement when tasks
are motor-oriented; and greater motivation to tasks which have tangible and
immediate goals.

[1] *Higher Horizons Progress Report*. Board of Education of the City of New York.
January 1963.

[2] Frank Riessman. *Some Suggestions Concerning Psychotherapy with Blue Collar Pa-
tients*. Mobilization for Youth and Department of Psychiatry, Columbia University, New
York City. Unpublished Mimeographed Paper. 1963. p. 4.

[3] Frank Riessman. *The Culturally Deprived Child*. Harper and Row, New York City.
1962.

An elementary science program for such children must be based on the positive elements of the characteristics, environment, and expectations of these children.

WHAT ARE THE FEATURES OF SUCH A PROGRAM?

An elementary science program must be based on the pupils' environment.

Children are concerned with the world about them; the sound of bells, thunder and lightning, automobiles, airplanes, trees, birds, and their own bodies. Disadvantaged children are no exception; however, their own world may not be the same as their teacher's world. To the teacher, larva, pupa, and butterfly are part of nature; to the pupils these may be meaningless because they may never have seen these things. Skyscrapers, concrete, and alley cats are more meaningful to these children than the Grand Canyon, sedimentary rocks, and protozoa. The culturally deprived child's environment is quite restricted, and we must seek from his environment those elements familiar to him and build our program upon them.

It is also important to enlarge the pupil's environment. This suggests that he be given direct experiences through audio-visual materials. A trip to the farm or zoo where the urban slum child can see and fondle farm animals, a lesson on magnetism where he and his fellow pupils can handle many different magnets, or a film which shows him what makes night and day are all experiences which will enlarge the pupil's concepts about his environment.

AN ELEMENTARY SCIENCE PROGRAM MUST BE BASED ON REAL PROBLEMS

Children ask questions about their environment and want answers to their questions. Some of these questions are: How does the school bell ring? What makes the light go on? Why do we want to explore outer space? How can we keep food from spoiling? How does the weatherman forecast weather? How does a telephone work? How can my skates roll more easily? What makes a car stop? Whereas many children frequently obtain the correct answers to their questions from parents or from books, the culturally deprived youngsters generally do not. Their parents are not able to help them and they are not able or motivated to help themselves. They must rely on the school for the correct answer, or else be satisfied with misinformation or no answer. The implications are clear. The teacher must gear her program to help these children find answers to questions about their environment. Indeed, the teacher may need to help the children verbalize questions which their environment has led them to submerge. Questions, such as those listed above, could and should serve as the aims of lessons in elementary science. By basing the aims of her lessons on real problems, the teacher can capitalize on pupils' interest and compensate for the learning they should, but do not, receive at home.

ELEMENTARY SCIENCE SHOULD NOT DEPEND ON
READING OR OTHER ACADEMIC SKILLS

A major weakness of the disadvantaged child is lack of achievement in reading and other academic skills. This lack of achievement in reading probably accounts, in large measure, for lack of success in other curriculum areas which depend on reading. If an elementary science program is to be successful, then the pupils must feel that they can succeed in science. I conceive of elementary science as a truly "democratic" subject—democratic to the extent that every child can participate in, and get a feeling of, achievement and success from it. Therefore, it is important that activities be so chosen that they do not discourage children. One way to do this is to use children's language skills, other than reading, in the elementary science program. Such skills as listening, speaking, reporting, observing, and note-taking (at the pupil's level) should be encouraged.

Teachers should plan lessons which draw on pupils' experiences, and the conclusions to each lesson should be elicited from the class in the pupils' own language. Audio-visual materials should be used extensively to provide basic information and material for research. Children can use filmstrips with individual viewers just as they would use books. The formation of soil and the operation of the water cycle can be demonstrated more effectively by films than by books.

Although the basic science program should not depend on textbooks, children should have contact with many science books at their own reading level. Thus, instead of 30 books of a basic series of texts on one grade level in a class, it might be possible to have 30 books of many series at different levels. Trade books on many topics at varying reading levels should be available. In this way, children could select those books which they are able to read, and which do not frustrate them.

ELEMENTARY SCIENCE SHOULD REINFORCE BASIC ACADEMIC SKILLS

Although this may seem contrary to what was previously stated, it is not. Elementary science can and should encourage and motivate growth in reading. As these children get a feeling of success from their science activities, they may be motivated to greater achievement. Thus, they can be encouraged to use some of the trade and textbooks that are to be found in the room. Elementary science can provide even more basic reading experiences. Labelling of specimens, models, and charts provide reading experiences, as do captions on filmstrips. In my own experience, at the end of each lesson I ask the children to tell me what they have learned from that lesson. Their own statements are written on large sheets of paper and the pupils copy these in their notebooks. Many weeks later the pupils are able to read their statements, although they may not be able to read at that level in their basal readers. They are able to read their experience charts because they are motivated to learn to read those statements which arise from their own experience. Elementary science is used to motivate these pupils.

A more formal experiment correlating science and reading is being conducted by Richard Kinney, at Public School No. 188 in Manhattan. In this experiment, reading lessons, based on the children's science experiences, are being prepared on three reading levels. The results so far have been encouraging and point to further study in this area.

ELEMENTARY SCIENCE SHOULD AFFORD CHILDREN OPPORTUNITIES TO HANDLE MATERIALS AND EQUIPMENT

A fundamental concept in teaching elementary science is that all children should have an opportunity to handle materials and equipment. This is especially true for the culturally deprived child since he seems to have greater achievement when tasks are motor-oriented. Teachers, therefore, should provide every opportunity for children to participate in demonstrations and experiments. If possible, there should be enough material so that every child can use the same materials at his seat that his teacher is using at her desk. Kits of materials can be organized which contain, for example, 30 dry cells, 30 switches, 30 bells, and pieces of wire, or 30 sets of different magnets. The materials that are used should be familiar to children. Esoteric and elaborate equipment should be avoided since it may be confusing to children; and assume importance rather than the science concepts being demonstrated. Children should be given recognition for their projects by having their exhibits displayed to other pupils as well as to their parents and to the community at periodic science fairs.

Through proper adaptation of the elementary science curriculum to the needs of this large portion of our children, we may bring about an enrichment of their lives which, in turn, will benefit our entire community. We have, so far, failed to tap America's greatest resources, the creative skills and abilities of all its children. Among these disadvantaged children, there is a large reservoir of future high-level, professional, and skilled personnel, if we learn how to help them realize their potential.

Throughout the country, experimentation with curriculum development for the culturally deprived children, such as the "Higher Horizons Program" and "Mobilization for Youth" in New York City are providing insights into the techniques of teaching such children. Through implementation of our new insights, both society and the child will benefit.

THE EVALUATION OF ELEMENTARY SCIENCE

INTRODUCTION

If the elementary science program is to be effective, then the program should be evaluated continuously. Definite and adequate provision should be made to ensure that the evaluation is dynamic and continuous rather than perfunctory and sporadic. All those who participate in the science program should be involved in the evaluation, and not just a small committee of teachers specifically appointed for that purpose. This is especially important when the elementary science program is part of a total K–12 program. Then the program should be evaluated by the elementary and secondary school teachers, by the science supervisor or consultant, and by the curriculum director, because all these persons are responsible for determining the content of the program.

If there is a curriculum guide, it too should be evaluated continuously. Teachers should be encouraged to evaluate the contents of the guide critically as they use it, and to forward criticisms and recommendations to the persons or committee responsible for conducting the evaluation and revision of the guide. The science content of the guide should be examined carefully for corrections, additions, or deletions. The sequence of topics in the guide should be checked for appropriate grade placement. Initiating activities should be evaluated for motivating and problem-raising potential. Learning activities should be tested critically to see if they are producing maximum learning, and should be replaced by newer, more creative activities as they appear in text and reference books. Even the evaluation techniques themselves should be scrutinized regularly.

In the classroom good teaching and learning call for continuous evaluation by both the teacher and the children. The teacher should constantly evaluate the content being learned, and also the methods and materials being used, to see if the children are achieving the objectives of the science program. The children should be encouraged to evaluate continually their strengths and weaknesses, their progress and growth in science learning, and their proficiency with the key operations, or processes, of science and the scientist.

Evaluation in the classroom can be used for a variety of purposes. First, it can be used to appraise achievement, by determining how well the children have learned science concepts and how competent they have become in performing the operations of the scientist. Second, it can be used for diagnostic purposes. As such, it can help identify the children's strengths and weaknesses. It can determine how well the children can work individually and in groups. It can be used as a pretest to learn how much the children already know about a topic before they begin the study of this topic. It can be used to diagnose the effectiveness of the teaching methods being used. Sometimes one method is more effective than another for different groups of children. Third, evaluation can be used for predictive purposes, where the teacher attempts to predict the children's behavior and achievement in the future or under different conditions.

There are a variety of methods of evaluation which the elementary school teacher can use. These methods are grouped into three categories: oral methods, written methods, and observation methods. Teachers may vary in their preference, but there is no one single best method of evaluating science learning. Actually, the objectives to be evaluated are more important than the method used, and very often the desired objectives or outcomes of learning will help determine which method should be selected. Also, the teacher should keep in mind that good test questions can be difficult and time-consuming to prepare, so tests should be constructed with much thought and care.

THE EVALUATION OF THE
ELEMENTARY SCIENCE
PROGRAM *

National Society for the Study of Education

A total elementary science program must be evaluated by all who participate in the program. Such evaluation must include children, teachers, supervisors or consultants, and administrators. Evaluation should be planned and should be a constant process. It can take place only after the characteristics of a good program are established. The following article presents eight such characteristics and the criteria for their evaluation. This article is an excerpt from Chapter 7, "Developing Science Programs in the Elementary School," of the Fifty-ninth Yearbook, Part I, of the National Society for the Study of Education, Rethinking Science Education. Members of the committee who wrote this chapter include Glenn O. Blough, Paul E. Blackwood, Katherine E. Hill, and Julius Schwartz.

A PROGRAM in elementary science can be effectively evaluated only when the objectives of a program are clear and have been accepted by the teachers and administrators in charge of the program. Too often the goals of a program are listed by a committee, printed at the beginning of a course of study, and then forgotten. Once goals have been accepted, they should be used as a basis for the selection of subject matter and the methods of teaching. If this is done, the adequacy of the program may be evaluated, at least in terms of its goals. Such appraisal may lead to redefinition of purposes and the establishment of new goals, which in turn may reasonably be expected to lead to experimenting with different teaching methods and subject matter. This is a process by which educational programs can be improved continuously.

Many curriculum guides and resource units include suggestions for evaluation. Some of the manuals for the development of courses of study that

---

* REPRINTED FROM *Rethinking Science Education*, 59th Yearbook of the National Society for the Study of Education, Part I (Chicago: University of Chicago Press, 1960), pp. 129–135, by permission of the publisher.

have been produced by state departments of education contain excellent suggestions for evaluation. However, few systematic attempts at evaluation of elementary-science programs have been reported.

WHO EVALUATES? If the evaluation of a total program in elementary science is sought, then all who participate in the program should be involved in the evaluation of it. Too often segments of the program have been evaluated in discrete units only by those most closely connected with the particular parts examined. For example, fifth-grade teachers in a school system have regularly evaluated the science taught in the fifth grades only. At times, the evaluation has been limited to the appraisal of the elementary-school program in science by the elementary-school faculty. This is too limited a group to evaluate elementary science as an integral part of a science program extending from the Kindergarten through Grade XII. A total science program must be assessed by elementary- and secondary-school teachers, by consultants in elementary science if they operate in the system, and by those administrators who are responsible for the development of curriculum. These are the persons primarily responsible for the selection of methods and content. All must be involved in the evaluation of the acceptability of the elementary-science program.

But the learner must not be forgotten. He must have a part in the evaluative process. Involving elementary-school children in assessing the *program* in science is a difficult undertaking, since their appraisal is apt to be related only to their most recent science experiences. Even so, the judgment of children may lead to reappraisal of a program. Older children, especially those in the upper-elementary grades and in the secondary school, may be used in helping the teaching and curriculum staffs find strong and weak features of the elementary-science program.

A third group sometimes involved in judging the merits of a program in elementary science is composed of parents and other members of the community. Often, they make judgments of the value of various aspects of the science program. At times, their judgments result in pressure being applied to influence school programs. The evaluation by members of the community may contribute to the over-all evaluation of the elementary science program.

The teacher and administrator have the responsibility of weighing and co-ordinating the various evaluations of the elementary-science program. Children, teachers, and other members of the community all express their views about the program. To make a difference, however, evaluation must affect the program. To use evaluations to modify and improve programs is a task for the administrators, who are responsible for the development of programs of elementary science.

WHEN AND HOW SHOULD EVALUATION TAKE PLACE? If a program in elementary science is to be dynamic, if it is to make a difference in the lives of children, then that program must undergo careful and constant scrutiny.

But, planning for the evaluative process must also be an integral part of the program in elementary science. This process must not be left to chance, to be considered in a cursory manner every few years by a committee of teachers. Ongoing and thorough examination of a science program should be considered part of the educator's responsibility, and there should be adequate provision for meeting this responsibility.

A description of the procedure for involving responsible personnel in evaluating the program follows: In one local school a group of three teachers, one who taught five-, six-, and seven-year-olds, one who taught eight- and nine-year-olds, and one who taught ten- and eleven-year-olds, were the nucleus of a committee for the evaluation of the science program in each elementary school. These three teachers had the responsibility for gathering information from their co-workers each eight weeks. Such information was gathered verbally or in writing and included responses to the following questions: What content, methods, or materials have you used or would you like to use? Have you evidence that your present group of children is making use of previous experiences? Have you evidence that your children are strengthening their insights and expanding their interests in science? If so, what is making this possible? What improvements are you planning to make in your own science program? What improvements would you like to see made in our total school program in science?

Such information is invaluable in appraising a school's science program and as a basis for its improvement. With such information, committees of teachers and administrators can plan a series of meetings with the total teaching staff. Such meetings can lead to continuing improvement of the science program in the elementary school.

For such important curriculum work, leadership is needed to organize the evaluation and to find means to insure that the outcomes of the evaluative process are reflected in the developing program. Adequate periods of time must be planned for evaluation, and administrative and secretarial assistance should be provided to facilitate the work of the committees. The machinery must be set up so that representatives of various groups of teachers and administrators can work together on evaluation.

SOME CHARACTERISTICS OF A GOOD ELEMENTARY-SCIENCE PROGRAM. Each teacher, each elementary school, and each school system is responsible for determining the goals toward which science teaching and learning are directed. It follows that each teacher, school, and school system must be intimately involved in judging the appropriateness of the goals and the methods and materials employed in reaching those goals. Science programs will vary from community to community and certainly will change with the passage of time. It seems appropriate, however, to present the following characteristics of a good elementary science program, together with the criteria for evaluation in the hope that they will be of specific aid to educators in judging their programs.

Characteristics of a Good Elementary-Science Program	*Criteria For Evaluating An Elementary-Science Program*
Elementary science should be recognized as an important part of the total elementary-school curriculum. Science experiences should be a part of the total school experiences at each grade level. Elementary-school science should be an integral part of a K–12 science program.	Is sufficient time for science provided in the program? (Some educators are suggesting that one-fifth of the elementary program be devoted to science, one-fifth to social studies, one-fifth to language arts, one-fifth to expressive and graphic arts, and one-fifth to the development of skills related to learning.)
	Has a curriculum in elementary science been developed for your school?
	Do the science experiences at each grade level build upon experiences in previous grades and lead to experiences in subsequent grades? Is an administrator responsible for assisting teachers in developing the science program from the Kindergarten through Grade XII? Are parents regularly informed of the achievement of their child in science?
A program in elementary science should be provided for *all* children.	Do the teachers and administrators view science as important in the life of each child?
	Realizing that all citizens must be aware of and understand the importance of science in a democracy, is a science program provided for all children?
	Is opportunity provided to extend the horizons of those children who are especially fascinated with science?
The development of scientific attitudes is basic in a good elementary science program.	Do teachers provide time for the exploration of ideas verbally and with materials?
	Is there evidence that scientific attitudes are becoming a part of the behavior of children?
An elementary-science program should provide a balanced content in science.	During each one- or two-year period, do children have an opportunity to explore in each of the several large areas of sci-

Characteristics of a Good Elementary-Science Program	Criteria For Evaluating An Elementary-Science Program
	ence, such as (a) our earth, its composition, and the changes occurring on it; (b) our earth in space; (c) the living things on the earth, how they grow, change, survive, and die; (d) the physical and chemical forces man uses; (e) man's place in his changing environment?
Children need to have an opportunity to participate in a variety of activities in elementary science.	There is no one best way to develop elementary-science experiences. A good elementary-science program is characterized by a variety of challenging experiences. Do children have a chance to participate in experiments, demonstrations, field trips, construction projects, library research, group discussions, and discussions with informed members of the community? Is the curriculum flexible enough to provide time for investigating important science questions not provided for in the planned program in elementary science?
Adequate materials are provided to carry on a good elementary-science program.	Are appropriate manipulative materials provided as regular equipment in each classroom? Is provision made for exploration of the out-of-the classroom environment? Is each classroom provided with a science library of at least two different books per child? Is there a selection of science books in the school library? Are films, film strips, TV programs, slides, records of bird songs, etc., readily available?

Characteristics of a Good Elementary-Science Program	Criteria For Evaluating An Elementary-Science Program
Expert help is available to the classroom teacher, who is the key to a good elementary-science program.	Are professional books and curriculum materials in science provided for teachers?
	Is some one administrator responsible for aiding teachers in the development of a program in elementary science?
	Is a consultant in elementary science available for each group of 18 to 24 classroom teachers in the school system to aid them in their work? Is this consultant trained both in working with elementary-school children and in science content?
	Are opportunities available to classroom teachers for in-service education in science?
Ongoing evaluation is a part of a good program in elementary science.	Is provision made for constant and thorough analysis of the elementary-science program?
	Has the program in elementary science been improved substantially during the last two years?

These are some characteristics of good elementary-science programs. Committees of elementary-school teachers and administrators working in cooperation with teachers and administrators from other schools in the school system can use those characteristics to examine and evaluate their programs of elementary science. Such evaluations can lead to the continuing improvement of children's experiences in this important area of the total elementary-school program.

A SUGGESTED CHECKLIST FOR
ASSESSING A SCIENCE
PROGRAM *

U.S. Office of Education

This checklist, prepared by Specialists for Science at the U.S. Office of Education, is designed to help identify the strengths and weaknesses of a science program. The checklist can be used at all grade levels, in schools of different sizes, and by teachers of varying degrees of experience. Suggestions are offered on how to provide for broad participation in the evaluation of ten areas of the science program. A chart is provided for making an evaluation profile of these areas, to decide which science program problems are most pressing.

MANY PERSONS in all parts of the country are concerned about the quality of their schools. Taxpayers want to know whether their tax dollars are well spent. Administrators want to know what they can do to strengthen their school programs, and conscientious teachers and supervisors want to know how well they are doing in light of present efforts to improve teaching.

How to go about assessing a school program is a problem, particularly in science where content and methods are changing rapidly—perhaps even more so than in other subjects.

To evaluate a program some kind of yardstick is needed. This publication contains a suggested checklist that can help identify the strong points of a science program as well as those that need to be strengthened. The checklist may be used at all levels, in schools of varying sizes, and by teachers of varying degrees of experience. Therefore, the following suggestions on the use of the list are not all applicable to every situation. Many have come from individual teachers and supervisors and have been found useful by them; and there are, among the suggestions, some which will be of use to any school undertaking an evaluation of its science program.

This service bulletin has been prepared by the U.S. Office of Education at the request of many schools. This fifth revision, which results from extensive field use over the past several years, has been submitted to competent spe-

---

* REPRINTED FROM *A Suggested Checklist for Assessing a Science Program*, U.S. Office of Education, Document OE-29034A, 1964, pp. 1–19.

cialists of science, professors of science education, science teachers, and others for comments and editorial suggestions. We wish to thank all who have had a part in making this checklist an improved instrument for the evaluation of a science program.

BROAD PARTICIPATION

The broader the participation of science teachers, supervisors, principals, and superintendents in the science program evaluation, the more satisfactory the results. To initiate it, each science teacher of a given school might fill out a copy of the suggested checklist. Then all the science teachers in each school of the district or system might, as a group (again using the checklist), evaluate their particular school's science program and prepare a composite checklist. Finally, the proper authorities could, in the same way, evaluate the science program of the entire school system. From the evaluations, a profile would emerge of the school system's strengths and weaknesses in science teaching. This profile would be the basis for setting up priorities in a plan to improve the science program.

RECENCY OF CONTENT AND METHODS

When using a checklist keep in mind the importance of *recency*. For example, a library collection in science cannot be considered up to date if few of the books, especially in rapidly developing science areas, have been published within the past 5 years. Similarly, a teacher's science background should be modern. Unless it has been updated by science refresher courses or independent study during the last few years, it too is out of date.

Teaching methods for science should be as modern as the content itself. It goes almost without saying these days that *how* children and young people learn is as important, really, as *what* they learn. Who would gainsay that they must be equipped to find answers to problems as well as to manipulate verbal and mathematical symbols in the three R's?

Merely to memorize facts is no longer considered sufficient in education. It has become increasingly clear that the apparent validity of a fact cannot be assured for any given length of time. But scientific methods of inquiry into the nature of things will stand the test of time and are as necessary in other areas of learning as they are in science.

In good science programs, pupils do not use the laboratory merely to confirm textbook statements or to follow step-by-step written procedures. Rather, they participate in activities that stimulate scientific creativity in identifying problems, stating hypotheses, designing experiments, and evaluating data from many sources. Open-end activities, where the pupil can continue an individual investigation in greater depth, have been designed for both elementary and secondary grades; and reports concerning them have been published. In science many resourceful teachers use pupil-teacher planning to develop their own unique investigative experiments.

A Profile for Determining Priorities

Everything cannot be done at once—outline a science curriculum for junior high school, develop an inservice education program for elementary teachers, plan a program for academically talented senior high school students, provide individual laboratory work in general science, and arrange a science fair. Confronted by all these urgent problems, decide which ones in your own school are most crucial. How to decide?

One help in deciding might well come from making an evaluation profile from the data provided from this checklist of the science program. At the end of this publication is a suggested chart for such a profile which ties in with the immediately preceding suggested checklist. When the profile chart is filled in from the answers appearing on the checklists, it will become apparent which science-program problems are most crucial and pressing. These problems would naturally be given top priority and, as such, could then serve as the starting point to plan improvements in the program.

How To Use the Checklist

The checklist items are merely suggestions. Many of the items are general statements because local school systems vary greatly. A school may want to revise them to fit local needs. In any case, it would want to examine each item—as it now stands or after revision—to make certain that when the entire list is applied to the local program it does in fact draw an accurate profile of that program.

More specific checklists will be required for followup use after this general checklist has been completed by the local schools. Such checklists will be available soon from the U.S. Office of Education for *elementary school science, junior high school science,* and *senior high school sciences* (biology, chemistry, and physics). These will search more intensively and more deeply into items which pertain especially to the levels mentioned above.

The checklist is provided with four answer columns, which may be used as suggested below, or the individual schools can write in their own headings, geared to local requirements.

Check (√) the column most applicable:
    3—There is *much* evidence that the practice exists
    2—There is *some* evidence that the practice exists
    1—There is *little* evidence that the practice exists
    Insert O in column headed "other" if the item *does not exist*
    Insert X in column headed "other" if the item *does not apply*

	3	2	1	other
1. (Item)				
2. (Item)				
3. (Item)				

etc.

An alternate method of using the checklist is to place a check in one of the first three columns that answers the item as in 1, 2, or 3 below.

3—Yes, there is *much* evidence that the practice exists

2—Yes, there is *some* evidence that the practice exists

1—No, there is no evidence that the practice exists

A SUGGESTED CHECKLIST FOR ASSESSING A SCIENCE PROGRAM [1]

The items marked with an asterisk (*) may be considered as being of major importance or most desirable for a minimum basic science program. If a school wishes to change or add to these basic items, it may do so.

I. FOUNDATIONS FOR LOCAL PROGRAM PLANNING

	3	2	1	other
*1. Has a local science advisory committee been established?				
*2. Have such representatives of the local community as scientists, engineers, school and lay personnel been involved—to the extent of action—on the local advisory committee?				
3. Has a survey or a listing been made of local science-related resources available for improving science teaching?				
4. Have resources of local business and industry been utilized, e.g., field trips, classroom presentations, and science materials?				
5. Are scientists from the local area *regularly* invited to participate in the school's science program?				
6. Are scientists and science educators from nearby colleges and universities invited to serve as consultants and speakers for the school's science program?				

---

[1] Adapted by permission. *School Management* Magazine, Inc., copyright 1959.

	3	2	1	other

*7. Are measurements made of factors such as changes in enrollment and interest in science classes and activities which might be significant in planning for facilities, staff, budget, and curriculum?

*8. Is there coordination to insure that conservation, health, safety, aerospace, and other like areas are being adequately included in the science program and at the same time are not being duplicated?

*9. Is attention being given to coordinating the science program with the mathematics, English, social studies, and other programs?

10. Is there provision for two-way communication between the community and school about changes in the science program, whether through the advisory committee or by some other means?

11. Has an effort been made to develop adjunct science activities within the community, such as a junior museum, nature trail, or wildlife preserve?

II. PUBLIC RESPONSIBILITY AND GOALS

*1. Has the local board of education and the school administration evidenced a sensitivity for the responsibility for public education in science:
   a. By establishing policies which are consistent with local, State, and national needs, such as providing for an education adequate to give the background needed for future scientists, engineers, technicians, and scientifically oriented nonscience citizens?
   b. By providing an opportunity for every child to study science at every grade level?
   c. By providing for the identification, encouragement, and development of boys and girls with special science talent?
   d. By considering the need for a science program for students with below-average ability?
   e. By recognizing that specific facilities and equipment as well as properly trained science teachers are a basic requisite to a good program, and by making plans to adequately finance such a program?

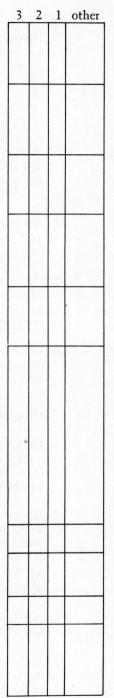

	3	2	1	other
*2. Have consistent long-range goals in harmony with the present American culture (as implied in the preceding statements) been established for your science program?				
*3. Do long-range goals give emphasis to the processes of scientific inquiry, e.g., problem recognition, assumption recognition, hypothesizing, observations as comparison and measurement, experimental design and conduct, data analysis and interpretation, and the extension and relating of understandings to new problems?				
4. Are the long-range goals for the science program used in determining short-range immediate objectives?				
5. Has competent outside professional guidance, both educational and scientific, been sought in the development of the long-range goals for your science program?				
6. Do the long-range goals consider the nature and importance of the history, philosophy, and lives of men of science as a major cultural influence?				

III. CURRICULUM

	3	2	1	other
*1. Does the content of science courses taught provide a valid impression of science as it exists today both in terms of major ideas and the evidence upon which these ideas are based?				
*2. Have criteria, based on long-range goals, been established for the selection and organization of course content?				
3. Are broad integrating themes used as the basis for developing an understanding of science?				
*4. Is science scheduled as a regular subject and is it available to each pupil at every grade level?				
*5. Is the amount of class time scheduled for science at every grade level sufficient for the full attainment of the desired goals?				

	3	2	1	other

*6. Are open-ended and problem-solving-type activities used extensively as a means of developing:
    a. Scientific attitudes?
    b. Skills in the processes of scientific inquiry?
    c. Functional understandings of scientific concepts?

*7. Do science courses provide frequent opportunities for each pupil to engage in laboratory work and other firsthand experiences?

8. Are double laboratory periods or extended class time scheduled each week for the science courses offered in grades 7 to 12?

9. Are the school's science laboratories and/or project work areas available to science talented pupils for independent projects and research outside of regular class time?

10. Are the pupils who have shown interest in science careers provided opportunities to take at least 4 years each of science and mathematics in grades 9 to 12?

11. Is every secondary school pupil required to take a minimum of 2 years of laboratory science, at least 1 each of biological and physical science, for graduation?

*12. Does the curriculum at all grade levels give emphasis to the historical, biographical (men of science), and philosophical aspects of science?

13. Have the following been utilized in the development of science curriculum materials:
    a. State department of education personnel?
    b. Science supervisor?
    c. Local teaching and administrative staff?
    d. College and university scientists and science educators?
    e. Business and industry personnel?
    f. Representatives of lay organizations, e.g., county farm agents, health department, hospital, and clinic personnel?

	3	2	1	other

14. Is there a trend in curriculum revision in your school to cover fewer topics (subject matter areas)? Are those areas that are selected for study covered in greater depth?

IV. TEACHING-LEARNING

*1. Are pupils at all levels given opportunities to:
   a. Learn and practice skills in scientific observation?
   b. Design, set up, and carry out controlled experiments to test hypotheses?
   c. Formulate and delimit problems?
   d. Recognize assumptions?
   e. Prepare and discuss hypotheses regarding the solutions to problems?
   f. Use appropriate instruments for making measurements?
   g. Use proper statistical and mathematical procedures for handling measurements?
   h. Evaluate and interpret evidence they have collected?
   i. Learn the value of withholding judgment until sufficient evidence has been collected?
   j. Recognize the nature of any conclusion and modify this conclusion on the basis of new evidence?

*2. Do pupils at all levels have the opportunity to discover science principles through participation in experiences rather than through mere reading or talking about science?

*3. Does the laboratory work consist of working on real problems which are genuinely thought-provoking rather than performing "cookbook" types of exercises?

4. Are teacher and pupil-teacher demonstrations used to promote critical thought and discussion rather than just to serve as illustrations of science principles?

*5. Are pupils encouraged to question evidence, challenge loose thinking, and develop hypotheses as an accepted part of classroom behavior?

6. Do science activities seek to relate new learnings to previous learnings?

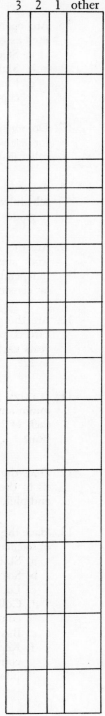

	3	2	1	other

7. Are pupils encouraged to develop investigations on their own?

V. EVALUATION

Evaluation of Pupil Performance

*1. Does the evaluation program make use of a variety of techniques and instruments such as the following:
    a. Anecdotal records?
    b. Performance tests?
    c. Objective tests?
    d. Essay examinations?
    e. Observations of laboratory procedures?
    f. Rating scales?

2. Are inservice or other opportunities available for teachers to discuss and prepare evaluation materials and procedures?

Evaluation of the Science Program

*1. Are criteria for evaluation available which are based on the stated goals for the science program?

2. Are materials (books, sample tests, and national norms) available within the school to help teachers evaluate pupil learnings in science?

*3. Is there specific evidence that attempts are made at all grade levels to evaluate growth in the processes of scientific inquiry?

4. Are efforts made to follow up the graduates of high school to determine whether or not the science program has met the needs of:
    a. Those who plan to follow careers in science?
    b. Those who plan to become science teachers?
    c. Those who plan to become science technicians?
    d. Those who do not plan to pursue science-related careers but who will become scientifically literate citizens?

*5. Are teachers encouraged and given the opportunity to evaluate their own teaching procedures?

VI. YOUTH ACTIVITIES

*1. Does your school science program include one or more of the following:

3 2 1 other

a. Science clubs?
b. Science seminars?
c. Annual science exhibits?
d. Participation in a statewide or national organization?
e. Participation in the Junior Academy of Science?
f. The Westinghouse Science Talent Search?

2. Do the secondary school science pupils conduct research projects which may be exhibited at science fairs or science congresses?

3. Do pupils prepare and read scientific and research papers at science congresses, junior academies of science, and other scientific meetings?

*4. Do projects for science students emerge from and, in part, contribute to the on-going classroom activities?

5. Are the science youth organizations affiliated with:
a. Local organizations?
b. State organizations?
c. National organizations?

6. Are the faculty sponsors of science youth activities given either compensatory time or a salary supplement?

7. Are science pupils encouraged to participate in:
a. Summer science camps?
b. Summer science institutes?
c. Summer science expeditions?
d. Summer employment in scientific laboratories?

VII. STAFF

*1. Are the NASDTEC-AAAS [2] recommendations for preparation in science and mathematics met by a substantial portion of:

2 *Guidelines for Science and Mathematics in the Preparation Program of Elementary School Teachers,* National Association of State Directors of Teacher Education and Certification in Cooperation with the American Association for the Advancement of Science, 1515 Massachusetts Avenue, NW., Washington, D.C., 1963.
Guidelines for Preparation Programs of Teachers of Secondary School Science and Mathematics, National Association of State Directors of Teacher Education and Certification in Cooperation with the American Association for the Advancement of Science, 1515 Massachusetts Avenue, NW., Washington, D.C., 1961.

	3	2	1	other
a. Elementary school teachers?				
b. Junior high school science teachers?				
c. Senior high school science teachers?				
*2. Have all science teachers completed at least:				
a. An undergraduate major in a science?				
b. A master's degree in science?				
3. Are inservice institutes conducted for science teachers as a regular part of their professional workload?				
4. Have most of the science teachers attended summer or academic year science institutes within the last 5 years?				
*5. Is consultant help available to all science teachers from:				
a. An elementary science consultant?				
b. A secondary science consultant?				
c. Scientists in local industry?				
d. Scientists and science educators in a nearby college or university?				
e. A State supervisor of science?				
f. Academies of science?				
*6. Do science teachers generally attend meetings of professional or scientific organizations at the:				
a. Local level?				
b. State level?				
c. Regional level?				
d. National level?				
7. During out-of-school time do all science teachers strive to improve their professional, scientific, and general cultural backgrounds through:				
a. Travel?				
b. Study?				
c. Work in science-based industry?				
d. Engaging in scientific research?				
e. Engaging in science education research?				
8. Do all the science teachers subscribe to or read:				
a. Educational journals?				
b. Scientific journals?				
c. Journals of research in science teaching?				
d. Science teaching journals?				

	3	2	1	other

9. Are science teachers given assistance by means of one or more of the following:
   a. Clerical help?
   b. Paid laboratory assistants?
   c. Volunteer laboratory assistants?
   d. Free periods for planning activities and caring for and setting up equipment?

10. Does the guidance staff include counselors who are sensitive to the needs of pupils interested in science?

*11. Do science teachers assume professional responsibility for career guidance of pupils interested in science?

12. Do science teachers work with other staff members to effectively coordinate teaching-learning activities?

13. Do science teachers assist pupils or refer them to appropriate personnel for assistance in the improvement of reading and study skills?

VIII. ADMINISTRATION

*1. Do the board of education and the administration have a policy to frequently review teacher assignments in terms of academic and other qualifications?

*2. Have the board of education and the school administration taken specific action to enable and encourage teachers to update their:
   a. Professional qualifications?
   b. Academic qualifications?

3. Are teachers on all grade levels encouraged to experiment with new content and new techniques?

4. Are science teachers allowed time with pay to attend professional conferences related to the science program?

5. Does the school have a policy that provides for, encourages, and regulates:
   a. Local field trips?
   b. School journeys to special areas?
   c. Summer excursions for scientific studies?

	3	2	1	other

*6. Does the administration exert leadership to encourage science teachers and other teachers to work together for overall science program planning as part of their regular assignment?

7. Does the administration maintain close contact with and seek consultant help from the school district and State supervisors of science?

*8. Does the administration recognize that good science teaching requires more in the way of specific facilities and equipment than other academic areas and that science classes should not be scheduled in standard classrooms?

9. Does the school district provide transportation for science field trips for:
   a. Science pupils?
   b. Science teachers?

IX. FINANCES

*1. Does the budget [3] provide realistically and adequately for science:
   a. Apparatus?
   b. Supplies?
   c. Instructional material?
   d. Teaching aids?
   e. Library books?
   f. Repair, maintenance, and replacement of equipment and materials?

2. Is science equipment purchased with the needs of specific science courses in mind?

3. Does the school science budget provide needed laboratory supplies for each student in every course throughout the year?

4. Is a petty cash fund or an equivalent source of money provided to purchase incidental science materials?

[3] Charles L. Koelsche and Archie N. Solberg, *Facilities and Equipment Available for Teaching Science in Public High Schools*, 1958–59. Toledo, Ohio: Research Foundation, University of Toledo, 1959, p. 26.
". . . (a) breakdown of budgeted funds for the various enrollment categories revealed that the average amount per science student in the 1–199 size group was $3.90; 200–499, $2.88; 500–999, $2.50; and 1000-up, $2.26."

	3	2	1	other

*5. Does the salary structure:
    a. Attract well-qualified science teachers?
    b. Include increments which will assure retention of well-qualified teachers?
    c. Eliminate the need for additional nonprofessional employment?

6. Does the school provide money and/or leave for professional travel for science teachers?

7. Have NDEA Title III funds been used to the limit of Federal matching funds?

8. Are science teachers consulted in the establishment of budgetary procedures and the formulation of the budget?

X. FACILITIES, EQUIPMENT, AND TEACHING AIDS

*1. Are the suggestions and recommendations of qualified science teaching personnel sought and incorporated in plans for new science facilities?

*2. Does each room where science is taught have the following characteristics:
    a. Proper heat and ventilation (including fume hoods where needed)?
    b. Good lighting with supplementary lighting where needed?
    c. Electrical wiring and outlets with voltage and amperage control where needed?
    d. Gas supply and outlets where needed?
    e. Running water taps and sinks where needed?
    f. Proper acoustics for potentially noisy areas?
    g. Room darkening facilities (blackout shades)?
    h. Area suitable for photographic darkroom work?
    i. Exhibit and display areas?
    j. Space for individual pupil project work?
    k. Suitable areas for maintaining living plants and animals near or in the biology laboratory?
    l. Acid resistant tabletop and floor covering where needed?
    m. Preparation area?

3. Are the following laboratory safeguards provided:
    a. Prevention and control of gas, chemical, and electrical fires (blankets or extinguishers)?

	3	2	1	other

   b. Electrical equipment (fuses, breakers, etc.)?
   c. Emergency shower and eye fountains?
   d. "Hot lab" facilities for radioactive chemicals?
   e. First aid kits or cabinets?
   f. Properly placed exits?

4. Are the science facilities, furniture, and equipment suitable for and adaptable to:
   a. Individual experimentation by pupils?
   b. Long-term pupil experiments or projects?
   c. Teacher and pupil demonstrations?
   d. Small and large group work?
   e. Effective use of supplementary aids?
   f. Science clubs, fairs, and project activities?

5. Does each science teacher have facilities for effective performance of:
   a. Preparatory activities?
   b. Conference activities with pupils and parents?
   c. The use of reference books and materials?
   d. Desk and office functions?

6. Are adequate storage facilities provided in:
   a. The rooms where science is taught?
   b. Separate storage and/or preparation rooms?

7. Are equipment and supplies stored and organized for effective use in:
   a. Classrooms and laboratories?
   b. Storage facilities?

8. Are adequate inventory records and controls maintained for science equipment and materials?

9. Are the science rooms equipped with the following instructional aids or are they readily available:
   a. Overhead projector?
   b. Microprojector?
   c. 16 mm. movie projector?
   d. Slide and filmstrip projector?
   e. Closed circuit television?
   f. Programed learning devices?

*10. Are suitable [4] types of basic equipment and instructional aids provided and readily available to:
   a. Teachers for instructional purposes?
   b. Pupils for project work?

---

[4] Should be interpreted as meaning sufficient for the full realization of the purposes and goals of the course.

3   2   1   other

    c. Pupils for team work?
    d. Pupils for individual work, both during and
       outside of classroom time?

*11. Are adequate [4] quantities provided of the following:
    a. Textbooks with recent copyright dates?
    b. Science periodicals for teachers?
    c. Science periodicals for pupils?
    d. Science reference books for teachers?
    e. Science reference books for pupils?
    f. Professional science journals?

12. Are the following types of facilities available in
    areas where possible:
    a. A school pond or wild life area?
    b. An area where activities related to conservation
       may be carried out?
    c. A greenhouse?
    d. A weather station?
    e. A planetarium?
    f. An area where the environmental conditions—
       temperature, light, and moisture—can be con-
       trolled and varied?

*13. Is the library adequately equipped with books for
    a comprehensive science program?

14. Does the science staff request additional titles to
    supplement existing references?

15. Is the library effectively and regularly used by the:
    a. Pupils?
    b. Science teachers?

EVALUATION PROFILE

AVERAGE RATING	I Foundations	II Goals	III Curriculum	IV Teaching-learning	V Evaluation	VI Youth activities	VII Staff	VIII Administration	IX Finance	X Equipment
3										
2½										
2										
1½										
1										
½										
0										

187

EVALUATION AS A PART OF THE
TEACHING-LEARNING PROCESS*

National Society for the Study of Education

Evaluation should be in terms of all the goals that are set for the teaching process. Of primary concern in evaluation is whether the desirable changes in behavior have taken place. In addition, it is of utmost importance that the teacher critically evaluate his teaching. The teacher, therefore, should constantly be asking two questions: "How well is the child doing?" and "How well am I doing?" This article is an excerpt from Chapter 8, "Teaching and Evaluating Science in the Elementary School," of the Fifty-ninth Yearbook, Part I, of the National Society for the Study of Education, Rethinking Science Education. *Members of the committee who wrote this chapter include Glenn O. Blough, Katherine E. Hill, Willard J. Jacobson, and Albert Piltz.*

E VALUATION should be considered an integral part of the total teaching-learning process, and it should be continuous. The assessment of the effectiveness of teaching is a day-by-day, perhaps even an hour-by-hour, procedure. The results of evaluation supply the impetus for the redirection of the teaching-learning process with all that this implies. The evaluation process will lead to the examination of previously accepted goals, of methods being used by teacher and learner in moving toward these goals, and of the merits of the very evaluation procedures themselves.

It seems apparent, then, that evaluation is a continuing part of teaching and learning and is directed toward the appraisal of the quality of the teaching-learning process. However, in order to assess quality, each teacher must have an awareness of the desired outcomes of teaching. True evaluation of teaching occurs only when that evaluation is in terms of the accepted goals of teaching in a particular institution.

It is not enough to evaluate in terms of only one goal, such as the retention of facts. Evaluation should be in terms of *all* of the goals that are set for the teaching process.

Our primary concern in evaluation is to determine the nature of the changes in behavior that have taken place. It is not enough for the pupil to

---

* REPRINTED FROM *Rethinking Science Education*, 59th Yearbook of the National Society for the Study of Education, Part I (Chicago: University of Chicago Press, 1960), pp. 144–149, by permission of the publisher.

be able to *recite* facts. Facts should make a difference in behavior. Children's science experiences should influence their patterns of thinking and acting. In evaluation we try to determine whether or not the pupils' science experiences have influenced their thinking and how teaching can be further improved. Perhaps an example which shows the dangers of limited, narrow evaluations will point up the importance of evaluating in terms of all goals and in terms of changes in behavior.

Late in April, the teacher of a group of ten-year-olds in a consolidated school was deluged with bouquets of wild flowers, gifts of the children. This fitted into the teacher's plan to teach the names of ten wild flowers common to the state. It was easy to arouse interest in the lesson, as specimens of seven of the flowers were in the room. There were even enough of five of the varieties of flowers for each child to press his own specimen, mount it in a booklet, and write the name of the flower beneath it. In the next few days, enough specimens of two rarer wild flowers were gathered by the eager children so that each child could also have a specimen of those flowers for his book. Specimens of the remaining three wild flowers on the list were discovered, and each of the finders graciously shared his spoils with his best friends. Those children not so fortunate as to have a specimen of these three rarer flowers drew a picture of each of them. So each individual booklet was complete with specimens or sketches of the ten wild flowers in question. Furthermore, on a test which required the children to name the ten common wild flowers, almost every child was successful. Those who were unsuccessful were retaught. On another test, the children showed they could do even more. They were able to match pictures of the flowers with the proper names, showing that they were not only capable of naming the flowers but also of identifying them. The teacher was proud of the results of the test because one of the goals had been to learn the names of the flowers. This goal had been surpassed, for most of the children were able to identify the flowers. In terms of the *one* goal, this traditional teaching-learning process had been eminently successful.

A more significant goal, however, might have been to develop an intelligent attitude toward conservation of natural resources. In terms of this goal, the teaching was not very successful. In their collections, the children had several specimens of hepatica, bluebell, redbud, and trailing arbutus which were on the "protected" list of the state. If this teacher had evaluated his program in terms of conservation behavior as well as of the retention of facts, he would have changed his approach to teaching and developed much more significant experiences.

As a result of such an evaluation, the teacher might be prompted to begin the project before the first spring flowers appeared. Pictures of the flowers might be put on the bulletin board so that children would be alerted to watch for these flowers and to report their observations in class. Trips to observe and study the flowers in their natural habitat might be arranged. Under sensitive and insightful handling, not one of these wild flowers would

be picked. Evaluation would be concerned with behavior and attitudes relating to conservation. The children would learn to recognize certain flowers
and to enjoy them. In addition, they would learn a great deal about the natural habitat of these wild flowers and how and why some are protected.
Evaluation in terms of all of our goals and in terms of desired behavior can
lead to desirable and effective science experiences.

Some teachers find it difficult to evaluate in terms of such a goal as conservation behavior. Yet, this is an important goal to keep in mind. It is a
goal toward which teachers may direct the learning process continuously
throughout the year. If this is the case, constant evaluation of the growth of
individuals toward this goal is in order. As children meet new situations calling for conservation practices, are they encouraged and helped to examine
their behavior in order to change their patterns of behavior if change seems
to be desirable?

If the goal of elementary-science teaching is to effect differences in the
lives of children, evaluation of that process must be focused on behavior.
This is difficult, but it is not impossible; it is time-consuming but rewarding.

TEACHERS EVALUATE PUPIL GROWTH IN SCIENCE

An important method of judging the effectiveness of the teaching process
is to appraise the growth of individual children. Such an appraisal requires
constant attention to the progress and growth of the child toward stated
science goals. If such goals as improved scientific attitudes, behavior consistent
with the best of scientific knowledge, and improved ability to think through
a question critically are held to be important, it then becomes necessary to
assess a child's growth frequently and in action.

A number of techniques have been developed which are useful in making
an appraisal. The cumulative science record of the pupil is basic to the
week-by-week and year-by-year analysis of individual progress. Such a cumulative record, kept by the school, may contain examples of a child's work, but,
even more important, it contains teachers' analyses of progress based upon
observation as well as upon other evidence.

Research workers have developed a number of effective techniques for
obtaining information that is useful for evaluation. The following are some
of these techniques:

(a) Recording anecdotes which reveal progress or lack of progress toward
such goals as improved critical thinking and skill in problem-solving.
Navarra, in his study of concept-development in a child,[1] developed
and refined useful techniques for observing children. A teacher selects
a few children each week and concentrates on observing and record-

[1] John Gabriel Navarra, *The Development of Scientific Concepts in a Child*. New York:
Bureau of Publications, Teachers College, Columbia University, 1955.

ing the behavior of these children. In the course of a month or six weeks, he gathers considerable evidence of value in assessing the growth of individual children.

(b) Using a tape recorder during discussion periods in science, Schenke found tape recordings of children's discussions a valuable tool in studying sources of children's science information.[2] This technique merits wider use than it now has. Tapes made at intervals of several weeks are analyzed by the teacher in order to ascertain progress of individual children. In addition, they are used by the children, especially those in the upper grades, in assessing their own progress from time to time.

(c) Recording on a check sheet the types of contributions that individuals are making, West and Hill developed check sheets for recording the observation of children's contributions.[3, 4] The use of a check sheet with entries for indicating a child's request for information, contribution of fact, suggestion for solving a problem, remark indicating skepticism, or statement revealing reservation of judgment makes it possible for the busy teacher to record the information. As a child makes a remark which fits one of the categories, his initials are entered in the proper category. Records made during several consecutive science discussions give a picture of the nature of the contributions of individuals.

After such data have been secured, it is necessary to evaluate critically the individual's growth toward specific goals. As an outcome of such an evaluation, a teacher may see the wisdom of changing his teaching process so that it will be more effective in stimulating and encouraging individual growth toward the desired goals.

TEACHERS EXAMINE THEIR TEACHING

In addition to evaluating pupil progress, the teacher should examine critically his approach to the teaching of elementary science. This is especially important since many teachers of elementary-school children have not been adequately prepared to teach science by their preservice training. Therefore, it might be well for each classroom teacher, each consultant, and each administrator responsible for curriculum development to ask himself such questions as the following:

[2] Lahron Schenke, "Information Sources Children Use," *Science Education*, XL (April, 1956), 232–237.

[3] Joe Young West, *A Technique for Appraising Certain Observable Behavior of Children in Science in Elementary Schools*. New York: Bureau of Publications, Teachers College, Columbia University, 1937.

[4] Katherine E. Hill, *Children's Contributions in Science Discussions*. New York: Bureau of Publications, Teachers College, Columbia University, 1947.

(a) In my teaching and in my professional studies am I concerned with the importance of science to society and of the layman's responsibility in relation to the progress and use of science?

(b) Am I constantly reading, televiewing, listening, or evaluating to enlarge my store of science content?

(c) Am I making science an important part of my curriculum by planning and providing sufficient time and adequate materials for it in the program? Am I emphasizing it in reporting to parents?

(d) Am I becoming more confident in approaching new problems in science and learning with the children?

(e) Do I make flexible, but careful, plans for science?

(f) Do I scrutinize my teaching constantly to determine whether or not my goals are desirable and attainable?

(g) Am I aware of the progress or lack of progress of individual children?

(h) Do I consult with colleagues in an ongoing appraisal of the total program in elementary science?

In evaluating the teaching process in relation to elementary science, consideration must be given to the degree of success attained in setting workable and reasonable goals, the use of techniques for appraising the progress of each child toward these goals, the constant self-appraisal by each teacher of his own attitudes and methods in the area of elementary science, and the ongoing evaluation of the process of evaluation itself.

EVALUATION IN ELEMENTARY SCIENCE BY CLASSROOM TEACHERS AND THEIR SUPERVISORS *

Harold E. Tannenbaum, Nathan Stillman, and Albert Piltz

This article is intended by the authors to serve a number of different purposes in the area of elementary school science. First, it should be helpful to

---

* REPRINTED FROM *Evaluation in Elementary School Science*, U.S. Office of Education, Document OE-29057, Circular No. 757, 1964, pp. 19–52. Dr. Tannenbaum is Professor of Education at Hunter College, New York. Dr. Stillman is Professor of Education at Yeshiva University, New York. Dr. Piltz is Specialist in Science Instructional Resources at the U.S. Office of Education.

supervisors and administrators on the state and local levels in evaluating the effectiveness of the elementary science program. Second, it should enable teachers to do a more effective job of evaluating the growth of their students in achieving the goals of the science program. Third, it should provide supervisors with material for in-service teacher education programs in evaluation. Fourth, it should aid supervisors by giving them guiding principles for measuring the effectiveness of teachers. This article is an excerpt from the U. S. Office of Education bulletin Evaluation in Elementary School Science.

"WHAT," "how," and "how well" are key words introducing three of the major questions faced by every supervisor and classroom teacher in the formal education of students. The first, "What should children learn?" is concerned with both the long-term goals and the consequent immediate objectives of the educational enterprise. The second, "How should they learn?" related to the problem of method or of determining the most effective means of helping students achieve the objectives. The third, "How well have they learned?" involves ascertaining the degree to which the objectives have been achieved. It is this careful appraisal of where a pupil is and how well he is progressing that comprises "student evaluation."

Teachers generally and rightly consider evaluation as one of the most complex problems in teaching and one for which they have been inadequately prepared. This is especially true in the area of elementary school science, where curriculums are undergoing extensive revisions not only in relation to content but also with respect to scientific attitudes and problem solving approaches. Standardized tests in elementary school science which would be appropriate for most schools are still nonexistent. Merely using a test labeled "science" could well result only in obtaining erroneous information about students and would be worse than not using tests at all. Thus, both the classroom teacher and the local personnel charged with the supervision of the elementary school science program are faced with the responsibility for learning how to develop, use, and interpret a variety of appraisal techniques for the purpose of furthering the teaching-learning process.

Measuring the outcomes of the teaching-learning process requires a great variety of evaluative techniques. For some purposes, testing devices such as objective tests or essay tests are not only satisfactory but even necessary. For example, objective tests can be used to determine if students can define such terms as "compound," "mixture," and "element"; essay tests can be used to determine if students are able to use these terms in formulating chemical explanations of natural or man-made phenomena.

Other kinds of achievement can be evaluated by nontesting techniques such as the rating of pupil-made products, or observation of a pupil's classroom performance, or the nature and extent of an individual child's behavior during selected science activities. Consider science fairs and the children's exhibits as an example. In addition to being excellent motivators, such activities can furnish the supervisor and teacher with many opportunities for evaluating how well given pupils are progressing towards pertinent goals of the science curriculum. Does the exhibit present scientific information clearly? Are the details of the exhibit relevant to the main concept? Can the student explain his exhibit so that it is obvious that he understands the principles involved? Such nontesting techniques are valuable in judging the progress of students and the effectiveness of programs.

Dependable evaluation is recognized as fundamental to both effective teaching and effective learning. Thus, evaluation procedures used by a teacher with his class can serve such functions as:

(1) Providing feedback information for the teacher and helping him decide how effective a given amount of teaching has been.
(2) Supplying diagnostic information concerning individual pupils.
(3) Providing motivation for students. As pupils see progress toward established goals, they can be motivated to further learning.
(4) Affording sound evidence for differentiating among pupils.

1. Defining Objectives

The first and most important step in evaluating teaching and learning is to define the objectives that are to be attained, and questions like the following may prove useful:

a. What problem-solving abilities is the student expected to achieve? Can he describe what he saw when he watched a candle being snuffed as a jar covered it? Can he formulate hypotheses about the observed phenomena? Can he plan experiments to test his hypotheses?

b. What information is the student expected to acquire? Has he learned the components of air? Does he know about changes in percentages of these components depending upon altitude or other variables?

c. What skills is he supposed to display? Can he measure amounts of air that are consumed by a candle burned in a jar? Can he manipulate science equipment so that he can perform experiments with air?

d. How is he expected to reveal his attitudes? Does he defer judgment when he observes a demonstration? Does he consider the reliability of a source of information?

e. What applications of his knowledge is the student expected to make? Can he apply what he learned about candles burning in a jar to other problems involving combustion? Does he understand that rusting of iron is another form of oxidation?

All school programs have objectives, but too often these are stated in very general terms and are vague and unclear. Before a supervisor or teacher can determine whether a student has reached certain objectives, he must be able to identify specifically what the student was supposed to achieve. For example, "to help students develop a wholesome attitude toward science" or "to help students appreciate the methods of science" are purposes that have little meaning and would not be useful as guides for evaluation. Objectives must be clearly and specifically defined in terms of pupil behavior, and the performance expected of a student if the objective has been achieved must be specified. If a teacher is unable to list the characteristic behaviors of a student who has reached a particular objective, it is meaningless.

The job of defining objectives in terms of student behavior is recognized as an extremely difficult one, but it is basic to effective evaluation. For example, consider the long-term goal "to help children learn some techniques of problem-solving." Among the specific pupil behaviors that might be expected when this goal is achieved are the abilities to:

(1) State a variety of hypotheses concerning the problem,
(2) Plan experiments for testing these hypotheses,
(3) Report observed phenomena, and
(4) Generalize from what has been observed.

As a second example, the long-term science goal "to help children develop rational attitudes toward the world around them" may be cited. When this is specified in terms of pupil behavior, it might require that the child be able:

(1) To identify certain superstitions, and
(2) To identify sources of information and consider their dependability.

In every science unit, certain of the attitudes, skills, and techniques that have been defined generally must be spelled out so that they relate to the science to be taught. Thus, in a study of weather, growing out of the goal of identifying superstitions might be the following immediate objectives. The pupil can:

(1) Distinguish between "weather superstitions" and "weather facts," and
(2) Offer explanations for the origins of some "weather superstitions."

In a similar manner, the goal of identifying sources of information and considering their dependability might be formulated as the following objective. The pupil can:

> Compare the reliability of weather information from such varied sources as the United States Weather Bureau and the *Farmer's Almanac*.

The examples cited above suggest only a few of the kinds of behavior which would indicate achievement of the desired goals. There are, in every case, many different kinds of behavior which could be examined. In fact, there are far too many behavioral characteristics for adequate consideration by teachers in elementary school classrooms, and some of the desired behaviors, while very important, do not lend themselves to evaluation in classroom situations. What the teacher must do is to choose those particular behavior patterns which he feels are important and measurable within the framework of his classroom, and use them as his criteria for evaluation.

2. Assigning Relative Emphasis to Objectives

Every unit in elementary school science has a variety of objectives which students are expected to attain. However, all of the objectives are not of equal importance. If an objective has been assigned major emphasis, it should be allotted a greater proportion of the class time; other objectives, which have been assigned lesser emphasis, should be allotted relatively smaller amounts of time. Therefore, to simplify the process of planning a unit of study, the weight assigned to each objective should be specified. This can be easily accomplished by using the numerical scale of 100 and distributing numerical weights to each objective. Higher weights should be assigned to major objectives and lower weights to minor objectives. If the objectives are all determined to be of equal importance, equal weight should be assigned to each.

This simple system of assigning weights to objectives has real value for the teacher in planning both the content and the evaluation. He now has a measure for determining how much class time should be allotted to the achievement of each objective, as well as an index of the degree to which the objective should be emphasized in the evaluation process. For example, if major emphasis is placed on helping students learn to use the microscope, this should be emphasized to a similar extent in the total evaluation of the student's achievement. If identifying the parts of the microscope is considered a minor objective, it should receive relatively little emphasis in the appraisal process.

The procedure of assigning weights to objectives does not have to follow a rigid formula but may be as flexible as a teacher desires. The emphasis allotted in a classroom quiz may differ from the emphasis assigned in a weekly test. In addition, the distribution of emphasis may be modified from group to group, depending on such factors as the students' readiness for achieving certain objectives, their current interests, and the availability of necessary materials and equipment for developing particular areas of the elementary science program. But regardless of what evaluation procedure is used, the important factor is that the procedure be planned so that it achieves the purpose for which it was intended.

3. Outlining the Content

Once the objectives have been clearly specified and defined, the next important step in the evaluation process is outlining the content. The content of the unit or area of study becomes the actual means of achieving the objectives. The term "curriculum" frequently is defined as a means to behavioral ends. The content of a unit is the curriculum for attaining the specific behavioral objectives of that unit. By outlining the content, the teacher is able to relate the particular objective to the method of achieving the objective. Frequently, the same content can be utilized in attaining several objectives; sometimes a variety of methods have to be developed for achieving a single objective. For example, if an objective of a science unit is to help children learn to use measuring instruments such as thermometers, the content might include activities like reading daily temperatures in and outside of the classroom, measuring temperatures in sun and shade, or measuring temperatures of hot and cold liquids. This content also could be used for achieving other objectives relating to heat absorption, heat reflection, heat transfer, or insulation.

Another way in which outlining the content can have value for the teacher is in predetermining the specific materials and equipment which must be available for achieving certain objectives. If children are to use thermometers, such instruments must be available in sufficient quantity so that each child may have several opportunities for using the instrument. If skill in doing reference work about geologic periods is in the objective, a variety of appropriate books on historical geology must be available so that each child may read from various sources and compare the information obtained.

Although this may appear to be a time-consuming task for the teacher, it actually can simplify the ardous job of preparing conventional lesson plans and, in addition, specify the evaluation procedure to be used in determining student progress toward particular objectives. A simple way of arranging objectives, content, and evaluation for a unit is to use a three-column table. The first column would contain the objectives; the second column would indicate the methods and materials necessary for achieving each objective; and the third column would specify the type of evaluation procedure to be used in determining student achievement of each objective.

In the first table one objective requires two procedures for evaluation:

OBJECTIVE	METHODS AND MATERIALS	TYPE OF EVALUATION
The ability to record and interpret temperature data from information gathered using outdoor thermometers	Make simple bar graphs of the daily temperature as found at noon in the shade next to the building. Use the graphs to find significant temperature information; make comparisons among the days studied and also among reading made by different children.	Examine the charts prepared by each child. Does the chart show that the child can make an accurate and understandable table of data. Devise written questions to be answered by individual children, each using his own chart: Which day was hottest? Which day was coldest?

OBJECTIVE	METHODS AND MATERIALS	TYPE OF EVALUATION
	Have sufficient supply of outdoor thermometers so that variations in readings can be observed.	On which two days was the temperature about the same at noon.
	Have necessary graph grids prepared so that each child has appropriate equipment.	

In the second table, two objectives may be evaluated through a single procedure:

OBJECTIVE	METHODS AND MATERIALS	TYPE OF EVALUATION
The ability to use library resources to do reference work	Introduce the use of the card catalog and encylopedias, to show a) How to search out appropriate references; b) How to make summaries; c) How to make a bibliography.	Examine the summaries for accuracy of reporting, comparison of material found in different sources, completeness of bibliography, comprehension of content.
The ability to prepare a summary of information found on the last glacial period in North America	Have each child find at least four appropriate references.	
	Make sure there are sufficient references for the children's use.	
	Make sure there are reading materials at the appropriate reading level for each of the children.	

EVALUATION TECHNIQUES

The teacher who is concerned with evaluation will recognize that he must select appropriate evaluation methods for each of his educational objectives. For certain objectives, the overt behavior of the student—in the classroom situation, in the library, in the laboratory—would yield the most appropriate information. For other objectives, where opportunities for students to demonstrate their actual behavior are very limited or do not exist, pencil-and-paper tests would be more satisfactory. Some objectives are more difficult to measure than are others; for some, appropriate measuring devices have not yet been developed. However, because of the intimate relationship which exists between the objectives and evaluation, objectives must be stated in concrete and specific ways if evaluative results are to lend themselves to precise statements; objectives that are stated in vague and general terms result in evaluation methods that yield incomplete and inaccurate results.

The various kinds of evaluation—observation of student behavior, appraisal of student projects, and the variety of paper-and-pencil tests—yield a wide range of information. But unless sufficient use is made of the results of such observations, appraisals, and measurements, they become a waste of time both for the supervisor or teacher and for students. Such evaluative techniques have three basic uses. In the first place, they can provide a means for assessing the growth of individual students. Secondly, such devices can help each student know his strengths and weaknesses. Finally, through the use of these techniques, a supervisor or teacher can learn how well the objectives of a program are being met.

It must be remembered, however, that the supervisor or teacher is the ultimate evaluator. A test or other evaluative device can gather information about a student or a program. But only the evaluator can look at this information, weight it, add and subtract related data, and come up with an appraisal of where a student is in relation to his potential, or how well a program is attaining its stated objectives.

1. Selection of Appropriate Devices

There is no single evaluation procedure which is best for judging student achievement. Each method has its advantages and limitations, depending on the situation in which it is used. The key to selecting the most appropriate technique is the behavioral objective the teacher wishes to measure. How should a teacher appraise a child's ability to work cooperatively with others on a science problem? A written test for this kind of appraisal would be pointless. Observation of the students in a variety of classroom situations would seem more appropriate in determining progress toward this objective, but even "observation" has its limitations and must not be counted on for evaluating too many objectives. Two criteria for the effectiveness of observation as an evaluative technique are suggested:

(1) Can the desired behavior be evoked in the classroom?
(2) Has the teacher sufficient opportunity to observe and record what he sees?

Take another example: How should skill in setting up laboratory apparatus be measured? Often, teachers wishing to make such a determination give a written test and make their evaluations on the basis of such test results. A moment's consideration, however, shows that such tests are nowhere near as appropriate as having the student actually carry out the desired laboratory procedure. In fact, it is quite conceivable that students could answer correctly all the questions relating to the ways in which a Bunsen burner should be lit, but, placed in the actual laboratory situation, be unable to light the burner correctly and safely. Again, the kind of test that is given must be determined by the kind of behavior to be observed and evaluated.

Under what conditions, then, are pencil-and-paper tests appropriate? What can such tests indicate? If the teacher is concerned with determining how well students 'can explain certain phenomena, compare materials from several sources, make inferences, draw conclusions, or select significant factors, pencil-and-paper tests are appropriate vehicles.

It is also necessary to recognize that for measuring certain desired outcomes present devices for evaluating student behavior are still inadequate. Results of attempts to evaluate such behaviors are highly unreliable and must be treated with this fact in mind. One such behavior pattern relates to the use of science information in the choice of a well-balanced diet. Obviously, young children are not in a position to purchase and prepare their own meals. Thus, the desired behavioral objective cannot be measured adequately at this time. In short, each teacher must recognize what he is trying to measure and to what extent his measuring device is effective.

2. Validity and Reliability of Evaluation Techniques

There are two important factors that teachers must consider before using any procedure or instrument for determining student growth. The first and foremost factor is validity, the second is reliability. An instrument is valid insofar as it measures what it is supposed to measure. An instrument is reliable insofar as it measures accurately. A thermometer can be perfectly reliable in that it measures temperature accurately, but the thermometer alone hardly would yield valid results in measuring the caloric content of a substance.

The distinction between reliability and validity can be seen clearly when one examines the stated objectives of a given science program and then considers almost any of the currently available achievement tests in elementary school science. The tests all report high reliability. In general, these reports are true; the tests do measure accurately what they set out to measure. But an inspection of the content of these tests and a comparison of the items in the test to the stated objectives of a particular science class readily show that there is little relationship between the items found in the test and the objectives for which elementary science is being taught. Actually, the validity of these tests for measuring what is being taught in science classes is extremely low. The ideal evaluation technique must serve the purposes for which it is intended and it must yield information that is accurate.

Since validity is so important in evaluation, teachers must be very much concerned with this factor both in selecting commercial testing instruments for measuring the work of the students in their classes and in preparing their own instruments. The validity of any teacher-made instrument will depend on the degree of correspondence between the behavior that is to be appraised and the objectives that have been set for given instruction. It is for this reason that so much emphasis has been placed on identifying the behavioral objectives as the first step in the evaluation process. If the teacher can spell out the way in which a student will act after he has learned a given item or successfully mastered a given unit of work, he can then construct valid evaluative instruments by developing situations in which the student will be able to indicate how effectively he has mastered the desired behavior. For example, if it is desired that a student know the parts of an electric motor, a pencil-and-paper test which requires the student to describe these parts could be satisfactory.

However, suppose the stated objective of a unit is to develop an understanding of the interrelationships of the parts of an electric motor. A test which asks students only to identify or describe the parts of the motor would not be valid in relation to the stated objective. Some kind of test situation which determined the extent to which the student understood the interrelationships among the parts would be necessary. A valid test might ask the student to explain the relationship of the armature to the brushes. Or he might be asked to explain the relationship between the stator and the rotor. For the test situation to be valid, it must elicit responses that are very similar or identical to the objectives of the unit being studied.

Another important factor which teachers should be aware of both in selecting and in making valid instruments is the vocabulary used for the test situation. If a test or an item in a test is worded so that it can be understood by only a few students in the class, such an item is not valid for measuring the learning outcomes of the other members of the class. This is especially true in the primary grades, but also holds true for other groups in which there are wide variations in reading ability and comprehension.

Reliability of commercially prepared testing materials is generally not a problem. Such materials usually are carefully designed and controlled for reliability. But the reliability of teacher-made classroom tests depends upon a few special considerations. The usual and conventional methods of developing reliable tests of the standardized variety generally are impractical for teacher-made tests. However, since the major reasons for the low reliability of teacher-made tests are that such tests are either too short or too difficult, remedies can be found which will help teachers prepare more reliable tests.

First, teachers should include large numbers of items in the test; second, each test should include an adequate number of items which most students will be able to answer. For example, if a test is to be constructed to determine the ability of students to classify foods as proteins, carbohydrates, or fats, listing merely three foods—nuts, dried beans, and apples—would make a test that has little reliability and, incidentally, little validity. To improve the reliability of the test, large numbers of foods of each of the three categories would need to be included. Furthermore, among the items included would need to be simpler ones such as meat, butter, and sugar. Adequate samplings must be included if an evaluation device is to have high reliability and high validity.

Finally, adequate samplings are needed so that the teacher can determine how well—to what extent—a student is meeting the objectives which have been established for him and for the class as a whole. It is the student's performance on the samples included in a test that enables the teacher to judge the student's progress in the total area which has been studied. To obtain sound results for such evaluations, test samples must be sufficiently large and sufficiently varied in difficulty.

CATEGORIES OF CLASSROOM TESTS

The classroom test is still the foundation of the day-to-day evaluation program of most schools. Yet many of these tests have poorly framed items, confusing directions, ambiguous statements, and other flaws that seriously impair the usefulness of the scores they yield. Some of the basic principles of test construction are summarized below so that teachers will be able to derive full value from the use of these instruments in evaluating student growth.

Classroom tests generally are classified into two broad categories, essay tests and objective tests. The essay or free-response examination permits the student to compose and express his answer in his own words. The response may range from a few sentences to several pages, and the accuracy and quality of the response is judged subjectively by a person who is competent in the field.

Objective tests restrict the student's response to a symbol, word, or phrase, and subjective judgment is practically eliminated in determining the accuracy of the answer. The term "objective" as applied to objective tests refers to the scoring of the response and not to the choice of the content. Objective-test items generally are classified as supply or selection items. In responding to a supply item, the student provides the necessary word, phrase, or symbol. In responding to a selection item, the student chooses a response from among those presented to him.

1. Essay Tests

Essay tests have certain advantages that cannot be matched by any other form of evaluation. The chief merit of the essay item is that it provides the student with an opportunity to demonstrate the degree to which he can analyze a problem, select relevant information, present evidence, and organize his answers logically and effectively. In addition, since no answer need be competely right or completely wrong, it is possible for a teacher to determine the degree of correctness of a student's response.

Despite these distinct advantages, essay tests have come under considerable attack in recent years because of certain glaring weaknesses. Many essay tests, as they are currently used in various schools, measure nothing more than the ability to reproduce information. Merely phrasing a question in essay form does not automatically guarantee that progress toward such goals as recognizing causal relationships, applying principles, or making generalizations will be assessed. In addition to poor design of questions, the essay test frequently suffers from inadequate sampling, from highly subjective and inconsistent scoring, and from the influence of such extraneous and irrelevant factors as literary skill and handwriting. However, these are weaknesses that can be overcome, and the following guidelines are suggested to help teachers develop greater skill in designing appropriate items and in improving their methods of evaluating student answers.

a. Limit the use of essay items to those objectives that are measured most efficiently by the essay format. For example, the question:

What is the accepted composition of air at sea level? tests only for specific facts, namely, the percentages of various components of air. It illustrates inefficient use of an essay item. The essay item should be reserved for evaluating progress toward more complex educational goals than merely reproducing information. The following example, based on the same general topic, is more appropriate for an essay item:

Compare the composition of the air of a large community and a small farm community, and account for the differences.

In answering this question, the student would have to demonstrate his ability to use information to interpret data.

b. Improve effectiveness of essay items by requiring the student to use knowledge in situations that have not been discussed directly in class. Thus, if students have studied the use of the lever, inclined plane, and wheel, the following instruction might be appropriate:

There is a large stone in the playground which is too heavy to lift and carry away. Explain how you could use simple machines to remove the stone.

In this situation, the student would be using information learned in class to solve a problem that has not been discussed previously.

Another example providing the student with an opportunity to demonstrate his ability to apply principles might result from a study of the properties of metals. In this case, the student could be asked to:

Explain three ways in which you could test the "lead" in a pencil to determine if it is a metal.

Similarly, after a study of experimental procedures, the student could be presented with the following situation:

John heard that weak tea makes plants grow better than tap water. He set up an experiment to find out if this is true. First, he obtained two identical plants.

He kept one plant on the shelf along the wall and the other plant on the window sill. He watered each plant daily. He used tap water on one plant and a weak tea solution on the other plant. He found that the plant which was given the tap water grew better than did the plant that was given a weak tea solution.

The student then could be asked any number of questions relating to this situation, such as:

On the basis of this experiment, should John conclude that tap water is better for plants than weak tea? Why?

or:

How would you perform the experiment to determine if weak tea is better for plants than tap water?

Naturally, the quality of the response would depend upon the grade level of the students, their familiarity with experimental methods, and their ability to make accurate inferences.

c. Frame essay items that measure ability to apply principles, recognize relationships, or make generalizations more effectively by starting with such phrases as "Explain how," "Explain why," "Compare," "Interpret," "Show the relationships," and "Give reasons for." Essay items which start with such words as "what," "who," or "list" generally require that the student merely reproduce certain facts. Essay items that start with such phrases as "What is your opinion of" or "What do you think of" are usually inappropriate for measuring various facets of educational achievement. Frequently, the teacher who uses this type of phrase actually is concerned with the student's ability to analyze a situation or support a particular position and not with the giving of a personal opinion. Therefore, it would be preferable for the teacher to rephrase the question so that the desired response could be elicited.

d. Word essay questions clearly so that the answers which students give will be limited to the specific objectives which are being measured. Too often essay items are so vague and ill-defined that pupils are forced to guess what the teacher wanted. If a student guesses wrong through no fault of his own, or if he interprets a question one way while the teacher wants a different interpretation, the responses become impossible to score, and the advantage of using essay items is lost. Thus, the question:

What effect will atomic energy have on the world? is much too broad and vague. The response could be limited to the destructive properties of atomic energy, or the constructive uses to which it can be set, or both. To be sure that each student will interpret it the same way, the following statement is better:

Plans are now being made for the peacetime use of atomic energy. Give two examples of how atomic energy could be used in agriculture.

In the rephrased statement, there is no uncertainty about what is wanted and about the specific areas to be discussed.

e. Allow sufficient time for students to answer essay questions. Since essay items are used to evaluate the more complex educational goals which require a good deal of thought, the student must have adequate time for analyzing the question, organizing his answer, and then writing it. When students are pressed for time, their responses frequently show careless thinking and sloppy writing.

f. Score every objective that is to be measured by the essay question independently. The grading of correct factual information should be judged separately from the grading of organization of material. If grammar, spelling, or writing style are included in the objectives of the unit, these areas should also be scored, but scored separately from the other educational objectives. If only a single score is given for an essay response, the student has no way of knowing how well he has progressed toward each of the objectives established for the particular science unit.

g. Prepare scoring guides in advance. By so doing, judging essay responses can be made more reliable. One of the chief disadvantages of using essay questions has been the inconsistency of the scoring methods. Not only have different teachers reading the same answer come up with divergent scores, but the same teacher reading the same answer has reported different scores on different days. To eliminate such inconsistencies, teachers can prepare a model answer in advance, indicating the factors that should be covered and the credits assigned to each factor. This guide can provide a more uniform basis for evaluating the written responses of each student.

h. Administer several essay tests during the school year to increase the sampling of subject matter. Generally, adequate subject matter sampling can be obtained more satisfactorily through the use of other measuring devices. However, where the essay test is the best instrument for measuring progress toward a goal, it should be used. In essay tests, adequate sampling of subject matter can only be provided for by increasing the number of essay items used. This is not feasible because of limitations of class time; therefore, several tests are necessary.

2. *Objective Tests*

The objective test was introduced into the classroom to overcome some of the weaknesses of the essay test. One obvious advantage of the objective test is that it permits extensive sampling of the topics covered, whereas the essay test tends to limit the amount of subject matter that can be sampled. Another advantage of the objective test is that the answers can be scored quickly and objectively. In the essay test, scoring is generally time-consuming and sometimes unreliable. The major complaint made against the use of the objective item is that it tends to measure bits of superficial and random information rather than broad understandings and more complex abilities. But this limitation, when examined carefully, seems to be more the fault of the person constructing the test items than of the inherent nature of the test itself. Items can be constructed that test not only for knowledge but also for the more complex abilities of understanding and reasoning. However, designing such items for an objective test is far more difficult than preparing similar items for an essay test.

It is no longer a question of which kind of test to use because both essay and objective tests can be used to advantage in the classroom. The most important factor is how well an item is constructed. A poorly constructed test fails to achieve its purpose and actually can interfere with the learning process. Therefore, certain guiding principles are offered here to assist the teacher in constructing objective tests so that greater benefits will be derived from the classroom evaluation program.

A. SUPPLY ITEMS. One major type of objective-test item is the supply item. In a supply-item test, the student is required to provide information, usually in the form of a word or a phrase. Generally speaking, there are two kinds of supply items, the short-answer and the completion item. If the problem is presented in question form, it is a short-answer item. If the problem is presented as an incomplete statement, it is a completion item. The following examples show how the same information can be elicited from both forms:

(1) Short Answer: What is the source of energy in a flashlight?
    Completion: The source of energy in a flashlight is _____.
(2) Short Answer: What is the atmospheric pressure at sea level in pounds per square inch?
    Completion: The atmospheric pressure at sea level in pounds per square inch is _____.
    or: The atmospheric pressure at sea level is _____ pounds per square inch.
(3) Short Answer: What is the chemical formula for hydrochloric acid?
    Completion: The chemical formula for hydrochloric acid is _____.

Supply items emphasize recall of information and are satisfactory for measuring knowledge of specific facts, names, dates, and simple computations. In addition, supply items allow the teacher to sample a large body of subject matter in a relatively brief period of time. In a supply test, the probability of a student guessing the correct answer is reduced to a minimum. However, these items are not well suited for measuring the more complex abilities of understanding and reasoning.

Suggestions for Constructing Supply Items

(1) Design items that avoid misinterpretation and require one correct response. The following shows how a poorly stated item can be improved:

Poor: The two most common gases in the air are _____ and _____.

Although the teacher expects students to respond with "oxygen" and "nitrogen," it would not be surprising to find some pupils responding with "invisible" and "important" or any two other qualities. It would be difficult to score such an answer since it is actually correct even though it is not the answer desired.

Improved: The names of the two most common gases in the air are _____ and _____.

(2) Design items that require only one or two completions to be made in a statement. When statements are interrupted by many blanks, the meaning of the item is destroyed, and students are forced to resort to guessing.

Poor: A _____ is an _____ for measuring the _____ of the air.
Improved: A barometer is an instrument for measuring the _____ of the air.

(3) Place blanks near or at the end of a statement. When blanks are placed at or near the beginning of statement, the student generally must read the statement twice before being able to supply the answer.

Poor: A(n) _____ measures the speed of the wind.
Improved: The speed of the wind is measured by a(n) _____.

(4) Do not provide clues to the correct answer. In the previous example, the article is listed as "a" or "an" so that the student who does not have accurate information cannot guess at the correct response. In addition, the length of the blank should not offer the student a clue to the length of the word omitted. It is a good policy to make all blanks a uniform length, but long enough so that the child has room to write his answer.
(5) Specify the units in which a numerical answer is to be given.

Poor: The freezing point of distilled water is _____ degrees.
Improved: The freezing point of distilled water is _____ degrees Fahrenheit.

B. SELECTION ITEMS. Another major group of objective tests is the selection item. In a selection test, the student is required to select a response from among those presented to him. Selection items are also referred to as recognition items and include true-false, multiple choice, and matching items.

(1) True-false items

The true-false test is perhaps the most widely used of all selection tests. It generally consists of a simple declarative statement to be judged true or false, such as:

True.   False.   It is the oxygen in the air which supports combustion.

A variation of the traditional true-false test is sometimes employed which requires the student to correct the item if it is false. The student must supply the correct answer in the blank provided, for example:

The sun is a planet. True. (False.) <u>Star</u>

This modified true-false item helps to reduce guessing, and thus provides the teacher with more valid information about the student's knowledge.

The chief advantage in using true-false tests is that the teacher can sample a large body of subject matter in a short period of time. However, the tests are appropriate only for measuring specific pieces of information, rather than broad understandings. True-false items are also very difficult to construct because they have to be limited to statements that are either completely true or absolutely false. As a result, many of the items that are seen on true-false tests are ambiguous and pose difficult problems, especially for the bright student. Another weakness of true-false tests is that they encourage guessing.

Suggestions for Constructing True-False Items

(a) Use statements that are completely true or absolutely false. One of the glaring weaknesses of true-false items is that the capable student generally can think of certain exceptions, and thus finds them difficult to answer, as in this example:

Poor: T. F. The boiling point of water is 212° Fahrenheit.

Improved: T. F. The boiling point of distilled water at sea level is 212° Fahrenheit.

In the first example, certain information related to atmospheric pressure and kind of water is omitted, which might pose a real problem for these students who see the need for additional qualifications before answering the statement as true. The second example takes these factors into account.

(b) Avoid using specific determiners that give students clues to the probable answer. Words that tend to identify a statement containing them as true or false are called specific determiners. For example, such words as "always," "never," "none," and "all" are found in statements that are likely to be false. On the other hand, words such as "sometimes," "may," "usually," and "could" are found in statements likely to be true, as for example:

T. F. Evaporation *always* takes place more rapidly in summer than in winter.

T. F. Evaporation *sometimes* takes place more rapidly in summer than in winter.

In the above examples, a student without specific knowledge in the area could probably answer these statements correctly by using the specific determiners "always" and "sometimes" as clues.

(c) Avoid using negative statements. Negatives tend either to confuse students by complicating the meaning of the statement or to cause careless errors when students overlook them, as in the following:

T. F. Mercury is *not* a metal.

(d) Avoid lengthy and involved statements. On the one hand, statements that are lengthy are frequently true. On the other hand, they needlessly prevent the pupil from readily recognizing the important factor in the item, for example:

T. F. When a person moves from New York City to Denver, he finds that the reduced atmospheric pressure at higher altitudes alters the forces exerted on water molecules, and as a result, water changes to steam at a lower temperature than along the seacoast.

(e) Avoid using statements that are partly true and partly false. This again leads to confusion and obscures the real purpose of the test item.

T. F. Oxygen, a gas which supports combustion, was discovered by Newton in 1736.

(2) Multiple-choice items

A second type of selection item is the multiple-choice test. In a multiple-choice item, the student is given an introductory statement, called the stem, and several alternative answers from which he must select the one that is most appropriate. The introductory statement or stem may be in the form of a question or an incomplete statement as follows:

Question form: Which of the following foods is the best source of vitamin C?
(a) raisins   (b) grapefruit   (c) pears   (d) cherries

Incomplete statement: We get the most iron from a normal serving of
(a) fish   (b) veal   (c) liver   (d) ham

Incomplete statement: We get the highest caloric value from one ounce of
(a) lean beef   (b) banana   (c) white bread   (d) butter

In the above examples, four options are included for each stem. There is no fixed rule regarding the number of options used, but generally four or five possible responses are listed because guessing is then reduced to a minimum. With younger children, however, fewer options can be given without destroying the effectiveness of the item.

The multiple-choice item is considered the most valuable and most flexible of all objective items. It can be used to measure the degree to which a student can recall factual knowledge as well as measure the degree to which he can use the more complex abilities of understanding and reasoning. Many content areas can be sampled adequately even though the amount of time needed for answering multiple-choice items is greater than for true-false items.

The most serious drawback of multiple-choice items is that plausible distractors are difficult to construct. As a result, teachers sometimes use options that are obviously incorrect or resort to such alternatives as "all of these" or "none of these," which are more often wrong answers rather than right answers. It would be preferable for teachers to use fewer options than to weaken the multiple-choice item by presenting distractors that do not seem plausible to the student. Another limitation of the multiple-choice item is that it cannot measure the ability of pupils to organize and present their ideas.

Suggestions for Constructing Multiple-Choice Items

(a) Word the stem clearly and meaningfully. The stem should present a single problem adequately. Teachers who have had little experience in constructing multiple-choice items probably will find that it is easier to state the central problem when the stem is in the form of a question than when it is in the form of an incomplete statement. When an incomplete statement does not present a specific problem, the alternatives merely become a series of independent true-false statements with the student deciding which one is more correct than the others, for example:

> Poor: A study of plants tells us that
> 1) green plants store food only in leaves and stems
> 2) some green plants grow from bulbs
> 3) green plants need only air, heat, and water to stay alive
> 4) green plants and animals do not have common needs.

It is rather obvious that this item does not present a definite problem. Instead of the student being asked to select the best of four choices concerning a single problem, he actually is involved in deciding which of four somewhat related true-false statements is more true than the others. One suggestion which has been made for determining whether there is a central problem in the stem of a multiple-choice item is to cover the alternatives and see whether the stem, standing by itself, points to a definite problem. This would not be the case in the stem illustrated above. However, it could be improved as follows:

> Improved: A study of the ways in which green plants react to sunlight shows . . .

(b) Include in the stem as much of the item as is possible and especially any words that would otherwise have to be repeated in each alternative. Thus, items are improved because after reading the stem, the student knows exactly what to look for before he examines the alternatives, as in the following:

The temperature of the water for sterilizing baby bottles at home should be 1) 112° F., 2) 212° F., 3) 100° F., 4) 312° F.

(c) Design distractors that are plausible to students. The distractors should appear to be reasonable answers to students who do not have the knowledge required by the item. When some alternatives are obviously incorrect, students with inadequate understanding of the material can arrive at the correct response by the process of elimination, for example:

> Poor: The process of nuclear fission normally is started in a nuclear reactor by
> 1) neutrons hitting atomic nuclei
> 2) earthquakes
> 3) releasing electrons
> 4) volcanic explosions

This item can be improved by substituting for the implausible responses 2) and 4) new responses that are more closely related to the others, such as:

> Improved: The process of nuclear fission normally is started in a nuclear reactor by
> 1) neutrons hitting atomic nuclei
> 2) uniting atomic nuclei
> 3) releasing electrons
> 4) neutralizing protons

(d) State the problem in positive form. The use of negatives tends to confuse the student and causes careless errors.

> Poor: Which of the following is not an element?
> 1) mercury 2) oxygen 3) salt 4) hydrogen

> Improved: Which one of the following is an element?
> 1) mercury 2) peroxide 3) salt 4) hydrocarbon

(e) Construct responses that are grammatically consistent with the stem. A correct sentence should be formed when each alternative is attached to the incomplete statement. Cues resulting from grammatical inconsistencies should be avoided.

> Poor: The voltage in an alternating current circuit can be stepped down
>   by a

1) transformer
2) induction coil
3) oscillator
4) alternator

Improved: The voltage in an alternating current circuit can be stepped down
by a
1) transformer
2) rectifier
3) magneto
4) condensor

The grammatical inconsistency in the first example could also be remedied by removing the article "a" from the stem and using the appropriate article with each option.

(f) Use situations that the student has not previously encountered in class when designing items to measure such abilities as reasoning, problem solving, or any of the other higher mental processes. If students are presented with items that have already been used in the text or discussed in the classroom, the teacher may be measuring only rote memory rather than thinking ability.

(3) Matching items

A third type of selection test is the matching-item test. Typically, such a test consists of two columns of items which are to be associated on some directed basis. The first column is called a list of premises and the second column a list of responses. In the simplest form, the two columns have the same number of items, but the matching test can be made more complex by increasing the number of responses or requiring the use of more than one response item for some items in the list of premises. For most elementary school programs, however, the simpler test is more appropriate:

Directions: In the space next to each item in Column I, place the letter of the phrase in Column II which defines it best.

Column I	Column II
_____1. Force	A. The rate of doing work
_____2. Energy	B. A push or pull
_____3. Power	C. Capacity for doing work
_____4. Speed	D. Rate of change of position

Matching tests are particularly well-suited for measuring a large body of factual information in a relatively short period of testing time. Matching tests can show whether a student is able to associate events with persons or places, terms with their definitions, principles with examples, and chemical symbols with names of chemicals. Matching items can be scored quickly and objectively, and when the items are well-designed, guessing is reduced to a minimum. The major disadvantage of the matching test is that its use is restricted to a limited number of subject areas. Since the items must bear some relationship to each other, it is often difficult and even impossible to find a sufficient number of related items in all areas of subject content. Another weakness of the matching test is that good items that are not completely obvious are hard to construct.

Suggestions for Constructing Matching Items

(a) The items in the list of premises and the items in the list of responses should be as homogeneous as possible. One method for determining homogeneity is to see whether all of the items in a column can be described accurately by one term. In the following example, this cannot be done:

Poor: *Column I*

_____1. mammal
_____2. insect
_____3. scientist
_____4. gas

Column II

A. Pasteur
B. cat
C. mosquito
D. hydrogen

It is obvious that the problem presented in this example could be solved by students with the most superficial knowledge merely by the process of elimination. The items are so heterogeneous that no item in Column I could in any way be related to more than a single item in Column II. In the next example, only homogeneous items are used:

Improved: *Column I*

_____1. anenometer
_____2. barometer
_____3. hygrometer
_____4. thermometer

Column II

A. measures atmospheric pressure
B. measures temperature
C. measures wind velocity
D. measures humidity

(b) The directions should specify clearly the basis for matching the items. The purpose in providing explicit directions is to avoid confusion and clarify for the student the task he is to perform even in situations where the basis for matching seems obvious.

Poor: Match items in Column I with Column II.

Improved: The following problem presents a column listing weather instruments and a column listing what they measure. In the space next to each item in Column I, place the letter of the phrase in Column II which defines it best.

(c) The premises and responses should be arranged in logical order whenever possible. If dates are used, they should be arranged chronologically, and if names are used, they should be arranged alphabetically. This simplifies the task for the student and reduces the amount of time needed for answering these items.

C. OBJECTIVE TESTS USING PICTURES. Objective test items based upon pictorial material can be adapted to measuring a variety of objectives including ability to recall information, interpret data, and apply principles. Furthermore, they are versatile enough to be used in all grades of the elementary school and especially for students with limited reading comprehension. Since relatively few words are needed for this sort of item to be understood, the teacher can give the instructions orally. Test items based upon pictures can provide the student with clear and unambiguous problems that are interesting, novel, and realistic. It is true that there are certain topics that do not lend themselves to pictorial representation and that some teachers may be poor artists. Nothing can be done about the first problem, but teachers who have little skill in art can find appropriate material in books and magazines which they can either copy or trace. Just using pictures is of little value unless the pictures improve the test item and communicate the problem more effectively than the words they replace.

The following are examples of objective-test items which are based upon pictorial material:

Directions: Mark an X across the picture that shows a complete circuit.

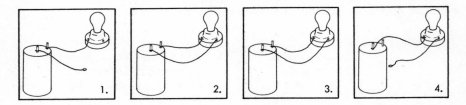

This is an example of a multiple-choice item based on pictorial material. It has been successful in first and second grades with the teacher reading the directions orally.

Directions: Here is a picture of a tree with names of some of its parts printed on it. Use these names to complete the statements about the tree.

1. The food for the tree is made in the _____.
2. The tree is held in the ground by the _____.
3. Water is taken into the tree through the _____.
4. The sap is carried to the branches through the _____.
5. The food for the tree is stored in the _____.

This is an example of a completion item using pictorial material. It has been used successfully in second and third grades. Where children have difficulty reading the statements, the teacher reads the statement orally and the children copy the appropriate word from the picture.

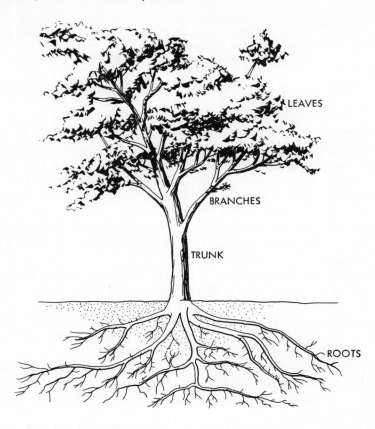

Directions: Look carefully at this picture of a sailboat being moved by the wind. There are two statements about the boat listed below. Mark an X across the word which makes each statement true.

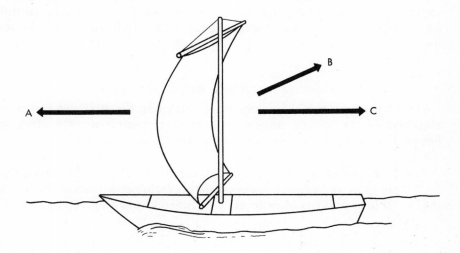

1. This boat will move because the wind is pushing the _____.
   SAIL   WATER   AIR
2. This boat will move toward _____.
   A.   B.   C.

This is another example of a multiple-choice item using pictorial material.

Summary Suggestions for All Testing Procedures

a. Check test items against the objectives of the unit to insure that the items relate to the goals and that the test items adequately cover all of the goals. One method of assuring a proper distribution of items is to use a simple coding system. Each objective can be numbered, and as each test item is constructed, it can be related to the objective by assigning it the appropriate number.

b. Check the reading level of each item so that students who are being evaluated in science are not penalized for deficiencies in reading speed or comprehension.

c. Arrange test items in order of difficulty. This provides for more efficient use of the testing time. When difficult items appear first, many students use up most of their time with a few questions and never have time to answer easier questions which may appear later. Furthermore, students who have difficulty at the beginning of a test may soon become discouraged and give up.

Group items also according to subject matter and to type of item, and always in order of increasing difficulty. This system has real merit because it reduces confusion and helps the student focus more efficiently on the task to be accomplished.

d. Word directions for pupils clearly, specifically, and without ambiguity. The student must know exactly the manner in which he is to select and record his response and also the amount of time allotted for the test.

e. Analyze and classify pupil's responses to tests. They should not just be scored and then forgotten, but can be used by the teacher to gain valuable information regarding student difficulties, teaching techniques, and the test itself.

OBSERVATION USED FOR EVALUATION

One of the most useful techniques for evaluating the attainment of many objectives of the science curriculum is teacher observation of student behavior. For example, two objectives of a unit on microbes might be

(1) To help students learn simple laboratory techniques with which they can grow and prepare micro-organisms for observation and study, and
(2) To help students learn to use a microscope and a microprojector.

Progress toward these objectives can be evaluated best when student behavior is observed in the realistic laboratory situation, but the observation cannot be random or casual. In the first place, the teacher should know exactly what he is looking for. Some indications of a student's ability to use a microscope properly are that he

(1) Handles the instrument with great care.
(2) Cleans the lenses only with lens tissue or with a soft, clean cloth.
(3) Never focuses the microscope downward toward the slides; always moves the objective downward while the eye is away from the eyepiece, and then focuses the microscope upward with the eye looking through the microscope.
(4) Arranges the mirror for optimum amount of light.
(5) Prepares material for observation, using the techniques most appropriate to whatever is being examined; uses depression slides or bridge arrangements for comparatively large material; uses cover slips to cover smaller items.

1. Checklists and Rating Scales

Having determined the desired behaviors, the teacher can prepare a checklist or a rating scale containing a list of all the actions that relate to student behavior in a particular area. By using a check mark, the teacher can record his observations of a student's performance. The following is an example of such a checklist:

	ALWAYS	SOMETIMES	NEVER
Is careful in handling microscope			
Cleans lenses properly			
Focuses instrument properly			
Prepares slides correctly			
Arranges mirror for correct amount of light			

The data yielded by this checklist can indicate how well students have achieved the objective of using a microscope properly. Such information is usually qualitative and subjective, but when teachers know what they are to observe, the subjective generally can be made more objective.

In the same way, to check whether the children have learned the simple laboratory techniques with which they can grow and prepare micro-organisms, direct observation of the students' behavior in the situation will provide the teacher with more accurate evidence for evaluation than will responses by the children to written questions. Obviously, answers to written questions can give some evidence and should be used too. But what is wanted from the children is not so much the ability to verbalize about what they should do, as actions which show that they can conduct themselves in the desired manner.

2. Areas Where Observation Is Indicated

An analysis of many areas of the curriculum reveals long-term goals which depend mainly upon observation for their evaluation. For example, there are goals like assuming responsibility, sharing and communicating with others, practicing proper health habits, developing sound attitudes toward learning, or participating in classroom activities. Attaining such long-term goals is an essential part of the science program. Observation is the most effective way by which to determine how well they are being achieved.

To sum up: Observation as an evaluation technique can be effective if the teacher has a clear understanding of the behavior to be assessed. Furthermore, it is incumbent upon the teacher to provide equal opportunities for all the students to respond in the desired manner; every child must have his chance. This requires a conscious effort on the part of the teacher. Finally, a written record of such observations is not only desirable, it is imperative. How these records are made out—whether they be in anecdotal form, in rating scales, or on check sheets—is not too important. Any of these forms can serve the teacher's purposes. What is essential, however, is that the teacher make a written appraisal of what each child actually has shown himself able to perform in certain areas of behavior according to a set of criteria.

APPRAISING CHILDREN'S PROJECTS

Another very significant way of finding out how well children are meeting the objectives of the science program is the teacher's examination of the material which the children produce. After all, what a child does and what he produces can tell much about the way he meets the objectives of the program. For example, we know that third and fourth-graders are collectors. But collections have little worth from a science point of view unless they are organized. One indication of a scientific attitude is the manner in which a person employs a theme for his ideas, and organizes his facts and information in a planned classification. A teacher of the third or fourth grade will want the children to begin to develop the ability to conceive of such themes and such frameworks, and to organize their collections and categorize them accordingly. Thus, the teacher examines a collection of rocks and looks to see how the rocks are grouped. Are they organized according to the place where the rocks are found? Are they grouped as igneous, sedimentary, and metamorphic? Are they exhibited to show certain interesting phenomena such as weathering, water erosion, or ice scratches? Or are they just a hodge-podge of pretty stones? Neatness, beauty, novelty are all important, but not for science. What is being evaluated as far as science is concerned is the ability to organize and classify materials in a sensible and reasoned way.

Then there are the experiments which children design and the models which they construct to illustrate applications of scientific principles. An analysis of such materials can reveal much more clearly the extent of a student's attainment of the goal of expanded understandings of science than can any paper-and-pencil test. A careful study of such materials is one important way of determining growth toward extended vision and richer insight into the meanings of science and the applications of these meanings to appropriate situations. But such study requires that the teacher be sure about the objectives he is trying to reach. If this evaluation procedure is to have validity, the teacher must appraise a project on the basis of the processes used by the student in reaching his conclusion. Extended vision of one's environment, insight into the scientific concepts derived from facts, and understanding of how such concepts may be applied to specific problems cannot be measured by the quality of the art work involved in lettering the parts of an exhibit. Rather, it is measured by the clarity of thinking that shows in the resultant project. It is measured by the extent to which the exhibit explains a scientific principle through clear and simple examples.

Science reports, too, need this same kind of evaluation. It is not a matter of how many pictures are included in a report. Rather, it is the appropriateness of the pictures as illustrative of the points being made. It is not the length of the report, but the thoughtful organization and clear explanation of the material presented. And, as far as writing goes, a teacher may very well refuse to accept a report from a child because it is not up to the level of neatness or standards of language skill of which he is capable. Misspelled words and poor grammar are not acceptable in science reports any more than they are in English reports. But having to return such a report for rewriting should have no bearing on the science evaluation. In evaluating a science report, the teacher should appraise its worth as science—its accuracy of information, its appropriate explanations, its resultant generalizations, its organization. Science reports must be judged in the light of science objectives.

The teacher must be certain that the objectives upon which the work will be built and upon which it should eventually be appraised are stated in such forms as to indicate the type of resultant behavior desired. If the objective of a weather unit is to have the children understand the water cycle, the exhibit or project which shows, simply and clearly, how water evaporates and then condenses is much more truly an example of sound science thinking than is an elaborate poster of the various kinds of clouds, beautiful as the art work may be. And a simple home-built model of the workings of a gasoline engine—a model made from cardboard, paper fasteners, and crayons —is a much more acceptable project than a plastic cross-sectional, commercial model of a complex Diesel engine, even though the Diesel engine is put together with great care. What is wanted is a demonstration of how children are thinking, of how well they understand the scientific principles which they are studying. The home-built model shows this; the purchased plastic model does not. Only as the teacher knows clearly the kind of behavior he eventually expects from his students, and as he helps his students carry out projects which lead to this kind of behavior, can he develop an adequate basis for evaluating the work which his students produce.

BIBLIOGRAPHY

AHMANN, J. STANLEY and GLOCK, MARVIN. *Evaluating Pupil Growth*. Boston: Allyn and Bacon, Inc., 1958.

AHMANN, J. STANLEY; GLOCK, MARVIN; and WARDEBERG, HELEN. *Evaluating Elementary School Pupils*. Boston: Allyn and Bacon, Inc., 1960.

REMMERS, H. H., and GAGE, N. L. *Educational Measurement and Evaluation*. New York: Harper and Bros., 1955.

THOMAS, R. M. *Judging Student Progress*. New York: Longmans, Green and Co., 1954.

THORNDIKE, ROBERT and HAGER, ELIZABETH. *Measurement and Evaluation in Psychology and Education*. New York: John Wiley and Sons, Inc., 1961.

TORGERSON, T., and ADAMS, G. *Measurement and Evaluation*. New York: The Dryden Press, 1954.

TRAVERS, R. *How to Make Achievement Tests*. New York: The Odyssey Press, 1950.

MATERIALS AND FACILITIES
FOR ELEMENTARY SCIENCE

INTRODUCTION

Of all the areas in the elementary school curriculum, science holds a unique position because it offers countless opportunities for the children to do experiments. When children are able to work with a wide variety of materials, their learning experiences become real rather than vicarious. Not only do the children acquire skill in manipulating the same kind of equipment that scientists use, but they also gain greater insight into the key operations, or processes, of science and the scientist.

The strong interest in science education during the past few years has resulted in the development of comprehensive elementary science programs throughout the country. These programs require adequate amounts of supplies and equipment if they are to be effective. Local, state, and federal authorities recognize this need and have shown their willingness to support elementary science financially. Money is now being allocated in school budgets for the purchase of supplies and equipment. The National Defense Education Act of 1958, Title III, was created to provide the schools with financial aid in purchasing laboratory, demonstration, and other special equipment.

It should be kept in mind that the materials should be built around the program, rather than the program built around the materials. The learning activities selected for the program should determine what science materials will be needed. If the science program has a well-developed curriculum guide, then the materials needed will be those necessary to conduct the learning activities described in the guide. This same rationale would apply if the science program is developed around a single or multiple science textbook series.

As a rule, simple supplies and equipment are used in elementary science. This makes it possible to purchase much more materials, and increases the possibility of allowing the children to experiment individually rather than in groups. Also, simple materials can be re-

placed more easily when they are damaged or broken. Homemade or improvised equipment can be very useful, if the learnings that result are worthwhile and if an inordinate amount of time and effort do not have to be spent in either finding or making the equipment. However, no science program can be maintained by using only homemade equipment. Many commercial materials must be purchased if the program is to be effective.

Very few elementary schools have adequate classroom facilities for teaching science. Each classroom should have a fixed or movable table for conducting experiments and demonstrations. Water should be easily accessible, and there should be electrical outlets in each room. The teacher should be provided with suitable sources of heat, such as a portable gas burner, a hot plate, and an alcohol lamp. Facilities should be provided for classroom storage of supplies and equipment. This can be accomplished by using either commercial or homemade storage cabinets. Another possibility would be the use of wall counters, with storage space and shelves below, installed along one wall of the classroom.

There will also be many items that are used only periodically. These include special pieces of equipment and an assortment of chemicals. All of these materials must be stored. Each school should have its own central storeroom for science materials. If this is not possible under existing conditions, perhaps some space can be allocated in another supply room. If necessary, large storage cabinets could be purchased or constructed and placed in a convenient location.

SCIENCE FACILITIES FOR OUR SCHOOLS K–12 *

National Science Teachers Association

The teaching of science is concerned with helping students understand the facts, concepts, principles, and generalizations of science. Greater emphasis is now given to helping students think critically, be creative in their approach to problem-solving, and develop skills and techniques in the use of scientific methods of thinking and acting. To accomplish these goals and accommodate changing procedures, time, space, and adequate facilities must be provided for a wide variety of learning activities and experiences. This excerpt, a portion of a larger article that deals with science facilities for elementary, junior high, and high schools, discusses nine current trends in science education and their concomitant effects on materials and facilities. Twenty principles for planning facilities are set forth. Finally, specific recommendations are made regarding facilities for elementary school science.

CURRENT TRENDS IN SCIENCE EDUCATION

Facilities that meet today's needs and yet look to the future must be related to trends, just as the trends themselves relate to the evolving goals of science.

An emerging pattern of changes in the teaching of science, as seen by identifiable trends, points toward the necessity for continuous evaluation of facilities and evaluation on the basis of sound educational specifications. Those who are planning facilities for science education today need to weigh their plans in relation to trends in science teaching. The resulting facilities should meet present needs and, at the same time, remain flexible for an evolving science program for the future.

Today's trends indicate . . .

1. Greater emphasis on inductive development of concepts and principles through the discovery or problem-solving approach in science teaching.

* REPRINTED FROM *The Science Teacher*, Vol. 30, No. 8, December 1963, pp. 48–60. Copyright, 1963, by the National Science Teachers Association, Washington, D.C. Reprinted by permission of the publisher.

Less emphasis is placed on the verification "of basic principles through demonstrations and laboratory exercises." As often as feasible, teachers permit students to discover principles for themselves through experimentation and problem-solving. Thus, the teacher often acts as a director of research rather than as the ultimate source of information. At other times, information is obtained through reading, discussion, lecture demonstrations, and even verification exercises.

The laboratories, then, must provide space and equipment for a wide variety of experiments performed by the students under the direction of the science teacher, as well as demonstration facilities. Space for reference work will also be needed.

2. A *shift away from teacher demonstration as a prime method of teaching and toward pupil experimentation.*

At all grade levels, teaching now attempts to involve the student in inquiry and discovery and uses a variety of methods to help the student learn the basic concepts of science. This trend seems to have special importance at the junior high school level since laboratory teaching at this level is thought to result in continued motivation for science study in the senior high school.

All grade levels need instruments, supplies, and equipment that the students can manipulate. Space should be available both inside and outside the building for pupil activity in all areas of science.

3. A *movement toward more pupil-teacher planned experiments and away from simple manipulation directed by detailed instructions.*

There is a decrease in the lockstep of requiring all pupils to perform the same experiment at the same time. The teacher also introduces students to methods of planning and carrying out activities that will test their own hypotheses.

Arrangement of facilities must be such that the teacher can direct varied activities with a minimum of traffic and confusion and with a maximum of safety and control. The kind and arrangement of furniture, the completeness of mechanical and electric services at work stations, and the adequacy of safety arrangements are important for success with this type of science teaching.

4. A *movement toward science for all students and away from science for only the college-bound students.*

Science for all students means not only serving more students but also serving many different levels of ability and motivation.

More classrooms and laboratories will be required, and it will be necessary to provide facilities suitable for a wide range of learning activities and abilities.

5. *The traditional science sequence of general science, biology, chemistry, and physics giving way to other sequences and patterns.*

New units and new courses in the curriculum, as well as renewed emphasis on earth science and the introduction of study about space, all make specific demands for science facilities in the junior and senior high schools.

Facilities will need to be adaptable to the teaching and learning of broad concepts, to the possible merging of certain subjects, and to the new needs of study of earth and space science. Facilities must also be prepared for the introduction of new subjects as well as rearrangement of the old.

6. *More homogeneous grouping of students in science classes.*

Such grouping facilitates flexibility in, and adaptation of, learning experience on various levels of ability and interest. For example, some educators believe that first-hand experiences may be even more important for the slow or average student than for those of greater intellectual ability.

Facilities and equipment should provide for a wide variety of learning experiences and for ways that these experiences can be appropriate to the learning potential and interest of students of all capabilities.

7. *Activities such as science fairs, science clubs, and out-of-class science projects on the increase.*

Any large-scale program of science project work places a heavy burden on school facilities.

Where participation in outside science activities is important to a school, adequate facilities must be provided if all of the objectives of the science program are to be achieved.

8. *Increased use of audio-visual instructional materials by small groups or by individual students.*

It is recognized that there are times, lessons, and objectives for which audio-visual materials are the most appropriate teaching tools available. In other instances, these materials may supplement laboratory or textbook. Such materials have an important role in the teaching and learning of science.

Provision should be made for use of audio-visual materials both by the whole class and by individuals or small groups. Educational television, programed instruction, and other teaching devices may also need to be considered.

9. *Increasing provision for flexibility in design and construction of science facilities.*

This trend reflects the need for changes in room arrangements required by evolving science curricula and the emerging philosophy which places increasing emphasis on learning science through inquiry and discovery. Flexibility also gives the possibility of adapting physical facilities to new methods and procedures and recognizes that there may be several such new methods during the lifetime of the building.

Flexibility in room arrangement will include furniture and major items of equipment, as well as work surfaces, storage space, and teaching materials.

PRINCIPLES FOR PLANNING FACILITIES

The importance of principles to be observed in the design of science facilities was recognized by the National Science Teachers Association in the report of its first study devoted to this phase of science teaching. The introductory chapter of this publication contained a list of "General Principles

Concerning Facilities for Science Instruction." In the study on which this present bulletin is based, respondents to the questionnaire commented on the principles and ranked them in order of importance for those who are planning science facilities today. At least 88 percent of the participants in the current study considered each principle to be valid today. The following list is arranged in order of importance, as they were judged by the present respondents.

1. *School facilities for science should include space for proper storage of all materials related to science.*

Adequate storage for the wide variety of materials and equipment needed in science teaching presents an acute problem in many old and new facilities. This is borne out by the number one rank given this principle. Planners must consider the need for generous and proper storage of such essentials as apparatus, equipment, chemicals, consumable materials, models, charts, audio-visual materials, and tools. Laboratory furniture makers have developed excellent cabinets and shelving for many kinds of storage needs. The quality and flexibility of such furniture will pay big dividends over the years in protecting students and teachers and in reducing loss of apparatus caused by improper or unprotected storage.

2. *The planning of science facilities should utilize the ideas of many qualified persons.*

Architects, administrators, school board members, and also science teachers, supervisors, and laymen in the community should all be a part of the planning team. If plans are to result in the best possible facility, each planner should recognize and respect the areas of competence of the others. Care must be exercised that the whimsy and idiosyncracy of any of the planning team not create unworkable or inflexible facilities. A wise balance between creativity and experience should be sought.

Administrators and teachers, for example, must agree on class sizes, number of classes that will be assigned to each room during a given day, number of periods per week a teacher will have for planning and preparation, and number of teachers using each classroom and laboratory.

The science teacher will often be the team member most able to contribute to the educational specifications area of planning. Such specifications should include the objectives of the science program; the variety of methods, techniques, and procedures that will be used; special requirements of the various courses and units of study; and the projected use of the facility both at the time of its completion and in the future.

3. *The unique needs of science teaching should be anticipated in planning such general features as floors, illumination, heating, ventilation, plumbing, and electrical services.*

The science area requires special planning for materials and structural details required for the science activities. The use of acids, bases, and a variety of solvents should be considered in selecting materials and finishes for floors as well as for laboratory furniture. Laboratory work requires optimum illumination at all work stations. Electric outlets for 110–120 volt alternating current are also essential at most work stations, and other outlets are needed for audio-visual devices and laboratory equipment. Ventilation will often require fume hoods and rapid venting with resultant adjustment in the heating system in cold climates. Plumbing needs include numerous sinks, especially for the biology and general science laboratories.

4. *The amount of space in the science rooms should be adequate for a wide range of essential learning activities.*

To accommodate the number and variety of learning activities taking place in modern science classes, more space per pupil will be required than for more formal academic courses; rooms should be wide, rather than long and narrow; and arrangement of laboratory furniture should help to cut down on traffic and confusion. The need for individual work stations in the laboratories has increased, and teachers have found that rooms with a width of 30 or more feet best accommodate such arrangements. Participants in the study agreed almost unanimously that from 35 to 45 square feet per student was essential for efficient classroom-laboratories.

The concept of a science suite or science center has prevailed in the design of many schools. In addition to the classroom-laboratories, some of the essential areas of such a suite are preparation and storage rooms, reading areas, project laboratories, shop facilities, darkrooms, plant growing areas, and animal rooms. Of the total space used for science, approximately three-fourths should be used for classroom laboratories and one-fourth for preparation and storage rooms, reading areas, project rooms, shop facilities, or other supplementary areas.

5. *Facilities for science instruction should include provisions for students to do individual experimental work.*

Recent trends in science curricula and teaching methods have greatly increased the need for individual experimental work stations. The degree of sophistication of experimental work will vary as the interests and abilities of students vary. Stations for experimentation by all students should be provided, but a project room for highly motivated students must also be included if the maximum potential of these students is to be attained.

6. *Furniture adaptable to class, small group, and individual work should be provided for science rooms.*

This principle is closely associated with the concept of flexibility in science facilities. Recent designs of furniture for science classrooms make possible rapid changes in work areas for a variety of learning activities. The classroom-laboratory in which rapid shifting from class instruction to laboratory work may take place at any appropriate time is an example of such a facility.

Perimeter arrangement of work counters with regularly spaced outlets for utilities allows the use of movable tables and chairs for different arrangement of work spaces. Fixed peninsular work stations also give considerable flexibility for a variety of learning activities.

7. School facilities for science should include provisions for the science teacher to work on plans, records, orders, tests, and the like.

Efficient utilization of the science teacher's time and energy should be considered in planning facilities. Effective science teachers must do as much paper work as do teachers in other academic areas. In addition, they must plan and prepare for many kinds of activities in their daily teaching. They must select and set up the materials and apparatus to be used in the classroom for demonstrations and laboratory experiments. They must select and prepare teaching aids and devices and try them out before the class meets.

Most classrooms and laboratories must be used every period during a school day to accommodate the increasing student population. In such cases a convenient and well-equipped preparation room including outlets for utilities should be provided. This room might also serve as an office for the teacher.

8. Rooms used for science should be so planned and equipped that their flexibility will provide for a variety of uses and for changes and adaptations to meet evolving needs.

Individual laboratory work, small-group activities, whole-class discussions, and demonstrations may require rearrangement of tables and chairs. As curriculum experiences and teaching methods evolve, school facilities must accommodate changes in furniture arrangement and space usage. Walls and utility services should be planned so that expansion of the science facilities into adjoining sections of the building is possible at reasonable costs if new needs become apparent. Increasingly, the rooms themselves are being grouped into a science suite or wing.

9. School facilities for science teaching should make provisions for use of an abundance of real materials and forces.

Developing a functional understanding of science concepts, of cause-and-effect relationships, and of the processes and safeguards of scientific thinking make experiences with real materials and forces essential elements in the methods of science teaching. Facilities must provide space for students to have these first-hand experiences and space for the materials and equipment necessary for a wide variety of such activities.

10. Schools should provide facilities for using audio-visual and other sensory aids in science teaching.

Certain kinds of science learnings may best be accomplished through the use of motion pictures, slides, filmstrips, tape recordings, or television. The need for such supplementary devices and material is important for any quality science program. Thus, the facilities must provide for effective and efficient use of audio-visual devices and materials.

11. Science facilities should permit students and teachers to carry on experimental projects without daily moving or dismantling of equipment.

Rooms for research and experimental projects have become an essential part of science facilities. Teachers must continue to grow in their understanding of science and in their skills in the methods of science. If teachers are to motivate pupils toward continuing in science, they must have an opportunity to demonstrate their own competence in carrying on scientific investigations. The able students may participate in such activities either with their own investigations or as a team working with the teacher on a broader problem.

Space for these activities must be separate from the classroom-laboratory, and at the same time it must be an integral part of the total facility. A well-planned project room with large work stations is needed.

12. School facilities for science should include provisions for students to use published materials in planning their work, interpreting their observations, and studying the activities and findings of scientists.

Students need a place where they can read, think, and plan if they are to experience the processes of the scientific enterprise. Every science classroom, therefore, should contain shelves and files for the wide range of printed materials needed in the science programs—for example, reference books, a variety of texts at different reading levels, pamphlets, research reports, periodicals, and instruction guides for apparatus. These should be readily available in an organized file in the science area, rather than in a library far from the place where they are immediately needed. A reading table and chairs where data can be noted and directions outlined will facilitate use of this resource area of the classroom-laboratory. Some schools are providing carrels, study alcoves, or other arrangements for individual study, either in a classroom or library area.

13. School facilities for science should include provisions for the science teacher to confer with students as individuals or as small groups, and with parents, with the privacy necessary for satisfactory conferences.

The concept of the office-conference room as an integral part of any teaching facility needs no justification in modern schools. Many planners have found that a room which serves both as a preparation room and as a teacher's office is a satisfactory provision for this need. Privacy must be assured, yet easy access to classroom-laboratories and storage areas must be provided. An entrance to the area from the corridor should also be considered to prevent interruption of classes when parents or others come for conferences with the teacher.

14. School facilities for science should reveal that science is a community as well as a school activity.

Many school systems have acquired and developed their own school camps, wooded parks, and nature trails. These areas as well as planetariums installed within the school, become an extension of the science facilities within the community. Learning experiences in earth science, ecology, and conservation are only a few of the science activities carried on in such areas. Supporting areas within the school building would include reference materials as well as space for display of, or work with, specimens brought back from field trips.

Facilities within the school should also offer opportunity for students to hear guest speakers and to be informed—through bulletin board space, for example—of science-related events and programs in the community.

15. Schools should provide facilities where experiments and projects may be carried on for others to observe.

A wider learning experience for all students is made possible through demonstration and exhibit of other students' individual projects. A demonstration table should be available for such student activities. Other areas for exhibiting the results of individual or group experimentation and projects should be provided within the science area.

16. Rooms used for science should be so designed and decorated that they are pleasant and attractive to the students, teachers, and others who use them.

The atmosphere of science as an active process is an important feature of the science classroom-laboratory. Many participants in the study also expressed the belief that students are attracted to science, in part, by the quality and atmosphere of facilities in the school. Both architects and furniture makers have recognized the importance of this principle. Color and form in room decoration and furniture must continue to be used in planning science facilities.

17. School facilities for science should include provision for constructing and repairing science apparatus and equipment.

Science teachers have found that it is often necessary or desirable to improvise equipment for developing an understanding of certain scientific concepts. Students also find the construction of equipment and apparatus for their own individual experiments to be highly effective in developing their understanding of the problem on which they are working. Therefore, an area within the facilities should provide appropriate work surfaces, materials, and tools for the construction of such equipment. This area may also provide for simple repairs on commercially obtained equipment. Safety considerations are important for this area.

18. School facilities for science should include provisions for students and teachers to use mass media in bringing science to the school and community.

Communication between the school and community is important in our democratic society. Moreover, adequate support for the science program in a school may result from the skillful use of mass media in presenting the activities taking place in the classrooms and laboratories. Facilities should provide opportunities for such activities as science assembly programs, science fairs, store window displays, programs for service clubs, television and radio programs, and news-type photographs of science activities in the school.

19. The selection of the site for a new building should be made, in part, with regard for the potential contributions of the site and its surroundings to the teaching of science.

In some instances, farsighted school boards have been able to acquire undeveloped land for school sites and to select and preserve the natural resources of the area for use in the school's science program. "School grounds are becoming increasingly valuable and recognized as important outdoor laboratories for school programs of study in science, agriculture, mathematics and other subjects." Ecology and conservation are receiving increasing emphasis in the new biological curricula. Therefore, it seems essential that the potential of school surroundings be explored and developed for maximum use in learning experiences. With the cooperation of the community, such areas as school gardens, wildflower and rock gardens, arboretums, school forests, wildlife sanctuaries, bog gardens, fish ponds, nature trails, weather stations, and outdoor classrooms should be developed.

20. *School facilities for science should include provisions for displaying both improvised and manufactured products and devices.*

Much learning will occur from observing well-planned displays, and students will often be motivated to further learning in science as a result of such vicarious experiences. Nor should the learning that takes place when students themselves plan and make good displays be overlooked. This activity may be a worthwhile learning experience for some students and may lead to further motivation in classroom activities. Therefore, modern science facilities should include display cases and tackboards, with some of these being placed in corridors as well as in the science rooms. Living things and their habitats are well displayed in the open courts of modern school buildings.

Facilities for Elementary School Science

In its earlier years, science in the elementary school was chiefly nature study. Natural objects were collected, identified, displayed, observed, and talked about. Incidental and accidental happenings made up a large part of the learning experiences in science. Little or no curricular design prevailed, and in many schools no science could be found.

Educators are now increasingly recognizing the importance of a K–12 program in science. They are also recognizing that such programs don't just happen—they must be carefully planned, constantly evaluated and strengthened, and energetically supported. Facilities, of course, play a large part in the program, but first must come understanding of what makes a good program, time planned for the program, and teachers competent to carry it out. Since not all elementary school teachers will be competent in science, administrators must provide inservice training programs, an atmosphere in which teachers are not afraid to try new methods of teaching, and continuing leadership for the program.

Objectives of Science Programs in the Elementary School

Programs of learning in science at the elementary school level should:

1. Provide experiences through which boys and girls can arrive at some of the concepts of science through observation, inquiry, problem-solving, and study of cause-and-effect relationships

2. Provide science experiences planned around activities of significance to boys and girls

3. Organize the learnings in science so that they will result in certain desirable outcomes by the time the child completes the elementary grades —for example, beginnings of habits of systematic observation, of quantitative thinking and representation; some acquaintance with modes of scientific thought; beginnings of a scientific vocabulary; and a desire for scientific explanation

4. Help the child, wherever possible, to apply the methods of science to arithmetic, language arts, and other studies

Space should be arranged and facilities and equipment chosen to support these objectives—not just to demonstrate or to be the center of attention in themselves.

Further guidance in planning for science in the elementary school can be gained from familiarity with apparent trends and recognition of relationship between school organization and facilities for science.

Trends in Elementary School Science

Analysis of replies from persons queried in this study indicate trends in elementary school science toward:

1. *Planning of experience in science.* Such planning includes both scope and sequence of science experiences. The content of the program has been broadened with much more emphasis being given to concepts in the physical and earth sciences.

2. *More adequate instructional materials in science.* This is especially true of printed material. Space is needed for housing and using these materials.

3. *Problem-solving activities in science.* The problem-solving approach, using both materials and equipment from the pupils' own environment and commercial scientific equipment is increasingly central to the elementary science program. No longer is the cluttered table in the science corner adequate for elementary school science teaching.

4. *More effective teachers and better programs for preparing teachers for elementary school science.* A deeper understanding of science for children also requires a greater competence in the use of science facilities.

5. *Increased specialized personnel with competence in science.* Resource teachers and supervisors for elementary science are increasingly being used, often as team teachers with the classroom teachers. The effective use of such resource persons depends, in part, upon the quality and arrangement of the facilities within the elementary school.

Science Facilities in the Self-contained Classroom

The organization of a school has a direct relationship to the kinds of facilities needed. Where the self-contained classroom is in the pattern of kindergarten through grade six, at least two alternatives are possible. In one arrangement, work surfaces, storage space, and electric outlets are provided in each classroom. Flexibility within the room is an essential feature, not only for science activities but for learning activities in all areas of the elementary school curriculum. Chalkboards, tackboard, display areas, provisions for projection, workbenches, movable tables, and storage cabinets are necessary for good elementary teaching whether it be in language arts, social studies, mathematics, art, or science. A reading area with a place for a wide range of printed materials should be available with science materials taking their rightful place among these resources.

A dynamic science program creates special needs to be met within the self-contained classroom. The following provisions are essential:

A work counter with one or more sinks provided with hot and cold water
A convenient electric outlet (110–120 volt AC) for a hotplate at the work counter
Safe sources of heat for experiments, such as the small liquid petroleum burners
Dry cells or a low-voltage direct and alternating current power pack for electrical experiments. (These electric substations may either be portable or permanently installed in the work counter; for safety, they should be installed beyond reaching distance of the sink and its hardware.)

Space for work and for storage should be planned together. Beneath the window ledge, counter tops of sufficient depth provide for some important science activities. They provide space for such things as terrariums and growing plants. Space for an aquarium may be provided but not in a position where it will get long hours of sunlight. When heating units allow, space below work counters can be used for excellent storage spaces for a variety of things for science. Adjustable shelves are essential for efficient use of all cabinet spaces.

Furniture within the room should be movable. Flat-top desks may be placed together for larger work areas, or the furniture can be moved to clear the center of the room for certain essential science activities. At least one suitable table in the elementary classroom is a great aid in carrying on science experiments and projects. The table, and other tables used for experiments, should have an acid- and water-resistant surface. The workbench with its tools for construction of simple apparatus is likewise an essential part of the facilities.

Many small and rather inexpensive items of equipment, such as glassware, magnets, dry cells, thermometers, pans, and plastic containers should be a permanent part of the equipment for each room. Adequate storage space must be provided, although the storage of science materials should not crowd out the materials needed for other areas of the elementary school program.

The Elementary School Science Center

A science center for the elementary school is an excellent provision for the science program and is an alternative to having all facilities in the classroom itself. The center may function both as a place for storing materials and equipment and as a place for preparing these materials for use in the classroom. At times the teacher may send a student or a small group of students to this area to prepare materials for a science project. A room smaller than a classroom but larger than a storage closet will serve for the center.

The science center needs large amounts of storage space in both closed cabinets and open shelves, a work counter with a sink with hot and cold running water, and electric outlets. A workbench or worktable greatly increases the center's value. Wood, hammer, nails, wire, cloth, metal, string, and many other kinds of construction materials should also be available in the science center.

Larger and more expensive pieces of equipment which should be shared by several classes may well be kept in the closed cabinets in this room. A rollable table may be provided to transport equipment and materials to and from the classrooms and as a table for class experimentation. Careful cataloging of equipment and supplies with storage space for each item increases effective use of the science center.

Elementary Science Laboratories

Another arrangement of facilities for elementary science teaching may be associated with a departmentalized organization of the school, at least in grades four, five, and six. Parenthetically, it should be noted here that many educators object seriously to a departmental arrangement. They claim that certain outcomes of the self-contained classroom cannot be achieved by the regimentation of a departmentalized program. However, until all elementary teachers can be brought to a much higher level of competence in science teaching than they now have, some special arrangements will be required. In schools that do have a departmental organization, a science classroom-laboratory with adjoining preparation and storage area should be provided. Classes participating in such a program would be regularly scheduled for this room.

The special science classroom-laboratory has many fascinating possibilities for the elementary school, if imaginatively furnished and arranged for young children. It need not be, in fact must not be, a miniature replica of a traditional high school science laboratory.

The teacher in charge must be especially prepared and highly competent in the teaching of elementary science.

Flexibility is an essential quality of a room for science. Rearrangement of the room must be possible with a minimum of effort and confusion. Tables and chairs should be movable and should come in several appropriate heights for the variety of students who will use this room. Folding tables may be used so that large areas of the floor can be cleared for various activities. Adjustable chairs may also be provided.

As much counter space as possible should be provided around the perimeter of the room. Several sinks with hot and cold running water should be spaced within the counter top. Storage below the counter should include both drawers and shelves. Electric outlets should be provided at various points in the room. Storage cabinets in various parts of the facility should include appropriate space for models, globes, charts, large and small pieces of apparatus, plastic items and glassware, hand tools, kits, and tote-trays. A variety of materials for construction should be available.

Facilities for elementary school science should also provide for living plants and animals. Many schools have inside courts. With careful planning and work, such areas may become excellent extensions of the science facility. Small ponds for fish and frogs, or a variety of living plants and small animals may be maintained in such an area. Trees, shrubs, and bird feeders will increase the interest and value of the school's surroundings for elementary science. The science room should be placed so that it can have an exit leading directly to the out-of-doors.

SELECTING EQUIPMENT AND MATERIALS
FOR A SCIENCE PROGRAM *

Albert Piltz

Albert Piltz discusses the role of equipment and materials in the elementary science program, and cautions against the use of too complicated materials. The uses of film, filmstrip, opaque, and overhead projectors are presented. Dr. Piltz briefly takes up science kits, and describes the place of both home-

* REPRINTED FROM *Science Equipment and Materials for Elementary Schools*, U.S. Office of Education, Document OE-29029, Bulletin 1961, No. 28, 1963, pp. 20–31. Dr. Piltz is Specialist in Science Instructional Resources at the U.S. Office of Education.

made and commercial materials in the science program. The need for adequate storage of equipment is stressed. This article is an excerpt from the U. S. Office of Education bulletin entitled Science Equipment and Materials for Elementary Schools.

I N LEARNING science, children plan, discuss, read, report, and listen, but these alone do not add up to effective science teaching. The vital elements are experimentation and demonstration.

EQUIPMENT IN RELATION TO PROGRAM

What is to be taught in a science program and how it is to be taught should determine the equipment and material needs. It would be untenable to purchase a model of a power dam, a science kit, or some object and then build a program around it. If children are to assemble or construct instruments for a weather station, the purpose of the instruction should determine what will be purchased and what will be constructed. For example, a barometer or thermometer may need to be purchased, but a weather vane may be constructed. In each instance the value to the learner should be considered.

Complicated materials and apparatus are usually not suitable for elementary school children, since they may confuse the child and sometimes actually interfere with the principle to be taught. Concepts developed with formal, complex laboratory equipment are often isolated thoughts in the mind of the child. Ideally, most demonstrations or experiments should be such that they can be repeated, varied, or extended at home.

The grade level, the geographical location, the textbook or the science guide or manual, availability of utilities in the classroom, and the ingenuity of the teacher are some of the factors which determine the materials and the equipment needs for a given classroom. Also, equipment which might be suitable for individual or small-group experimentation might be too small to be seen easily if used for demonstration purposes. Thus, content and method are factors which bear directly on the needed materials.

Since careful observation is an important aspect of science learning, much valuable experience may be gained by simply viewing the natural environment either in the immediate vicinity of the school or on an extended field trip in which ecological relationships are sought. Often observations which children make of the day and the night sky, of natural habitats of plants and animals, and of land and rock formations require no equipment or materials but result in considerable learning.

The teacher as well as the children can be alert to science materials in the environment. Collections of materials, besides being useful in study, may often lead to careers, hobbies, and leisure-time activities. Children may sometimes be encouraged to bring to school specimens from the out-of-doors or articles from home. It is natural for a youngster to bring a cocoon, a new toy, or a budding twig to school to "show and tell." This becomes a re-source for the teacher and a stimulus to learning. A personal contribution helps the child to identify more closely with the project and to develop self-direction and resourcefulness. However, too much dependence by the teacher on the contribution of the children is impractical, since responses are often capricious. The practice of engaging children in participation by having them contribute material or construct apparatus should in no way replace the use of essential equipment and materials provided through the school budget.

PROJECTION EQUIPMENT AND MATERIALS

Motion picture and filmstrip projectors have become almost standard equipment for most elementary schools and, in general, are accessible to teachers. For easy handling, many projectors are mounted on mobile carts which can be moved to the room where they are to be used. Classrooms are either equipped with projection screens and darkening facilities or special rooms are equipped and designated as projection rooms. With the greater availability of motion picture films on elementary school science and with funds for purchase being greatly increased, the use of films is becoming more widespread. The quality of films is constantly improving and they are geared more and more to the instructional program. Science films for elementary school children deal with subject matter that emphasizes, to some degree, the process and the application of scientific principles, as well as the products of science. Films that emphasize the products of science are oriented to the social studies and center around themes of transportation, communication, and devices which have made life easier in the home.

Filmstrips (or slidefilms) are usually 35 mm. in width and often present a sequence of still pictures on a specific area in science. The teacher may use all or a portion of the sequence. Sometimes individual frames from a film-strip are used for instruction. Synchronized recordings of commentary can be used to create a "sound filmstrip."

There is a great versatility in the use of slides, since the teacher can do his own photography and make or procure a slide for almost any subject. Slides may also be used with sound accompaniment—mainly from record discs or tape recordings. Bird calls and various animal sounds have been effectively used with picture projection. Many teachers make a hobby of taking their own slides in color.

Microscopes have many uses in elementary classrooms. Magnifying a specimen in science often helps the teacher get across an idea which may not be in evidence when the specimen is viewed macroscopically. However, it is important with children not to use so high a power of magnification as to make the part which is enlarged seem totally unrelated to the whole specimen being examined. Even if the teacher helps the pupil properly focus and adjust the microscope for viewing, he is not always certain that he will see what is actually on the slide or even the section of a slide that needs to be observed for study. The problem is even greater with live and moving material. Microprojectors have some advantages in this respect. Although microprojectors are usually limited in magnification compared to some microscopes, the enlargement in projection will generally suffice for most elementary school children. While a microscope can be used by one person at a time, the microprojector projects the object or specimen on the screen so that the entire group can see it. This enables pupils to discuss the material shown on the screen and helps the teacher to clear up certain points for the entire class. In addition, each individual has the same focus on the image at the same time. This may be useful in certain instances.

Since an opaque projector can project on a screen nontransparent pictures, flat specimens, and even shallow containers, its possibilities for elementary science are manifold. Photographic and hand-drawn or hand-written illustrations are commonly used. In addition, botanical and animal specimens of some types can easily be projected. Opaque projectors can be used for children in almost all grades. Some specimens too fragile to be passed around for individual examination can be projected for an entire class. Children also can prepare material for projection.

Overhead transparency projectors have a distinct advantage in elementary science classes because the teacher can face the pupils in front of the class when projecting the material. The teacher can also draw or write on a plastic sheet in the course of his presentation with an overhead projector. The chalkboard may be comparatively limited in this respect, since a greater number of pupils can readily view an overhead projection with ease. Much of the material used can be prepared by teacher and pupil, using various colored wax pencils for color if desired. With successive layers of transparencies or overlays, various stages in a scientific process may be illustrated or changes which occur in a life science sequence shown dramatically.

As projective techniques and materials are developed further, their place in instruction must be constantly evaluated by both teachers and administrators. It is well to keep in mind that projective techniques are used mainly with groups of children, whereas nonprojective techniques are more for individual use. Both types have their place in a good science program.

KITS, CARTS, AND PACKAGE MATERIALS

Science kits and so-called "packaged science" are of particular concern to program builders because of their popularity and their potential misuse. The busy administrator who lacks the time to select and order separate items from the various catalogues looks upon the kit as a solution to his program and equipment problems. Likewise the teacher who is inexperienced in building a science curriculum welcomes the readymade program. Although the cost of some kits may exceed that of the same items purchased separately, the kits do contain useful materials. Some supervisors of science, however, have emphasized that an overdependence on science kits may have a limiting effect on an instructional program. This equipment, like other types of equipment, can be used effectively or ineffectively. Some persons are concerned with the stereotyped use of equipment, leading to the so-called "cookbook" science. To a large extent the kit may determine the program.

The several commercial kits familiar to most teachers and available in elementary schools have quite a range of price depending on the amount and quality of the contents. They contain a variety of physical science items, such as magnets, spring-balance, thermometer, and magnifier. They are usually marketed in specially built boxes with handles, which makes them convenient to carry.

Some schools or school systems make their own kits; they construct the box and obtain the materials for it from many sources. One type of school-built kit is designed to provide materials for the study of concepts in a specific unit or area in elementary science, such as earth science, the night sky, light, heat, sound, magnets, and weather. In some school systems these kits are called "shoebox kits"; in other places they are called "science-concept boxes."

Some kits emphasize the assembly of a particular kind of equipment, such as a toy motor, telegraph set, question-and-answer boards, or optical system. The skills developed in putting the component parts together would justify the activity, providing the purpose of the activity is clear at the outset.

To relieve the problem of storing and transporting materials and equipment, a cart or mobile arrangement has been made available to teachers in various school systems. Some carts have been constructed in local mill shops; others have been built by school personnel. The cart usually contains basic science materials, both commercial and improvised, arranged in an orderly fashion. Much of the material is contained in boxes or in compartments, according to topics, and is labeled and inventoried. Some mobile units contain a source of water and a source for heat, and can be moved from classroom to classroom.

There are currently available several commercially designed laboratory units for use in elementary schools. Much like the handmade cart, they are more elaborate in construction and are intended to provide the laboratory facilities which many elementary classrooms lack. They come in a wide range of prices, depending on construction, features, and size. In the opinion of many school people these carts have solved, in part, some of the problems of work space, utilities, availability of demonstration equipment when needed, and mobility of use.

THE PLACE OF COMMERCIAL AND IMPROVISED EQUIPMENT

There is clearly a place in the science program for both commercial and improvised equipment. The value of each for its contribution to the educational process must be studied carefully, and the determination to purchase or improvise can then be made in relation to program needs and the purposes to be achieved in the learning activities.

In many areas of science study there are a number of satisfactory ways to demonstrate the same principle. To show the effects of air pressure, for example, the teacher may use either an elaborate vacuum pump or the classical "egg in bottle" demonstration. Each can show the effects of reduced or increased pressure. If resources are plentiful, a variety of experiments may be used. To reinforce learning and stimulate critical thinking, children should be challenged to devise their own methods of illustrating principles and experimenting.

To avoid frustration, all projects for construction should be carefully considered in terms of the children's ability and the availability of tools and materials. Adequate raw materials, tools, and work space are essential. If small-group experimentation is to be encouraged, equipment should be sufficient to allow all children to participate.

In a successful activity in which a model of a solar system was contrived, children used numerous references for information, many aids, creativity in mounting, and arithmetical concepts in measuring distances and making models to scale. They soon learned the limitations of the models but were stimulated to learn more about the night sky and achieved great appreciation of telescopes and optical equipment. If in construction of equipment a child is helped to better understand a science concept or can better apply a principle of science, then the activity is warranted.

In the past, because science and equipment facilities were often inadequate, teacher education emphasized skills designed to develop resourcefulness in borrowing, salvaging, and improvising materials and equipment to provide low-cost aids for teaching science. As a result, valuable teaching time and effort often were spent in the creation of makeshift facilities. As greater amounts of equipment and materials become available, more instruction can be done with commercial scientific equipment. Elementary school pupils may continue to build thermometers so that they may better understand the principles of temperature and measurement, but they will need precision thermometers for exact readings of temperature. Simple materials from the child's environment can provide rich learning experiences, but dry cells, wire, meters, and other apparatus cannot all be improvised. The child who constructs a telegraph set or miniature motor from metal, wood scraps, wire and nails, learns about materials, electromagnets, and principles of rotation. He also exercises manipulative skill in the activity. The commercial motor, however, gives him opportunity to study construction and, further, to explore the operation that makes motors useful.

ORGANIZATION, STORAGE, AND DISTRIBUTION OF EQUIPMENT

To insure adequate classroom control during periods of class activity, the teacher will need to work out a plan for distributing and collecting materials.

Frequently used items should have storage facilities close at hand. When a classroom is being designed to include adequate storage, consideration should be given to the characteristics of each item, such as kind, quantity, size, shape, durability, and frequency of use, and, then, the storage facilities planned accordingly. Storage appropriate for chemicals differs from that necessary for telescopes, microscopes, large charts, or demonstration apparatus. Delicate or expensive equipment which requires special handling, such as galvanometers or microscopes, should be kept under lock and key. Chemicals should also be stored some distance from any equipment that will corrode.

Some costly equipment items which are used infrequently might be stored in a central location either in a school building or central warehouse or in a cooperating children's museum, materials center, curriculum laboratory, or audiovisual center. Much will depend on the facilities available in the school system. If items are distributed to classrooms from a central supply room in a building, a system of classification, labeling, and inventory will help in locating and distributing them.

Whether equipment is stored in a school building or at an instruction center, it is important that an easy method be devised of making it available to teachers if frequent use of the item is desired. Some provision also should be made for repair and replacement of materials and equipment.

NATIONAL DEFENSE EDUCATION ACT *

Albert Piltz

Briefly and concisely, Albert Piltz presents eight questions and answers about the science aids available to schools and teachers through Title III of the National Defense Education Act.

1. WHAT IS THE NATIONAL DEFENSE EDUCATION ACT (NDEA)?

The National Defense Education Act, first passed in 1958 and recently extended and expanded, is based on the premise that every American should have the opportunity to develop his skills and competencies to the fullest

---

* REPRINTED FROM *Science and Children*, Vol. 2, No. 7, April 1965, pp. 9–10. Copyright, 1965, by the National Science Teachers Association, Washington, D.C. Reprinted by permission of the author and the publisher. Dr. Piltz is Specialist in Science Instructional Resources at the U.S. Office of Education.

extent, and that only in this way can the nation develop the trained man-power and insure the leadership essential for the preservation of democracy. The Act, as recently amended, has eleven titles. The purpose of Title III of NDEA is to strengthen instruction in science, mathematics, modern foreign language, history, civics, geography, English, and reading in elementary and secondary schools. This is accomplished through federal grants and loans for the acquisition of laboratory and other special equipment and materials, and for minor remodeling of space to make effective use of such equipment; and through federal grants for state programs of supervisory and related services in the critical subject area.

2. How Does A School Arrange to Participate in an NDEA Project?

School administrators contact the Title III coordinator or administrator in the state educational agency. The states supply application forms which teachers and local administrators use to submit projects to the state educational agency. The application asks the administrators to show the scope and content of their programs in science and other critical subjects, instructional goals, equipment and materials used and needed, ways in which new equipment and materials or minor remodeling would strengthen instruction, qualifications of teachers, predicted enrollment, and available matching funds.

A project is a proposal submitted by a local educational agency or other public school authority below the state level, or by the highest administrative officer of a public elementary or secondary school or audiovisual library operated by the state educational agency. The proposal must itemize and estimate the cost of the equipment to be acquired or minor remodeling to be done, and explain how the proposed acquisitions or minor remodeling will improve instruction in one of the critical subjects.

3. How Does A Teacher Determine the Equipment and Material Needs for the Classroom?

What is to be taught in a science program and how it is to be taught should determine the equipment and material needed. Building the activity around the equipment is educationally unsound—like "putting the cart before the horse."

4. What Types of Equipment and Materials May Be Bought With Federal Financial Participation?

Only those items for use in providing education in the critical subjects are eligible for NDEA funds. The following are the general categories of eligible items of laboratory and other special equipment: pupil-laboratory equipment, teacher-demonstration equipment, and special equipment and instructional materials not consumed in use. Student-laboratory equipment for science includes glass and porcelain ware such as battery jars, beakers, and bottles; electrical devices such as hot plates, meters, and switches; kits such as electrical circuit and soil testing; models and display materials such as anatomical models, insect, rock, and plant collections, and specimen mounts; measuring and recording devices such as balances and weights, calorimeters, and thermometers; optical devices such as binoculars, microscopes, and telescopes; and other laboratory devices such as gauges, magnets, and pulleys.

Among pieces of teacher-demonstration equipment eligible for purchase under the Act for science are aquariums, simple machine apparatus, terrariums, and gyroscopes. Fixtures such as potting benches, laboratory carts, teacher-demonstration desks and tables for science, and special chalkboards may be eligible.

General purpose classroom furniture and equipment such as bulletin boards, wall clocks, pencil sharpeners, teachers' desks, chairs, and air conditioners are not eligible, nor are maintenance equipment and replacement parts.

5. What Is the Place of Science Kits in a Program?

Science kits are packaged collections of items for use in experiments or demonstrations in teaching the physical or biological sciences. They are currently available for every grade level and for most science subjects. Whether to use a kit or some other type of science equipment is an educational decision, since the needs of the instructional program govern the choice of materials and equipment. If kits are to be used, it should be clear before any particular selection is made how and by whom the kit will be used in instruction and what it can contribute to the pupils' progress in science. No one can know what a specific kit is or what value it will be to him until he has examined its physical makeup and assessed its potential use in the learning situation for which it is intended. Such an examination should be made by the teacher before recommending its purchase. The educator's main question about the use of kits has to do with their misuse, since dependence upon kits may limit the instructional program and stifle ingenuity and creativeness on the part of teachers and pupils alike. The discerning teacher will select a kit or any other equipment only if it is geared to the instructional program.

6. What Audiovisual Materials May Be Eligible?

Audiovisual equipment is eligible if used primarily in the teaching of critical subjects. The following is a partial list of audiovisual equipment which may be eligible: darkening shades, blinds, or curtains; filmstrip or slide previewers; flannel and magnetic boards; projection screens, stands, and tables; projectors; record or transcription players; tape recorders and playbacks; teaching machines; or television receivers. Some examples of eligible materials are: charts, diagrams, globes, graphs, maps, and mockups; films and filmstrips; pamphlets for reference or supplementary use; periodicals of special use in one of the critical subjects; programmed books, if not used as textbook; reference books; tapes and discs; and transparencies. The Act excludes textbooks or supplies and materials consumed in use.

7. How Can a School Use a Grant Most Effectively?

Basic items of equipment and materials should be acquired before special ones, and those of wide use should be preferred to others of limited application. The equipment purchased must meet the standards established by the state. Similar products should be examined and compared before the selection is made. Competitive estimates and bids should be obtained, and other sound purchasing practices should be followed. The science teacher may request consultative help from the state supervisor of science. The state supervisor may also help plan new laboratories or arrange in-service teacher educational programs.

8. How Are Payments Made?

The U.S. Commissioner of Education pays to the state an amount equal to half of the state and local expenditures for acquiring equipment or doing minor remodeling. Allotments are made on the basis of a formula provided in the Act. Unneeded portions of state allotments may be reallotted to other states. The state reimburses the local school district for its share of expenditures for approved projects. Loans to nonprofit private schools are made by the U.S. Commissioner of Education.

NDEA PURCHASE GUIDE *

Leo Schubert

Leo Schubert describes the Purchase Guide, *prepared by the Council of Chief State School Officers, and tells how it is to be used. The Guide makes available to the teacher and administrator the very best opinion in the*

* REPRINTED FROM *Science and Children*, Vol. 2, No. 7, April 1965, pp. 7–8. Copyright, 1965, by the National Science Teachers Association, Washington, D.C. Reprinted by permission of the author and the publisher. Dr. Schubert is Chairman of the Chemistry Department at the American University, Washington, D.C.

country as to what the equipment can do and the grade level at which it can be used most effectively. Dr. Schubert believes that the Guide can be one of the most important resources in elementary school education, and that no school should be without it.

T HE PASSAGE of the National Defense Education Act (NDEA) made it almost mandatory that a responsible organization establish a set of standards for the purchase of equipment in the sciences, mathematics, and modern foreign languages. One of the possibilities was that this function reside in the government itself. It seemed to some that it would be more advisable for a set of standards to be established outside of the government; this was undertaken by the Council of Chief State School Officers under the direction of Edgar Fuller, Executive Secretary of the Council.

The first step was accomplished at a meeting held at Michigan State University. A list of equipment helpful in the teaching of the sciences, mathematics, and modern foreign languages, was drawn up. This list was printed, and over one hundred thousand copies were sent out to interested teachers. The list proved inadequate because no attempt was made to indicate the educational level of the items or the technical standards by which they could be purchased in a sound way. In consequence, Dr. Fuller then set about organizing a *Purchase Guide* with specifications. Financial support for this project was given by the Educational Facilities Laboratories, the Scientific Apparatus Makers Association, and the National Audio-Visual Association. Indirect support was provided through the U. S. Office of Education, the National Bureau of Standards, and some professional organizations.

The organization was simple. A Committee of Seven representing some learned societies was established. Organizations represented in this Committee were the American Chemical Society, the American Institute of Physics, the American Institute of Biological Sciences, the American Association for the Advancement of Science, and the Modern Language Association. This Committee of Seven had as its function the establishment of policy.

FIRST GUIDE PRODUCED IN 1959

Items of equipment were submitted to the National Bureau of Standards, and Bureau personnel drew up technical specifications. These specifications were reviewed by the Council staff for educational meaningfulness and usefulness. More than 50,000 copies of the first *Purchase Guide*, which was issued in 1959, were distributed. A Supplement to the guide was issued two years later, to update the original and to improve its usefulness.

Because science and its teaching change so rapidly, it was obvious that a revised *Purchase Guide* would have to be issued. Major financial support for this revised guide was assumed by the National Science Foundation. Additional funds were provided by the Scientific Apparatus Makers Association and Educational Facilities Laboratories. The *Purchase Guide* revision project took two years, and publication was scheduled for early 1965.*

The revised guide is a document of about 400 pages and contains information on the sciences and mathematics; the modern foreign languages are not included. Equipment is listed on all levels from elementary school through junior college. Not only are the items themselves listed and described through specification, but also through use information. These items are described in terms of what the equipment can do and the level at which it may be used effectively. If an item is deemed to be essential to a science or mathematics program, it is designated a *basic* item, and no respectable program may be without it. If a school can afford average financial support for its science and mathematics programs, the items listed for such programs are described as *standard*. Those schools which expect to receive above-average support, find that the items for such programs are described in the *Purchase Guide* as *advanced*. In this way, the prospective teacher or other purchaser can have available to him the very best opinion in the country as to the level of equipment to be purchased and used. A school system purchasing apparatus or equipment for the first time has available guidance so that it need not purchase the most advanced equipment instead of the most essential equipment.

ELEMENTARY SCHOOL STRESSED IN REVISION

The elementary schools were emphasized in the *Purchase Guide* revision. A great deal of work has gone into describing equipment which can be of use to elementary school teachers with no special training in the sciences. The assumption is not made that the list is a perfect one or complete. Nor is it regarded as being entirely up to date because new equipment is constantly being made available. However, the list does provide the teacher not only with the items to be used, but also with uses for these items. The use information in the guide is an integral part of it. It tells the teacher what to use, how to use it, and the educational function.

In addition to the listing and specifications of items, the guidelines contain much else that is of value. For example, there is an essay on science furniture which describes the different kinds of laboratory furniture that are available. The guide gives advice as to how the furniture may be selected and the use for which the furniture is intended. Advice is included on the care of furniture. There is an essay on surplus property and how one may go about acquiring it. This essay lists the kind of items that a school system may obtain through surplus. An important part of the guide is devoted to a well-annotated bibliography of books in science and mathematics. This bibliography was developed through the combined work of scientists, educa-

---

* The revised *Purchase Guide* is now available from Ginn and Company, Boston, Massachusetts. $4.25. (A 25 percent discount is given to schools and teachers.)

tors, and librarians and comprises the most careful thinking of these different groups. Still another section of the guide is concerned with the new curricula that are being developed in the sciences and mathematics. The section on audiovisual aids was made as authoritative as possible through the assistance of the National Audio-Visual Association and the Department of Audio-Visual Instruction of the National Education Association. In this listing, as well as in the guidelines devoted to this field, will be found a most up-to-date description of the very latest items that may be used as audiovisual materials in teaching programs.

This guide is one of the most important resources in elementary school education. No assumptions are made as to previous background. Care has been taken to make the guide as complete and authoritative as is possible. The consultants for this guide were drawn from all over the country, and the professional societies contributed unstintedly toward the excellence and reliability of the book. A teacher or purchaser who uses this book can be certain that the items selected are the best possible items for educational use. The information contained in the guidelines and in the bibliography will prove to be invaluable. No school or school system should be without this *Purchase Guide,* and teachers should refer to it constantly in support of their equipment acquisitions and teaching programs.

SCIENCE EQUIPMENT STORAGE *

William J. Walsh

With the advent of increased emphasis in elementary school science and the availability of special funds from Title III of the National Defense Education Act, many schools find themselves with much equipment and materials, but with little or no planned thought given to their storage. The development of central storage facilities for science supplies and equipment is vital if the elementary science program is to be effective. William J. Walsh discusses the need for cooperative planning in selecting a location, identifying and classifying materials, providing for the taking of inventory, and allowing for expansion of storage facilities.

* REPRINTED FROM *Science and Children,* Vol. 1, No. 5, February 1964, pp. 8–10. Copyright, 1964, by the National Science Teachers Association, Washington, D.C. Reprinted by permission of the author and the publisher. Dr. Walsh is Associate Professor of Education at Michigan State University.

F EW TEACHERS would question the need for a continuous improvement of science instruction in the elementary school. Accompanying the demand for quality instruction is the need for more science equipment. With financial encouragement from local resources and the entitlement features of state and federal agencies (National Defense Education Act), it is obvious that more equipment is being purchased for use by the teacher in developing the elementary science curriculum.

Yet, these encouraging developments are not paralleled by similar advancements in centralizing equipment and supplies and making them readily available to all teachers of the elementary school. Orders for equipment, which is seldom used or which duplicates available items, indicate that steps should be taken to render maximum service to the school program of diverse needs as well as quality supply in selected areas.

Few school systems can financially afford to provide the maximum amount of science equipment desired in each self-contained classroom of the elementary school. The requirements of storage alone poses a serious problem to the classroom teacher. Moreover, as the program moves from sole teacher-demonstration emphasis to laboratory-type student project approach, a wider range of equipment needs becomes more evident.

Obviously, it is not an either/or proposition. Each teacher is entitled to minimum or basic science equipment in the individual room. Often this is confined to a box or a drawer. It generally includes some simple tools, wire, tape, a source of heat, assorted pieces of glassware, a dry cell, and perhaps a few clamps. As the teacher moves to new units of investigation with the multitude of activities now associated with them, there is a need for specific equipment. Activities for a weather unit, for example, often include equipment requirements for a barometer, also soda straws, nylon thread, petri dishes, metersticks, and assorted pieces of glassware. In most instances, the availability of equipment such as this will affect the planning, execution, and (probably) the success of the unit. But, how can such requirements be met in the self-contained classroom?

Before World War II, many schools depended upon teachers' pocketbooks for supplying scientific equipment. In recent years, however, this arrangement has moved beyond the pocketbook and memory of most teachers, and school systems are providing funds for science equipment at the elementary level. The complexity of school operations and increased enrollments of students has pointed to the need for the establishment of a central facility for the storing of major items of science equipment and supplies.

In some large school systems, a central budget or purchasing office has been established to centralize inventory and purchase science equipment. In other school arrangements, forms of teaching in departmentalized fashion have eased individual teacher requests. Systems which feature the self-contained classroom, however, have not been able to meet student and teacher demands in an adequate fashion without centralizing a common supply of science equipment somewhere in the building. The development of a teacher-planned central storage facility for science equipment and supplies would assist the development of an improved elementary school science curriculum.

COOPERATIVE PLANNING

Any centralized facility must be developed by and for the teachers it will service. The physical location must be decided as must be the manner in which it will be used. The wishes of all members of the staff must be considered in initial planning as well as in future development. Some teachers will hesitate to endorse and support the initial plans unless they are assured that equipment contributed to the centralized storage area will be available when they need it. Other individuals who have successfully leaned upon incidental teaching-motivation will be wary of changing habitual preparation patterns. Such common and understandable questions of philosophy and practice should be answered before the move to centralize storage is taken in final form.

CENTRAL LOCATION

A convenient and centrally located space can be found in most schools for centralized science storage. Because of the hourly need for check-out and return of equipment, a large closet is preferable to a corner of the principal's office. For the same reason, a corner of the boiler room, properly outfitted, will be used more advantageously than a corner of a single classroom. Some schools start with a movable supply center such as a large cabinet by which, upon rolling it from one location to another, a site of maximum convenience can be determined. Small schools can begin with the storage afforded by a portable demonstration table. Its limited space, however, often requires augmentation from other storage areas.

IDENTIFICATION AND CLASSIFICATION

Whether a school uses a large bookcase or a series of shoe boxes, the central storage area should be divided into sections that are easily identified and located. This process is often the most difficult to accomplish. Some systems use one box or space for magnets, another for electricity. It is not uncommon to see common teaching units or concepts used as segments of the total classification. For example, a unit or box labeled "Heat" will include thermometers, expansion strips, conduction bars, etc.

Whatever method is used for classification, it should be used consistently. Keep it simple for maximum utilization. In some instances, a simple alphabetical listing might suffice in the beginning stages with permanent groupings selected at a later date.

Physical grouping of the material into boxes, trays, drawers, or other containers is desirable. Commercial storage cabinets with removable drawers or trays lend themselves handily to the science storage area. Carrying boxes with handles as well as wheeled carts will augment the transportation of equipment.

Wherever possible, separate the chemical supplies from other equipment. This will prevent the formation of corrosion and subsequent deterioration of valuable instruments and metal equipment.

PROVIDE FOR EXPANSION

The contents of the original centralized storage area of the school will in most cases result from a pooling of the equipment and supplies formerly divided between each of the elementary classrooms. In terms of future needs, the original collection will probably occupy less than one-third of the space that may be required after a five- to seven-year growth period.

Some schools have discovered corners or blind hall ends which serve nicely as storerooms by "boxing-in" with wallboard or plywood. If remodeling or new space such as this is contemplated, triple the space now needed to provide for future needs.

Bulk purchases of both equipment and supplies will conserve future budgets, but does demand present storage space. A year's supply of glassware or dry cells for a ten- to twelve-room school is not an expensive package but necessitates space that makes these materials available over an extended period of time.

INVENTORY NEEDS

Often overlooked in planning storage facilities, is a means of determining what is stocked in the storage area and when to replace or reorder existing items. This procedure is particularly critical with supplies. A simple card system can be used to indicate, for example, how many ounces or containers of iron filings are in stock. When a classroom teacher or an appointed checker notes the supply is dwindling, a note on an order list should suffice. If the third-grade teacher needs more centigrade thermometers, she should be able to record her request on a list or sheet in the storage room. Planning for the future rests heavily upon anticipating the needs of the individual class as well as the total school.

With an important link in the total science program resting upon inventory, it is helpful for teachers to rotate or share responsibility for ordering and replacing present equipment and supplies as well as processing requests for additional stocks. Where possible, honorary or paid high school student assistance should be considered.

FITTING FACILITIES TO THE PROGRAM

The development of central storage facilities should go far to aid the implementation of a desirable science education program. The availability of equipment and supplies should encourage an upward revision of former goals and objectives associated with the curricula. In no instances should the availability or unavailability of an item indicate teaching aims. The knowledge that microscopes are available should encourage the teacher to plan an improved unit on microorganisms. The presence of the instruments should not in itself trigger a study of the microscope merely as an exercise or busy work.

Many schools work cooperatively with teachers of science at the junior and senior high school levels in securing and developing specific materials that can be used advantageously by all grade levels. Decisions concerned with adding to present equipment should be made in the light of future as well as present needs of the total kindergarten through twelfth-grade curriculum. The possibility of the development of a school or community museum would have serious implications upon the biological specimens, charts, and models contemplated for a system where museum facilities had not previously been available.

The degree of centralization can be overdone. Narrowing the center to a total school system has less promise than centers in individual buildings. Problems of use and return multiply when facilities outside of the building are developed. The test of the degree to which centralization can be made includes the responsibility for providing the maximum utilization of all school facilities. If the teacher loses touch with the program through unnecessary complications, the additional facilities will not be of material benefit to anyone.

IMPROVING THE QUALITY OF ELEMENTARY SCIENCE TEACHING

INTRODUCTION

A well-structured elementary science program requires the teacher to be cognizant of key concepts from the three broad branches of science: physical, biological, and earth science. This knowledge calls for a more extensive science background than most elementary school teachers now receive in their pre-service training. At the same time, the rapid and continuing increase in knowledge in science makes it difficult for the teacher in the classroom to keep abreast of new developments. It is a well-known fact that when teachers have a limited science background, they become extremely reluctant to teach science. Consequently, if the elementary science program is to be effective, consideration must be given to the preparation and professional growth in science of the elementary teacher.

The elementary teacher should be provided with a broad general education which includes preparation in the humanities, the arts, and the sciences. This is necessary because the teacher must teach not only science but also language arts, social studies, and mathematics. Very often the teacher is also responsible for the teaching of music, art, and physical education. A broad education, then, should enable the teacher to coordinate all the learning experiences of the children during the day. Because the teacher is working with children, the education of the teacher should also include an insight into the growth and development, learning, and behavior of the child.

The preparation of the elementary teacher in science should include the learning of as many key concepts in biological, physical, and earth science as time and effort will permit. The teacher should also learn something about the relationship of these branches of science to each other and about the relationship of science to other areas of knowledge.

253

Since teachers tend to teach in the same manner as they have been taught, it is important that the science courses for elementary teachers stress scientific inquiry and the opportunity to work with the materials of science. Finally, the elementary teacher should be given the opportunity to acquire depth in science, as well as breadth, if the teacher so desires.

In-service education is needed for the elementary teacher to grow professionally and to acquire increased competency in the teaching of science. Typical in-service activities include workshops, seminars, study groups, college courses, and special programs by state and national agencies.

The growth of elementary science and in-service education in science has created a strong need for supervision. Many school systems are now beginning to employ science supervisors. These persons, also called science coordinators or consultants, are experienced and competent teachers who have leadership qualities and a strong science background. Science supervisors can do much to make the science program more effective. They can help teachers by demonstrating special teaching procedures, preparing and distributing instructional materials, and showing how to organize and plan for teaching science. They can help develop in-service programs and, when necessary, conduct the programs. They can inform teachers, administrators, and the public about new developments in science education and research. They can assist in the selection of supplies, equipment, facilities, books, films, and other instructional materials. They can work with elementary, junior high, and high school teachers to develop a continuous K–12 science program for the school system. Finally, they can maintain a liaison with college, university, and state department personnel in science.

The improvement of science education in our elementary schools has become a matter of local, state, and national concern. On the local level the principal and superintendent are beginning to take a leadership role in fostering and instituting curriculum developments and innovations in the teaching of science. State departments of education are strengthening their position and efforts in improving science education in the schools. On the national level the U.S. Office of Education, through its specialists, continues to make excellent contributions to science education. The National Science Foundation, in existence only since 1950, has extended its broad program to include institutes for improving the science background of elementary teachers.

GUIDELINES FOR THE SCIENCE AND MATHEMATICS PREPARATION OF ELEMENTARY SCHOOL TEACHERS *

NASDTEC-AAAS

Due to the continuing increase in new knowledge in science, it is necessary to reconsider the preparatory program for elementary teachers. This study is concerned with the nature and quality of programs for the preparation of elementary teachers in the subject areas of science and mathematics. The recommendations suggested here are the results of much intensive and cooperative thinking. The study was sponsored by the National Association of State Directors of Teacher Education and Certification (NASDTEC) in cooperation with the American Association for the Advancement of Science (AAAS) and supported by the Carnegie Corporation of New York.

BASIC ASSUMPTIONS

Guideline I

> *The faculty of each institution should design its program for the preparation of the elementary school teacher after careful analysis of the role of (1) the elementary school in American society, (2) the elementary school teacher, and (3) the institutions preparing teachers.*

In designing these *Guidelines* to aid college faculties in the preparation of their teacher education programs several assumptions were made. These assumptions should serve as a basis for understanding the recommendations of the NASDTEC-AAAS Studies. They may be taken as a point of departure by faculties in developing their own statements of objectives and in designing appropriate teacher education programs.

THE ROLE OF THE ELEMENTARY SCHOOL IN AMERICAN SOCIETY. The elementary school is responsible for providing educational opportunities

---

* REPRINTED FROM *Guidelines for Science and Mathematics in the Preparation Program of Elementary School Teachers,* American Association for the Advancement of Science, Misc. Publ. No. 63–7, 1963, pp. 1–15, by permission of the publisher.

for all children. For most children it is the first formal experience with a program devoted to building those general attitudes, understandings and skills needed by every member of society. The program must provide for the continuous mental, emotional, physical and social growth of each child and must recognize that children differ both in potential for growth and in their rate of development. Growth occurs best in an environment that is permeated by the spirit of inquiry, exploration and discovery and one that encourages each child to work toward his maximum self-realization.

THE ROLE OF THE ELEMENTARY SCHOOL TEACHER.   The elementary school teacher must provide a rich, human and cultural environment in the classroom. He must accept children at their level of development and guide them to further discovery and understanding of their world. He must assist children at their level of development and guide them to further discovery and understanding of their world. He must assist children in using materials and in gaining experiences which develop concepts and stimulate further learning in all the subject areas for which he is responsible. He must relate each new concept to those previously learned in the expansion of the child's knowledge and understanding.

RESPONSIBILITY OF THE TEACHER EDUCATION INSTITUTION.   An institution will wish to design a program that will prepare teachers to guide the learning activities of elementary school children. In order to do this, it will select highly qualified candidates, devise ways to study the qualifications and needs of its entrants, the needs and opportunities in its service area schools, and take measures to keep its staff up to date and enthusiastic.

The teacher preparation program will give the student an opportunity to acquire a broad background in liberal arts and sciences, preparation in professional education, and, if he so desires, specialization in a major field of interest.

A teacher education institution that assumes the responsibility for the post-baccalaureate education of elementary school teachers by offering regular graduate study or other types of inservice education will wish to plan its offerings in relation to its four year program and to meet the diverse needs of students.

LIBERAL EDUCATION

Guideline II

> *The program of preparation for the elementary school teacher should include a broad general education with attention to human growth.*

Since children's interests know no boundaries, the preparation of the elementary school teacher must be sufficiently comprehensive to enable him to encourage and guide these interests into productive channels. In addition, he must be prepared to teach all subject fields offered in the elementary school: language arts, social studies, the sciences, mathematics, health, the fine arts, physical education, and in some cases, a foreign language. To do this well, he must have, beyond subject matter, a working knowledge of human growth, learning, and behavior.

The liberal education of an elementary school teacher should, then, include preparation in the humanities, the sciences, the arts, and human growth, learning, and behavior.

Processes of Scientific Inquiry

Guideline III

> *Instruction in science and mathematics should be conducted in ways that will develop in teachers an understanding of and facility in the processes of scientific inquiry and mathematical thinking.*

The study of science and mathematics with an emphasis on processes can be a most stimulating experience. When the student has an opportunity to investigate and to discover for himself scientific phenomena and mathematical properties and to formulate principles which he can test, he achieves that sense of accomplishment which should be a product of all scholarly efforts.

In the area of sciences an essential ingredient in the proper education of elementary teachers is the development of skills in scientific inquiry. Such skills include: investigating; observing accurately and reporting concisely results of investigations; formulating and stating questions clearly; designing and executing experiments; conducting field studies; using equipment for counting, measuring and weighing; documenting findings with evidence; classifying materials and ideas; organizing and interpreting data; and, analyzing and critically reviewing scientific literature.

In the area of mathematics, concepts and manipulating skills are both of high importance. Skills without conceptual understanding are relatively sterile as are concepts unaccompanied by skills to give them succinct expression. Mathematics courses should be organized and taught so that there will be continuing emphasis on understanding the deductive nature of mathematics; the importance of mathematical structure in arithmetic, algebra, and geometry and recognition of common ideas that tend to unify these areas; the patterns of logical reasoning; recognition of the role of experience and intuition in mathematical discovery and appreciation of their significance when they appear in the classroom; the importance of the role of precise definitions and the use of mathematical terminology; and, proficiency in manipulating skills.

To accomplish these ends college teachers must look critically at the instructional procedures in their courses as well as at organization and content. It becomes necessary that college study for prospective elementary school teachers include a wide variety of techniques and materials which lend themselves to the development of these skills. For instance, individual and group laboratory experiences must be provided and should include experimental activities as well as the more traditional exercises involving verification.

An appreciation of the processes of mathematics and sciences can be derived only from an active participation in these disciplines on the part of the student. Prospective teachers must receive preparation that will develop in them the attitudes that they should cultivate in their students.

Subject Matter in Science and Mathematics

Guideline IV

> *The program of preparation for the elementary school teacher should include breadth of preparation in the sciences and in mathematics most appropriate as background for the elementary school program, with emphasis on concept development and interdisciplinary treatment.*

The education of elementary school teachers in the sciences and mathematics should be viewed as a continuous process beginning with the elementary school, including the substantive courses in science and in mathematics in the high school, continuing through the liberal education courses in these fields in college with opportunities for advanced study in the sciences and in mathematics.

In planning a program careful attention should be given to the previous achievement of the prospective elementary school teacher in high school courses. If full recognition is given for the proficiency level already reached by the student, the amount of time required in science and mathematics may not be as great as the following paragraphs appear to suggest. However, for the student who enters college inadequately prepared, more than four years may be necessary to complete an appropriate program.

The preparation needed is in the spirit of the best new liberal education courses. The scope must be very broad with emphasis on the underlying concepts, scientific principles, and the nature of scientific inquiry and mathematical discovery.

Every elementary school teacher should be educated in the fundamental concepts of the biological sciences, physical sciences, earth sciences, and mathematics; in particular those with implications for the education of the elementary school children. Colleges should explore the development of interdisciplinary courses designed to draw upon the subject matter of the various sciences to illustrate these fundamental concepts. The educational program should be organized so that the appropriate sequences of experiences in the sciences and mathematics are provided. It is essential that scientific inquiry be stressed in all science and mathematics courses designed for prospective elementary school teachers. These elements are to be obtained by providing:

1. Experiences which lead to increased understanding, knowledge and skills in science and mathematics appropriate to the needs and capabilities of children;
2. Experiences which lead to understanding the relationships between branches of science and mathematics and between these areas and other branches of learning;
3. A study of the current and historical developments and philosophies of science and mathematics;
4. Experiences which lead to awareness and appreciation of the continuous expansion of knowledge and the changing emphasis in science and mathematics;
5. Work which will be acceptable as prerequisite for intermediate level undergraduate study in various science fields.
6. Student teaching of many kinds, especially laboratory and field experiences, which illustrate how the methods of science are communicated; and,
7. Opportunities to increase understanding of problem solving, critical thinking, and methods of inquiry and discovery in science and mathematics.

It is recognized that the skeletal statements of course content which follow are subject to varied interpretations and realizations by institutions. Institutions should expect to devote continuing attention to the ordering and articulation of the separate offerings.

EARTH SCIENCE AND SPACE SCIENCE. Earth science is concerned with the description and interpretation of earth phenomena in all their intermingled, physical, chemical, biological, and mathematical aspects. Its data come largely from field observations, often at widely spread data points, and it is, therefore, concerned with sampling, broad extrapolation of data, and analysis of controlled variables.

Because every child naturally encounters the rocks and the hills, the wind and the rain, and the sun and the stars, earth science serves as a focal point for introduction of other sciences. Furthermore, field examples are available to teachers everywhere that can stimulate creative, disciplined imagination and focus attention on existing phenomena in a search for explanations of our natural world.

The program in earth science for elementary school teachers should consider descriptions and interpretations of features of the earth, the oceans, the atmosphere, and the relation of the earth to the solar system and the universe. The study of earth science for elementary teachers might contain the following elements: field observations, incorporating elements of sampling, the multiple working hypothesis, methods of making measurements, and the limitations and uncertainties of observations; laboratory measurements including development of experiments, control of variables, and the development of ideas about scale and theory of scale models; display of data, including development and use of maps and cross-sections; and, interpretation and extrapolation of data.

Subject matter should include:

1. Ideas about the origin of the earth in the context of the solar system;
2. The development of an earth model and the methods, sources of data, and uncertainties inherent in the construction of this model;
3. Ideas about the origin and distribution of continents and oceans;
4. Something about geochronology and the history of the earth, including the methods used to determine time relations, such as isotope dating;
5. The distribution and origin of elements, the nature of solids and crystal structure, and derivation of rocks and minerals from silicate and aqueous systems;
6. The sources of the earth's energy and energy changes relating to processes on the surface of the earth;
7. The origin of the earth's atmosphere, climate, and the hydrologic cycle;
8. Evolution of life and the character of the fossil record in extending concepts of evolution backward in geologic time; and,
9. Something about the economic utilization of earth materials and the relation of earth materials to human affairs.

BIOLOGICAL SCIENCES. For the purposes of instruction, the discipline of biology can be organized in a variety of ways. It is recommended that biology instruction for elementary school teachers present a coherent view of the field of biology and also focus on aspects of the field which are most meaningful and useful for future work and elementary school students. Such foci are:

A. Kinds of living organisms-microbes, plants and animals;
B. The functioning of organisms, including complementarity of structure and function;
C. Growth and development of organisms, including genetic continuity; and,
D. Interrelations of organisms and environment.

In organizing the foregoing aspects of biology into a coherent view of the field, there are three essential considerations. The first is the reciprocal relationship between biological inquiry and the development of biological knowledge. To illustrate and develop an understanding of this relationship, college instruction in biology should emphasize: descriptive and experimental aspects of investigation, significant experiences in scientific inquiry (this can be achieved through critical analysis of research reports as well as through laboratory experiences planned to illustrate design of experiments relative to a problem, gathering and interpretation of data, etc.); experience in selection and use of biological literature and, laboratory experience as an integral part of the course. (Living and preserved materials, instrumentation techniques, and field experiences which demonstrate development of biological concepts should be used.)

The second essential consideration in presenting a coherent view of the discipline is to show the interrelationships among the various areas of biology. Broad concepts such as the following can provide a basis for such interrelationships: evolution, diversity of type and unity of pattern; biological roots of behavior; and, community (molecular and cellular as well as ecological). In addition to these concepts, macromolecular biology can be used as a unifying thread.

The third essential consideration is to stress the interrelationships between biology and other disciplines. Some areas in which these are most readily seen are: photosynthesis and respiration; kinematics of enzyme systems; probability and statistics; studies of behavior; ecosystems; biological evolution and culture evolution; and, history of the controversy over spontaneous generation.

To illustrate the foregoing principles to be used in selecting and organizing material from biology for elementary school teachers the following descriptions are provided:

A. *Kinds of living organisms.* Experience in careful observation, description and discrimination with the construction and use of keys for classification often provides experience in the ordering of knowledge. It can provide an understanding of the development of taxonomy as an area of biology by showing the need for frequent review in setting up criteria used in classifying organisms.

B. *The functioning organism.* Consideration should be given to all major kinds of organisms—plants, animals and microbes. Also, life functions should be studied on the level of the behavior of organisms as well as on the molecular-cellular and organ-tissue level. Concepts of significance in studying the functions of organisms are exchange of materials and energy between organism and environment (illustrated by respiration and photosynthesis); regulation and homeostasis; and interaction between environmental stimuli and the organisms. The similarities and differences in these phenomena as they occur in major kinds of organisms—microbes, plants, animals—should be stressed. Differences in kinds of biological problems and modes of experimentation can be readily brought out by comparing key studies of exchange of materials and energy, homeostasis and regulation, and behavior.

Of course, throughout, the complementarity of structure and function should be emphasized. This would entail careful morphological studies of a variety of organisms. In its broadest sense, morphology explains the gross structural differences between plants and animals; in its narrowest sense, it interprets the molecular organization or the structural unit of living organisms—the cell. By drawing upon the equipment and procedures of conventional microscopy and electron microscopy it can be shown how the biological and physical scientists integrate their efforts, their skills, their investigative approaches and their problem solving to interpret taxonomy, ecology, embryology, genetics and physiology. However, these outcomes are not likely to be developed if morphology is restricted to preserved materials. Living materials should be used as much as possible. In this way the elementary school teacher can become familiar with opportunities for studying the live materials abundantly on hand in every elementary school environment.

C. *Growth and development.* The unique contribution which *genetics* can make to the education of elementary teachers is an understanding of how both similarity and variation in successive generations of organisms is possible.

The study of genetics also provides an excellent opportunity for developing an understanding of biological inquiry. Examination of a sequence of key papers in genetics can reveal the development and revision of concepts and the revision of modes of investigation in light of the developing concepts. In addition, the concept of genetic continuity, built up through numerous particular examples of transmission of hereditary characteristics can be used to integrate many areas of study of biological phenomena.

To develop these understandings it is necessary to have first, a precise, disciplined knowledge of the phenomena of mitosis and meiosis; second to understand that there have been different explanations of the mechanisms of these phenomena and why the current explanation is considered most adequate; third, to understand the relationship between the phenomena of mitosis and meiosis and the evidence pertaining to the transmission of hereditary characteristics—i.e., how evidence from cytological, molecular-biochemical and hereditary studies supplement one another; fourth, to see how mathematical concepts have been crucial to the development of the field of genetics; and fifth, to recognize the importance of shifting the unit of study in genetics from individuals to populations.

D. *Interrelations between organisms and environment.* Modern biology should approach the study of living organisms in relation to their total environment, both animate and inanimate. Emphasis should be placed on the interactions between an individual organism and into environment as well as on interrelations between populations. Changes in the behavior patterns in response to changes in environmental factors such as radiation, temperature, moisture, mineral elements and associated organisms are subjects for profitable investigation. Any classroom teacher has within his immediate surroundings a ready-made situation for ecological study, without the necessity of costly equipment. Furthermore, ecology provides an excellent means of bringing the earth sciences, physical sciences, social sciences, and biological sciences into a unified whole. Adequate ecological studies lead directly into the areas of health, safety, and conservation of natural resources.

PHYSICAL SCIENCES. The teaching of elements of physics and chemistry in the elementary schools will probably undergo a considerable change during this decade as a result of the work of various study groups. These groups are exploring the questions of concept formation in the sciences, and their findings will have a great effect on ways in which science is presented to children.

It is important that physical science be taught in a way that will emphasize the investigative nature of science. The teaching of physical science should reveal the way in which these disciplines have developed theoretical and abstract concepts. The physical sciences should be appreciated equally for freeing man from the limitations of common sense observation and for providing the technology that has changed man's environment.

In general, emphasis should be placed on depth of treatment, rather than breadth of coverage. Each course should examine at least one specific topic so that the student acquires an understanding of the application of one or more aspects of chemistry and physics in the development of a rigorous and penetrating scientific argument. Guidance for the role of laboratory to accompany these courses may well come from recent course content experimentation in both high school and college. Opportunities must be provided for students to develop their scientific powers through designing and conducting their own laboratory investigations.

An interdisciplinary approach might well be explored by colleges in offering courses that cover the appropriate topics. Emphasis should be put upon the unity of the sciences, however these topics are presented, and every opportunity taken to show interdisciplinary connections. The history and philosophy of physics and chemistry offer many opportunities to relate the physical sciences to studies in the humanities and social sciences, and historical and philosophical topics should be judiciously introduced into the physical science courses.

Studies in the physical science for elementary school teachers should include topics selected from such major areas as:

1. Measurement and experimental errors in chemistry and physics;
2. Kinematics in one and two dimensions;
3. Dynamics of a particle—Newton's laws, motion of a projectile, Keplerian orbits;
4. Conservation principles: conservation of mass-energy, momentum and charge;
5. Structure of matter and origins of the atomic theory; kinetic-molecular theory, gas laws, atomic species and the periodic table;
6. Descriptive chemistry of important elements and compounds: formulas and equations;

7. Heat phenomena: temperature, transfer of heat, change of phase;
8. First and second laws of thermodynamics: mechanical equivalent of heat, order and disorder;
9. Waves: waves on strings, acoustic waves;
10. Electric and magnetic fields: electrostatics, electric currents, electromagnetism, electromagnetic induction;
11. Electromagnetic waves: geometrical and physical optics developed for optical waves, but extended to other electromagnetic radiations; the electromagnetic spectrum;
12. The atom-quantum theory of Planck and Einstein, discrete spectra, Rutherford model of the atom, Bohr theory, matter-waves and indeterminacy;
13. Chemical bonding: ionic, covalent, metallic;
14. Chemical reactions: rates, equilibrium, energy of reaction. The solid state; and,
15. The nuclear atom and nuclear energy—radioactivity and isotopes, mass-energy equivalence, fission and fusion, models of the nucleus.

MATHEMATICS. The recommendations of the Committee on Undergraduate Program in Mathematics of the Mathematical Association of America for the preparation in mathematics of prospective elementary teachers are strongly endorsed in principle. The amount of time needed to satisfy the CUPM recommendations is dependent upon the ability and previous preparation of the teacher candidate and will vary from student to student. Programs should be based on at least two years of college preparatory mathematics and more if feasible.

The following are brief descriptions of essential mathematical preparation of the elementary teacher:

A. *Algebraic structure of the number system.* This is a study of the numbers used in elementary school whole numbers, common fractions, irrational numbers. Emphasis should be on the basic concepts and techniques: properties of addition, multiplication, inverses, systems of numeration, and the number line. The techniques for computation with numbers should be derived from the properties and structure of the number system, and much attention should be paid to approximation. Some elementary number theory, including prime numbers, properties of even and odd numbers, and some arithmetic with congruences should be included.

B. *Algebra.* Basic ideas and structure of algebra, including equations, inequalities, positive and negative numbers, absolute value, graphing of truth sets of equations and inequalities, examples of other algebraic systems—definitely including finite ones—to emphasize the structure of algebra as well as simple concepts and language of sets.

C. *Intuitive foundations of geometry.* A study of space, plane, and line as sets of points, considering separation properties and simple closed curves; the triangle, rectangle, circle, sphere, and the other figures in the plane and space considered as sets of points with their properties developed intuitively; the concept of deduction and the beginning of deductive theory based on the properties that have been identified in the intuitive development; concepts of measurement in the plane and space, angle measurement, measurement of the circle, volumes of familiar solids; and, the treatment of coordinate geometry through graphs of simple equations.

These recommendations are minimal. Students who have already covered much of the material recommended by CUPM should be encouraged to extend their studies. A good percentage of the prospective elementary school teachers should enroll in a program comparable to the CUPM recommendations for level II. All students should be prepared to meet changes in content, terminology, and methods in elementary school mathematics with a minimum of inservice assistance. The required flexibility of mind can best be attained by an emphasis on fundamental, widely applicable concepts, such as: set, relation, function, operation, one-to-one correspondence, and isomorphism.

With the inevitable increased future dependence of society on quantitative thinking throughout the many areas served by mathematics it is vital that the teacher bring to the elementary school as much related academic background as possible. For example, elementary notions of probability and statistics may find their way into the secondary and elementary curricula of the future. The applications of these ideas to the physical and social sciences are increasing. Thus some experience with probability and statistics is desirable. Some knowledge of the significance of the computer and its place in society, as well as some idea of the things that programmers do, would be appropriate.

Elementary school teachers should be thoroughly acquainted with the curricula of the higher grades (junior and senior high school) toward which their pupils are moving. This is in keeping with the more general principle that any teacher should thoroughly understand the subject matter at levels beyond the one that he is teaching.

ELEMENTARY SCIENCE AND MATHEMATICS CURRICULUM AND METHODS

Guideline V

> *The program of preparation for the elementary school teacher should include study of the aims and methods of teaching science and mathematics in the elementary school.*

The prospective elementary school teacher should have ample and appropriate opportunity to relate the concepts, information and techniques of college science and mathematics to the educational needs and potentialities of elementary school pupils.

The professional courses should provide both classroom and laboratory experiences specifically designed to develop skill in teaching science and mathematics in the elementary schools. Attention should be given to the identification and development of teaching procedures according to the unique abilities of each prospective teacher.

Professional experiences should include:

1. Systematic consideration of purposes, methods, materials, and evaluation procedures appropriate to the teaching of mathematics and science to children;
2. Study of current trends and research in the teaching of science and mathematics;
3. Laboratory and field opportunities to encourage development of individual initiative in conducting experiments, devising demonstration equipment, developing teacher resources, and planning other types of learning activities;
4. Study of the implications of psychology for the teaching and learning of science and mathematics; and,
5. Opportunities for prospective teachers to become acquainted with the professional organizations in science and mathematics, their services to teachers, and the importance of active participation in selected organizations including the encouragement they provide for professional growth.

Teachers of methods courses should be well informed about basic mathematical and scientific concepts; the concepts, problems, and literature of mathematics and science education; the nature of the learner; and, the nature of American public schools. They should be excellent teachers who have the confidence of the mathematics, science and education departments.

EXPERIENCES WITH CHILDREN

Guideline VI

> *Professional ·laboratory experiences, including observation and student teaching, should provide opportunities for the prospective teacher to work with experienced elementary school teachers who are competent in the subject area, skilled in nurturing the spirit of inquiry, and effective in helping children benefit from the study of science and mathematics.*

The institution should have a well-developed program of professional laboratory experiences for future elementary school teachers. With reference to science and mathematics, there should be provision for the effective utilization of personnel appropriately sensitive and competent in science, mathematics and education. This includes the director of laboratory experiences, the immediate supervisor of student teaching experience, the college visitors from the sciences and mathematics departments, and the local cooperating teachers.

The young teacher's confidence in his own ability to teach children science and mathematics in the elementary school is important in initiating and carrying out his own activities. His college experience, including student teaching, should encourage self-confidence. Important in his preparation to teach science and mathematics is contact with teachers who know how to teach science and mathematics to children of differing interests, backgrounds and abilities. Observations and demonstrations should be planned to help prospective teachers relate both content and professional education courses to the interests and maturity levels of children.

The student teaching experience should be under the control of a supervising teacher who has the experience and ability necessary to plan and execute a well-balanced classroom program in which science and mathematics are effectively taught. The cooperating teacher should help the student teacher to develop and utilize teaching plans that integrate effectively science and mathematics in the total elementary school curriculum. He should provide opportunities for student teachers to guide and stimulate children through problematic approaches, and through activities that will result in learning. He should teach student teachers to carry on varied and responsible evaluations with their pupils.

The student teaching supervisory staff should include staff members who have strong backgrounds in science or mathematics education. In addition, these staff members should be well acquainted with the characteristics of children as learners, with the teaching process, should have practical insights into the program of the elementary school, and should make an effort to work with the cooperating teacher.

ADDITIONAL UNDERGRADUATE STUDY

Guideline VII

> *The program for the preparation of the elementary school teacher should provide opportunities for pursuit of additional undergraduate study in a carefully planned program in science and mathematics.*

Prospective teachers should seek depth in a subject matter area, whether it be in the humanities, in the sciences or in the arts. The demands of elementary teacher preparation within a four year college program may restrict specialization to something less than a conventional academic major but there should be opportunities to pursue a subject beyond the introductory level. Additional emphasis on specialized content and instructional techniques in both science and mathematics, for instance, should be available in professional methods courses, in the study of elementary school curriculum and in pre-professional participation and student teaching.

In the material suggested below opportunities for study should go beyond those recommended in the preceding *Guidelines*.

Biological Sciences. For those who seek depth in biological science, additional study of biology should be provided with problem solving laboratory and field experiences deliberately oriented in favor of an investigative approach. Further depth in concepts should be developed in accordance with material listed in *Guideline IV*.

Physical Sciences. For those who seek depth in physical science additional study in chemistry and physics might be selected from such areas as general chemistry, analytical chemistry, biochemistry, organic chemistry, physical chemistry, introductory classical physics, and introductory modern physics.

Earth Sciences. For those who seek depth in the earth sciences, the study selected will depend on the background of the student. Additional study may be done in such areas as astronomy; meteorology and climatology; geology; mineralogy and paleontology; and oceanography.

Mathematics. For those who seek depth in mathematics, study should continue into mathematical analysis (including the fundamentals of analytic geometry), abstract algebra, geometry, and probability from a set-theoretic point of view. This program is spelled out very well by the Committee on the Undergraduate Program in Mathematics (CUPM) but currently would probably not be adequately covered by standard programs in mathematics departments over the country.

Fifth and Sixth Programs

Guideline VIII

> *Fifth year and sixth year programs for the elementary school teacher should offer appropriate science courses and mathematics courses which might be applied toward an advanced degree.*

Post-baccalaureate opportunities should be available within the institutions or through cooperation with other institutions so that elementary school teachers can extend their competence in the sciences and mathematics with the purpose of becoming better teachers, special teachers, or supervisors. In working out the details of any such program, primary attention must be focused on what would best contribute to increasing the competence and effectiveness of the teacher.

Institutions are encouraged to experiment with new approaches to the development of science and mathematics programs for elementary school teachers at the post-baccalaureate level.

It is recommended that institutions offer graduate level credit for the courses developed. Courses so designed should be considered as adequate to permit further study in regular programs of the departments included under science and mathematics.

In the fields of science, these courses will probably differ from those designed for the preparation of professional scientists in the following ways. There will be an emphasis on simple but revealing laboratory experiments; more attention will be paid to an interdisciplinary approach; greater emphasis will be placed on concepts of science relevant to the teaching of science in the elementary school; use will be made of a simple quantitative approach with emphasis on quantitative representation; the historical development of science will be emphasized; and, less emphasis will be placed on the enumeration of scientific facts.

Teachers who engage in fifth and sixth year programs of study should have an opportunity to take additional work in science and mathematics to enable them to teach these subjects more effectively. Teachers who have a special responsibility for science and mathematics in a team teaching plan in their schools will need to strengthen their backgrounds of experience in the study of science and mathematics and to be kept up-to-date on new developments in scientific research, curriculum, and teaching methods.

For fuller realization of a program of science and mathematics in an elementary school, the use of science and mathematics specialists should be considered. Post-baccalaureate programs for the preparation of these specialists should be developed by colleges and universities with qualified staff members who are particularly interested in this endeavor. Such programs should produce specialists who have at least a masters degree which includes substantial work in science and/or mathematics.

A specialist may be a consultant, special teacher, resource person, supervisor, or coordinator. The functions of mathematics and science specialists may include: preparing instructional materials and coordinating resources available from the immediate community; assisting in selection of equipment, facilities and instructional materials; developing inservice programs; facilitating articulation of K–12 programs in science and mathematics; providing liaison with college, university and state department personnel in science and mathematics; interpreting new developments in research and teaching to administrators and the public; teaching demonstration lessons; and, providing leadership for evaluation of science and mathematics programs.

INSERVICE EDUCATION

Guideline IX

> *Inservice education should provide opportunities for the elementary school teacher continuously to improve and extend the competencies required for effective teaching of science and mathematics.*

Guidelines I to VIII recommend that elementary teachers have four years of preservice undergraduate education and that they spend a fifth year in rounding out their preparation for elementary teaching and in pursuing advanced work in areas of particular interest. Inservice offerings must take into account the needs of those now teaching whose preservice preparation does not meet *Guideline* standards. Inservice education is interpreted to mean both planned group and planned independent study. Its primary aim is to keep teachers alert to changes in content and method.

The preservice education of teachers should encourage and develop those qualities which enable teachers to supplement inservice course opportunities with a continuing program of independent study. The object should be to develop those habits, ideas, techniques, and powers of judgment and understanding that will not only enable but will also inspire the postgraduate to an active continuation of self-education throughout life. Due to the present explosive rate of growth of knowledge in mathematics and in the sciences, the preservice teacher trainees of today will be required in the future to judge programs and teach materials which they have never studied formally and for which inservice programs will not always be available.

Teacher education institutions, state, and local agencies are urged to provide appropriate inservice programs. School systems are urged in turn to provide time and incentives for teacher participation in these programs. The suggestions made earlier in these *Guidelines* for the preservice preparation of elementary school teachers should be considered in planning inservice programs for teachers in modern mathematics and science.

These programs should: provide the teacher with analyses of current research pertinent to the teaching of science and mathematics; the study and evaluation of contemporary learning materials for science and mathematics education; and, assist teachers in planning effective applications and in orienting their subject matter to the general or unique needs of their students.

Effective methods of conducting inservice education should be investigated; e.g., programmed instruction, radio, television, correspondence, guides, films, supplementary materials, tapes, and laboratory and field experiences. Mass media coupled with actual personal involvement should be explored.

It is assumed that increasingly young teachers will enter teaching better prepared in science and mathematics. Recurring surveys of inservice education programs will be required to keep up with the changing needs of teachers.

MODEL PROGRAMS FOR THE
EDUCATION OF TEACHERS
IN SCIENCE *

Stephen S. Winter

This article is a portion of a progress report from the Eastern Section of the Association for the Education of Teachers in Science. Four groups presented recommendations for the preparation of elementary, junior high, and high school teachers in science. The individual reports of the four groups were edited into one comprehensive report by Stephen S. Winter. This portion of the report is concerned only with the professional education (reported by Harold E. Tannenbaum of Hunter College) and with the pre-service science education (reported by Paul S. Hiack of Trenton State College) of elementary teachers.

I. RECOMMENDATIONS FOR PROFESSIONAL EDUCATION—NON-SCIENCE

Group I considered the desired behavioral characteristics of beginning teachers in the professional, non-science areas. The group generally agreed upon three areas of concern:

A. Philosophic foundations
B. Social foundations
C. Psychological foundations.

The major portion of the group's time was spent considering the first two of these areas. It was agreed that the third area should receive further consideration at the next conference of the group.

A summary of the discussion follows:

A. *Philosophic Foundations*

A prospective teacher of science (K–12) should through his actions, even more than through his oral and written statements, indicate the beginnings of a mature personal and social philosophy consistent with the characteristics

---

* REPRINTED FROM *Journal of Research in Science Teaching*, Vol. 3, Issue 2, 1965, pp. 102–104, by permission of the author and the editor. Dr. Winter is Associate Professor of Education at the State University of New York, Buffalo.

of American society. He should demonstrate a consistent value system through the ways he behaves, not only professionally but personally. It was the consensus of the group that one important aspect of the personal behavior of the beginning professional should be determined by his attitudes towards the scientific enterprise of the contemporary world. Included in the desired behavior patterns should be an active understanding of the roles of science in modern society: what science can do *for* us; what science can do *to* us. Furthermore, the beginning teacher should demonstrate his appreciation not only of the rational aspects of science processes but also of the creative and intuitive aspects of these processes.

Finally, the group agreed that an essential behavior of the beginning teacher would be found in his philosophic approach to his teaching assignment. The purposes of education to which he adheres as well as his own views on the role of the teacher in the general framework of the educational enterprise should be clearly evident from his written and oral statements. Even more important, his views and positions on matters of educational philosophy should be evident from his professional behavior.

It seemed to the group that the curricular work related to developing a personal philosophy needed to come early in the pre-service education of the teacher while those aspects of the curriculum related to the development of a consistent and functional educational philosophy might well come toward the close of the pre-service program, concurrent with or following an internship experience.

B. Social Foundations

The group generally agreed that the social behavior of the young professional would be a very significant indicator of his education. Does the young teacher indicate concern for the social issues of the day both through his own out-of-school activities and through the kinds of activities he fosters and encourages in his classroom? Does the young teacher, through his own behavior, indicate an awareness of the significant contributions of the behavioral sciences to the understanding of contemporary society? Does the young teacher, through professional behavior, indicate a consistency in the philosophy he espouses and the personal and professional activities in which he participates?

The group recognized that social foundations had been included in most curricular designs for at least the past thirty years. It was noted with considerable emphasis, however, that a curriculum was being advocated which included not mere courses in sociology, anthropology, social psychology, and the like, but opportunities for active social participation by students during their pre-service education.

C. Psychological Foundations

As was pointed out earlier, the psychological foundations for teacher preparation did not receive the needed attention from the group. However, the group was in agreement that the young teacher needs to demonstrate his awareness of the characteristics of children and youth of all ages and to be particularly cognizant of the psychological characteristics and needs of the age group with which he is working. A further discussion of this aspect of teacher preparation is contemplated for the next meeting of the group.

D. Other Considerations and Summary

Running through the entire discussion was a constant emphasis on the importance of personal experience in the education of the prospective teacher. We want our pre-service personnel to have experiences in various parts of the nation, to know our cities, our rural areas, our various geographic sectors, our many ethnic groups, and our neighbors, near and far. These should be provided, in so far as possible, through personal activities; where such personal involvement cannot be achieved, the best available vicarious experiences that modern educational media can provide should be substituted. We want our young teachers to have worked with children and youth from many social, economic, and ethnic backgrounds during their pre-service preparation. We are convinced that a well-planned internship, jointly sponsored by the preparing institution and the employing school system, offers great promise (if it is not, indeed, the *sine qua non*) for sound professional preparation. We want our future science teachers to have personal experiences in the science centers and workshops of the nation, under the supervision of practicing scientists.

In short, we see the education of a future teacher as something much broader and deeper than a mere series of college courses, either in the liberal studies or in professional education. We propose during our further deliberations to turn to a consideration of the kinds of activities we would advocate for the preparation of such teachers.

II. Recommendations for Pre-Service Education of Elementary Teachers

Group II considered that the science education of the individual teacher will depend in part on the extent of his responsibility for teaching science. Various organizational patterns based on this assumption were discussed. It was recognized that additional research is needed to resolve the question of which pattern will best support the teaching of science in the elementary school. Therefore, at present the general classroom teacher should be trained to assume responsibility for the teaching of science and should have available adequate consultant help in this area. Adequate help in this context was defined as a science consultant for each building and, in addition, a teaching staff of which 20–25 per cent has a science emphasis pre-service preparation. A staff so prepared would seem to offer good flexibility should it become apparent that some other administrative pattern is more desirable.

The group then identified the needs of the personnel in this organization for scientific instruction. The needs of all teachers were identified and recommendations were made for the pre-service education programs of the three types of teachers: the general classroom teacher, the teacher with a pre-service emphasis in science, and the science consultant. However, the group also recognized that additional research is needed in all areas of elementary school science, especially in the area of teacher preparation.

A. *General Competencies for Elementary Science*

Among the competencies necessary for effective teaching of elementary science which are directly related to pre-service education in science are the following:

1. Awareness of content and structure of science, of the relationship among the branches of science, and the relationship of science to other areas of knowledge.
2. Skill in working with the materials of science.
3. A knowledge of and skill in the use of methods which have been shown to be useful in achieving the objectives of elementary school science.
4. The ability to work with children who have special interest or ability in science and to assist further in the development of that interest and ability.

B. *The General Classroom Teacher*

This preparation would include training in each of the broad course areas of science, *i.e.*, physical, biological, and space science. Twelve to twenty hours of such science courses should be completed. These are to be courses in which the major ideas of these areas are used as unifying concepts. Laboratory and field work are considered essential. In addition, a methods course specifically directed toward teaching of science in the elementary school must be included.

C. *The Teacher with Pre-Service Emphasis in Science*

Preparation here includes all the requirements for the general teacher plus additional courses in formal science comprising about one fourth of the total pre-service preparation. Student teaching in science is assumed to be an integral part of the pre-service preparation and is not included in the formal science course preparation.

D. *The Science Consultant*

This area requires the above preparation plus teaching experience on the elementary level and at least one year of courses on the graduate level.

IN-SERVICE SCIENCE ACTIVITIES FOR THE ELEMENTARY SCHOOL TEACHER *

Marjorie S. Lerner

Marjorie Lerner describes how elementary school teachers can continue their professional growth through varied in-service activities. In-service education in elementary school science can be derived from three basic sources: programs occurring within the local school system, opportunities provided by colleges and universities, and activities that can be self-initiated by the teacher. Dr. Lerner also discusses briefly the role of the school administrator in promoting effective in-service education.

THE PROFESSIONAL growth of the elementary school teacher is a necessity as long as the teacher continues to teach. In order to develop and maintain a high level of competence, the teacher must be provided with continued opportunities for in-service education in all areas of the elementary school curriculum.

Today there is a vital need for in-service education in the area of elementary school science. There are several factors responsible for creating this need. A number of new programs have been developed based on an approach to the teaching of science in the elementary school which stresses the development of the skills or processes of science, and which also aims for the inculcation of scientific attitudes and critical thinking. Programs such as these require elementary school teachers to review and extend further their understanding of the different ways of teaching science.

The recent explosion of science knowledge has produced an impact all the way down to the elementary school, making it imperative for teachers who are already in service to upgrade their science knowledge and background. The National Defense Education Act and also the Elementary and Secondary Education Act have made it possible for the elementary schools to acquire a large quantity and variety of much-needed scientific equipment. As

* REPRINTED FROM a presentation made on July 13, 1966, at the Summer Conference on Science Education sponsored by the Northwestern University School of Education in Evanston, Illinois, by permission of the author. Dr. Lerner is principal of the Donoghue Elementary School in Chicago.

a result, teachers must now become familiar with many different kinds of equipment, learn the purposes for which the equipment can be used, and develop proficiency in manipulating the equipment.

THREE BASIC SOURCES FOR IN-SERVICE EDUCATION

In-service education in science for the elementary school teacher can be derived from three basic sources. First, there are programs that can operate within the local school system. Second, there are opportunities provided by colleges and universities. Third, there are in-service activities that can be initiated and sustained by the teacher alone.

Within the Local System

WORKSHOPS. Science workshops can be helpful to teachers in a number of ways. They can be used to evaluate and revise an existing science program, to organize and develop a new science program with scope and sequence, to coordinate a science program so that it becomes part of an over-all K–12 science program, to construct teaching units, to investigate and determine ways of obtaining and using materials and equipment, to select textbooks and reference books, to provide the teachers with a series of lecture-demonstrations by science specialists, and to help the teachers become more proficient in methods of teaching science to children.

Science workshops are usually conducted under the leadership of a science supervisor, if the school has one, or by a special committee appointed for that purpose. In some workshops academically and professionally trained persons are asked to serve as consultants and as resource specialists to provide either science information or methodology or both. Some workshops make use of their high school and junior high school science teachers as well.

What characteristics are necessary for a successful workshop? To begin with, workshops cannot be artificial situations with manufactured problems. The problems must be of real concern to the teachers who are participating in the workshop.

In order to ensure that teachers have profitable experiences, workshops should be cooperatively planned with carefully designated objectives. These objectives may be immediate objectives or long-range objectives. For example, a workshop for elementary teachers to acquaint them with the use of several new pieces of equipment has an immediate objective of developing teacher competency in using this new equipment. This new equipment is then scrutinized in perspective with other science equipment, and decisions are made as to where and how this new equipment will best be used. An example of a workshop with long-range objectives would be one where all the science equipment is evaluated, for the purpose of determining specific needs for the future rather than ordering new materials on a "guess" basis.

Some workshops should be specifically designed for the teacher new to the local system. New teachers need orientation to the guiding philosophy in the science program. New teachers also have to see the entire scope and sequence of the science program in order to understand their specific role in the program. Workshops designed to help new teachers learn what resources are available to them and where they may obtain assistance in their science teaching can be of tremendous assistance.

The experienced teacher usually has problems that are different and more sophisticated than those of the new teacher, and therefore needs a workshop with different objectives: How do I apply new approaches to teaching science at my grade level? How do I recognize changed scientific behavior? How do I evaluate my teaching in terms of desired changed behavior? How do I construct valid tests for the objectives set forth in the science program? How do I individualize science instruction? What textbooks are best suited to the program?

COMMITTEE WORK.   Teachers can further their professional growth by serving on both small and large committees. Committees provide a wide range of opportunity for in-service education because they permit teachers to engage in many types of activities. Teachers may be encouraged to try out new science programs and report on the progress of such programs. Perhaps the teacher will design new activities to be incorporated into new programs. The teacher can become involved in writing curriculum materials. The study of current research and literature is an important facet of science curriculum development. There are opportunities for the exchange of ideas with other teachers and with various science supervisors and consultants. In evaluating programs and materials, the goals for teaching science in the elementary school become clarified.

THE SCIENCE SUPERVISOR.   Quite often elementary teachers fail to realize that their most immediate source for a wide range of in-service activities lies within their grasp by making proper use of their science supervisor. The following is only a partial list of the various ways teachers can obtain help from the science supervisor.

1. Request the observation and evaluation of the teaching-learning situation.
2. Have the science supervisor teach a science session, perhaps one that involves the use of science equipment.
3. Discuss new ideas or approaches to the teaching of science, and request aid in carrying them through.
4. Request assistance in locating needed equipment or in constructing simple equipment.
5. Seek aid in locating or evaluating instructional material.
6. Ask for a specific type of workshop to help solve special problems.
7. Seek advice on local resources.
8. Request aid in planning profitable field trips that will enrich the science program.

9. Ask for help on how to use new equipment or materials.
10. Request the recommendation of certain teachers to be visited and observed for competence in teaching science.
11. Ask for recommendations for professional literature that will assist the teacher in teaching science.
12. Request aid in the construction of tests that will best suit the goals and objectives of the science program.
13. Seek aid in the selection of appropriate films, filmstrips, and other audio-visual materials.
14. Seek advice on summer offerings at local colleges and universities.

Even though this is a partial list of the ways the science supervisor can help the elementary school teacher, it clearly shows how the science supervisor can be a valuable resource person for assisting teachers to continue their professional growth while teaching.

THE ROLE OF TELEVISION. Television possesses tremendous opportunities for use in in-service education of teachers. Television has the advantage of being able to reach large numbers of teachers through a single telecast or series of telecasts. Teachers can learn much by observing a skillful classroom teacher work in her classroom. By using television, this one skillful teacher can be observed by a great many teachers.

The science supervisor often needs to serve large numbers of teachers. His time and efforts can be conserved through the use of television. New advances in science can be brought to the immediate attention of teachers through the use of science consultants. Entire college courses are now being taught on television. Perhaps here is the opportunity for the elementary teacher to obtain needed knowledge and background in physics, chemistry, geology or astronomy. Some instructional courses are presented during the pre-school hours, others during the school day.

Colleges and Universities

An examination of the backgrounds of most new elementary school teachers reveals in most cases a woeful lack of science background. Our colleges and universities often allow the science requirements for graduation to be fulfilled by the election of just one year of a science in an area which the college student chooses. It is, therefore, not uncommon for the elementary school teacher to arrive on the job with a one-year sequence in biology and, perhaps, the professional science methods course. In many instances, it is possible for the new teacher to have had absolutely no laboratory experience in fulfilling the college science requirement. Even the elementary school science methods may be part of a multiple methods course involving other elementary curricular areas such as social studies and/or mathematics. Yet a cursory examination of elementary science textbooks reveals that only about one third of the science content is in the area of the biological sciences. Approximately another third is devoted to the area of physics. The remaining third is concerned with the areas of astronomy, geology, meteorology, and chemistry.

It is quite evident that a four-year college program cannot produce elementary teachers with the proper science background to teach elementary school science effectively. After a year or two of teaching, therefore, elementary teachers should begin to become aware of the gaps in their science background and should begin to fill these needs. Summer study at colleges and universities can fill these gaps.

The teachers must be careful, however, to select courses that truly fill their needs. An introductory course in geology can be more immediately fruitful to the elementary school teacher than an advanced course in educational psychology. The teacher should select science courses that will provide laboratory experience. Teachers without such experiences are generally fearful of science equipment. As a result, experiments and/or demonstrations will rarely occur when such teachers are teaching science.

Many school systems base salary increments only upon graduate study and additional degrees. As a result, teachers cannot gain recognition or credit by taking the introductory course, even though such a course meets a definite need for the professional growth of the teacher. Consequently, teachers are discouraged from taking beginning courses in a science area. There is a great need for school systems to re-evaluate their attitudes toward such introductory courses. In the long run, it is the child in the classroom who benefits by the teacher who seeks and attains competence in subject matter. This, then, should be the criterion used by school systems rather than the level of the college course taken by the teacher.

National Science Foundation

The National Science Foundation supports a variety of projects designed to help elementary school teachers become acquainted with new developments in science and in elementary science education, and thus increase their competence as teachers. These projects are generally in the form of summer institutes given at host colleges and universities under grants provided by the National Science Foundation. In many of these projects, stipends and allowances are available to participants. These institutes can fill many gaps in the background of elementary teachers. In order to meet the needs of teachers with varied backgrounds, these institutes offer courses of an introductory nature as well as courses for those teachers who will have had some prior study in a specific area.

An examination of a list of National Science Foundation elementary school summer institutes reveals course offerings in physics, chemistry, biology, astronomy, geology, physical science, biological science, earth science, mathematics, and methods of teaching elementary school science. Participants in these summer institutes often become key science personnel for a local school system and act as resource people for in-service programs. In this way the influence of the institutes is eventually extended to a larger number of teachers.

Self-Initiating Activities

Elementary teachers can and should afford themselves the opportunity for professional growth through reading current professional literature. *Science and Children* is an excellent publication of the National Science Teachers Association, devoted exclusively to science for grades K–6. Frequently, this publication presents outstanding talks from the association's annual convention or from regional conferences. *The Grade Teacher* and *The Instructor* have devoted entire issues to science for the elementary grades. *School Science and Mathematics* (the publication of the Central Association of Science and Mathematics Teachers) and *The Science Teacher* (another publication of the National Science Teachers Association) occasionally feature articles pertinent to elementary school science. The same holds true for the *National Education Association Journal*. If these publications do not appear in your professional school library, consult your school librarian. She is usually eager to obtain subscriptions to those professional publications that will be helpful to the teacher.

Membership in a professional science education organization on a local, state, or national level will afford many opportunities for professional growth through bulletins, newsletters, publication announcements, or attendance at meetings, regional conferences, and conventions. Many publishers of elementary science textbooks issue curricular bulletins and charts, and are always interested in communicating with teachers. In school systems where in-service education is entirely an individual matter, self-initiating activities make it possible for elementary teachers to continue their professional growth.

THE ROLE OF THE SCHOOL ADMINISTRATOR

The school administrator plays a crucial role in the effectiveness of any in-service education program. He must be aware of the strengths and weaknesses of his teachers, be able to identify their widely divergent problems and needs, and provide a variety of opportunities to help the teachers according to their specific needs.

He should encourage teachers to seek new approaches to the teaching of science. Provisions must be made for teachers to observe good teaching practices and to attend workshops, conferences, and conventions. He must provide necessary materials, establish effective schedules, and coordinate the activities of teachers, supervisors, and consultants. Unless the administrator plans for school in-service activities, they will not take place, and professional growth will be held to a minimum.

THE SUPERVISION OF THE
SCIENCE PROGRAM *

National Society for the Study of Education

Supervision plays an extremely important role in any school organization. As the school system grows, specialists in science education are needed to provide for the constant growth and improvement in the science curriculum and instruction. This comprehensive discussion considers the various roles of the supervisor on the state, county, and local levels. The special problems that arise at each of these levels are presented, and suggestions are made as to how to meet these problems. This discussion is an excerpt from Chaper 12, "The Supervision of the Science Programs," of the Fifty-ninth Yearbook of the National Society for the Study of Education, Part I, Rethinking Science Education. Members of the committee who wrote this chapter include Donald Stotler, Lorenzo Lisonbee, Elra Palmer, Samuel Schenburg, and Henry Shannon.

The Nature and Importance of Supervision

Operational problems of one kind or another will quite certainly confront any established organization. If an organizational group is to remain dynamic, it must struggle toward equilibrium in structure at the very time that it is seeking ways to unbalance the equilibrium in order to improve the structure. This conflict between stability and change is blended most successfully in organizations where the expectancy is one of "structural mobility" or "organized change." In such situations the energy typically spent in resisting change is channeled into seeking and fostering types of change designed for the improvement of the whole organization.

The Need for Supervision

Supervisors are needed to help an organization live successfully as a "family" within its structural plan while at the same time helping to rebuild the structure. Doing this is difficult enough, but doing it with methods which permit acceptance of the supervisor as a member of the "family" is the acid test of modern supervision.

For this difficult role effective supervisors are in constant demand, for the

---

* REPRINTED FROM *Rethinking Science Education*, 59th Yearbook of the National Society for the Study of Education, Part I (Chicago: University of Chicago Press, 1960), pp. 213–224, 226–228, by permission of the publisher.

part they play in an organization is somewhat like the role of the catalyst in an organism. Membership in smaller educational organizations is often limited to planners (administrators) and teachers. Such an organization may be very successful; or it may result in the development of an arbitrary plan of action with little provision for reorganization and growth. More flexibility often results if the administrator provides some time for supervisory work or arranges to have a teacher released on a part-time basis for this type of service.

As a school system grows in size, both advantages and disadvantages emerge. One advantage arises from the fact that, between the administrative and the implemental levels, specialists in subject matter and methodology can be provided to play the catalytic role.

The Supervisor as a Consultant

When a supervisory program becomes more inhibiting than catalytic, the reasons are usually less obvious than those indicated in the preceding paragraphs. The latter may be only contributing influences. In an honest attempt to reduce friction and increase the effectiveness of a program, especially in larger systems, a stifling accumulation of rules, procedures, clearances, and general protocol may accrue. Out of this complexity may arise an atmosphere known in popular jargon as "bureaucratic." In this type of organization, the supervisor tends to become so preoccupied with procedure that proceedings grind to a snail's pace. It becomes so difficult or irritating to bring about change that initiative and creativity are stifled.

A new concept is arising in the field of supervision. In some systems the title of supervisor has actually been replaced by the title of consultant. Even where the title has been retained, the supervisor has become a consultant. The word itself denotes the change. A consultant is a person who is sought for suggestions and assistance in planning. The emphasis upon being sought is an invitation to initiative in others. It also means that to be successful a consultant must have something to offer in the way of knowledge and method.

Supervision: A Cooperative Endeavor

The modern concept of supervision is one of helping people help themselves. This is also the modern concept of classroom instruction. The supervisor is wise, therefore, to make all details of his approach consistent with the approach he advocates for teachers. If he believes teachers should set a wholesome emotional tone in the classroom, then he should seek a similar tone in the educational system. If he believes teachers should develop experimental-mindedness, curiosity, leadership, and self-analysis, he should seek to bring out these qualities in the adults with whom he works. If he believes that the teacher should use multiple approaches, employ diverse materials, encourage problem-exploration, and emphasize individual differences, this belief should be reflected in his own activities.

All of this calls for that healthy give-and-take called cooperative planning.

The supervisor by no means abdicates the role of leadership, nor does the classroom teacher who organizes the classroom in such a manner that she is freed to be a consultant. People seek the consultant in order to become oriented and to discuss new pursuits. The consultant, in approaching problems cooperatively, helps draw a larger circle with new problems. This may be an extension of a new interest or an enlargement of an old one, but it leads to a desire for leadership in opening up new frontiers.

Teachers may use the consultant approach with students, and consultants may use a similar approach with adult personnel within the educational system—and still the education of youth could be jeopardized if the community does not understand the modern approach. The supervisor uses the same approach with the community which he uses with the adult personnel in the school system and which he encourages teachers to use in the classroom. The attitude is not one of salesmanship of a finished program but cooperative problem-exploration in improving the program.

THE STATE CONSULTANT FOR SCIENCE

A typical state school system might have one thousand secondary schools in operation in one hundred fifty local school units. Each of these schools is an integral part of a complex machine devoted to the job of educating youth. If one were to evaluate the science programs in these schools, a normal distribution would probably be the result. The schools would vary in the effectiveness of their programs from very poor to very good, in much the same manner that members of a heterogeneous biology class would vary in their achievements. However, there would be many schools which failed to realize their potential and operated below their capacity, thus providing sufficient reason for initiating plans for improvement.

The Need for the Consultant

The state consultant for science occupies a unique and challenging position in programs for improvement. He works with all schools and with groups within the schools including administrators, teachers, pupils, and school boards. He endeavors to direct their energies into appropriate channels and to help them formulate plans of action for long-range improvement. He performs a motivating function, an analysis function, and a synthesizing function. The schools with weaker programs are encouraged to analyze their resources with the view of preparing a program which will raise the instruction to a higher level. Schools with strong science programs are guided into well-planned experiments to discover more effective ways of handling the various aspects of the curriculum, and these are translated into procedures which can be used later by all schools.

The Role of the Consultant

The science consultant representing a state department of education will find himself involved in the thinking and other activities of many groups.

He must work with all groups which are genuinely interested in providing the best scientific education for youth. With these groups his role will be that of a listener, an originator of ideas, a co-ordinator of activities, a pro-curer of help, and an encourager. In short, he will serve as the director of a team composed of many members, each of whom must be placed in the type of work which will assure the best results.

All of this means that the state consultant in science must know and understand the spectrum of science education in his state, which will include bases of the curriculum; relation of administration, teachers, and students to the program; physical facilities; experimentation; and new curriculum materials. When he finds there are gaps in this spectrum, he must work in such a manner that these voids are gradually filled. Unfortunately, this is an un-ending task for, as one gap is filled, another appears. Therefore, review of the spectrum and efforts to keep it unbroken must be continuous.

Responsibilities of the Consultant

As indicated in the preceding paragraph, the consultant, to be effective, must contribute to the achievement of the general goals by assisting in the solution of a variety of problems as they arise or become acute. A number of serious gaps have appeared in the science-education spectrum in recent years. One of these is the inadequacy of teaching personnel with respect to both numbers and training. This problem has arisen because of the upsurge in school enrollments, low salaries, poor working conditions, and the rapid change from an agricultural to a technological society. To make this situa-tion more serious, the subject matter in the various science courses has neces-sarily undergone rapid change. Perhaps an answer is needed to the question, "What kind of program should be established to provide science teachers who will be able to channel the energies of youth into more productive efforts?"

The solution to this problem must be a co-operative affair, involving the science consultant, the state department of education, the colleges, the sci-ence teachers, administrators, and resource persons such as industrial chem-ists and conservationists. With the consultant as a co-ordinator, these groups can participate in science-teacher work conferences in local school systems and in programs on sectional and state levels. The work of these conferences might be centered on such topics as the cell, the atom, photosynthesis, me-tabolism, chromatographic analysis, materials, and professional organizations. However, such conferences affect directly only those persons already teach-ing. Paralleling these activities must be others which deal with pre-service teacher education. With vitalized programs at the pre-service level, progress should be noticeable within a few years.

A second gap in the spectrum has occurred in the area of curriculum. The large volume of scientific information collected cannot be covered in the courses, and, as a result, important questions have been asked: What should be eliminated? What should be added? What sequence should be followed? What should be provided for the rapid learner? What background in science is needed by all citizens? These are only a few of many questions, most of which are difficult to resolve. Again, the science consultant is in a position to provide leadership in the development of good curriculum bulletins and in the planning of workshops and work conferences to attack these problems. But placing a bulletin in the hands of administrators and teachers will not insure beneficial changes. To accomplish needed changes, the science consultant must organize groups of teachers and selected consultants to develop the bulletin and then hold work conferences to study the finished product.

A third gap has occurred in the spectrum in regard to physical facilities for teaching science. The filling of this gap involves more than the provision of funds. A prerequisite is a clear understanding of the activities in which modern-day science students should engage and the type of facilities and equipment which will encourage the many aspects of problem-solving. In helping to fill this gap, the role of the consultant is obvious. He must present ideas to school personnel and architects and lend assistance in designing programs and facilities which reflect the best of available ideas.

Another responsibility of the science consultant is to provide the public with accurate information regarding the status of the science programs in the state. To do this effectively, he will find it necessary to collect and summarize pertinent data each year, and to make his findings available through the press, the radio, and television.

SUPERVISION AT THE COUNTY LEVEL

Harold Spears is quoted as authority for the statement that "The improvement of instruction for about half of the nation's school children is largely dependent upon the supervision that comes out of the office of the county superintendent." [1] He also reports that half of the counties do not employ supervisors, the superintendent carrying all supervisory responsibility.[2]

In a survey of the 49 states made for this study,[3] it was revealed that science supervision is, to the extent that it exists, provided by general supervisors or by the county superintendent. In some counties, certain county staff members with some competence in science education are employed. A few state departments reported that excellent work in science education was being done by these specialists. Leaders in a number of state departments reported a need for specialized supervisors at the county level, while others indicated

---

[1] Harold Spears, *Improving the Supervision of Instruction* (New York: Prentice-Hall, Inc., 1953), p. 235.

[2] *Ibid.*, p. 236.

[3] In June, 1958, an inquiry concerning the status of science supervision at the county level was mailed to all the state departments of education. There were 45 replies.

a preference for general supervisors who would concentrate their efforts on teaching methods rather than on subject matter.

Special Problems

AT THE ELEMENTARY LEVEL. Replies to the questionnaire from the state departments can be summarized thus: (a) Elementary teachers, in the main, lack sufficient training in science and tend to shy away from science. (b) The combination of not having specially trained supervisors at the county level and not having classroom teachers trained in science renders unlikely any attempt on the part of the two groups to co-operate in the improvement of science education. (c) The lack of training indicated in (a) and (b) above is responsible, in large measure, for the lack of minimum physical facilities for a minimum program in science.

The consensus indicated that the first step in upgrading science-teaching in schools of the county is to obtain competent supervisors who have an interest in science and who would encourage the schools to employ science teachers who are competent and are interested in teaching science. This appears to be essential if children of high ability in science and mathematics are to be identified early and started on their way to science careers.

The Role of the County Consultant

Responses to the questionnaire from state departments gave general support to the idea that county consultants should be specialists in (a) supervision and curriculum, (b) the basic sciences, (c) methods of teaching science, and (d) human relations. The consultant is a resource person, ready to serve where and when needed. His association with teachers in the county should make them more confident of their ability to teach science. He is a leader in the broadest sense.

The science consultant provides liaison between teachers and administrators. He advises the superintendents and principals and reports to them on the progress and needs of the schools. He attempts to develop a unity of purpose among the schools of the county and co-ordinates the over-all effort from Kindergarten through Grade XII. He recognizes weaknesses in the programs of the schools and, in a democratic way, helps teachers and administrators correct them. He places proper emphasis on science instruction and assists in integrating science into the curriculum.

Responsibilities of the County Consultant

All of the science consultant's efforts are pointed toward upgrading science education in the county. He works constantly with teachers and administrators to improve instruction and to expand the opportunities afforded children for the study of science. He develops or assists in the development of a science program from the elementary grades through high school; helps develop programs of in-service training; trains teachers in methods of instruction, giving classroom assistance where needed and wanted. The consultant co-ordinates the county program as a whole and evaluates the curriculum in individual schools annually. He assists teachers and administrators in the reorganization of the curriculum and makes arrangements for institutes and workshops for the improvement of instruction.

SUPERVISION IN LARGE CITY SYSTEMS

The attributes of good supervision are the same regardless of the size of the school system; the problems involved, however, are of a different order of magnitude. The number and nature of opportunities for supervision differ from level to level and even at the same level. Although ideas do not easily flow among a large number of teachers, the existence of a large staff makes possible the addition of consultants, specialists, and supervisors with only a small percentage increase in the school budget.

Special Problems

AT THE ELEMENTARY LEVEL. The increase of dependence of our way of life upon scientific achievements has convinced educators that science must become an essential part of the elementary school curriculum. Elementary science is being increasingly introduced in many parts of the country, and the preparation of the elementary teachers to teach with confidence in that field is one of the primary aims of elementary education today. Since many school principals are not science specialists and many elementary teachers have little or no background in science, the problem of adequate supervision becomes a formidable one. A supervisor at the elementary level is called upon to perform many important functions. Among these the following are suggestive:

1. He must participate in the formulation of a science program which will explore scientific concepts and provide experiences for children from the Kindergarten through Grade XII.
2. He must participate in the preparation of resource publications which describe a variety of appropriate activities for implementing the science program.
3. He must engage in a broad teacher-training program designed to provide background and engage in workshop courses which will enable teachers to secure first-hand experiences with science subject matter, materials, and techniques.
4. He must recommend selections of supplies and equipment and proper procedures for obtaining them.
5. He must participate in the formulation of programs for talented students.
6. He must participate in the formulation of continuous in-service science

programs which will supplement the initial background courses and workshops and will insure the professional growth of teachers throughout their teaching lifetime.

7. He must evaluate instruction through such methods as direct classroom visitations and follow-up conferences.

There are some elementary-science supervisors who are performing only part of the foregoing functions. In some cities some of these functions are being performed by science specialists. They are usually highly successful teachers with good backgrounds in science, who are freed from teaching to operate from a field superintendent's office. The specialists visit elementary school teachers in accordance with an arranged schedule or upon specific request of principals and teachers. The specialists can usually assist only in the performance of a few of the functions. They work with the teachers individually and in small groups. One consultant to every 120 to 150 elementary teachers is recommended.

The evaluation function, together with one or more of the other functions, is usually performed by the principal or assistant principal of the school. Either operates under a disadvantage when he attempts classroom supervision because his background in science may be too meager. Also, principals and assistant principals are so occupied with administrative duties and the entire program of elementary education that they are often unable to provide the leadership needed for science work at the elementary school level.

In this period of transition, when in-service science training of the present corps of elementary teachers is paramount, effective elementary supervision should remain the joint responsibility of the science specialist and the principal of the school.

To assure the proper supervision of classroom instruction and the professional growth of the elementary-school teachers, it is recommended by some that at least one person who possesses an adequate science background and supervisory training should be assigned to each elementary school. He would be responsible for the supervision of science instruction in addition to other duties.

Supervisors should not disregard the fact that the elementary and secondary schools are operating upon the *same* child at different stages of his development. Supervision on one level cannot, therefore, ignore the fields of science as they are explored on other levels if it is to assure the proper ordering of scientific concepts and activities for the maturing child. Thus vertical articulation, so obviously needed in our school systems, should be a prime responsibility of the science supervisor.

SUPERVISION IN SMALLER CITY AND SUBURBAN SYSTEMS

The large number of relatively small school systems in the country makes it necessary to study problems of supervision in such systems. Statistics indicate that 75 per cent of American high schools have enrollments of less than three hundred pupils, while 90 per cent have fewer than a thousand.

The Role of the Consultant

Supervision is an expert professional service which is primarily concerned with the improvement of learning. Thus, supervision deals with the improvement of the total teacher-learning process; orients learning and its improvement within the general aim of education; and co-ordinates, stimulates, and directs the growth of teachers through co-operative leadership. It is deeply concerned with the long-range improvement of science education.

To accomplish these aims and those stated in the first part of this chapter, the supervisor or consultant offers such services as:

1. Developing in-service educational programs.
2. Developing a science curriculum.
3. Visiting classrooms.
4. Establishing and implementing educational goals.
5. Planning demonstration lessons.
6. Coordinating services.
7. Suggesting and supplying resource materials.
8. Helping in the selection and purchase of textbooks and equipment.

The supervisor or consultant also has obligations to raise professional standards, build teacher morale, serve as a resource person, encourage advanced study and research, and interpret the science program to the staff and the community.

One of the major advantages that the science consultant in smaller cities has is the opportunity to know his teachers well and to recognize their strengths and weaknesses. The possibility of developing an exceptional *esprit de corps* is greater than in the larger cities.

Providing for Adequate Supervision

In this period of increasing emphasis upon science education, it is imperative that small city and suburban systems provide adequate science supervisory service. It is a prime factor in the improvement of science instruction.

Wherever feasible, a full-time science consultant should be employed to assist with the program in Grades I through XII. In those cities of approximately 200,000, an assistant may be employed who is a specialist in the field of elementary science. In small districts science leadership can be provided by the head of the school science department. This individual should be given adequate time and compensation for performing the services needed to facilitate an on-going science program.

Within the framework of the American philosophy of education, the schools belong to the people. The schools reflect this concept, and, therefore, will generally be only as good as the citizenry demands.

General Qualifications of the Science Consultant

The science consultant should have a thorough subject-matter background, a basic knowledge in the major branches of science and their interrelationship. In addition to the subject-matter qualifications, the consultant should have professional training in supervision and administration. It is important that the supervisor be familiar with recent developments in the fields of science and education. The consultant certainly must qualify as a superior teacher and should have at least five years of successful teaching experience in the grade levels concerned. It is unrealistic to require previous experience in science supervision since such a small percentage of the school systems, up to the present time, have employed science consultants. A lack of experience in supervision may well be offset by experience within a school system. One of the most important competencies lies in the field of personality. The consultant must be able to work well with his peer group and possess a deep insight into the problems of human relations. He must establish rapport with his teachers in order to carry on free and frank discussions. He must have the ability to assume a leadership role. He should bring to the position a high degree of imagination and creativity. He should be able to recognize the need for specific kinds of help—corrective, preventive, constructive, and creative. He should possess a sense of humor and the maturity to accept decisions adverse to those he has made or would make. These traits and abilities may well serve as guideposts for the selection of a consultant, and it is hoped that they will develop more fully with experience on the job.

IMPROVING THE EDUCATION OF
THE SCIENCE SUPERVISOR *

J. Darrell Barnard

J. Darrell Barnard defines the qualities that make a good science supervisor. He groups these qualities into two categories. First, there are attributes, which refer to those qualities that one innately possesses or comes to possess by processes not clearly revealed. Second, there are competencies, which refer to

* REPRINTED FROM a paper presented on March 30, 1965, at the Thirteenth Annual Convention of the National Science Teachers Association in Denver, Colorado, by permission of the author and the National Science Teachers Association. Dr. Barnard is Chairman of the Department of Science and Mathematics Education at New York University.

those qualities that one learns or may learn as a part of his professional education or experiences. Dr. Barnard lists ten attributes and sixteen competencies, which should become the goals of a graduate program for the education of science supervisors.

I T SEEMS reasonable to begin an exploration of this topic by asking the question: What is a science supervisor? The question can be asked but there is no simple answer. Based upon the findings of his survey of the science supervisor, Ploutz concludes, "Due to differing conditions within school systems throughout the United States, there is probably no such thing as *the model supervisor*." [1] Among the 100 supervisors of science included in his study, he found four different models. There was the K–8 or elementary school model; the 9–12 or secondary school model; the K–12 or total curriculum model; and finally the state department model. He also found a variety of titles given to persons who assumed a science supervisory role in schools: science-helping teacher, science-resource person, science consultant, and science coordinator. We could add others such as departmental chairman and director of science.

It is my understanding that NSSA has had a commission working upon the problem of defining a science supervisor model based upon the duties he should properly perform. Until such a time as the NSSA model has been developed, we shall have to resort to our own definitions. For purposes of this paper a science supervisor is any one in a school system who has been trained in science education and who, because of this training, has been given official responsibility for the management of all or some part of the science program, beyond the specific science courses that he teaches. He may assume this responsibility on a full or part-time work schedule. I realize that this is a broad definition, but so is the present status of science supervision in the schools. A part of this might be accounted for by the fact that little distinction has been made between the education of the science teacher and the science supervisor. I am hopeful that this paper may help to clarify some of the confusion—not compound it further.

Working within this rather nebulous concept of the science supervisor, I have attempted to define qualities that go to make a good one. In part this has been done by making case studies of some science supervisors as I have come to know them and their work. The remaining qualities have been identified by analyzing duty lists for supervisors prepared by school administrators, teachers (both the beginning teacher and the experienced one), and by supervisors themselves. I have divided my items of quality into two categories. For want of a better term, I refer to my first category as *attributes* and to my second category as *competencies*. As you can predict, the distinc-

[1] Ploutz, Paul F. "Survey of the Science Supervisor," *The Science Teacher* 28: p. 411 (October, 1961).

tion between these two categories is a relatively tenuous one. *Attributes* refer to those qualities that one innately possesses or comes to possess by processes not clearly revealed. *Competencies* are those qualities that one learns or may learn as a part of his professional education or experience.

None of the persons included in my case studies arrived at his position as a supervisor by satisfactorily completing a collegiate program specifically designed to educate him for his position as a supervisor. Excluding school systems where qualifying or licensing examinations are required, there are probably as many ways to become a science supervisor as there are science supervisors. Be that as it may, I have found what appears to be certain common prerequisite qualities possessed by my subjects.

Some time prior to being made a supervisor, they had demonstrated that they were "good" science teachers. (I have put good in quotes because this may mean slightly different things to different evaluators.) Second, they had identified themselves as "leaders" among their peers. (Again I have put leaders in quotes for much the same reason.) Third, they were not satisfied with models of science teaching as they had observed them. Fourth, they had "ideas." These included ideas about improved models of science teaching. Fifth, they were "aggressive." I do not mean aggressive in a derogatory sense, but in the sense they moved out to get things done.

The above are five attributes generally shared by my subjects. However, there are five other attributes that are possessed in varying degrees by different subjects. And yet they appear to be qualities of a high order of importance in becoming a good supervisor. They include modesty, adaptability, critical mindedness, a well developed system of values, and respect for the worth and dignity of each teacher with whom he works.

For the most part these qualities are beyond the purview of formal education. Or to put it another way, if the prospective candidate for a supervisory position does not possess a good proportion of these qualities, not much more can be done to help him become a supervisor. It would seem that these attributes represent a basic list of qualities which one should possess before he is admitted into a graduate program for science supervisors. How to determine their possession becomes a perplexing admissions problem.

As I mentioned before, the second list of qualities represents competencies, or "abilities to do," which to a large extent can be developed, in fact, they should become the goals of a graduate program to educate science supervisors. I hold no brief for the completeness of this list, however, I do consider the 16 listed here to be important ones based upon analyses of the various lists of duties:

1. He should be able to envision the essential features of an articulated K–12 science sequence. This does not mean that he should have a neat little K–12 package worked out on paper or in the head. But he should be able to tell what the principal features of a good one would be, and therefore to provide leadership in developing one or in evaluating "ready-made" packages that may be available to schools.

2. He should be able to innovate and objectively to evaluate the innovations of others as they relate to methods, content, equipment and sequences. This would mean that he has developed a rational frame of reference, philosophically and psychologically, which he consistently applies in evaluating "new" ideas.

3. He should be able to distinguish clearly between effective and ineffective teaching practices and to rationalize the bases for the distinctions he makes. He must be more than an intuitive evaluator of teaching.

4. He should be able to motivate teachers to seek means of improving their practices and to counsel them regarding effective ways of going about it.

5. He should be able to use effective procedures for evaluating the progress of students, as well as the effectiveness of teachers in directing the learning experiences of students.

6. He should be able to design and conduct investigations that will yield reliable evidence regarding the effectiveness of instructional programs.

7. He should be able to interpret science education, in general, and his school's science program, in particular, to other educators and to laymen in the school community.

8. He should be able to design and administer inventory systems and prepare defensible budgets for the procurement and proper maintenance of science materials and equipment.

9. He should be able to initiate and direct in-service science curriculum studies and workshops or institutes for upgrading and updating science teachers.

10. He should be able to keep teachers informed regarding current developments in science education and promising innovations in science teaching.

11. He should be able to demonstrate effective ways of teaching for the various outcomes, especially the less tangible ones such as critical thinking.

12. He should be able to adapt his method of working with teachers to the idiosyncrasies of teachers. Teaching is basically a personal accomplishment. He should not only accept it as such, but strive to get teachers to do so.

13. He should be able to *listen* to teachers and to gain insights regarding their points of view, their aspirations, their frustrations, their fears and their needs. Just as a good teacher listens more than he talks, so should a supervisor.

14. He should be able to identify the strengths and weaknesses of individual teachers and to help each teacher overcome his weakness without depreciating the teacher's self image.

15. He should be able to conduct group conferences and work sessions in ways that maximize the contributions of participants.

16. He should be able to help teachers understand the objectives of science teaching in terms of their consequent behaviors. He should be able to operationalize objectives.

The above list of 16 competencies, supplemented by the 10 attributes mentioned earlier, should provide basis for thinking about ways in which the education of supervisors might be improved.

It would seem that we begin with the assumption that one who would become a supervisor must first have been a teacher. Next, we assume that all science teachers will not or should not become supervisors; that the prerequisites for becoming a supervisor involve something more than being a teacher. Finally, we assume that the education of science supervisors is a joint responsibility of public school systems and collegiate institutions. Just what the relative roles of each should be have not been clearly delineated. In fact, I am hopeful that the remainder of this paper might throw some light upon the subject.

There is a pre-service and an in-service phase to the education of science supervisors. The in-service phase has to do with those who are practicing the profession of supervision. The pre-service phase has to do with those who seek to prepare themselves to be supervisors.

What has been the pre-service education of supervisors? Most of those in supervisory positions began their careers as secondary school science teachers. Their academic preparation was basically that required to be certified as secondary school science teachers. Their science content courses were those that were assumed to prepare them to be either chemistry, physics, earth science, or biology teachers. Outside of the foundations courses in philosophy of education, history of education and/or educational sociology, their professional courses were geared to the secondary level: principles of secondary education, general methods of teaching at the secondary level, methods of teaching secondary school science, and adolescent psychology. Pre-student teaching observation and student teaching were limited to secondary schools. In other words, their orientation was almost exclusively secondary, which represents only the upper half of the K–12 science sequence. I do not believe that this pattern is adequate either for the secondary school science teacher or for the prospective science supervisor.

How should the pre-service education of prospective science supervisors be improved? The content background required to be competent science supervisors, precludes prospective candidates coming to such positions through the elementary school. Most will continue to enter supervision by way of the secondary-school-science-teacher route. Secondary school science teachers know relatively little about elementary education, and more specifically about elementary school science. In part, this accounts for some of the difficulties which schools encounter in their efforts to develop K–12 articulated programs in science. Why shouldn't secondary school science teachers be more knowl-edgeable in elementary education? I believe they should and propose the following changes in the professional courses which they are required to take in preparation for teaching at the secondary school level.

Instead of a course in principles of secondary education, I would propose a course in principles of education. In this course the principles would be applied to both elementary and secondary education. Instead of a course in adolescent psychology, they should have one or more courses that deal with growth and development from 5 years to 17 years of age. The concepts of growth and development as they relate to learning should be high-lighted. The general methods of teaching at the secondary school level would become a general methods course for teaching at both the elementary and secondary school level. The science methods courses would deal with methods of teaching science at the various grade levels. Pre-student teaching observation would include observation in both elementary and secondary schools. Student teaching would be done at both levels.

The implementation of such a proposal calls for some radical changes in our colleges of education where specialization in elementary and secondary education has become unreasonably entrenched. In spite of the tenability of assumptions underlying such a proposal, the specialists in elementary education and the specialists in secondary education will probably contend that such courses cannot be taught within the conventional limitation of credits allocated for professional courses. After some radical surgery of present courses, I believe they could.

With this broad-based background in elementary and secondary education, secondary school science teachers should be much better equipped to perform their duties within a K–12 science sequence. Furthermore, the potential pool of candidates for supervisory positions in science at the various levels will become enlarged.

It would seem to me that science teachers who aspire to prepare themselves for supervisory positions should have taught a minimum of five years. They should have had experience at the elementary, junior high school and senior high school levels. They should take at least one year of graduate study beyond the masters. Whether the advanced work is recognized academically by a sixth-year certificate or applied toward a doctorate, it should be designed to accomplish the following:

1. Bring the candidate's science background up to a minimum of 18 points in graduate courses. (6)
2. Provide an internship in supervision for at least one semester. (6)
3. Include a full-year practicum to deal with such topics as: (6)
   a. The K–12 science sequence
   b. Innovations in science teaching
   c. Evaluation of teaching practices
   d. Objectives as behavioral goals
   e. Demonstration teaching
   f. Adapting methods of supervision to the idiosyncrasies of schools and teachers
   g. How to listen to teachers
4. Include these courses

    a. Research design and statistics (6)
    b. Tests and measurements (3)
    c. Group dynamics (3)

Let's look next at the in-service phase of the supervisor's education. Except in large school systems, the science supervisor finds few professional associates within the system who share his specific interests and problems. In various ways he may become associated with supervisors of other subject fields when general problems of supervision are considered, and this can make an important contribution to his education as a science supervisor. Through membership in NSSA, he may become involved in conferences and clinics dealing with problems of the science supervisor. He may read the professional literature and even contribute articles. He may have the good fortune of working with a group of science teachers who stimulate him to push out beyond the fringes of established routines. From time to time he may even seek assistance with certain problems from the professors in nearby collegiate institutions. He may spend all or part of several summers at institutes and work conferences for supervisors. He may have the privilege of working on one of the course improvement projects. Along the way he may even complete his doctorate in science education and thereby earn his union card. Through these and other self-initiated activities, he provides for his in-service education as a science supervisor. My guess is that the above is representative of the logs of many of the supervisors attending this conference. Does the procedure need to be improved? If so, should collegiate institutions become more actively involved?

Collegiate institutions have three major responsibilities: 1) Inquiry; 2) Instruction; and 3) Service. There are two of these that have particular implications for improving the in-service education of science supervisors.

Some institutions have distinguished themselves for the consultant services which their professors have provided to schools. In fact, the demands from schools for such services have often diverted professors from their more fundamental responsibility, inquiry. Professors have rationalized their neglect of research by citing their busy consultation schedules and contending that the feed-back from this effort is helping to advance knowledge in science education. Except in those institutions, such as Florida State University, where the service to the schools is one of conducting formal inquiry into teaching problems on a cooperative basis, such contentions of productive feed-back are largely wishful thinking.

If institutions were to limit their school services to cooperative research projects, both schools and institutions would profit. Schools would profit through the involvement of its supervisory staff and its teachers in research, as well as getting more definitive answers to many of their questions. The collegiate institution would profit through the redirection of its energy into channels that are more traditionally the responsibility of the university, a fundamental responsibility not generally assumed by any other institution in our society.

In terms of their professional performance, supervisors share with many college professors a critical deficiency. Few, if any of them, are actively involved in research designed to advance our understanding of problems related to science teaching. It is toward the correction of this situation that collegiate institutions could contribute most to the improvement of the in-service education of science supervisors and to the upgrading of its own contributions to the profession.

If the research is to be cooperative it should deal with unresolved problems faced by the schools in their efforts to advance science teaching. The processes involved in the identification of these problems and in asking the questions that should, and can, be researched not only represents a real challenge to the schools but will also require the best research talents that collegiate institutions can provide.

It is unreasonable to assume that sustained cooperative research efforts of any significance will be accomplished by forcing supervisors and/or professors to become involved. The consequences of such "forced feeding" is that as soon as the pressure is removed, the research effort terminates. For example, how many of those who were "forced" to do research in fulfilling their requirements for the doctorate have continued to be active in research? It would seem that the one-shot deal immunizes against further research rather than spreads the infection.

Somehow we need to develop a climate in which we habitually turn to research for answers to the many unresolved and critical questions that face us in science education. Many of the persistent problems in science education result from practices based upon *superstitious* beliefs and pedagogical *folklore*.

In our efforts to change the intellectual climate of science education we should begin with the research that has been done. I cannot agree with those who contend that most, if not all, of the research in science education is worthless. For 25 years prior to the recent efforts to improve science curriculums we had evidence that something was wrong. Furthermore, there was abundant evidence from the research that the teaching methods so commonly practiced were not only ineffective, but actually deleterious. But it was not until the scientists intuitively arrived at this conclusion that it was given effective visibility. And they have had their problems in convincing some teachers whose behavior has been guided by superstitious beliefs and the folklore of science teaching.

In professional courses for science teachers and supervisors, research findings should be used in dealing with the basic questions of what, how, and why. Where the findings from research are not adequate, it should be clearly indicated that we tentatively rely upon best judgments. Teachers, supervisors, and professors should become conditioned to distinguish between fact and opinion in dealing with curriculum problems in science. We should adopt the attitude of Dr. Anton J. Carlson, the distinguished physiologist, who became a thorn in the side of many a glib physiologist by repeatedly asking the question: What is your evidence? But Dr. Carlson did not merely ask the question. Where there was no evidence, he set about to find it. This led to many of his classical experiments on the physiology of hunger and digestion. Furthermore, his book, *The Machinery of the Body*, is an exemplary physiology text in which the concepts of physiology are largely taught by reviewing the research that led to them.

Why, in the community of science educators, is there not a greater professional interest with opinions lacking the support of evidence? Is it because we have become enamored with the doctrine of expediency? Is it because we are unwilling to subject ourselves to the discipline required of him who would search for evidence? Is it because the profession and the public put higher premiums upon other kinds of performance, such as attending conferences, conducting institutes, developing "new" curriculums, making speeches, and writing textbooks? Is it because our "busy" schedules allow no time for the reflective thinking, reading and probing that is required to get started?

Money buys time and increasing amounts of money are becoming available to buy a part of the time of those qualified persons who would commit themselves to do research. In our own institution, released time from one or more classes is now given to professors who wish time to design investigations. Funds are also available for travel and consultant assistance. I imagine that our institution is not unique in this respect; that other institutions are also developing climates that are conducive to the spawning of a greater research effort in science education. As this becomes more of a way of academic life at institutions where supervisors and potential supervisors obtain their training, there will be more research infections and fewer research immunizations.

If I seem to have overemphasized involvement in cooperative research as an approach to the improvement of the in-service education of science supervisors, it is because I strongly believe that it is the most neglected aspect of our efforts to advance professionally. If more of it were being done, conventions such as this one might become disturbing, enlightening, dynamic forums rather than polite gatherings for purposes of listening to rehashes of ideas such as those presented in this paper.

THE PRINCIPAL'S ROLE IN THE
ELEMENTARY SCIENCE PROGRAM *

Paul F. Ploutz

Paul F. Ploutz discusses the importance of the principal's role in establishing a good science program in the elementary school. The principal, as the instructional leader, should provide the necessary stimulation to increase the effectiveness of the science program. Dr. Ploutz provides a twenty-question check list for self-assessment by elementary school principals. The check list can identify areas of weakness where the principal is failing to provide the kind of leadership that he alone can provide. Dr. Ploutz also outlines five desirable areas for involving the teacher in the development of a good science program.

ELEMENTARY teachers have frequently been blamed for dereliction of duty in teaching science.

Colleges of education have been accused of granting elementary teaching certificates to those who "didn't like" or to those "afraid" of science.

Personnel and employment directors for public school systems ask the routine questions when interviewing teacher candidates but avoid questions relating to science. When "you need teachers," you don't scare candidates with science questions.

As for science supervision and in-service education, a recent study revealed that even "elementary supervisors of science have less authority, status, experience, assistance or training than other groups of supervisors." [1]

In one report or another virtually everyone from the Board of Education to the kindergarten child has been charged with neglect in the elementary science program. In all probability, the reason different groups have been charged with neglect hinges on the fact that a good curriculum is a result of effort by many people. The failure of a science program to meet existing needs is conversely apt to be a neglect by many.

As the instructional leader, the elementary principal can and should be the key person in stimulating teachers and other administrators in recognizing

---

* REPRINTED FROM *Science Education*, Vol. 47, No. 3, April 1963, pp. 250–253, by permission of the author and the publisher. Dr. Ploutz is Associate Professor of Education at Ohio University, Athens, Ohio.
1 Paul F. Ploutz, "The Science Supervisor," unpublished Field Study Number 1, Colorado State College, Greeley, Colorado, May 1960.

and implementing an elementary science program that has previously stalled in passive indifference, lack of funds, or out-dated concepts of the importance of science in our way of life.

It is the purpose of this article to assist the elementary principal in appraising the need for increased (1) physical facilities, (2) science apparatus, equipment and materials, and (3) student science activities in his school. The need for science equipment at the elementary level continues to keep many experiments and demonstrations from taking place. Insufficient equipment limits the effect of in-service education efforts for both new and experienced teachers. In many instances, new equipment can be used to motivate teacher interest in science. While it is generally conceded that many elementary teachers either partially or wholly neglect science, the science equipment situation in many instances is even worse. A strong case can be made for the fact that the present importance of science is so immense that elementary schools, virtually without exception, do not prepare their students with science concepts and understandings necessary for the present, much less future anticipated needs.

Many elementary children with interest and ability in science get more science instruction in their out-of-school environment than at school. It is still commonplace to find fifth or sixth grade students constructing or owning crystal radio sets, transistor radio sets, microscopes, and the like; while the school they attend owns less equipment than the children.

Elementary principals are frequently aware that the students in their buildings are "pushing" the teachers in the area of science—not an impressive situation from an administrative or Board of Education viewpoint. Even in those situations where the school board and administration provide sufficient leadership, there is a lot of time, training, and money involved between recognizing the importance of science and implementing an acceptable elementary science program.

School systems have, to varying degrees, recognized the urgency for elementary science, yet many have done very little other than stating the need. In respect to personnel and finances required for a modern-day program, some school systems have made little, if any, progress.

While we legitimately continue to emphasize the importance of science to elementary teachers, have we provided equipment necessary to implement the program? In the face of the financial squeeze and budget reductions in which 23 per cent of all 1960 public school bond issues in the United States failed at the polls,[2] have we rationalized our thinking into believing that string, milk cartons, and balloons can replace a microscope, tuning fork, and aquarium? Has the over-worn concept of homemade gadgetry, coupled with slogans of teacher inventiveness and creativity, sold principals into thinking that teachers can teach science without equipment?

In a mid-western state where teachers' salaries and the educational tax

[2] Phi Delta Kappan, Vol. XLIII, No. 2, November 1961, p. 53.

base are well above the national average, this writer recently visited a well-known system noted for high standards and excellence. It was discovered that of the twenty-six elementary schools involved, eighteen had less than $150 worth of science equipment per school. While this particular community had demonstrated its continued desire to have and support superior programs, the elementary science program was based on an inaccurate curriculum guide prepared by teachers. The teaching, or lack of teaching science in the schools was left to the whims or strengths of twenty-six principals working individually. There were no budget provisions for science equipment; in-service education consisted of an occasional college extension course accommodating only twenty or twenty-five of the 600+ elementary teachers in the system. In those few schools where the elementary principal had an interest or a college minor in science, the science activities in the school were clearly evident. In these situations, the elementary principal was the instructional leader in reality, rather than in theory.

It seems increasingly obvious that while many factors are in play in determining the nature and caliber of a good science program, the role of the elementary principal is *singularly* important.

The likelihood of having a good elementary science program in a school where the principal is not active and interested in science activities is obviously not good.

But what of NDEA? [3] Have elementary principals made themselves aware of how NDEA funds are secured and been aggressive in pursuing their needs? Perhaps with the secondary schools adding courses in earth science, electronics, and biology, and "beefing up" general science, the secondary program has absorbed most of the funds available. Perhaps, however, the elementary principal has not made his "pitch." There is no controversy in the need for outfitting newly constructed and existing secondary science facilities. The question may well be, however, have NDEA funds passed by the elementary school by default?

The following check list is designed to assist in identifying those ways in which the principal, as instructional leader, can work to increase the effectiveness of the elementary science program in his building or in his system.

CHECK LIST FOR ELEMENTARY PRINCIPALS [4]

1. Have you informed yourself how much money your system obtains through NDEA?
2. Do you feel the elementary schools receive financial assistance reasonably proportionate to what secondary schools are securing through NDEA?

[3] National Defense Education Act, Title III (passed September, 1958, providing federal funds for science, mathematics and foreign languages; effective until 1964).

[4] A three-column check space with captions "Yes," "No," or "Don't Know" was placed to the right of the questions. Deleted here for space reasons.

3. Have you identified one, two, or more teachers in your school to put on building science workshops or promote science activities?
4. Have you encouraged teachers to report their science equipment and material needs to you?
5. Do you develop an equipment-needs list during the school year for inclusion on budget for the following year?
6. Are there provisions for ordering small amounts of simple chemicals and expendable materials *during* the year?
7. Does your library meet American Library Association standards and subscribe to science reference books and magazines for both teachers and pupils?
8. Is your library securing many of the new science and mathematics books prepared for children?
9. Do you have, or have you considered forming, a science club in your school?
10. Has your school taken advantage of streams, planetariums, industry, and other field trip resources in your area?
11. Do you keep your teachers aware of science films available in various areas of science? (Astronomy—"How Many Stars," Moody Institute of Science, et al.)
12. Are your teachers convinced that *you* consider science important?
13. Do you encourage science displays, bulletin boards, collections, etc., in halls, library, or other places in school buildings?
14. Are you aware and have you informed your teachers of the professional organizations related to elementary science?
15. Are science concepts presented and expanded upon in a grade-to-grade sequential manner?
16. Do you involve the P.T.A. and related groups in the school science program through a school fair and student science display; and have you encouraged or supported Boy Scouts, 4-H Clubs, Brownies, and other groups interested in science?
17. Is the copyright date on every science textbook now in use less than five years old?
18. Are proper storage facilities available with easy teacher-access to science equipment?
19. Does every teacher have access to projectors, film strip machines, and other audio-visual aids in classrooms which may be easily darkened for audio-visual and demonstration purposes?
20. Does each teacher have some facility for a science table, corner aquarium, hobby display, science materials shelf, stand, or table?

Twenty "Yes" answers could be considered ideal.
Six or more negative answers should offer stimulation.

The preceding check list can identify areas of weakness existing system-wide or in only one elementary school.

It is recognized that involvement is one of the keys to creating interest and affecting change in students' behavior. The technique for teachers is the same.

In developing an elementary science program, it is desirable, when possible, to involve the teacher in:

1. Selecting the content and concepts to be presented at each sequential grade level.
2. Determining what experience seems most effective in children's learning concepts from grade-to-grade.
3. Determining what equipment is needed to teach concepts selected in the K–6 program.
4. Organizing an in-service education program around need for all science content areas as well as most effective utilization of equipment.
5. The evaluation of the effectiveness of the total K–6 instructional program in science.

Since many elementary science programs are ineffectual or generally inadequate in emphasis, rather than non-existent, the problem is generally more often one of "stimulating" an existing program, rather than creating a totally new program.

The elementary principal must now, more than ever before, assure each student the opportunity to develop his potential in science.

"Though only a few students will ever become research scientists, local schools still hold the great responsibility of providing an up-to-date science program, continuous from the kindergarten through the twelfth grade, to provide the academic atmosphere that will allow certain students to greatly excel." [5]

We need only to further encourage and develop the existing inborn natural qualities of curiosity in children. Our country is in great need of scientists in every field. It is equally true that we need statesmen as much as physicians, missionaries, and technicians.

The elementary principal must accept his tremendous share of the responsibility that future generations do not run out of top soil, or starve in attempting to feed the overwhelming population increase. The boys and girls in today's elementary schools must prevent us from smothering in smog or losing the battle with the bugs. The youth of today must soon mend our hearts and cure our cancers. The one question keeps returning, however: are we doing enough in science to prepare them for the challenge immediately ahead?

[5] Paul F. Ploutz, "The Science Supervisor," unpublished Field Study Number 1, Colorado State College, Greeley, Colorado, May 1960, p. 115.

THE NATIONAL SCIENCE FOUNDATION AND ELEMENTARY SCIENCE *

National Science Foundation

The National Science Foundation was established in 1950 by an act of the Congress and was assigned the problem of finding ways to bring the resources of the Federal Government to bear on the task of strengthening science education in the United States. This includes the improvement of elementary school science. Accordingly, institutes are offered for elementary school teachers, designed to improve their subject-matter background in science. Also, financial grants are given to groups, for the purpose of developing appropriate course materials in elementary science.

GENERAL INFORMATION

The National Science Foundation, established in 1950 by Public Law 507, 81st Congress, is an independent agency of the Federal Government. It is concerned primarily with the support of basic research, training and education in the sciences, and interchange and dissemination of scientific information.

A 24-member National Science Board and Director of the Foundation, all appointed by the President of the United States by and with the advice and consent of the Senate, develop the plans and policies of the Foundation and guide its operation.

The support of basic research is accomplished through grants primarily to investigators at colleges and universities and is administered through the Division of Biological and Medical Sciences; Division of Mathematical, Physical, and Engineering Sciences; Division of Social Sciences; and the Office of Antarctic Programs. Basic research support also includes grants for equipment and specialized facilities. The Office of Institutional Programs provides matching funds for construction, modernization, and refurbishment of graduate research laboratories.

Programs in support of training and education in the sciences are supported by the Division of Scientific Personnel and Education.

* REPRINTED FROM *Programs for Education in the Sciences*, National Science Foundation, 1963, p. 41, and from *14th Annual Report*, National Science Foundation, 1965, pp. 79–81, by permission of the publisher.

The function of the Foundation's Office of Science Information Service is to increase the availability of scientific literature in all languages. The Office, at the national level, stimulates and supports efforts to improve the existing system for disseminating information, including abstracting, indexing, and translation activities. Research is also supported to develop new methods, including mechanized systems, for making scientific information available.

The Science Resources Planning Office serves as a focal point for studies relevant to the formulation of national policy for research and education in science and engineering. It coordinates long-range planning within the Foundation. The Office of Economic and Statistical Studies directs or conducts detailed economic analysis and statistical surveys of the national research efforts measured by both funds and manpower.

The Office of International Science Activities encourages and supports cooperative international science activities and the improvement of liaison between U.S. scientists and scientists abroad (by direct contact and via international governmental organizations).

More detailed information is contained in the pamphlet entitled *The National Science Foundation*, available upon request.

ELEMENTARY SCHOOL PROGRAMS

Elementary School Personnel

A major consideration in providing supplementary training in science and mathematics for elementary school teachers is the fact that very few of the approximately 1,100,000 elementary school teachers in the United States (kindergarten through grade 6) have any appreciable training in these subjects and are qualified to teach them. Consequently, the Foundation has chosen necessarily to concentrate on training leaders who may, in turn, influence and instruct their colleagues. This training is conducted in summer institutes for which participants are selected on a national scale and in the more numerous in-service institutes, which are oriented to local needs.

The institutes for elementary school teachers are directed toward improving the subject-matter background in science and mathematics of those individuals holding key positions in (1) introducing the teaching of science and (2) improving the teaching of mathematics in the elementary grades. This group of individuals includes specialist teachers, subject-matter supervisors, principals, and regular classroom teachers who are leaders in science instruction in their schools. Most of these individuals have had minimal training in either science or mathematics, yet they are being called upon to lead their schools in adjusting to new curricular ideas which introduce science, the scientific method, and an understanding of fundamental mathematical concepts. As a result of grants made in fiscal year 1964, about 3,350 elementary school personnel in the categories mentioned will receive training next year. This represents a 37 percent increase in the number of individuals as compared with last year's participants.

Although funds for institutes for elementary school personnel were increased this year, the Foundation continues to receive many more meritorious proposals for these institutes than it can support; and at the same time, the number of applications received by the grantee institutions is about fifteen times the number of places available. The Foundation is considering means of assisting more teachers. One plan is to encourage local instructional programs supervised by university scientist-educators, but staffed by local secondary or elementary school teachers who have received special training for the purpose. This arrangement should materially reduce the operating costs as well as the manpower demand on colleges and universities.

Improving Elementary School Courses

The lack of clarity concerning what in science and mathematics can and should be taught in the elementary grades has made approaches to improvement at this level particularly difficult to determine. However, in the last few years, greatly increased attention has been given to this question and to the development of appropriate course materials for science and mathematics instruction in elementary schools. Experiments with new course materials have revealed that students at all age levels are capable of understanding subject matter of a relatively high degree of sophistication when the instructional materials are properly designed and appropriately presented.

Course materials in mathematics, developed under an NSF grant to the School Mathematics Study Group, are presently used by many elementary schools in the United States. To cite more recent developments, the Commission on Science Education of the American Association for the Advancement of Science is studying such general issues as: appropriate objectives for science instruction in elementary and junior high schools; variations in scope and sequence of science content; the education or re-education of teachers; effective evaluation of curriculum developments; and cooperative coordination among curriculum improvement projects. In addition, the Commission has prepared and tested a first version of one curriculum stressing basic processes of science for kindergarten through grade 3. During 1964–65 this curriculum will be revised and extended to grade 5 for further experimental trial.

A number of novel approaches to elementary science teaching are being tried out at the University of California, Berkeley; State University of New York, Stony Brook, Long Island; Utah State University, and elsewhere. These experiments may well supply ideas on how to foster in younger pupils an enduring curiosity about scientific studies. One project group is devising ways of leading second graders to an intuitive understanding of the relativity of motion, and fourth graders to a grasp of fundamental ideas of thermodynamics.

As is true of other educational levels, future changes in mathematics and science instructional materials at the elementary school level will undoubtedly be built upon the rapidly evolving structure and content of the subjects themselves, new insights into the capabilities and needs of our greatly diverse school population, and new possibilities for better instruction which have emerged from the results of earlier work in course content reform.

A NATIONAL CURRICULUM
IN SCIENCE? *

Stanley E. Williamson

Stanley E. Williamson presents arguments for and against the establishment of a national science curriculum. Dr. Williamson, however, believes that the dangers inherent in a national curriculum in science are greater than its potential benefits. He believes that such standardization violates the basic processes of science. In lieu of nationalization, the author believes more can be accomplished by improving teacher competence, by providing the necessary funds for curriculum improvement at the local level, by providing competent supervisory staff and consultants, and by providing schools with important research information concerning curriculum revision.

D URING the past few years, science educators, teachers, and school administrators have expressed concern over the possibility of the establishment of a national curriculum in science. Such an eventuality might come about as a result of the curriculum materials developed by foundations and other national groups. The belief that we are moving toward a national curriculum in science, stems, in part at least, from comments made by recognized leaders in education and by influential lay citizens favoring the establishment of a national council or commission charged with the responsibility of designing and developing curriculum materials. Paul R. Hanna has proposed such a plan. He believes that:

Few states and relatively fewer local communities possess or can afford to assemble the rare and costly resources (personnel) necessary for continuous research. . . .

 * REPRINTED FROM *Theory Into Practice*, Bureau of Educational Research and Service, The Ohio State University, Vol. 1, No. 5, December 1962, pp. 245–252, by permission of the author and the publisher. Dr. Williamson is Chairman of the Department of Science Education at Oregon State University.

Few local and state governments can assign qualified people to full time curriculum designing and development. The very survival of our nation and of free men everywhere demands that our schools throughout the nation present teaching-learning experiences that guarantee today's youth—tomorrow's citizens—will be taught and have the opportunity and encouragement to learn the highest priority understandings, values, and competencies essential to win the war being waged against free men by both communist and fascist forces.

. . . .

Such curriculum designing requires a national effort of laymen, academic scholars, and professional school teachers. We need a nationwide commission, or a council, or an academy that is nongovernmental and has no power except the force of its rational proposals for possible curriculums.[1]

Many support Mr. Hanna's proposal and consider it the only way to solve complex curriculum problems today.

Other leaders oppose this proposal, both in theory and in practice. They believe that a national council or commission would be the first step toward a national curriculum. Some contend that science programs developed by grants from the National Science Foundation and other groups are also a step toward a national curriculum in science. They are concerned that these new programs will be accepted without careful evaluation and analysis.

Still others maintain that, to the extent that the majority of teachers have used only a few textbooks in each area of science, we have always had a form of national curriculum in science. They reason that if the classroom teacher accepts the textbook as *the* course in science—to be followed to the exclusion of other materials—there is national conformity in science education.

The sections that follow indicate the major arguments for and against the establishment of a national curriculum in science. In presenting each one, I have made no attempt to examine its validity. However, in the concluding section of the paper, I have indicated my position toward such a curriculum.

ARGUMENTS FOR A NATIONAL SCIENCE CURRICULUM

1. *A national curriculum in science is needed because of the explosion of knowledge in the basic sciences.* The doubling of knowledge in the basic sciences during the past decade makes it increasingly difficult for the classroom teacher to determine the content and experiences that will have lasting importance for the student preparing to live in a modern scientific society. It is impossible for the teacher to keep up-to-date in his field of interest and at the same time to assume responsibility for the design and development of curriculum materials.

A science curriculum prepared by a national committee, composed of experts in the field, would identify the major concepts or common under-

1 "Is the Traditional Concept of Local Control of Public Education Still Valid?" *Journal of Secondary Education*, May, 1962, 37, 303.

standings needed by all pupils. These persons would have specialized training and sufficient resources to do the job far more effectively than any teacher or group of teachers working in a local setting. They would be in a position, too, to design experiments using newly developed curriculum materials and to evaluate the program in terms of their findings.

All too frequently, in final analysis, the science curriculum for many schools is little more than the traditional textbook, which becomes out-of-date in a few years. Authors and publishers can hardly be expected to revise their textbooks annually, but a national committee responsible for the science curriculum could spend the time necessary to keep curricular and instructional materials abreast of the explosion in knowledge.

A national curriculum could be modified each year as new scientific knowledge and further research in the psychology of learning became available. These changes would be passed on to the classroom teacher periodically and thus eliminate the need for local or state curriculum-revision committees. The time and energy that the teacher would normally spend in selecting and organizing content could be spent more profitably in refining instructional techniques and in solving other teaching problems.

2. *A national science curriculum would be uniform and hence more easily understood and implemented than a multiplicity of programs.* The varying objectives, content, and methods of local, state, and national programs tend to confuse rather than enlighten those responsible for using them. A national curriculum would be kept simple, its objectives clearly stated in terms of nationally accepted purposes, and its suggested materials of instruction easily understood. It would provide a common denominator for science teachers attending meetings and conferences.

The administrator would find it easy to follow and administer such a curriculum plan in the local situation. He would no longer have the problem of analyzing various curriculum proposals in order to select the best plan for his particular school. He would have the assurance, and the security that comes from knowing, that by following the national curriculum in science, his school would be able to offer as good a science program as any other school.

The establishment of a common body of science knowledge for all students would also facilitate the freedom of movement that characterizes today's population. As population mobility increases, it becomes more and more essential that students be able to transfer from community to community, or from state to state, without encountering major differences in the curriculum. Parents who move about freely should have the assurance that their children will not miss out on some of the important concepts and experiences developed through the science program.

3. *A national curriculum would make possible the standardization of materials, equipment, and facilities.* Increased school enrollments have produced serious financial problems in many communities. A major expense item is the money needed for science materials, equipment, and facilities. Many

teachers, administrators, and lay persons believe that a national curriculum in science would tend to standardize science classrooms, materials of instruction, and equipment, and thereby, in the long run, effect a reduction in the initial cost of these items. Such a curriculum would promote the design of truly functional science facilities that would meet the needs and interests of present and future science teachers.

Standardization of materials, equipment, and facilities would tend to make the same program and materials of instruction available to all students in all communities. The existing differential between rich and poor districts, in respect to science education, would be reduced to a minimum. Further, if all schools followed a national curriculum, Federal funds could be used more efficiently in remodeling structures and in purchasing science materials.

4. *A national curriculum in science would lead to the development of national standards for teacher preparation and certification.* A national science curriculum would make it possible to determine the academic preparation that prospective teachers need to teach the program effectively. Uniform certification requirements could then be set up on a national basis.

The present policy of having each state determine its own teacher-preparation program and specify certification requirements has resulted in fifty different solutions to problems of preparation and certification. As a result, teachers find it difficult to transfer from one state to another because they are confronted with a new set of regulations in each state. Many contend that this situation is an extravagant waste of the teacher's time and money during a period when critical teacher shortages exist.

Other arguments that favor a national curriculum in science may be advanced. However, each argument has in the background a rather special concept of curriculum planning and development: the idea that the curriculum consists of a selected body of knowledge that should be made available to everyone. The curriculum, in this sense, is static and uniform for every community at a given time and place. There is no room for consideration of specific local problems. (This point is taken up in the next section in some detail.) Whether it is desirable to have conformity in science-curriculum experience, standardization of equipment and facilities, and even standard background preparation and certification of teachers, should be carefully studied.

Arguments Against a National Science Curriculum

1. *A national science curriculum would not meet the varying needs of students from community to community.* John W. Gardner establishes as one of the national goals in education the idea that

each child should be dealt with in terms of his own abilities. Every child should have the benefit of an educational program designed to suit his capacities and to develop him to the limit of his potentialities—whatever that limit may be. None should be required to fit a pace and pattern of education designed for children of other capacities.[2]

Individual differences among students vary from community to community, and even in the same community, to such an extent that a single curriculum pattern cannot possibly meet them, regardless of the expertness with which curricular materials are designed. Those who advocate a national science curriculum fail to make clear just how individual differences would be considered. Programs prepared for use on the national level, in general, tend to be more rigid than those prepared at the local level.

The real need today is for curricular materials that provide for increased flexibility, with greater attention given to the individual student. To promote conformity at the expense of individuality, the opportunity to develop creative imagination, and other special aptitudes is a serious threat to our national purposes.

2. *A national science curriculum would limit local and state curriculum innovation and experimentation.* Teachers must not only accept, but cherish, the integrity of their personal decisions on problems related to the curriculum. They are in a position to recognize the problems and needs of their students and to devise the kinds of experiences that will enable students to meet these needs. A national curriculum would, at the least, minimize this important teacher activity. The teacher should be free to innovate and experiment in an environment that is without pressure or control from external committees, commissions, or institutions.

Decisions on major curriculum problems made by individuals far removed from the local situation can have little meaning for the classroom teacher. The strengths and weaknesses of the teacher's personality must be considered in every classroom teaching situation. The teacher must be free to create, invent, try out, and explore his own ideas in teaching. The creative mind, whether it be that of the teacher or student, is still the most precious resource of our generation.

3. *A national science curriculum would place the control of science education in the hands of a special group or groups.* A real danger exists when one individual or a small group of individuals gains control of the educational program or of a segment of that program. A national committee responsible for designing and developing the science curriculum would enjoy a special authoritative status. Administrators and teachers might regard it as a committee of experts capable of handling any and all curricular problems. Individuals at the local level would find it difficult to oppose such recommendations. In fact, teachers and administrators might even use recommendations made by the curricular committee to excuse their own failures.

4. *A national science curriculum would not solve the critical problems in science education.* Current literature in science education gives one the

---

[2] "National Goals in Education," in *Goals for Americans,* President's Commission on National Goals. New York: Prentice-Hall, Inc., 1960, pp. 84–85.

impression that the number of unresolved issues has increased rather than diminished. In fact, some of these have become so critical that attempts to devise a national curriculum would be folly until they have been resolved. For example, there is still wide divergence of opinion on such matters as the nature of the learning process, the meaning of basic education in the sciences, and the way in which the process of scientific inquiry can be taught to secondary-school students.

Some of the problems relate directly to the work of the national groups. One criticism of the in-service programs designed to enable teachers to teach the new science courses effectively is that they are teacher-training rather than teacher-education programs. *Training* is used in the sense that a teacher masters the content to be taught and the specific techniques needed to teach it. A teacher-education program, on the other hand, would alert the teacher to the need for creativity, adaptation, experimentation, and continuous evaluation of materials in the local situation.

A Vote Against a National Science Curriculum

The dangers inherent in a national curriculum in science are greater than its potential benefits. Conformity in science teaching brought about as a result of standardized instructional materials, equipment, and facilities, and even standardized teacher preparation and certification, must be regarded with suspicion. While some conformity in curriculum materials may meet temporary goals or solve immediate problems, it is the "long look ahead"— the ultimate influence on society and on democratic ideals that is of major importance. In a sense, such standardization violates the basic processes of science.

In the years ahead, the problems in curriculum planning and development will become more critical. Increased enrollments, lack of facilities, teacher shortages, and continued progress in the various science areas will add to the complexity of curricular problems. That curriculum changes must be made to meet changing conditions is evident. However, curriculum change, at any level, does not always mean that progress is being made. There are certain steps which must be taken to improve curriculum design and development in the future. The following measures, I believe, would enable public schools to prepare curriculum materials far superior to those found in a national curriculum.

1. *Improve teacher competence.* Colleges and universities preparing science teachers need to strengthen their instructional programs. Competent teachers are essential to curriculum improvement. Teachers must not only have command of the content area they teach and adequate professional preparation, but they must also have strong preparation in general education. Science teachers must be made aware of our national goals and of the great social and political issues of our time. There are no short-cuts to improving the curriculum and classroom instruction. A national curriculum cannot ensure

teacher competence, but a competent teacher can provide the school and community with a sound, well-designed curriculum.

2. *Provide funds (state and/or national) for curriculum inprovement at the local level.* Progress in education costs money—more money than many communities want to spend. A program for the continuous study and improvement of the curriculum may cost more than the individual school or community can afford. Sums of money made available, from state and national sources, to study, evaluate, and revise the curriculum, and to bring in outside consultants would stimulate local communities, administrators, and teachers to action. Community interest in the educational program would increase as local problems were identified and solved, whereas such interest would be likely to decrease if a national curriculum was prepared and distributed by someone far removed from the local scene.

3. *Provide competent supervisory staff and consultants.* Local school units should be of such size that supervisors and/or consultants could be retained as a part of the regular staff to identify local curriculum problems and to seek solutions for them.

In-service programs, skillfully designed and presented, could offer up-to-date curriculum methods and new science materials while helping science teachers to solve their individual curriculum problems. Supervisors and consultants would provide the leadership necessary to keep the educational program abreast of ever-changing local conditions. For small school units, supervisors and consultants could be provided on a regional basis.

4. *Provide schools with important research information concerning curriculum revision.* Better lines of communication must be developed between educational-research groups and the classroom teacher. The results of curriculum studies relating to objectives, content, methods, and evaluation are of major importance to the individual teacher or group of teachers responsible for curriculum revision. Practicing scientists could identify the major concepts or conceptual schemes that should be considered in designing a science course. Teachers would then be in a better position to appraise and select the content that would be most beneficial in their local situations.

Instituting such measures would provide for curriculum planning and development at all levels—local, state, and national. Schools could work cooperatively with state agencies to carry on research in the design and development of science programs that will meet local needs and conditions. National groups, with their greater resources and highly specialized abilities, should conduct large-scale research and evaluation programs and then make curricular recommendations based on their findings. The local school, however, must not look to any national group for all the answers; local and state officials have, and should continue to have, the responsibility for making curricular decisions that affect their school system.

INQUIRY AND PROCESS IN
ELEMENTARY SCIENCE

INTRODUCTION

In the past few years a strong movement has gotten under way to change the emphasis in the teaching of science. This change in emphasis has to do with the objectives of science education and is associated, interestingly enough, with a difference of opinion about the proper definition of science. For a long time the standard definition of science has been "a body of systematized knowledge resulting from observation, study, and experimentation." Many scientists have objected strongly to this definition. They insist that science is "a process of inquiry, resulting in a body of systematized knowledge."

The two major objectives of science education are to help the child develop (1) knowledge of science concepts—the content of science— and (2) facility in scientific skills and attitudes—the processes of science and scientific inquiry. These objectives are essentially the same in the elementary and secondary school, the only difference being in how much and how well these objectives will be developed.

Science yearbooks, methods books, articles, and curriculum guides all have consistently urged for years that both objectives be given equal consideration when teaching science. Teachers have been encouraged to use the processes of science to achieve the learning of science content. However, all too often the major emphasis has been on content, and process has been ignored. This has resulted in memorization rather than thinking and in the learning of facts rather than concepts and principles. Furthermore, the children have been deprived of needed experiences with scientific inquiry and the processes of science.

It is easily understandable, then, why today there is widespread preoccupation with revising existing science programs and developing new programs in such a way that the process approach to the learning of science is stressed. The following are some of the key processes, or operations, of science and the scientist that are being suggested for inclusion in the elementary science program: observation, analysis, classi-

315

fication, description, interpretation, inference, deduction, hypothesis, prediction, planning, experimentation, measurement, use of controls, and communication. Thus, concerted efforts are being made to bring the spirit as well as the substance of science into the classroom.

New knowledge of the ways children discover and learn, together with a re-discovery of psychological principles that had almost disappeared from view, are helping us decide the kind and amount of science that children should learn. We now know how the natural curiosity and investigative nature of the child can be utilized effectively to motivate inquiry and real science learning. We know that children go through a number of stages of intellectual development, in which the order of appearance of these stages does not vary. However, the time of appearance of these stages will vary with the individual child and with the society in which the child lives. We also know that we have underestimated greatly what children in the elementary school can learn.

This enthusiasm about the process approach to learning science has become so great that the pendulum is swinging the other way, and process is beginning to be emphasized at the expense of content. Some of the new programs are paying little attention to the learning of concepts. The science content in the program is almost completely unstructured, and whatever content that is included is used only as a means of getting the child to learn process. Many persons have already expressed some concern about this. They claim that the dual objectives of content and process are of equal importance. They maintain that both objectives are not mutually exclusive, but are complementary and mutually interdependent. They contend that when we teach for content, the child should be learning process; and when we teach for process, the child should be learning content.

However, this overemphasis of process should not constitute any real cause for alarm. It helps bring strongly into focus the need for process as well as content in the teaching and learning of science. Eventually a happy medium of both process and content in elementary science should result.

PIAGET REDISCOVERED *

Eleanor Duckworth

Eleanor Duckworth, a former student of Piaget's, served as his translator at the Jean Piaget Conferences on Cognitive Studies and Curriculum Development. These conferences were held in 1964 first at Cornell University and then at the University of California in Berkeley. Dr. Duckworth summarizes Piaget's theory of intellectual development, as presented at the conferences, and discusses the implications of his theory for education.

EVERYBODY in education realizes that Piaget is saying something that is relevant to the teaching of children. For the most part he is understood to be underestimating the value of teaching. He is understood to be saying something like this: Children go through certain stages of intellectual development from birth through adolescence. These stages materialize, fully constructed, when their time has come, and there is little we can do to advance them. What we must do in education is to realize the limits of children's understanding at certain ages, and plan our teaching so it falls within these limits.

In two recent conferences, one at Cornell, one at Berkeley, Piaget made clear that the implications of his psychology for education are a good deal more fecund than this. In fact, the only one of these statements that he would support is that children go through certain stages of intellectual development. Contrary to the view most often attributed to him, he maintains that good pedagogy *can* have an effect on this development.

I will start with the essentials of Piaget's theory of intellectual development, as presented at these conferences, and then go on to some implications for education.

Development of intellectual capacity goes through a number of stages whose order is constant, but whose time of appearance may vary both with the individual and with the society. Each new level of development is a new coherence, a new structuring of elements which until that time have not been systematically related to each other.

Piaget discussed four factors contributing to this development: nervous

* REPRINTED FROM *Journal of Research in Science Teaching*, Vol. 2, Issue 3, 1964, pp. 172–175, by permission of the author and the editor. Dr. Duckworth is associated with Educational Services Incorporated, Watertown, Massachusetts.

maturation, encounters with experience, social transmission, and equilibration or auto-regulation. While the first three do indeed play a role, Piaget finds each of them insufficient in itself. His findings lead him to conclude that an individual's intellectual development is a process of equilibration, where the individual himself is the active motor and coordinator of his own development.

What the first three factors have in common is that the individual is passive. Something is done *to* him; his physiological system matures, or he is presented with physical or linguistic material to absorb. But intellectual development is not this passive. Piaget finds it necessary to call upon the factor of the individual's own activity. An individual learns to see the world as coherent, as structured, to the extent that he acts upon the world, transforms it, and succeeds in coordinating these actions and transformations.

Development proceeds as partial understandings are revised, broadened, and related to one another. Piaget's model for this is one of auto-regulation to attain even broader and more stable equilibrium in the individual's dealing with his world.

As far as education is concerned, the chief outcome of this theory of intellectual development is a plea that children be allowed to do their own learning. Piaget is not saying that intellectual development proceeds at its own pace no matter what you try to do. He is saying that what schools usually try to do is ineffectual. You cannot further understanding in a child simply by talking to him. Good pedagogy must involve presenting the child with situations in which he himself experiments in the broadest sense of that term—trying things out to see what happens, manipulating things, manipulating symbols, posing questions and seeking his own answers, reconciling what he finds at one time with what he finds at another, and comparing his findings with those of other children.

Beyond this general implication, Piaget does not claim to be an educator. During the course of the two conferences he made no single discourse on pedagogy. But he made a number of points which I have gathered together here. Most of them are not new ideas, but it seems to me that it is of importance, somehow, to realize that this is what he is saying.

I shall start with comments on one or two teaching practices often associated with Piaget's name because of some relationships to his research. One is the head-on attack on a specific notion in a precise and limited way. This is the type of attack engaged in by psychological experimenters, in trying to teach four- and five-year-olds, for example, that the amount of liquid stays the same when poured into a glass of a different shape. (In Piaget's own research, when a child asserts that the same amount of liquid is conserved, this is taken as an indication of a certain structure of mental operations. For this reason, performance on this task is an important indicator of intellectual level.)

Piaget sees little sense in intensive specific training on tasks like this one. His feeling is that no learning of significance will take place. Even if the child does manage to learn something about this situation, the learning is not likely to have a general effect on his level of understanding.

But notice that he is *not* thereby saying that a young child's mental structure cannot be touched. He is only saying that this type of specific attack is rather trivial. Modifying a child's effective set of mental operations depends on a much wider, longer-lasting, and fundamental approach which involves all of the child's activity.

Piaget amplified this point about the importance of investigative activity in general in reply to a question on cross-cultural comparisons. Montreal psychologists, using Piaget's material as tests, found children in Martinique to be delayed several years compared to children in Montreal. Similarly, there is a significant delay of children in Iranian villages over children in Iranian cities. Piaget was asked what factors in the adult societies might account for these differences.

In reply, he first pointed out that the schools in Martinique follow the same curriculum as the schools in France, so that scholastic preparation was not likely to account for the difference. Then he quoted the psychologist who had done the research in Martinique, who pointed out that the climate is fine, agriculture flourishes, and living poses few problems. There seems to be little call for questioning and struggling for solutions in general, little call for either physical or intellectual activity. Piaget speculated that this could be the significant factor.

Another pedagogical approach often associated with Piaget's name has to do with teaching the "structure" of a subject matter area. This has been associated with him because of the importance that mental structures play in his psychological theory. The word "structure" is seized upon as the link.

The pedagogical idea is that children should be taught the unifying themes of a subject matter area, after which they will be able to relate individual items to this general structure. (This seems to be what Bruner often means by 'teaching the structure' in *The Process of Education*.) Commenting on this procedure, Piaget made the following statement:

The question comes up whether to teach the structure, or to present the child with situations where he is active and creates the structures himself. . . . The goal in education is not to increase the amount of knowledge, but to create the possibilities for a child to invent and discover. When we teach too fast, we keep the child from inventing and discovering himself. . . . Teaching means creating situations where structures can be discovered; it does not mean transmitting structures which may be assimilated at nothing other than a verbal level.

Piaget addressed two remarks to problems of teacher training. The first is that adults, as well as children, can learn better by doing things than by being told about them. He was talking about teachers in training, when he said, "If they read about it, it will be deformed, as is all learning that is not the result of the subject's own activity."

The second is that prospective teachers ought to spend some time questioning children in a one-to-one situation, in order to realize how hard it is to understand what children mean, and even more, how hard it is to make oneself understood by children. Each prospective teacher should work on an original investigation to find out what children think about some problem, and thus be forced to phrase the problem and establish communication with a number of different children. Facing the difficulties of this type of research will have a sobering effect on a teacher who thinks he is talking successfully to a whole class of children at once.

Permit me one other point of psychological theory as context for another of Piaget's remarks. Piaget sees the process of equilibration as a process of balance between assimilation and accommodation in a biological sense. An individual assimilates the world which comes down to saying he sees it in his own way. But sometimes something presents itself in such a way that he cannot assimilate it into his view of things, so he must change his view; he must accommodate if he wants to incorporate this new item.

The question arose in this conference as to whether school situations could lead a child to accommodate wrongly, that is, to change his ideas on the wrong basis. Piaget replied:

This is a very interesting question. This is a big danger of school—false accommodation which satisfies a child because it agrees with a verbal formula he has been given. This is a false equilibrium which satisfies a child by accommodating to words—to authority and not to objects as they present themselves to him. . . . A teacher would do better not to correct a child's schemas, but to provide situations so he will correct them himself.

Here are a few other remarks at random:

Experience is always necessary for intellectual development. . . . But I fear that we may fall into the illusion that being submitted to an experience (a demonstration) is sufficient for a subject to disengage the structure involved. But more than this is required. The subject must be active, must transform things, and find the structure of his own actions on the objects.

When I say "active," I mean it in two senses. One is acting on material things. But the other means doing things in social collaboration, in a group effort. This leads to a critical frame of mind, where children must communicate with each other. This is an essential factor in intellectual development. Cooperation is indeed co-operation.

(The role of social interaction is important in Piaget's theory of development. A characteristic phenomenon in intellectual difficulties of pre-school children is that they have difficulty conceiving of any point of view other than their own. Coming to an awareness that another child sees something differently from the way he sees it plays an important role in bringing a child to accommodate, to rebuild his point of view, and to come closer to a coherent operational structure.)

The best idea I have heard from a pedagog at the International Bureau of Education in Geneva was made by a Canadian. He said that in his province they had just decided every class should have two classrooms—one where the teacher is, and one where the teacher isn't.

The teacher must provide the instruments which the children can use to decide things by themselves. Children themselves must verify, experimentally in physics, deductively in mathematics. A ready-made truth is only a half-truth.

One participant asked what Piaget thought of having children of different ages in a class together. He replied that it might be helpful especially for the older ones. They could be given some responsibility of teaching younger ones. "Nobody knows better than a professor that the best way to learn something is to teach it."

Yes, the element of surprise is an essential motor in education and in scientific research in general. What distinguishes a good scientist is that he is amazed by things which seem natural to others. Surprise plays an important role; we might well try to develop an aptitude for surprise.

Words are probably not a short-cut to a better understanding. . . . The level of understanding seems to modify the language that is used, rather than vice versa. . . . Mainly, language serves to translate what is already understood; or else language may even present a danger if it is used to introduce an idea which is not yet accessible.

The principal goal of education is to create men who are capable of doing new things, not simply repeating what other generations have done—men who are creators, inventors, and discoverers. The second goal of education is to form minds which can be critical, can verify, and do not accept everything they are offered. The great danger today is from slogans, collective opinions, ready-made trends of thought. We have to be able to resist individually, to criticize, to distinguish between what is proven and what is not. So we need pupils who are active, who learn early to find out by themselves, partly by their own spontaneous activity and partly through material we set up for them; who learn early to tell what is verifiable and what is simply the first idea to come to them.

DEVELOPMENT AND LEARNING *

Jean Piaget

This article is an address given at the Conferences on Cognitive Studies and Curriculum Development described in the previous article. Jean Piaget maintains that the development of intellectual capacity in children goes

* REPRINTED FROM *Journal of Research in Science Teaching*, Vol. 2, Issue 3, 1964, pp. 176–185, by permission of the author and the editor. Professor Piaget is associated with the Center for Genetic Epistemology in Geneva, Switzerland.

through a number of stages, whose order is constant but whose time of appearance may vary with the individual and with the society. These stages are fully constructed when their time has come, and there is little we can do about them. Piaget discusses four factors which contribute to this intellectual development: (1) maturation of the nervous system, (2) experiences, (3) social transmission, and (4) equilibrium, or self-regulation. In education we must realize that there are limits of children's understanding at certain ages, and we must plan our teaching so that it falls within these limits.

M Y DEAR colleagues, I am very concerned about what to say to you, because I do not know if I shall accomplish the end that has been assigned to me. But I have been told that the important thing is not what you say, but the discussion which follows and the answers to questions you are asked. So this morning I shall simply give a general introduction of a few ideas which seem to me to be important for the subject of this conference.

First I would like to make clear the difference between two problems: the problem of *development* in general and the problem of *learning*. I think these problems are very different, although some people do not make this distinction.

The development of knowledge is a spontaneous process, tied to the whole process of embryogenesis. Embryogenesis concerns the development of the body, but it concerns as well the development of the nervous system and the development of mental functions. In the case of the development of knowledge in children, embryogenesis ends only in adulthood. It is a total developmental process which we must re-situate in its general biological and psychological context. In other words, development is a process which concerns the totality of the structures of knowledge.

Learning presents the opposite case. In general, learning is provoked by situations—provoked by a psychological experimenter; or by a teacher, with respect to some didactic point; or by an external situation. It is provoked, in general, as opposed to spontaneous. In addition, it is a limited process—limited to a single problem, or to a single structure.

So I think that development explains learning, and this opinion is contrary to the widely held opinion that development is a sum of discrete learning experiences. For some psychologists development is reduced to a series of specific learned items, and development is thus the sum, the cumulation of this series of specific items. I think this is an atomistic view which deforms the real state of things. In reality, development is the essential process and each element of learning occurs as a function of total development, rather than being an element which explains development. I shall begin, then, with a first part dealing with development, and I shall talk about learning in the second part.

To understand the development of knowledge, we must start with an idea which seems central to me—the idea of an *operation*. Knowledge is not a copy of reality. To know an object, to know an event, is not simply to look at it and make a mental copy or image of it. To know an object is to act on it. To know is to modify, to transform the object, and to understand the process of this transformation, and as a consequence to understand the way the object is constructed. An operation is thus the essence of knowledge; it is an interiorized action which modifies the object of knowledge. For instance an operation would consist of joining objects in a class to construct a classification. Or an operation would consist of ordering, or putting things in a series. Or an operation would consist of counting, or of measuring. In other words, it is a set of actions modifying the object, and enabling the knower to get at the structures of the transformation.

An operation is an interiorized action. But, in addition, it is a reversible action; that is, it can take place in both directions, for instance, adding or subtracting, joining or separating. So it is a particular type of action which makes up logical structures.

Above all, an operation is never isolated. It is always linked to other operations, and as a result it is always a part of a total structure. For instance, a logical class does not exist in isolation; what exists is the total structure of classification. An asymmetrical relation does not exist in isolation. Seriation is the natural, basic operational structure. A number does not exist in isolation. What exists is the series of numbers which constitute a structure, an exceedingly rich structure whose various properties have been revealed by mathematicians.

These operational structures are what seem to me to constitute the basis of knowledge, the natural psychological reality, in terms of which we must understand the development of knowledge. And the central problem of development is to understand the formation, elaboration, organization, and functioning of these structures.

I should like to review the stages of development of these structures, not in any detail, but simply as a reminder. I shall distinguish four main stages. The first is a sensory-motor, pre-verbal stage, lasting approximately the first 18 months of life. During this stage is developed the practical knowledge which constitutes the substructure of later representational knowledge. An example is the construction of the schema of the permanent object. For an infant, during the first months, an object has no permanence. When it disappears from the perceptual field it no longer exists. No attempt is made to find it again. Later, the infant will try to find it, and he will find it by localizing it spatially. Consequently, along with the construction of the permanent object there comes the construction of practical or sensory-motor space. There is similarly the construction of temporal succession, and of elementary sensory-motor causality. In other words, there is a series of structures which are indispensable for the structures of later representational thought.

In a second stage, we have pre-operational representation—the beginnings of language, of the symbolic function, and therefore of thought, or representation. But at the level of representational thought, there must now be a reconstruction of all that was developed on the sensory-motor level. That is, the sensory-motor actions are not immediately translated into operations. In fact, during all this second period of pre-operational representations, there are as yet no operations as I defined this term a moment ago. Specifically, there is as yet no conservation which is the psychological criterion of the presence of reversible operations. For example, if we pour liquid from one glass to another of a different shape, the pre-operational child will think there is more in one than in the other. In the absence of operational reversibility, there is no conservation of quantity.

In a third stage the first operations appear, but I call these concrete operations because they operate on objects, and not yet on verbally expressed hypotheses. For example, there are the operations of classification, ordering, the construction of the idea of number, spatial and temporal operations, and all the fundamental operations of elementary logic of classes and relations, of elementary mathematics, of elementary geometry, and even of elementary physics.

Finally, in the fourth stage, these operations are surpassed as the child reaches the level of what I call formal or hypothetic-deductive operations; that is, he can now reason on hypotheses, and not only on objects. He constructs new operations, operations of propositional logic, and not simply the operations of classes, relations, and numbers. He attains new structures which are on the one hand combinatorial, corresponding to what mathematicians call lattices; on the other hand, more complicated group structures. At the level of concrete operations, the operations apply within an immediate neighborhood: for instance, classification by successive inclusions. At the level of the combinatorial, however, the groups are much more mobile.

These, then, are the four stages which we identify, whose formation we shall now attempt to explain.

What factors can be called upon to explain the development from one set of structures to another? It seems to me that there are four main factors: first of all, *maturation*, in the sense of Gesell, since this development is a continuation of the embryogenesis; second, the role of *experience* of the effects of the physical environment on the structures of intelligence; third, *social transmission* in the broad sense (linguistic transmission, education, etc.); and fourth, a factor which is too often neglected but one which seems to me fundamental and even the principal factor. I shall call this the factor of *equilibration* or if you prefer it, of self-regulation.

Let us start with the first factor, maturation. One might think that these stages are simply a reflection of an interior maturation of the nervous system, following the hypotheses of Gesell, for example. Well, maturation certainly does play an indispensable role and must not be ignored. It certainly takes part in every transformation that takes place during a child's development. However, this first factor is insufficient in itself. First of all, we know practically nothing about the maturation of the nervous system beyond the first months of the child's existence. We know a little bit about it during the first two years but we know very little following this time. But above all, maturation doesn't explain everything, because the average ages at which these stages appear (the average chronological ages) vary a great deal from one society to another. The ordering of these stages is constant and has been found in all the societies studied. It has been found in various countries where psychologists in universities have redone the experiments but it has also been found in African peoples for example, in the children of the Bushmen, and in Iran, both in the villages and in the cities. However, although the order of succession is constant, the chronological ages of these stages varies a great deal. For instance, the ages which we have found in Geneva are not necessarily the ages which you would find in the United States. In Iran, furthermore, in the city of Teheran, they found approximately the same ages as we found in Geneva, but there is a systematic delay of two years in the children in the country. Canadian psychologists who redid our experiments, Monique Laurendeau and Father Adrien Pinard, found once again about the same ages in Montreal. But when they redid the experiments in Martinique, they found a delay of four years in all the experiments and this in spite of the fact that the children in Martinique go to a school set up according to the French system and the French curriculum and attain at the end of this elementary school a certificate of higher primary education. There is then a delay of four years, that is, there are the same stages, but systematically delayed. So you see that these age variations show that maturation does not explain everything.

I shall go on now to the role played by experience. Experience of objects, of physical reality, is obviously a basic factor in the development of cognitive structures. But once again this factor does not explain everything. I can give two reasons for this. The first reason is that some of the concepts which appear at the beginning of the stage of concrete operations are such that I cannot see how they could be drawn from experience. As an example, let us take the conservation of the substance in the case of changing the shape of a ball of plasticene. We give this ball of plasticene to a child who changes its shape into a sausage form and we ask him if there is the same amount of matter, that is, the same amount of substance as there was before. We also ask him if it now has the same weight and thirdly if it now has the same volume. The volume is measured by the displacement of water when we put the ball or the sausage into a glass of water. The findings, which have been the same every time this experiment has been done, show us that first of all there is conservation of the amount of substance. At about eight years old a child will say, "There is the same amount of plasticene." Only later does the child assert that the weight is conserved and still later that the volume is conserved. So I would ask you where the idea of the conservation of substance can come from. What is a constant and invariant substance when it doesn't yet have a constant weight or a constant volume? Through perception you can get at the weight of the ball or the volume of the ball but perception cannot give you an idea of the amount of substance. No experiment, no experience can show the child that there is the same amount of substance. He can weigh the ball and that would lead to the conservation of weight. He can immerse it in water and that would lead to the conservation of volume. But the notion of substance is attained before either weight or volume. This conservation of substance is simply a logical necessity. The child now understands that when there is a transformation something must be conserved because by reversing the transformation you can come back to the point of departure and once again have the ball. He knows that something is conserved but he doesn't know what. It is not yet the weight, it is not yet the volume; it is simply a logical form—a logical necessity. There, it seems to me, is an example of a progress in knowledge, a logical necessity for something to be conserved even though no experience can have lead to this notion.

My second objection to the sufficiency of experience as an explanatory factor is that this notion of experience is a very equivocal one. There are, in fact, two kinds of experience which are psychologically very different and this difference is very important from the pedagogical point of view. It is because of the pedagogical importance that I emphasize this distinction. First of all, there is what I shall call physical experience, and, secondly, what I shall call logical–mathematical experience.

Physical experience consists of acting upon objects and drawing some knowledge about the objects by abstraction from the objects. For example, to discover that this pipe is heavier than this watch, the child will weigh them both and find the difference in the objects themselves. This is experience in the usual sense of the term—in the sense used by empiricists. But there is a second type of experience which I shall call logical–mathematical experience where the knowledge is not drawn from the objects, but it is drawn by the actions effected upon the objects. This is not the same thing. When one acts upon objects, the objects are indeed there, but there is also the set of actions which modify the objects.

I shall give you an example of this type of experience. It is a nice example because we have verified it many times in small children under seven years of age, but it is also an example which one of my mathematician friends has related to me about his own childhood, and he dates his mathematical career from this experience. When he was four or five years old—I don't know exactly how old, but a small child—he was seated on the ground in his garden and he was counting pebbles. Now to count these pebbles he put them in a row and he counted them one, two, three, up to ten. Then he finished counting them and started to count them in the other direction. He began by the end and once again he found ten. He found this marvelous that there were ten in one direction and ten in the other direction. So he put them in a circle and counted them that way and found ten once again. Then he counted them in the other direction and found ten once more. So he put them in some other arrangement and kept counting them and kept finding ten. There was the discovery that he made.

Now what indeed did he discover? He did not discover a property of pebbles; he discovered a property of the action of ordering. The pebbles had no order. It was his action which introduced a linear order or a cyclical order, or any kind of an order. He discovered that the sum was independent of the order. The order was the action which he introduced among the pebbles. For the sum the same principle applied. The pebbles had no sum; they were simply in a pile. To make a sum, action was necessary—the operation of putting together and counting. He found that the sum was independent of the order, in other words, that the action of putting together is independent of the action of ordering. He discovered a property of actions and not a property of pebbles. You may say that it is in the nature of pebbles to let this be done to them and this is true. But it could have been drops of water, and drops of water would not have let this be done to them because two drops of water and two drops of water do not make four drops of water as you know very well. Drops of water then would not let this be done to them, we agree to that.

So it is not the physical property of pebbles which the experience uncovered. It is the properties of the actions carried out on the pebbles, and this is quite another form of experience. It is the point of departure of mathematical deduction. The subsequent deduction will consist of interiorizing these actions and then of combining them without needing any pebbles. The mathematician no longer needs his pebbles. He can combine his operations simply with symbols, and the point of departure of this mathematical deduction is logical-mathematical experience, and this is not at all experience in the sense of the empiricists. It is the beginning of the coordination of actions, but this coordination of actions before the stage of operations needs to be supported by concrete material. Later, this coordination of actions leads to the logical-mathematical structures. I believe that logic is not a derivative of language. The source of logic is much more profound. It is the total coordination of actions, actions of joining things together, or ordering things, etc. This is what logical-mathematical experience is. It is an experience of the actions of the subject, and not an experience of objects themselves. It is an experience which is necessary before there can be operations. Once the operations have been attained this experience is no longer needed and the coordinations of actions can take place by themselves in the form of deduction and construction for abstract structures.

The third factor is social transmission-linguistic transmission or educational transmission. This factor, once again, is fundamental. I do not deny the role of any one of these factors; they all play a part. But this factor is insufficient because the child can receive valuable information via language or via education directed by an adult only if he is in a state where he can understand this information. That is, to receive the information he must have a structure which enables him to assimilate this information. This is why you cannot teach higher mathematics to a five-year-old. He does not yet have structures which enable him to understand.

I shall take a much simpler example, an example of linguistic transmission. As my very first work in the realm of child psychology, I spent a long time studying the relation between a part and a whole in concrete experience and in language. For example, I used Burt's test employing the sentence, "Some of my flowers are buttercups." The child knows that all buttercups are yellow, so there are three possible conclusions: the whole bouquet is yellow, or part of the·bouquet is yellow, or none of the flowers in the bouquet are yellow. I found that up until nine years of age (and this was in Paris, so the children certainly did understand the French language) they replied, "The whole bouquet is yellow or some of my flowers are yellow." Both of those mean the same thing. They did not understand the expression, "some *of* my flowers." They did not understand this *of* as a partitive genitive, as the inclusion of some flowers in my flowers. They understood some of my flowers to be my several flowers as if the several flowers and the flowers were confused as one and the same class. So there you have children who until nine years of age heard every day a linguistic structure which implied the inclusion of a subclass in a class and yet did not understand this structure. It is only when they themselves are in firm possession of this logical structure, when they have constructed it for themselves according to the developmental laws which we shall discuss, that they succeed in understanding correctly the linguistic expression.

I come now to the fourth factor which is added to the three preceding ones but which seems to me to be the fundamental one. This is what I call the factor of equilibration. Since there are already three factors, they must somehow be equilibrated among themselves. That is one reason for bringing in the factor of equilibration. There is a second reason, however, which seems to me to be fundamental. It is that in the act of knowing, the subject is active, and consequently, faced with an external disturbance, he will react in order to compensate and consequently he will tend towards equilibrium. Equilibrium, defined by active compensation, leads to reversibility. Operational reversibility is a model of an equilibrated system where a transformation in one direction is compensated by a transformation in the other direction. Equilibration, as I understand it, is thus an active process. It is a process of self-regulation. I think that this self-regulation is a fundamental factor in development. I use this term in the sense in which it is used in cybernetics, that is, in the sense of processes with feedback and with feedforward, of processes which regulate themselves by a progressive compensation of systems. This process of equilibration takes the form of a succession of levels of equilibrium, of levels which have a certain probability which I shall call a sequential probability, that is, the probabilities are not established *a priori*. There is a sequence of levels. It is not possible to reach the second level unless equilibrium has been reached at the first level, and the equilibrium of the third level only becomes possible when the equilibrium of the second level has been reached, and so forth. That is, each level is determined as the most probable given that the preceding level has been reached. It is not the most probable at the beginning, but it is the most probable once the preceding level has been reached.

As an example, let us take the development of the idea of conservation in the transformation of the ball of plasticene into the sausage shape. Here you can discern four levels. The most probable at the beginning is for the child to think of only one dimension. Suppose that there is a probability of 0.8, for instance, that the child will focus on the length, and that the width has a probability of 0.2. This would mean that of ten children, eight will focus on the length alone without paying any attention to the width, and two will focus on the width without paying any attention to the length. They will focus only on one dimension or the other. Since the two dimensions are independent at this stage, focusing on both at once would have a probability. of only 0.16. That is less than either one of the two. In other words, the most probable in the beginning is to focus only on one dimension and in fact the child will say, "It's longer, so there's more in the sausage." Once he has reached this first level, if you continue to elongate the sausage, there comes a moment when he will say, "No, now it's too thin, so there's less." Now he is thinking about the width, but he forgets the length, so you have come to a second level which becomes the most probable after the first level, but which is not the most probable at the point of departure. Once he has focused on the width, he will come back sooner or later to focus on the length. Here you will have a third level where he will oscillate between width and length and where he will discover that the two are related. When you elongate you make it thinner, and when you make it shorter, you make it thicker. He discovers that the two are solidly related and in discovering this relationship, he will start to think in terms of transformation and not only in terms of the final configuration. Now he will say that when it gets longer it gets thinner, so it's the same thing. There is more of it in length but less of it in width. When you make it shorter it gets thicker; there's less in length and more in width, so there is compensation—compensation which defines equilibrium in the sense in which I defined it a moment ago. Consequently, you have operations and conservation. In other words, in the course of these developments you will always find a process of self-regulation which I call equilibration and which seems to me the fundamental factor in the acquisition of logical-mathematical knowledge.

I shall go on now to the second part of my lecture, that is, to deal with the topic of learning. Classically, learning is based on the stimulus-response schema. I think the stimulus-response schema, while I won't say it is false, is in any case entirely incapable of explaining cognitive learning. Why? Because when you think of a stimulus-response schema, you think usually that first of all there is a stimulus and then a response is set off by this stimulus. For my part, I am convinced that the response was there first, if I can express myself in this way. A stimulus is a stimulus only to the extent that it is significant, and it becomes significant only to the extent that there is a structure which permits its assimilation, a structure which can integrate this stimulus but which at the same time sets off the response. In other words, I would propose that the stimulus-response schema be written in the circular form—in the form of a schema or of a structure which is not simply one way. I would propose that above all, between the stimulus and the response, there is the organism, the organism and its structures. The stimulus is really a stimulus only when it is assimilated into a structure and it is this structure which sets off the response. Consequently, it is not an exaggeration to say that the response is there first, or if you wish at the beginning there is the structure. Of course we would want to understand how this structure comes to be. I tried to do this earlier by presenting a model of equilibration or self-regulation. Once there is a structure, the stimulus will set off a response, but only by the intermediary of this structure.

I should like to present some facts. We have facts in great number. I shall choose only one or two and I shall choose some facts which our colleague, Smedslund, has gathered. (Smedslund is currently at the Harvard Center for Cognitive Studies.) Smedslund arrived in Geneva a few years ago convinced (he had published this in one of his papers) that the development of the ideas of conservation could be indefinitely accelerated through learning of a stimulus-response type. I invited Smedslund to come to spend a year in Geneva to show us this, to show us that he could accelerate the development of operational conservation. I shall relate only one of his experiments.

During the year that he spent in Geneva he chose to work on the conservation of weight. The conservation of weight is, in fact, easy to study since there is a possible external reinforcement, that is, simply weighing the ball and the sausage on a balance. Then you can study the child's reactions to these external results. Smedslund studied the conservation of weight on the one hand, and on the other hand he studied the transitivity of weights, that is, the transitivity of equalities if A = B and B = C, then A = C, or the transitivity of the inequalities if A is less than B, and B is less than C, then A is less than C.

As far as conservation is concerned, Smedslund succeeded very easily with five- and six-year-old children in getting them to generalize that weight is conserved when the ball is transformed into a different shape. The child sees the ball transformed into a sausage or into little pieces or into a pancake or into any other form, he weighs it, and he sees that it is always the same thing. He will affirm it will be the same thing, no matter what you do to it; it will come out to be the same weight. Thus Smedslund very easily achieved the conservation of weight by this sort of external reinforcement.

In contrast to this, however, the same method did not succeed in teaching transitivity. The children resisted the notion of transitivity. A child would predict correctly in certain cases but he would make his prediction as a possibility or a probability and not as a certainty. There was never this generalized certainty in the case of transitivity.

So there is the first example, which seems to me very instructive, because in this problem in the conservation of weight there are two aspects. There is the physical aspect and there is the logical-mathematical aspect. Note that

Smedslund started his study by establishing that there was a correlation between conservation and transitivity. He began by making a statistical study on the relationships between the spontaneous responses to the questions about conservation and the spontaneous responses to the questions about transitivity, and he found a very significant correlation. But in the learning experiment, he obtained a learning of conservation and not of transitivity. Consequently, he successfully obtained a learning of what I called earlier physical experience (which is not surprising since it is simply a question of noting facts about objects), but he did not successfully obtain a learning in the construction of the logical structure. This doesn't surprise me either, since the logical structure is not the result of physical experience. It cannot be obtained by external reinforcement. The logical structure is reached only through internal equilibration, by self-regulation, and the external reinforcement of seeing that the balance did not suffice to establish this logical structure of transitivity.

I could give many other comparable examples, but it seems useless to me to insist upon these negative examples. Now I should like to show that learning is possible in the case of these logical-mathematical structures, but on one condition—that is, that the structure which you want to teach to the subjects can be supported by simpler, more elementary, logical-mathematical structures. I shall give you an example. It is the example of the conservation of number in the case of one-to-one correspondence. If you give a child seven blue tokens and ask him to put down as many red tokens, there is a pre-operational stage where he will put one red one opposite each blue one. But when you spread out the red ones, making them into a longer row, he will say to you, "Now, there are more red ones than there are blue ones."

Now how can we accelerate, if you want to accelerate, the acquisition of this conservation of number? Well, you can imagine an analogous structure but in a simpler, more elementary situation. For example, with Mlle. Inhelder, we have been studying recently the notion of one-to-one correspondence by giving the child two glasses of the same shape and a big pile of beads. The child puts a bead into one glass with one hand and at the same time a bead into the other glass with the other hand. Time after time he repeats this action, a bead into one glass with one hand and at the same time a bead into the other glass with the other hand and he sees that there is always the same amount on each side. Then you hide one of the glasses. You cover it up. He no longer sees this glass but he continues to put one bead into it while at the same time putting one bead into the other glass which he can see. Then you ask him whether the equality has been conserved, whether there is still the same amount in one glass as in the other. Now you will find that very small children, about four years old, don't want to make a prediction. They will say, "So far, it has been the same amount, but now I don't know. I can't see any more, so I don't know." They do not want to generalize. But the generalization is made from the age of about five and one-half years.

This is in contrast to the case of the red and blue tokens with one row spread out, where it isn't until seven or eight years of age that children will say there are the same number in the two rows. As one example of this generalization, I recall a little boy of five years and nine months who had been adding the beads to the glasses for a little while. Then we asked him whether, if he continued to do this all day and all night and all the next day, there would always be the same amount in the two glasses. The little boy gave this admirable reply. "Once you know, you know for always." In other words, this was recursive reasoning. So here the child does acquire the structure in this specific case. The number is a synthesis of class inclusion and ordering. This synthesis is being favored by the child's own actions. You have set up a situation where there is an iteration of one same action which continues and which is therefore ordered while at the same time being inclusive. You have, so to speak, a localized synthesis of inclusion and ordering which facilitates the construction of the idea of number in this specific case, and there you can find, in effect, an influence of this experience on the other experience. However, this influence is not immediate. We study the generalization from this recursive situation to the other situation where the tokens are laid on the table in rows, and it is not an immediate generalization but it is made possible through intermediaries. In other words, you can find some learning of this structure if you base the learning on simpler structures.

In this same area of the development of numerical structures, the psychologist Joachim Wohlwill, who spent a year at our Institute at Geneva, has also shown that this acquisition can be accelerated through introducing additive operations, which is what we introduced also in the experiment which I just described. Wohlwill introduced them in a different way but he too was able to obtain a certain learning effect. In other words, learning is possible if you base the more complex structure on simpler structures, that is, when there is a natural relationship and development of structures and not simply an external reinforcement.

Now I would like to take a few minutes to conclude what I was saying. My first conclusion is that learning of structures seems to obey the same laws as the natural development of these structures. In other words, learning is subordinated to development and not vice-versa as I said in the introduction. No doubt you will object that some investigators have succeeded in teaching operational structures. But, when I am faced with these facts, I always have three questions which I want to have answered before I am convinced.

The first question is: "Is this learning lasting? What remains two weeks or a month later?" If a structure develops spontaneously, once it has reached a state of equilibrium, it is lasting, it will continue throughout the child's entire life. When you achieve the learning by external reinforcement, is the result lasting or not and what are the conditions necessary for it to be lasting?

The second question is: "How much generalization is possible?" What makes learning interesting is the possibility of transfer of a generalization. When you have brought about some learning, you can always ask whether this is an isolated piece in the midst of the child's mental life, or if it is really a dynamic structure which can lead to generalizations.

Then there is the third question: "In the case of each learning experience what was the operational level of the subject before the experience and what more complex structures has this learning succeeded in achieving?" In other words, we must look at each specific learning experience from the point of view of the spontaneous operations which were present at the outset and the operational level which has been achieved after the learning experience.

My second conclusion is that the fundamental relation involved in all development and all learning is not the relation of association. In the stimulus-response schema, the relation between the response and the stimulus is understood to be one of association. In contrast to this, I think that the fundamental relation is one of assimilation. Assimilation is not the same as association. I shall define assimilation as the integration of any sort of reality into a structure, and it is this assimilation which seems to me to be fundamental in learning, and which seems to me to be the fundamental relation from the point of view of pedagogical or didactic applications. All of my remarks today represent the child and the learning subject as active. An operation is an activity. Learning is possible only when there is active assimilation. It is this activity on the part of the subject which seems to me to be underplayed in the stimulus-response schema. The presentation which I propose puts the emphasis on the idea of self-regulation, on assimilation. All the emphasis is placed on the activity of the subject himself, and I think that without this activity there is no possible didactic or pedagogy which significantly transforms the subject.

Finally, and this will be my last concluding remark, I would like to comment on an excellent publication by the psychologist Berlyne. Berlyne spent a year with us in Geneva during which he intended to translate our results on the development of operations into stimulus-response language, specifically into Hull's learning theory. Berlyne published in our series of studies of genetic epistemology a very good article on this comparison between the results obtained in Geneva and Hull's theory. In the same volume, I published a commentary on Berlyne's results. The essence of Berlyne's results is this: Our findings can very well be translated into Hullian language, but only on condition that two modifications are introduced. Berlyne himself found these modifications quite considerable, but they seemed to him to concern more the conceptualization than the Hullian theory itself. I am not so sure about that. The two modifications are these. First of all, Berlyne wants to distinguish two sorts of response in the S-R schema: (*a*) responses in the ordinary, classical sense, which I shall call "copy responses"; (*b*) responses which Berlyne calls "transformation responses." Tranformation responses consist of transforming one response of the first type into another response of the first type. These transformation responses are what I call operations, and you can see right away that this is a rather serious modification of Hull's conceptualization because here you are introducing an element of transformation and thus of assimilation and no longer the simple association of stimulus-response theory.

The second modification which Berlyne introduces into the stimulus-response language is the introduction of what he calls internal reinforcements. What are these internal reinforcements? They are what I call equilibration or self-regulation. The internal reinforcements are what enable the subject to eliminate contradictions, incompatibilities, and conflicts. All development is composed of momentary conflicts and incompatibilities which must be overcome to reach a higher level of equilibrium. Berlyne calls this elimination of incompatibilities internal reinforcements.

So you see that it is indeed a stimulus-response theory, if you will, but first you add operations and then you add equilibration. That's all we want!

PIAGET'S DEVELOPMENTAL THEORY OF LEARNING AND ITS IMPLICATIONS FOR INSTRUCTION IN SCIENCE *

Celia B. Stendler

Celia B. Stendler discusses Piaget's concept of intelligence, his concept of the properties of logical thinking, and his concept of stages in the development of logical thinking. Dr. Stendler points out that Piaget's concept of stages in logical thinking is not based upon ages but rather upon changes in the child's comprehension of logic. Dr. Stendler presents some promising leads about how the child develops logical thinking. Finally, she discusses the impact of early environmental deficits upon the culturally disadvantaged child. She sees the urgent need for systematic studies of the impact of cultural deprivation upon logical thinking.

I AM GOING to begin with a few background remarks about Jean Piaget. Chances are that all of you are familiar with at least some of his work. He is, as you know, a Swiss psychologist who has been studying children for

* REPRINTED FROM a paper presented on March 28, 1965, at the Thirteenth Annual Convention of the National Science Teachers Association in Denver, Colorado, by permission of the author and the National Science Teachers Association. Dr. Stendler is Professor of Education at the University of Illinois.

almost 50 years, and is still actively engaged in research at the Institute de J. J. Rousseau in Geneva. Those of you who are of my vintage may be best acquainted with his early work on language and moral development, first published in the twenties and still widely read. Even then Piaget's main concern was with epistemology. He asked and still asks, how does the child acquire knowledge, and what happens to mental processes during the acquisition? When his own children were infants, he made close observations and conducted little experiments with them, testing out his theory of how intelligence develops. Since then he has been busy refining theory and directing research, until today we have from his pen the best put-together picture of how intellective development takes place. When Piaget talks about the development of intelligence, he means the development of logical thinking, which he regards as man's highest attribute. There are, of course, other aspects considered to be part of intelligence—memory, for example—but I will be talking today about logical intelligence when I use the term.

All teachers, especially science and math teachers, must necessarily be concerned with logical thought processes in children. Many times throughout the day a teacher calls upon pupils to define, compare, contrast, find other examples of a phenomenon, deal with whole-part relations, and hypothesize. When a teacher asks a child to say what makes a bird a bird, or to give an example of adaptation, or to discover the relationship between angle of incidence and angle of reflection, he is calling upon the child to think logically, to perform some logical operations in thought. Note that such questions cannot be answered with responses learned through reinforcement. These questions require that the child manipulate data already stored in his mind, that he perform some mental operation to come up with his answer.

But what if the child cannot answer, or gives the wrong answer? What does the teacher do? Chances are he will call on another pupil, or he will say to the first, "Think! Think about my question. See if you can't find a better answer." Rarely does he ask, "How do you go about answering such a question?" to see if the pupil understands that *there are mental processes by which he can arrive at the correct answer*. More rarely still does he teach the pupil what that process is.

Note that I am using "process" in a different way from what you may be accustomed to. Bruner's book, *The Process of Education*, has popularized the word "process" in terms of the structure of subject matter, of the general principles that structure a body of knowledge. But *how* does a pupil grasp the principles? *How* does he make discoveries? When I talk about process, I have in mind what goes on in the gray cells that makes possible the acquisition of knowledge. It is process used in this sense that Piaget's theory is concerned with.

I have selected from the wealth of ideas that Piaget has given us three that I thought most relevant to the work of science educators. They are: Piaget's concept of intelligence; his concept of the properties of logical thought; and his concept of stages in the development of logical thinking. I will discuss each of these in turn.

First, his concept of intelligence. For Piaget, intelligence is not something that is qualitatively or quantitatively fixed at birth, but rather, is a form of adaptation characterized by equilibrium. Part of man's biological inheritance is a striving for equilibrium in *mental* processes as well as in other physiological processes. Twin processes are involved: assimilation and accommodation. The child assimilates information from the environment which may upset existing equilibrium, and then accommodates present structures to the new so that equilibrium is restored. A six-year-old may think that cubes of sugar dropped into a jar of water will make the water level go up, but that after the sugar dissolves, the water level will go down again. But there is order in the physical world; as the child carries on interactions with things in his environment he gets feedback. At first when he sees that water level does NOT go down when the sugar dissolves, he is shaken, but stumped. With repeated experiences and reflection upon outcome, he may come to see by eleven years that when we add something to a substance, it stays added. In the child's language, "Stuff doesn't go away by itself; you have to do something to it." The mental structure or schema involving conservation has been accommodated to the new information. Throughout the formative years, the child carries on countless transactions involving space, time, matter and causality, and as he assimilates information from the regularities in the physical world, old ideas are shaken and mental structures formed anew.

Note that the child must be mentally active; *he* must transform the data. In one demonstration session, I was testing a boy and girl together on a conservation of volume problem. Each child was presented with two cylinders identical in appearance, but one made of steel and the other of aluminum. No mention was made of weight, but the child held a cylinder in each hand and was asked to predict what each would do to the water level in the glasses, equal to begin with. The girl confidently predicted that the heavier one would make the water rise higher in the glass; the boy equally confidently predicted that water level would be the same. Then the cylinders were put in water and the girl's confidence was shaken. She had no explanation; *probably* she had been wrong, she thought. In the next step, the children were asked to find smaller objects that would make the water level go up the same as the steel cylinder. The girl chose heavy objects; the boy estimated overall size or volume. Then the girl reversed her decision. "He's probably right again," she said, "I'll say the same as he does; *but I don't really believe it.*" This last remark is *most* revealing. As Piaget says over and over again, children do not acquire knowledge of something merely by being told or by reading about it; the child *must act upon it.* Acting upon it may or may not involve a physical action, but it must involve a mental action. When a physical action is needed is a problem that I hope our panel will address itself to.

The second part of Piaget's theory that I have chosen to talk about is his concept of the properties of logical thought. What do we do when we think logically? Let us look at a classroom example. A sixth-grade class has been studying about the ways in which animals are adapted to their environment. The teacher asks, "Can you give me an example of an animal that lives in the desert, and explain how this is possible?" Assuming that the question is one that has not been dealt with directly in the text and so mere recall of information is not enough, what must a pupil do to answer the question? He has to manipulate data stored in his mind, shuffle different sets of facts around, or in Piaget's language, the child must perform some logical operations. First he may recall what extreme conditions with respect to basic needs of life are found on the desert and, second, select a particular desert animal and check out how that animal gets what it needs for survival under these extreme conditions. Let's take the kangaroo rat. First we have a set of desert conditions, made up of "little water"; "extremes of temperature"; "scarcity of food"; "little ground cover." In the next set, we put the characteristics of the rat, "eats seeds and gets water from seeds"; "sharp claws and so burrows; stays underground during heat of day and so needs less water"; "eyes have many rods and so the animal can see to hunt for food at night when there is less competition and few enemies." In other words, we take the set of desert conditions and the set of kangaroo rat characteristics and we do a one-to-one correspondence between each. If for every member of one set there is a corresponding member in the other set, then we know the two sets are identical. When I talk about teaching children how to go about answering questions, I have in mind teaching them processes like this one.

Actually, there are two logical operations involved here. The first is to put together the elements making up each set. This operation is additive composition or combinativity. One of the properties of logical thought is that elements can be combined to make a total class; we can put two and two together figuratively as well as literally.

The second operation involved in the example of the kangaroo rat is an identity operation. You will recall that the child first postulated a set of conditions of desert life and then checked out known characteristics of the rat against these conditions by doing a one-to-one correspondence. Whenever we ask children to compare, contrast, or give an example of some concept, an identity operation is involved. Some pupils know how to perform such an identity operation; they know what must be done to see if two sets are identical. Others do not discover for themselves what mental process is necessary to get the right answer; they need to know that there *is* a process and what the steps in the process are.

Two additional properties of logical thinking are associativity and reversibility. One of the operations possible when we think logically is to put together elements in different ways to achieve the same result. This is associativity, which simply put, means that we can reach the same goal by different paths. In one of Piaget's tests the young child is shown two identical paths, each made up of rods of equal length. He is told that two dolls are going for a walk, one on each path. Does each doll take as long a walk as the other? Is each path as long? The child agrees that each is the same length. Then one of the paths is rearranged in zig-zag fashion and the question is repeated. The young child will think that now the straight path is longer, "for it goes way over to here," while by six or seven the child will say, "You've got the same sticks in each path and it doesn't matter how you put them. It'll be the same walk." Older children often use the associative principle in solving the displacement of water problem involving cylinders of different weights. Those who realize that the steel cylinder will displace exactly the same amount of water as the one made of aluminum will be able to select objects of various sizes and shapes to total approximately the same volume as the metal cylinders. They will say of the one narrower in diameter, "It's skinnier, but it's longer. It makes up for being less here by being more here."

Of the displacements the child performs on data, one of the most critical to develop is that of reversibility. Every change, every displacement that we carry on mentally is reversible. We can combine robins and all birds-not-robins to make up a class of birds, and we can also separate the class into the original subclasses. We can construct hypotheses and then discard them and return to the starting point. We can follow one path in thinking and then retrace our steps without affecting the ideas employed. This ability to reverse thought is for Piaget the most clearly defined characteristic of logical intelligence.

The model that Piaget believes mirrors the thought of the child is a group-like structure or *groupement*. In fact, it is sometimes difficult to identify one of these logical properties in any mutually exclusive fashion for they are tightly knit ensembles. The child may say when one of the two balls of clay has been elongated, "They've got to be the same. Take some off the length and add it to the thickness and you're back where you started." He takes the data and puts them together in various ways to arrive at the solution to a problem.

Note, too, that the Piaget model is a logico-mathematical one. Those of you who are familiar with the principles of arithmetic as taught in the schools today will recognize in the four properties of thought the properties of algebraic structures. Piaget's model is a logico-mathematical one, for he sees the same structures in logical intelligence that have been identified in mathematics. The properties of the group correspond to the properties of thought in the child. In other words, mathematical structures and psychological structures resemble each other.

These operations that I have been describing characterize the thought processes of the child during the elementary school years, but during adolescence, there are changes that occur in modes of thinking. Piaget describes the kind of thinking that develops (and that, hopefully, characterizes adult thought) as *propositional thinking*. The child states propositions in terms of the variables he has identified, and then proceeds to systematically combine the propositions so as to test all possible combinations. A thirteen-year-old is presented with four flasks containing colorless, odorless liquids that look exactly the same, plus a bottle containing potassium iodide. He is shown that a few drops of the potassium iodide can turn the proper mixture of liquids yellow, and he is asked to reproduce the mixture. The boy's statements as he tries to solve the problem reveal certain characteristics of thinking that we do not find in younger children. For example, the boy states, "If this liquid (in the bottle) is water, then when you put it with a mixture of the first and third flasks it wouldn't prevent the yellow from forming." In effect, he is saying, "If it's water, it wouldn't do this"; one statement logically implies another.

There are four ways in which propositions can be combined. We can combine by conjunction, as when we say, "It's got to be this *and* this"; by disjunction, "It's got to be this or this"; by negation, "It's neither this nor this"; and by implication, "If it's this, then this will be true." In addition to combining propositions in these four different ways, we can also transform each of the combinations in four different ways, yielding a possibility of sixteen different products. Let's suppose, for example, that you are interested in the problem of visual stimulation and whether design and/or color is more attractive to certain insects. How to combine the two variables? The possible combinations are:

Is it design and not color?
Is it color and not design?
Is it design and color?
Is it neither?

Each one of these questions must be systematically checked out. The various types of conjunctions and disjunctions must be continuously linked to implications. Suppose we start with "Is it design and not color?" Then we have to say, "If it's color and not design, then when we present both stimuli, we ought to attract more insects to the color." But note that immediately there are problems involving an identity transformation. If it's color, is it any color? Does red work as well as yellow? Do fluorescent colors work better than nonfluorescent? If it's the case that color red is equal to color yellow, the number of insects should be the same. Back and forth the mind goes, combining propositions and then performing operations upon the propositions like identity operation that we just illustrated. Or the operation may be one of negation, of reciprocity or of correlation. "A change in the amount of fluorescence in the paint is going to result in a corresponding change in number of insects caught" is a statement of correlation. "If I vary designs from simple to complex and still don't attract as many insects as with color, then it can't be design" is an example of negation.

Propositional thinking is what our science teaching should help to develop; and again I would urge that we can best develop propositional thinking by letting pupils in on the fact that there *is* a set of operations consistently used in logical thinking. Students should *know* that there *are* systematic ways in which we combine propositions for testing hypotheses, and they should know what these systematic ways are. We have given lip service to the scientific method by teaching that children should observe carefully, state hypotheses, test hypotheses, note results, and come to some kind of conclusion. But notice the holes in such a procedure. We teach the importance of observation, but the *young* child *is* an observer. He does indeed observe carefully, but he judges in terms of perceptual data, of how things look to him, instead of performing logical operations on the data. And we emphasize stating and testing hypotheses without giving any clues as to how we can combine propositions and test *so as to exclude as well as to include*. Some so-called experiments are set up so that the child never has a chance to state as a proposition what he really thinks makes a difference. A third grade class was observing a demonstration in which lighted candles were covered with jars of various sizes and the children correctly hypothesized that the taller jar would provide more air and so the candle would burn longer. Usually this particular demonstration stops with the testing of the correct hypothesis. But the smart teacher in this case knew that there was a prior question: what determines the amount of air in the jar? Would the number of candles burning under each jar make a difference? This question gave the children no difficulty; they could state the case correctly. Then the teacher asked what else *might* make a difference? What about height of candle? Would a tall candle go out more quickly than a short one? The answer for the third-graders was yes! Demonstration and experimentation must be carried on so as to test for the exclusion of variables as well as to test the significant one that *we* know works.

So much, then, for an overview of what is involved in logical thinking. Now we turn to the developmental process. How do logical operations develop in the child? For Piaget the development of intelligence begins at least in the cradle and goes through stages from birth to maturity. The first stage Piaget calls the sensori-motor. The infant comes into the world with two kinds of reflexes: those like the knee jerk that are not altered by experience, and others like grasping and sucking that *are* modified as the infant exercises them. The modification occurs through assimilation and accommodation. The infant, for example, accommodates the grasping reflex to the shape of the object to be grasped, curving his fingers one way for a long narrow object, and in a different way for a ring. During the first eighteen months, the infant carries on countless transactions involving space, time, matter, and causality which build and reshape developing mental structures. Witness what happens with respect to the notion of permanence of object. To the neonate, the game of peek-a-boo is meaningless; for him, an object ceases to exist when it disappears from view, and out-of-sight is out-of-mind. But later in the first year, the infant knows that an object continues to exist and delights in searching for it when it is hidden. He "knows," not in words, but in his sensori-motor system, in much the same way that we may "know" how to find our way through a building the second time. For Piaget, sensori-motor intelligence is the intelligence of action. The infant must first carry out displacements in his actions, searching for an object first in one place and then in another, for he cannot do this in his mind. However, physical actions gradually become internalized, and by eighteen months the child is capable of "representation," of imagining the environment other than as he directly perceives it.

I move quickly to the next stage, the pre-operational, which extends from eighteen months, roughly, to about seven years. It is in this stage that we find most kindergarten and first-grade children, some second-grade, and of course, some children even older than seven years. This stage is called pre-operational because the child does not use logical operations in his thinking. Piaget characterizes mental processes at the pre-operational stage as follows:

1. The child is perceptually oriented; he makes judgments in terms of how things *look* to him. He may, for example, be confused in thinking about space by the objects placed in that space. When given a problem where two lines of ten segmented sticks are laid out in parallel rows, he will see that both are equal in length; that two dolls, walking along each path, would walk the same distance. But if one of the rows is rearranged in this fashion:

$$\bigwedge\!\bigwedge$$

and the child is again asked if each doll takes as long a walk as the other, the child says "no." Even when he counts the segments, he denies equality; the child does not see that there is a logical necessity by which ten must equal ten. Piaget has shown that this same type of perceptual judgment enters into the child's thinking about space, time, number and causality. It is only as the child goes beyond his perceptions to perform displacements upon the data in his mind (for example, visualizing the second row of sticks straightened out again) that conservation appears.

2. The child centers on one variable only, and usually the variable that stands out visually; he lacks the ability to coordinate variables. A kindergarten child is pouring juice into paper cups. The standard size cups run out, and the teacher substitutes some that are much higher but are also smaller in diameter. As the children drink their juice, several comment on the fact that Jimmy, Eddie, and Danny have more juice. And why? Because their cups are taller. The dimension of height stands out, not that of width, in this case. The child's thinking is rigid; he does not perform operations on what he sees. Later he will reason that "higher than" is compensated for by "skinnier than" and that both kinds of cups may hold the same amount of juice. This ability to see reciprocal changes in two sets of data is an important logical tool available to older children but not in the pre-operational child.

3. The child has difficulty in realizing that an object can possess more than one property, and that multiplicative classifications are possible. It is hard

for the child to see that one can live in Champaign and in Illinois at the same time; that a bird is also an animal; and that an Impala is also a Chevy. The operation of combining elements to form a whole and then seeing a part in relation to the whole has not as yet developed, and so hierarchical relationships cannot be mastered.

So far, this consideration of pre-operational thinking has been largely negative. We have seen that the child lacks the ability to combine parts into a whole, to put parts together in different ways, and to reverse processes. What, then, can the child do? The development of logical processes is not at a standstill during this period, and there are some positive accomplishments. We see, for example, the rudiments of classification; the child can make collections of things on the basis of some criterion. He can also shift that criterion. Thus if we present a kindergarten child with a collection of pink and blue squares and circles, some large and some small, and ask him to sort them into two piles with those in each pile being alike in some way, he can usually make two different collections on the basis of color and shape (a few children discover the third criterion of size). Such an ability, of course, is essential to the formation of classes and eventually to the notion of hierarchy of classes. Science provides countless opportunities for having children discover more than one variable. Sounds, for example, can be high or low, loud or soft, to make four possible combinations, as shown on this matrix.

The child is also beginning to arrange things in a series. He can compare two members of a set within a series when they are in consecutive order; he knows that Tuesday comes after Monday. But since Friday comes after Tuesday, which is after Monday, does Friday also come after Monday? This operation involving seeing logical relations between things or events that are arranged in a series is not yet possible to the pre-operational child, but experiences with seriation are preparatory to the development of such operations.

By seven years of age, the logical operations of reversibility, associativity, etc., that I have already described begin to appear. Piaget calls this the stage of concrete operations, because while the child uses logical operations, the content of his thinking is concrete rather than abstract. Fifth-grade pupils, if given a billiard-game problem when they are studying light, can do serial ordering and establish a one-to-one correspondence between the two slopes of directions. "The more I put it like that (inclined to the right), the more the ball will go like that," a ten-year-old will explain. That the total angle can be divided into two equal angles does not occur to them, for they lack the formal operations necessary to such a discovery. They solve problems and give explanations in terms of the concrete data available to them; they do not try to state generalizations.

This stage of concrete operations lasts until 12 years which is roughly the age for the onset of the state of formal operations or propositional thinking. According to Piaget, most children at the high school level tend to do the "If this happens, then that is likely to happen," or not to happen, kind of thinking. They are also more likely to think in terms of abstractions and can state, as in the case of the billiard game, the general principle involved.

Critics of Piaget have made his notion of development as occurring in stages one of their targets. Some mistakenly think that Piaget uses the concept as does Gesell. For Piaget, however, stages are convenient for helping us to think coherently about the course of development. His descriptions of stages are based upon changes in the child's comprehension of logic. They are not tied in any hard-and-fast way to age. In fact, as the students in Geneva discovered when they tried the Piaget tasks on husbands or wives, or other adults including themselves, adults are spotty in their ability to solve the tasks. With respect to cognitive processes at each of the stages, Piaget describes these in terms of probability; he would say that at a particular stage there is a probability which can be set at a certain figure that the child will select a particular strategy for solving a problem. Thus when the ball of clay is transformed into a sausage, there is a strong probability that the child will at one stage mention length rather than thickness, and an even stronger probability that he won't think of two dimensions.

The question arises, once we assume that stages in logical thinking are not rigidly tied to age, as to whether we can then speed up the development of logical thinking. This is a question that never fails to amuse students and faculty in Geneva, for they regard it as typically American. Tell an American that a child develops certain ways of thinking at seven, and he immediately sets about to try to develop those same ways of thinking at six or even five years of age. Actually investigators in countries other than America have tried to accelerate the development of logical thinking, and we have available today a considerable body of research on what works and what doesn't work. Most of the research has not worked. It hasn't worked because experimenters have not paid attention to equilibrium theory. The researchers have tried to teach an answer, a particular response, rather than to develop operations. They have tried to teach the child that of course the hot dog will weigh as much as the clay ball; just put both on a two-pan-balance and you'll see. But the child is completely unconvinced unless he shuffles the data around in his mind, using one or more of the operations I've described. Learning a fact by reinforcement does not in and of itself result in mental adaptation.

What does work? Research by some investigators (Smedslund and Wohlwill in particular) offers some promising leads. These might be summarized as follows:

1. It has been possible to accelerate the development of logical intelligence by inducing cognitive conflict in subjects. Smedslund devised a training procedure with the balls of clay where he both elongated the clay and also took away a piece of it, thus forcing the child to choose between two conflicting explanations. Can the hot dog weigh more when a piece has been taken away? Given this kind of choice, the child veers toward consistency.

2. Training children to recognize that an object can belong to several different classes at once aids in the development of logical classification.
3. There is a tendency for children, trained to see that addition and subtraction of elements changes numerical value to achieve conservation earlier than a non-trained group.
4. To help children move from the pre-operational stage to the stage of concrete operations, it is helpful to make gradual transformations in the visual stimulus, and to call the child's attention to the effects of a change in one dimension to a change in another.

There is a fifth possibility that I'd like to suggest, and that is that children, as they study subject-matter, should also be alerted to *process* in terms of the logical operations that I have been describing. At the present time, I am working on a research project in University City, Missouri, sponsored by the Ford Foundation. We are trying to introduce more intellectual stimulation into the kindergarten curriculum. Kindergartens, as you know, do a very good job for the most part in helping the child adjust to group life and to school routines. They also provide many fine activities designed to foster creativity. But kindergartens haven't quite known what to do to stimulate intellectual development. Some have turned to the teaching of reading, but the actual process of learning to read, while of course essential, does not really involve much in the way of logical thinking. In University City we are giving children equipment and opportunity to work with equipment designed to help them develop logical multiplication (that is, that an object can belong to several classes at once), the concept of a grid system, matrix-type thinking, the concept of unit iteration in measurement, and certain other processes. Underlying these processes, is the group-structure I have described. After five months when all 400 children have had a chance to play with equipment, to act upon it, we will give training on the operations themselves to part of the group. We have controls in another community. We will then be able to compare children's performance after six months of working on Piaget tasks with children without such experience. We will also be able to compare a smaller group of children who have received special training with a group that has experienced free play with Piaget tasks but no training. My subjective judgment is that the free play is effective.

A word in closing about the culturally disadvantaged. The evidence is overwhelming that early environmental deficits leave their impact upon the developing organism. Years ago, Goldforb found that children who spent the first three years of their lives in foundling institutions were deficient in concept development and in language, and since that time, as one writer has noted, there is a dreary repetition to the studies finding over and over again mental deficits resulting from environmental deprivation.

Poverty contributes to environmental deprivation. That "the poor are segregated and have no chance to learn from their more fortunate neighbors" was observed by Mme. Montessori in the Roman slums in 1907; it is just as

true today. Poverty is not always accompanied by environmental deprivation; some families in America with low incomes manage to provide children
with an environment conducive to development of intelligence, but this only
happens when parents themselves have had an opportunity to know that a
different way of life is possible, and to have some idea of how their children
might achieve what they missed. The history of immigrant families in
America attests to the truth of this generalization. Nor is poverty the only
prerequisite to cultural deprivation. There are rural families and blue-collar
families who are above the subsistence level, but whose home environment
is at such a low cultural level that the children are essentially culturally deprived when they enter school and have learning problems.

We have been in home after home of the culturally disadvantaged where
there are no books, no toys, nothing for small children to do except to look
for hours at the ever-present television set or carry on boisterous play with
their siblings. Piaget talks about logical intelligence developing as the child
carries on transactions upon objects or events in the environment. Thus
children acquire notions oʃ the world of space, time, matter and causality,
have their notions jarred and have equilibrium restored at a higher level,
all this in what we have assumed to be a *normal* pattern of living. But today the voices of Luci and Desi and Andy Griffith and As the World Turns
provide the stuff to stretch children's minds. Small wonder that we find these
minds are not developing as they should and that there are nine- and ten-
year-olds who are not mentally retarded, but who are still at the pre-operational level in logical thinking. There are no systematic studies of the
development of logical thinking in culturally disadvantaged children. In
Champaign-Urbana, however, we have administered the Piaget tests to more
than 100 poor children in the last three years and the retardation is obvious.
When we ask a nine-year-old boy, for example, to look at a set of geometric
figures (circles, squares and triangles) in two sizes and colors, and to separate them into two piles, putting those in one pile that go together in some
way, he can classify by one criterion (shape, most likely), but he cannot see
that one can group in terms of color and also of size. Language is, of course,
a handicap. Seven-year-olds sometimes don't know what we're talking about
when we use terms like "top" and "bottom," "up" and "down." Shown a
bottle half filled with water and then turned on its side, the child is asked,
"How high-up is the water now?" It is the word "up" in the question that
bothers the child. Interestingly enough, however, these children often do
better in problems involving operations upon relations than they do those
involving operations upon classes. When we deal with class concepts, language becomes a handicap, but when we present the child with a cube
3 x 3 x 4 and ask him to make a "house" on a 1 x 3 base with just as many
"rooms" out of one-inch blocks, the child reveals that he is using logical
operations such as combining elements, seeing more than one dimension and
it may be that in certain areas of thinking cultural deprivation takes a
stronger toll than in others. We need systematic studies of the impact of

cultural deprivation upon logical thinking so that we can provide for the problem of match.

In closing I would like to say that while I hope I have made Piaget's theory clearer to most of you, I believe firmly with Piaget that more than sitting and listening is necessary for accommodation to occur. I would urge you for a fuller understanding to administer some of the Piaget tests yourselves to children. Listen to the answers that children give to the standard questions and one will be forever humbled by the knowledge that in teaching one often fails to hit upon the very elementary but very basic misunderstanding that is interfering with logical thinking. Today we pride ourselves in science teaching that the curriculum is stronger in respectable subject-matter than ever before. Let's make sure that we aren't trying to teach atomic theory to children who have not yet grasped the conservation principle in its simplest form.

READINESS FOR LEARNING *

Jerome S. Bruner

The following article consists of key excerpts from Chapter III of Jerome S. Bruner's book, The Process Of Education. *Dr. Bruner proposes his widely quoted hypothesis that "any subject can be taught effectively in some intellectually honest form to any child at any stage of development." To clarify the implications of this hypothesis, he examines three general ideas: the process of intellectual development in children, the act of learning, and the notion of the "spiral curriculum." All three ideas have broad significance for curriculum development.*

WE BEGIN with the hypothesis that any subject can be taught effectively in some intellectually honest form to any child at any stage of development. It is a bold hypothesis and an essential one in thinking about the nature of a curriculum. No evidence exists to contradict it; considerable evidence is being amassed that supports it.

To make clear what is implied, let us examine three general ideas. The

* REPRINTED FROM *The Process of Education* (Cambridge: Harvard University Press, 1961), pp. 33–40, 48–49, 52–54, by permission of the author and the publisher. Dr. Bruner is Professor of Psychology and Director of the Center for Cognitive Studies at Harvard University.

first has to do with the process of intellectual development in children, the second with the act of learning, and the third with the notion of the "spiral curriculum" introduced earlier.

INTELLECTUAL DEVELOPMENT. Research on the intellectual development of the child highlights the fact that at each stage of development the child has a characteristic way of viewing the world and explaining it to himself. The task of teaching a subject to a child at any particular age is one of representing the structure of that subject in terms of the child's way of viewing things. The task can be thought of as one of translation. The general hypothesis that has just been stated is premised on the considered judgment that any idea can be represented honestly and usefully in the thought forms of children of school age, and that these first representations can later be made more powerful and precise the more easily by virtue of this early planning. To illustrate and support this view, we present here a somewhat detailed picture of the course of intellectual development, along with some suggestions about teaching at different stages of it.

The work of Piaget and others suggests that, roughly speaking, one may distinguish three stages in the intellectual development of the child. The first stage need not concern us in detail, for it is characteristic principally of the pre-school child. In this stage, which ends (at least for Swiss school children) around the fifth or sixth year, the child's mental work consists principally in establishing relationships between experience and action; his concern is with manipulating the world through action. This stage corresponds roughly to the period from the first development of language to the point at which the child learns to manipulate symbols. In this so-called preoperational stage, the principal symbolic achievement is that the child learns how to represent the external world through symbols established by simple generalization; things are represented as equivalent in terms of sharing some common property. But the child's symbolic world does not make a clear separation between internal motives and feelings on the one hand and external reality on the other. The sun moves because God pushes it, and the stars, like himself, have to go to bed. The child is little able to separate his own goals from the means for achieving them, and when he has to make corrections in his activity after unsuccessful attempts at manipulating reality, he does so by what are called intuitive regulations rather than by symbolic operations, the former being of a crude trial-and-error nature rather than the result of taking thought.

What is principally lacking at this stage of development is what the Geneva school has called the concept of reversibility. When the shape of an object is changed, as when one changes the shape of a ball of plasticene, the preoperational child cannot grasp the idea that it can be brought back readily to its original state. Because of this fundamental lack the child cannot understand certain fundamental ideas that lie at the basis of mathematics and physics—the mathematical idea that one conserves quantity even when one partitions a set of things into subgroups, or the physical idea that one conserves mass and weight even though one transforms the shape of an object. It goes without saying that teachers are severely limited in transmitting concepts to a child at this stage, even in a highly intuitive manner.

The second stage of development—and now the child is in school—is called the stage of concrete operations. This stage is operational in contrast to the preceding stage, which is merely active. An operation is a type of action: it can be carried out rather directly by the manipulation of objects, or internally, as when one manipulates the symbols that represent things and relations in one's mind. Roughly, an operation is a means of getting data about the real world into the mind and there transforming them so that they can be organized and used selectively in the solution of problems. Assume a child is presented with a pinball machine which bounces a ball off a wall at an angle. Let us find out what he appreciates about the relation between the angle of incidence and the angle of reflection. The young child sees no problem: for him, the ball travels in an arc, touching the wall on the way. The somewhat older child, say age ten, sees the two angles as roughly related —as one changes so does the other. The still older child begins to grasp that there is a fixed relation between the two, and usually says it is a right angle. Finally, the thirteen- or fourteen-year-old, often by pointing the ejector directly at the wall and seeing the ball come back at the ejector, gets the idea that the two angles are equal. Each way of looking at the phenomenon represents the result of an operation in this sense, and the child's thinking is constrained by his way of pulling his observations together.

An operation differs from simple action or goal-directed behavior in that it is internalized and reversible. "Internalized" means that the child does not have to go about his problem-solving any longer by overt trial and error, but can actually carry out trial and error in his head. Reversibility is present because operations are seen as characterized where appropriate by what is called "complete compensation"; that is to say, an operation can be compensated for by an inverse operation. If marbles, for example, are divided into subgroups, the child can grasp intuitively that the original collection of marbles can be restored by being added back together again. The child tips a balance scale too far with a weight and then searches systematically for a lighter weight or for something with which to get the scale rebalanced. He may carry reversibility too far by assuming that a piece of paper, once burned, can also be restored.

With the advent of concrete operations, the child develops an internalized structure with which to operate. In the example of the balance scale the structure is a serial order of weights that the child has in his mind. Such internal structures are of the essence. They are the internalized symbolic systems by which the child represents the world, as in the example of the pinball machine and the angles of incidence and reflection. It is into the language of these internal structures that one must translate ideas if the child is to grasp them.

But concrete operations, though they are guided by the logic of classes and the logic of relations, are means for structuring only immediately present reality. The child is able to give structure to the things he encounters, but he is not yet readily able to deal with possibilities not directly before him or not already experienced. This is not to say that children operating concretely are not able to anticipate things that are not present. Rather, it is that they do not command the operations for conjuring up systematically the full range of alternative possibilities that could exist at any given time. They cannot go systematically beyond the information given them to a description of what else might occur. Somewhere between ten and fourteen years of age the child passes into a third stage, which is called the stage of "formal operations" by the Geneva school.

Now the child's intellectual activity seems to be based upon an ability to operate on hypothetical propositions rather than being constrained to what he has experienced or what is before him. The child can now think of possible variables and even deduce potential relationships that can later be verified by experiment or observation. Intellectual operations now appear to be predicated upon the same kinds of logical operations that are the stock in trade of the logician, the scientist, or the abstract thinker. It is at this point that the child is able to give formal or axiomatic expression to the concrete ideas that before guided his problem-solving but could not be described or formally understood.

Earlier, while the child is in the stage of concrete operations, he is capable of grasping intuitively and concretely a great many of the basic ideas of mathematics, the sciences, the humanities, and the social sciences. But he can do so only in terms of concrete operations. It can be demonstrated that fifth-grade children can play mathematical games with rules modeled on highly advanced mathematics; indeed, they can arrive at these rules inductively and learn how to work with them. They will flounder, however, if one attempts to force upon them a formal mathematical description of what they have been doing, though they are perfectly capable of guiding their behavior by these rules. At the Woods Hole Conference we were privileged to see a demonstration of teaching in which fifth-grade children very rapidly grasped central ideas from the theory of functions, although had the teacher attempted to explain to them what the theory of functions was, he would have drawn a blank. Later, at the appropriate stage of development and given a certain amount of practice in concrete operations, the time would be ripe for introducing them to the necessary formalism.

What is most important for teaching basic concepts is that the child be helped to pass progressively from concrete thinking to the utilization of more conceptually adequate modes of thought. But it is futile to attempt this by presenting formal explanations based on a logic that is distant from the child's manner of thinking and sterile in its implications for him. Much teaching in mathematics is of this sort. The child learns not to understand mathematical order but rather to apply certain devices or recipes without understanding their significance and connectedness. They are not translated into his way of thinking. Given this inappropriate start, he is easily led to believe that the important thing is for him to be "accurate"—though accuracy has less to do with mathematics than with computation. Perhaps the most striking example of this type of thing is to be found in the manner in which the high school student meets Euclidian geometry for the first time, as a set of axioms and theorems, without having had some experience with simple geometric configurations and the intuitive means whereby one deals with them. If the child were earlier given the concepts and strategies in the form of intuitive geometry at a level that he could easily follow, he might be far better able to grasp deeply the meaning of the theorems and axioms to which he is exposed later.

But the intellectual development of the child is no clockwork sequence of events; it also responds to influences from the environment, notably the school environment. Thus instruction in scientific ideas, even at the elementary level, need not follow slavishly the natural course of cognitive development in the child. It can also lead intellectual development by providing challenging but usable opportunities for the child to forge ahead in his development. Experience has shown that it is worth the effort to provide the growing child with problems that tempt him into next stages of development. As David Page, one of the most experienced teachers of elementary mathematics, has commented: "In teaching from kindergarten to graduate school, I have been amazed at the intellectual similarity of human beings at all ages, although children are perhaps more spontaneous, creative, and energetic than adults. As far as I am concerned young children learn almost anything faster than adults do if it can be given to them in terms they understand. Giving the material to them in terms they understand, interestingly enough, turns out to involve knowing the mathematics oneself, and the better one knows it, the better it can be taught. It is appropriate that we warn ourselves to be careful of assigning an absolute level of difficulty to any particular topic. When I tell mathematicians that fourth-grade students can go a long way into 'set theory' a few of them reply: 'Of course.' Most of them are startled. The latter ones are completely wrong in assuming that 'set theory' is intrinsically difficult. Of course it may be that nothing is intrinsically difficult. We just have to wait until the proper point of view and corresponding language for presenting it are revealed. Given particular subject matter or a particular concept, it is easy to ask trivial questions, or to lead the child to ask trivial questions. It is also easy to ask impossibly difficult questions. The trick is to find the medium questions that can be answered and that take you somewhere. This is the big job of teachers and textbooks." One leads the child by the well-wrought "medium questions" to move more rapidly through the stages of intellectual development, to a deeper understanding of mathematical, physical, and historical principles. We must know far more about the ways in which this can be done.

* * *

THE ACT OF LEARNING. Learning a subject seems to involve three almost simultaneous processes. First there is *acquisition* of new information—often information that runs counter to or is a replacement for what the person has previously known implicitly or explicitly. At the very least it is a refinement of previous knowledge. Thus one teaches a student Newton's laws of motion, which violate the testimony of the senses. Or in teaching a student about wave mechanics, one violates the student's belief in mechanical impact as the sole source of real energy transfer. Or one bucks the language and its built-in way of thinking in terms of "wasting energy" by introducing the student to the conservation theorem in physics which asserts that no energy is lost. More often the situation is less drastic, as when one teaches the details of the circulatory system to a student who already knows vaguely or intuitively that blood circulates.

A second aspect of learning may be called *transformation*—the process of manipulating knowledge to make it fit new tasks. We learn to "unmask" or analyze information, to order it in a way that permits extrapolation or interpolation or conversion into another form. Transformation comprises the ways we deal with information in order to go beyond it.

A third aspect of learning is *evaluation*: checking whether the way we have manipulated information is adequate to the task. Is the generalization fitting, have we extrapolated appropriately, are we operating properly? Often a teacher is crucial in helping with evaluation, but much of it takes place by judgments of plausibility without our actually being able to check rigorously whether we are correct in our efforts.

In the learning of any subject matter, there is usually a series of episodes, each episode involving the three processes. Photosynthesis might reasonably comprise material for a learning episode in biology, fitted into a more comprehensive learning experience such as learning about the conversion of energy generally. At its best a learning episode reflects what has gone before it and permits one to generalize beyond it.

A learning episode can be brief or long, contain many ideas or a few. How sustained an episode a learner is willing to undergo depends upon what the person expects to get from his efforts, in the sense of such external things as grades but also in the sense of a gain in understanding.

We usually tailor material to the capacities and needs of students by manipulating learning episodes in several ways: by shortening or lengthening the episode, by piling on extrinsic rewards in the form of praise and gold stars, or by dramatizing the shock of recognition of what the material means when fully understood. The unit in a curriculum is meant to be a recognition of the importance of learning episodes, though many units drag on with no climax in understanding. There is a surprising lack of research on how one most wisely devises adequate learning episodes for children at different ages and in different subject matters.

* * *

THE "SPIRAL CURRICULUM." If one respects the ways of thought of the growing child, if one is courteous enough to translate material into his logical forms and challenging enough to tempt him to advance, then it is possible to introduce him at an early age to the ideas and styles that in later life make an educated man. We might ask, as a criterion for any subject taught in primary school, whether, when fully developed, it is worth an adult's knowing, and whether having known it as a child makes a person a better adult. If the answer to both questions is negative or ambiguous, then the material is cluttering the curriculum.

If the hypothesis with which this section was introduced is true—that any subject can be taught to any child in some honest form—then it should follow that a curriculum ought to be built around the great issues, principles, and values that a society deems worthy of the continual concern of its members.

*   *   *

If the understanding of number, measure, and probability is judged crucial in the pursuit of science, then instruction in these subjects should begin as intellectually honestly and as early as possible in a manner consistent with the child's forms of thought. Let the topics be developed and redeveloped in later grades. Thus, if most children are to take a tenth-grade unit in biology, need they approach the subject cold? Is it not possible, with a minimum of formal laboratory work if necessary, to introduce them to some of the major biological ideas earlier, in a spirit perhaps less exact and more intuitive?

Many curricula are originally planned with a guiding idea much like the one set forth here. But as curricula are actually executed, as they grow and change, they often lose their original form and suffer a relapse into a certain shapelessness. It is not amiss to urge that actual curricula be reexamined with an eye to the issues of continuity and development referred to in the preceding pages. One cannot predict the exact forms that revision might take; indeed, it is plain that there is now available too little research to provide adequate answers. One can only propose that appropriate research be undertaken with the greatest vigor and as soon as possible.

THE ACT OF DISCOVERY *

Jerome S. Bruner

Jerome S. Bruner believes that it is only through the exercise of problem-solving and the effort of discovery that one learns the working heuristics of discovery; and the more one has practice, the more likely is one to generalize what one has learned into a style of inquiry that serves for any kind of task. Dr. Bruner discusses what the act of discovery entails. He also describes four major benefits derived by children when they learn how to investigate and discover for themselves: (1) an increase in intellectual potency, (2) a shift from extrinsic to intrinsic rewards, (3) learning the heuristics of discovery, and (4) aid in memory processing.

M AIMONIDES, in his *Guide for the Perplexed*,[1] speaks of four forms of perfection that men might seek. The first and lowest form is perfection in the acquisition of worldly goods. The great philosopher dismisses such perfection on the ground that the possessions one acquires bear no meaningful relation to the possessor: "A great king may one morning find that there is no difference between him and the lowest person." A second perfection is of the body, its conformation and skills. Its failing is that it does not reflect on what is uniquely human about man: "he could (in any case) not be as strong as a mule." Moral perfection is the third, "the highest degree of excellency in man's character." Of this perfection Maimonides says: "Imagine a person being alone, and having no connection whatever with any other person; all his good moral principles are at rest, they are not required and give man no perfection whatever. These principles are only necessary and useful when man comes in contact with others." The fourth kind of perfection is "the true perfection of man; the possession of the highest intellectual faculties . . ." In justification of his assertion, this extraordinary Spanish-Judaic philosopher urges: "Examine the first three kinds of perfection; you will find that if you possess them, they are not your property, but the property of others. . . . But the last kind of perfection is exclusively yours; no one else owns any part of it."

---

[1] Maimonides, *Guide for the Perplexed* (New York: Dover Publications, 1956).

* REPRINTED FROM *Harvard Educational Review*, Vol. 31, No. 1, 1961, pp. 21–32, by permission of the author and the publisher. Dr. Bruner is Professor of Psychology and Director of the Center for Cognitive Studies at Harvard University.

It is a conjecture much like that of Maimonides that leads me to examine the act of discovery in man's intellectual life. For if man's intellectual excellence is the most his own among his perfections, it is also the case that the most uniquely personal of all that he knows is that which he has discovered for himself. What difference does it make, then, that we encourage discovery in the learning of the young? Does it, as Maimonides would say, create a special and unique relation between knowledge possessed and the possessor? And what may such a unique relation do for a man—or for a child, if you will, for our concern is with the education of the young?

The immediate occasion for my concern with discovery—and I do not restrict discovery to the act of finding out something that before was unknown to mankind, but rather include all forms of obtaining knowledge for oneself by the use of one's own mind—the immediate occasion is the work of the various new curriculum projects that have grown up in America during the last six or seven years. For whether one speaks to mathematicians or physicists or historians, one encounters repeatedly an expression of faith in the powerful effects that come from permitting the student to put things together for himself, to be his own discoverer.

First, let it be clear what the act of discovery entails. It is rarely, on the frontier of knowledge or elsewhere, that new facts are "discovered" in the sense of being encountered as Newton suggested in the form of islands of truth in an uncharted sea of ignorance. Or if they appear to be discovered in this way, it is almost always thanks to some happy hypotheses about where to navigate. Discovery, like surprise, favors the well prepared mind. In playing bridge, one is surprised by a hand with no honors in it at all and also by hands that are all in one suit. Yet all hands in bridge are equiprobable: one must know to be surprised. So too in discovery. The history of science is studded with examples of men "finding out" something and not knowing it. I shall operate on the assumption that discovery, whether by a schoolboy going it on his own or by a scientist cultivating the growing edge of his field, is in its essence a matter of rearranging or transforming evidence in such a way that one is enabled to go beyond the evidence so reassembled to additional new insights. It may well be that an additional fact or shred of evidence makes this larger transformation of evidence possible. But it is often not even dependent on new information.

It goes without saying that, left to himself, the child will go about discovering things for himself within limits. It also goes without saying that there are certain forms of child rearing, certain atmospheres that lead some children to be their own discoverers more than other children. These are both topics of great interest, but I shall not be discussing them. Rather, I should like to confine myself to the consideration of discovery and "finding-out-for-oneself" within an educational setting—especially the school. Our aim as teachers is to give our student as firm a grasp of a subject as we can, and to make him as autonomous and self-propelled a thinker as we can—one who will go along on his own after formal schooling has ended. I shall return in the end to the question of the kind of classroom and the style of teaching that encourage an attitude of wanting to discover. For purposes of orienting the discussion, however, I would like to make an overly simplified distinction between teaching that takes place in the *expository mode* and teaching that utilizes the *hypothetical mode*. In the former, the decisions concerning the mode and pace and style of exposition are principally determined by the teacher as expositor; the student is the listener. If I can put the matter in terms of structural linguistics, the speaker has a quite different set of decisions to make than the listener: the former has a wide choice of alternatives for structuring, he is anticipating paragraph content while the listener is still intent on the words, he is manipulating the content of the material by various transformations while the listener is quite unaware of these internal manipulations. In the hypothetical mode, the teacher and the student are in a more cooperative position with respect to what in linguistics would be called "speaker's decisions." The student is not a bench-bound listener, but is taking a part in the formulation and at times may play the principal role in it. He will be aware of alternatives and may even have an "as if" attitude toward these, and as he receives information he may evaluate it as it comes. One cannot describe the process in either mode with great precision as to detail, but I think the foregoing may serve to illustrate what is meant.

Consider now what benefit might be derived from the experience of learning through discoveries that one makes for oneself. I should like to discuss these under four headings: (1) The increase in intellectual potency, (2) the shift from extrinsic to intrinsic rewards, (3) learning the heuristics of discovering, and (4) the aid to memory processing.

1. INTELLECTUAL POTENCY. If you will permit me, I would like to consider the difference between subjects in a highly constrained psychological experiment involving a two-choice apparatus. In order to win chips, they must depress a key either on the right or the left side of the machine. A pattern of payoff is designed such that, say, they will be paid off on the right side 70 per cent of the time, on the left 30 per cent, although this detail is not important. What is important is that the payoff sequence is arranged at random, and there is no pattern. I should like to contrast the behavior of subjects who think that there *is* some pattern to be found in the sequence— who think that regularities are discoverable—in contrast to subjects who think that things are happening quite by *chance*. The former group adopts what is called an "event-matching" strategy in which the number of responses given to each side is roughly equal to the proportion of times it pays off: in the present case R70:L30. The group that believes there is no pattern very soon reverts to a much more primitive strategy wherein *all* responses are allocated to the side that has the greater payoff. A little arithmetic will show you that the lazy all-and-none strategy pays off more if indeed the environment is random: namely, they win seventy per cent of the time. The event-matching subjects win about 70% on the 70% payoff side (or 49% of the

time there) and 30% of the time on the side that pays off 30% of the time (another 9% for a total take-home wage of 58% in return for their labors of decision). But the world is not always or not even frequently random, and if one analyzes carefully what the event-matchers are doing, it turns out that they are trying out hypotheses one after the other, all of them containing a term such that they distribute bets on the two sides with a frequency to match the actual occurrence of events. If it should turn out that there is a pattern to be discovered, their payoff would become 100%. The other group would go on at the middling rate of 70%.

What has this to do with the subject at hand? For the person to search out and find regularities and relationships in his environment, he must be armed with an expectancy that there will be something to find and, once aroused by expectancy, he must devise ways of search and finding. One of the chief enemies of such expectancy is the assumption that there is nothing one can find in the environment by way of regularity or relationship. In the experiment just cited, subjects often fall into a habitual attitude that there is either nothing to be found or that they can find a pattern by looking. There is an important sequel in behavior to the two attitudes, and to this I should like to turn now.

We have been conducting a series of experimental studies on a group of some seventy school children over the last four years. The studies have led us to distinguish an interesting dimension of cognitive activity that can be described as ranging from *episodic empiricism* at one end to *cumulative constructionism* at the other. The two attitudes in the choice experiments just cited are illustrative of the extremes of the dimension. I might mention some other illustrations. One of the experiments employs the game of Twenty Questions. A child—in this case he is between 10 and 12—is told that a car has gone off the road and hit a tree. He is to ask questions that can be answered by "yes" or "no" to discover the cause of the accident. After completing the problem, the same task is given him again, though he is told that the accident had a different cause this time. In all, the procedure is repeated four times. Children enjoy playing the game. They also differ quite markedly in the approach or strategy they bring to the task. There are various elements in the strategies employed. In the first place, one may distinguish clearly between two types of questions asked: the one is designed for locating constraints in the problem, constraints that will eventually give shape to an hypothesis; the other is the hypothesis as question. It is the difference between, "Was there anything wrong with the driver?" and "Was the driver rushing to the doctor's office for an appointment and the car got out of control?" There are children who precede hypotheses with efforts to locate constraint and there are those who, to use our local slang, are "pot-shotters," who string out hypotheses non-cumulatively one after the other. A second element of strategy is its connectivity of information gathering: the extent to which questions asked utilize or ignore or violate information previously obtained. The questions asked by children tend to be organized in cycles, each cycle of questions usually being given over to the pursuit of some particular notion. Both within cycles and between cycles one can discern a marked difference on the connectivity of the child's performance. Needless to say, children who employ constraint location as a technique preliminary to the formulation of hypotheses tend to be far more connected in their harvesting of information. Persistence is another feature of strategy, a characteristic compounded on what appear to be two components: a sheer doggedness component, and a persistence that stems from the sequential organization that a child brings to the task. Doggedness is probably just animal spirits or the need for achievement—what has come to be called *n-ach*. Organized persistence is a maneuver for protecting our fragile cognitive apparatus from overload. The child who has flooded himself with disorganized information from unconnected hypotheses will become discouraged and confused sooner than the child who has shown a certain cunning in his strategy of getting information—a cunning whose principal component is the recognition that the value of information is not simply in getting it but in being able to carry it. The persistence of the organized child stems from his knowledge of how to organize questions in cycles, how to summarize things to himself, and the like.

Episodic empiricism is illustrated by information gathering that is unbound by prior constraints, that lacks connectivity, and that is deficient in organizational persistence. The opposite extreme is illustrated by an approach that is characterized by constraint sensitivity, by connective maneuvers, and by organized persistence. Brute persistence seems to be one of those gifts from the gods that make people more exaggeratedly what they are.[2]

Before returning to the issue of discovery and its role in the development of thinking, let me say a word more about the ways in which information may get transformed when the problem solver has actively processed it. There is first of all a pragmatic question: what does it take to get information processed into a form best designed to fit some future use? Take an experiment by Zajonc [3] as a case in point. He gives groups of subjects information of a controlled kind, some groups being told that their task is to transmit the information to others, others that it is merely to be kept in mind. In general, he finds more differentiation and organization of the information received with the intention of being transmitted than there is for information received passively. An active set leads to a transformation related to a task to be performed. The risk, to be sure, is in possible overspecialization of information processing that may lead to such a high degree of specific organization that information is lost for general use.

I would urge now in the spirit of an hypothesis that emphasis upon dis-

---

[2] I should also remark in passing that the two extremes also characterize concept attainment strategies as reported in *A Study of Thinking* by J. S. Bruner et al. (New York: J. Wiley, 1956). Successive scanning illustrates well what is meant here by episodic empiricism; conservative focusing is an example of cumulative constructionism.

[3] R. B. Zajonc (Personal communication, 1957).

covery in learning has precisely the effect upon the learner of leading him to be a constructionist, to organize what he is encountering in a manner not only designed to discover regularity and relatedness, but also to avoid the kind of information drift that fails to keep account of the uses to which information might have to be put. It is, if you will, a necessary condition for learning the variety of techniques of problem solving, of transforming information for better use, indeed for learning how to go about the very task of learning. Practice in discovering for oneself teaches one to acquire information in a way that makes that information more readily viable in problem solving. So goes the hypothesis. It is still in need of testing. But it is an hypothesis of such important human implications that we cannot afford not to test it—and testing will have to be in the schools.

2. INTRINSIC AND EXTRINSIC MOTIVES. Much of the problem in leading a child to effective cognitive activity is to free him from the immediate control of environmental rewards and punishments. That is to say, learning that starts in response to the rewards of parental or teacher approval or the avoidance of failure can too readily develop a pattern in which the child is seeking cues as to how to conform to what is expected of him. We know from studies of children who tend to be early over-achievers in school that they are likely to be seekers after the "right way to do it" and that their capacity for transforming their learning into viable thought structures tends to be lower than children merely achieving at levels predicted by intelligence tests. Our tests on such children show them to be lower in analytic ability than those who are not conspicuous in overachievement.[4] As we shall see later, they develop rote abilities and depend upon being able to "give back" what is expected rather than to make it into something that relates to the rest of their cognitive life. As Maimonides would say, their learning is not their own.

The hypothesis that I would propose here is that to the degree that one is able to approach learning as a task of discovering something rather than "learning about" it, to that degree will there be a tendency for the child to carry out his learning activities with the autonomy of self-reward or more properly by reward that is discovery itself.

To those of you familiar with the battles of the last half-century in the field of motivation, the above hypothesis will be recognized as controversial. For the classic view of motivation in learning has been, until very recently, couched in terms of a theory of drives and reinforcement: that learning occurred by virtue of the fact that a response produced by a stimulus was followed by the reduction in a primary drive state. The doctrine is greatly extended by the idea of secondary reinforcement: any state associated even remotely with the reduction of a primary drive could also have the effect of

---

[4] J. S. Bruner and A. J. Caron, "Cognition, Anxiety, and Achievement in the Preadolescent," *Journal of Educational Psychology* (in press).

producing learning. There has recently appeared a most searching and important criticism of this position, written by Professor Robert White,[5] reviewing the evidence of recently published animal studies, of work in the field of psychoanalysis, and of research on the development of cognitive processes in children. Professor White comes to the conclusion, quite rightly I think, that the drive-reduction model of learning runs counter to too many important phenomena of learning and development to be either regarded as general in its applicability or even correct in its general approach. Let me summarize some of his principal conclusions and explore their applicability to the hypothesis stated above.

I now propose that we gather the various kinds of behavior just mentioned, all of which have to do with effective interaction with the environment, under the general heading of competence. According to Webster, competence means fitness or ability, and the suggested synonyms include capability, capacity, efficiency, proficiency, and skill. It is, therefore, a suitable word to describe such things as grasping and exploring, crawling and walking, attention and perception, language and thinking, manipulating and changing the surroundings, all of which promote an effective—a competent—interaction with the environment. It is true, of course, that maturation plays a part in all these developments, but this part is heavily overshadowed by learning in all the more complex accomplishments like speech or skilled manipulation. I shall argue that it is necessary to make competence a motivational concept; there is *competence motivation* as well as competence in its more familiar sense of achieved capacity. The behavior that leads to the building up of effective grasping, handling, and letting go of objects, to take one example, is not random behavior that is produced by an overflow of energy. It is directed, selective, and persistent, and it continues not because it serves primary drives, which indeed it cannot serve until it is almost perfected, but because it satisfies an intrinsic need to deal with the environment.[6]

I am suggesting that there are forms of activity that serve to enlist and develop the competence motive, that serve to make it the driving force behind behavior. I should like to add to White's general premise that the *exercise* of competence motives has the effect of strengthening the degree to which they gain control over behavior and thereby reduce the effects of extrinsic rewards or drive gratification.

The brilliant Russian psychologist Vigotsky[7] characterizes the growth of thought processes as starting with a dialogue of speech and gesture between child and parent; autonomous thinking begins at the stage when the child is first able to internalize these conversations and "run them off" himself. This is a typical sequence in the development of competence. So too in instruction. The narrative of teaching is of the order of the conversation.

[5] R. W. White, "Motivation Reconsidered: The Concept of Competence," *Psychological Review*, LXVI (1959), pp. 297–333.

[6] *Ibid.*, pp. 317–318.

[7] L. S. Vigotsky, *Thinking and Speech* (Moscow, 1934).

The next move in the development of competence is the internalization of the narrative and its "rules of generation" so that the child is now capable of running off the narrative on his own. The hypothetical mode in teaching by encouraging the child to participate in "speaker's decisions" speeds this process along. Once internalization has occurred, the child is in a vastly improved position from several obvious points of view—notably that he is able to go beyond the information he has been given to generate additional ideas that can either be checked immediately from experience or can, at least, be used as a basis for formulating reasonable hypotheses. But over and beyond that, the child is now in a position to experience success and failure not as reward and punishment, but as information. For when the task is his own rather than a matter of matching environmental demands, he becomes his own paymaster in a certain measure. Seeking to gain control over his environment, he can now treat success as indicating that he is on the right track, failure as indicating he is on the wrong one.

In the end, this development has the effect of freeing learning from immediate stimulus control. When learning in the short run leads only to pellets of this or that rather than to mastery in the long run, then behavior can be readily "shaped" by extrinsic rewards. When behavior becomes more long-range and competence-oriented, it comes under the control of more complex cognitive structures, plans and the like, and operates more from the inside out. It is interesting that even Pavlov—whose early account of the learning process was based entirely on a notion of stimulus control of behavior through the conditioning mechanism in which, through contiguity, a new conditioned stimulus was substituted for an old unconditioned stimulus by the mechanism of stimulus substitution—that even Pavlov recognized his account as insufficient to deal with higher forms of learning. To supplement the account, he introduced the idea of the "second signalling system," with central importance placed on symbolic systems such as language in mediating and giving shape to mental life. Or as Luria [8] has put it, "the first signal system [is] concerned with directly perceived stimuli, the second with systems of verbal elaboration." Luria commenting on the importance of the transition from first to second signal system says: "It would be mistaken to suppose that verbal intercourse with adults merely changes the contents of the child's conscious activity without changing its form. . . . The word has a basic function not only because it indicates a corresponding object in the external world, but also because it abstracts, isolates the necessary signal, generalizes perceived signals and relates them to certain categories; it is this systematization of direct experience that makes the role of the word in the formation of mental processes so exceptionally important." [9, 10]

[8] A. L. Luria, "The Directive Function of Speech in Development and Dissolution," *Word*, XV (1959), pp. 341–464.

[9] *Ibid.*, p. 12.

[10] For an elaboration of the view expressed by Luria, the reader is referred to the forthcoming translation of L. S. Vigotsky's 1934 book being published by John Wiley and Sons and the Technology Press.

It is interesting that the final rejection of the universality of the doctrine of reinforcement in direct conditioning came from some of Pavlov's own students. Ivanov-Smolensky [11] and Krasnogorsky [12] published papers showing the manner in which symbolized linguistic messages could take over the place of the unconditioned stimulus and of the unconditioned response (gratification of hunger) in children. In all instances, they speak of these as *replacements* of lower, first-system mental or neural processes by higher order or second-system controls. A strange irony, then, that Russian psychology that gave us the notion of the conditioned response and the assumption that higher order activities are built up out of colligations or structurings of such primitive units, rejected this notion while much of American learning psychology has stayed until quite recently within the early Pavlovian fold (see, for example, a recent article by Spence [13] in the *Harvard Educational Review* or Skinner's treatment of language [14] and the attacks that have been made upon it by linguists such as Chomsky [15] who have become concerned with the relation of language and cognitive activity). What is the more interesting is that Russian pedagogical theory has become deeply influenced by this new trend and is now placing much stress upon the importance of building up a more active symbolical approach to problem solving among children.

To sum up the matter of the control of learning, then, I am proposing that the degree to which competence or mastery motives comes to control behavior, to that degree the role of reinforcement or "extrinsic pleasure" wanes in shaping behavior. The child comes to manipulate his environment more actively and achieves his gratification from coping with problems. Symbolic modes of representing and transforming the environment arise and the importance of stimulus-response-reward sequences declines. To use the metaphor that David Riesman developed in a quite different context, mental life moves from a state of outer-directedness in which the fortuity of stimuli and reinforcement are crucial to a state of inner-directedness in which the growth and maintenance of mastery become central and dominant.

3. LEARNING THE HEURISTICS OF DISCOVERY. Lincoln Steffens,[16] reflecting in his *Autobiography* on his undergraduate education at Berkeley, comments that his schooling was overly specialized on learning about the known and that too little attention was given to the task of finding out about what was not known. But how does one train a student in the techniques of

[11] A. G. Ivanov-Smolensky, "Concerning the Study of the Joint Activity of the First and Second Signal Systems," *Journal of Higher Nervous Activity*, 1, (1951), p. 1.

[12] N. D. Krasnogorsky, *Studies of Higher Nervous Activity in Animals and in Man*, Vol. 1 (Moscow, 1954).

[13] K. W. Spence, "The Relation of Learning Theory to the Technique of Education," *Harvard Educational Review*, XXIX (1959), pp. 84–95.

[14] B. F. Skinner, *Verbal Behavior* (New York: Appleton-Century-Crofts, 1957).

[15] N. Chomsky, *Syntactic Structure* (The Hague, The Netherlands: Mouton & Co., 1957).

[16] L. Steffens, *Autobiography of Lincoln Steffens* (New York: Harcourt, Brace, 1931).

discovery? Again I would like to offer some hypotheses. There are many ways of coming to the arts of inquiry. One of them is by careful study of its formalization in logic, statistics, mathematics, and the like. If a person is going to pursue inquiry as a way of life, particularly in the sciences, certainly such study is essential. Yet, whoever has taught kindergarten and the early primary grades or has had graduate students working with him on their theses—I choose the two extremes for they are both periods of intense inquiry—knows that an understanding of the formal aspect of inquiry is not sufficient. There appear to be, rather, a series of activities and attitudes, some directly related to a particular subject and some of them fairly generalized, that go with inquiry and research. These have to do with the *process* of trying to find out something, and while they provide no guarantee that the *product* will be any *great* discovery, their absence is likely to lead to awkwardness or aridity or confusion. How difficult it is to describe these matters— the heuristics of inquiry. There is one set of attitudes or ways of doing that has to do with sensing the relevance of variables—how to avoid getting stuck with edge effects and getting instead to the big sources of variance. Partly this gift comes from intuitive familiarity with a range of phenomena, sheer "knowing the stuff." But it also comes out of a sense of what things among an ensemble of things "smell right" in the sense of being of the right order of magnitude or scope or severity.

The English philosopher Weldon describes problem solving in an interesting and picturesque way. He distinguishes between difficulties, puzzles, and problems. We solve a problem or make a discovery when we impose a puzzle form on to a difficulty that converts it into a problem that can be solved in such a way that it gets us where we want to be. That is to say, we recast the difficulty into a form that we know how to work with, then work it. Much of what we speak of as discovery consists of knowing how to impose what kind of form on various kinds of difficulties. A small part but a crucial part of discovery of the highest order is to invent and develop models or "puzzle forms" that can be imposed on difficulties with good effect. It is in this area that the truly powerful mind shines. But it is interesting to what degree perfectly ordinary people can, given the benefit of instruction, construct quite interesting and what, a century ago, would have been considered greatly original models.

Now to the hypothesis. It is my hunch that it is only through the exercise of problem solving and the effort of discovery that one learns the working heuristics of discovery, and the more one has practice, the more likely is one to generalize what one has learned into a style of problem solving or inquiry that serves for any kind of task one may encounter—or almost any kind of task. I think the matter is self-evident, but what is unclear is what kinds of training and teaching produce the best effects. How do we teach a child to, say, cut his losses but at the same time be persistent in trying out an idea; to risk forming an early hunch without at the same time formulating one *so* early and with so little evidence as to be stuck with it waiting for appropriate evidence to materialize; to pose good testable guesses that are neither too brittle nor too sinuously incorrigible; etc., etc. Practice in inquiry, in trying to figure out things for oneself, is indeed what is needed, but in what form? Of only one thing I am convinced. I have never seen anybody improve in the art and technique of inquiry by any means other than engaging in inquiry.

4. CONSERVATION OF MEMORY. I should like to take what some psychologists might consider a rather drastic view of the memory process. It is a view that in large measure derives from the work of my colleague, Professor George Miller.[17] Its first premise is that the principal problem of human memory is not storage, but retrieval. In spite of the biological unlikeliness of it, we seem to be able to store a huge quantity of information—perhaps not a full tape recording, though at times it seems we even do that, but a great sufficiency of impressions. We may infer this from the fact that recognition (i.e., recall with the aid of maximum prompts) is so extraordinarily good in human beings—particularly in comparison with spontaneous recall where, so to speak, we must get out stored information without external aids or prompts. The key to retrieval is organization or, in even simpler terms, knowing where to find information and how to get there.

Let me illustrate the point with a simple experiment. We present pairs of words to twelve-year-old children. One group is simply told to remember the pairs, that they will be asked to repeat them later. Another is told to remember them by producing a word or idea that will tie the pair together in a way that will make sense to them. A third group is given the mediators used by the second group when presented with the pairs to aid them in tying the pairs into working units. The word pairs include such juxtapositions as "chair-forest," "sidewalk-square," and the like. One can distinguish three styles of mediators and children can be scaled in terms of their relative preference for each: *generic mediation* in which a pair is tied together by a superordinate idea: "chair and forest are both made of wood"; *thematic mediation* in which the two terms are imbedded in a theme or little story: "the lost child sat on a chair in the middle of the forest"; and *part-whole mediation* where "chairs are made from trees in the forest" is typical. Now, the chief result, as you would all predict, is that children who provide their own mediators do best—indeed, one time through a set of thirty pairs, they recover up to 95% of the second words when presented with the first ones of the pairs, whereas the uninstructed children reach a maximum of less than 50% recovered. Interestingly enough, children do best in recovering materials tied together by the form of mediator they most often use.

One can cite a myriad of findings to indicate that any organization of information that reduces the aggregate complexity of material by imbedding it into a cognitive structure a person has constructed will make that material more accessible for retrieval. In short, we may say that the process of memory, looked at from the retrieval side, is also a process of problem solving: how can material be "placed" in memory so that it can be got on demand?

[17] G. A. Miller, "The Magical Number Seven, Plus or Minus Two," *Psychological Review*, LXIII (1956), pp. 81–97.

We can take as a point of departure the example of the children who developed their own technique for relating the members of each word pair. You will recall that they did better than the children who were given by exposition the mediators they had developed. Let me suggest that in general, material that is organized in terms of a person's own interests and cognitive structures is material that has the best chance of being accessible in memory. That is to say, it is more likely to be placed along routes that are connected to one's own ways of intellectual travel.

In sum, the very attitudes and activities that characterize "figuring out" or "discovering" things for oneself also seem to have the effect of making material more readily accessible in memory.

THE LEARNING REQUIREMENTS
FOR ENQUIRY*

Robert M. Gagné

Robert M. Gagné agrees with other authors that enquiry is a necessary and vital objective of science instruction. He maintains, however, that if the practice of enquiry is to be carried out successfully, there are two major prerequisites: (1) a suitable background of broad generalized knowledge, which can be used in solving problems to make the inductive leap that characterizes enquiry, and (2) the possession of incisive knowledge, which makes it possible to discriminate between a good idea and a bad one. Dr. Gagné believes that, as the child progresses from kindergarten through college, there should be four levels of instruction which would enable the child to become progressively a competent performer, a student of knowledge, a scientific enquirer, and an independent investigator. There is constant overlap in the competencies and capabilities that are acquired at each level of instruction.

ONE OF the most interesting and important ideas which has been given emphasis in recent discussions of science education is the idea of enquiry. It has been stated to be perhaps the most critical kind of activity that the

* REPRINTED FROM *Journal of Research in Science Teaching*, Vol. 1, Issue 2, 1963, pp. 144–153, by permission of the author and the editor. Dr. Gagné is Professor of Psychology at the University of California, Berkeley.

scientist engages in, and for that reason to represent one of the most essential objectives of science instruction. Accordingly, there appears to be a very widespread agreement that enquiry is a worthwhile objective—something that our various educational efforts should deliberately try to achieve. And there is a widespread consensus that an instructional program for the student of science most clearly achieves this rightful goal when it enables such a student to adopt the procedures of scientific enquiry in response to any new unsolved problem he encounters.

Along with this emphasis on the importance of the method of enquiry there has been an accompanying realization that many traditional courses in science, at all levels of education, exhibit serious deficiencies insofar as they fail to get across to students the elements of this method. Many such courses seem to be neglecting the student in the most important sense that they do not encourage him to acquire the attitudes of enquiry, the methods of enquiry, the understanding of enquiry. They may provide him with a great many facts, with knowledge of important principles, even with the capability of using previously discovered principles in situations novel to him. But they omit this essential part of his education as a scientist, or even as an informed citizen, by not establishing within him the disposition which makes him able to employ enquiry in the manner so well-known to scientists.

Perhaps no writer has described this deficiency in science education so cogently and so thoroughly as has Schwab. It is worthwhile to quote here a short passage from his Inglis Lecture: [1]

It is the almost total absence of this portrayal of science which marks the greatest disparity between science as it is and science as seen through most textbooks of science. We are shown conclusions of enquiry as if they were certain or nearly certain facts. Further, we rarely see these conclusions as other than isolated, independent "facts." Their coherence and organization—the defining marks of *scientific* knowledge—are underemphasized or omitted. And we catch hardly a glimpse of the other constituents of scientific enquiry: organizing principles, data, and the interpretation of data.

The problem, then, seems pretty well-defined and agreed upon. It is, "How can one go about introducing, or perhaps restoring, to the process of instruction the necessary conditions which will make it more probable that the student learns about science as enquiry?" Obviously this is not as simple a matter as is "adding material" on neutrinos in atomic structure, or even as is "revising material" such as that on the reactivity of inert chemical elements. It is more complicated than either of these, because it is more difficult to identify and specify what it is that the student must learn. Yet this is the task that must be faced, complicated or not, if the desired change is to be brought about.

Let us assume, then, that there is general agreement about the problem and about the objective to be sought in its solution. Now, what, if anything, can the methods and results of research on the learning process contribute to this problem? This is the interest of the student of learning theory. Obviously, dealing with science as enquiry must be something that is learned. What do we know about learning that is relevant in establishing such a capability in the student?

Analysis of the Problem

As is the case with other users of scientific methods, the investigator of human learning customarily begins by defining or specifying what the problem is in terms which have served this function in the past. These terms serve to separate the general aspects of the problem situation from the specific and therefore incidental ones, and thus enable him to think about it in a rigorous fashion.

When this basic method is applied to the problem, the first distinction which becomes apparent is this: First, there is something we may call a *terminal capability*, something that the student is able to do after he has learned. That is to say, if we have been successful in establishing the correct conditions for learning, we will be able to infer that the student is or is not capable of employing the methods of scientific enquiry. To make this inference possible, of course, we must observe some kinds of behavior, which may also be specified, and we might refer to these observed events as *terminal behaviors*.

Second, the other major category of events with which we must deal in this problem is a set of conditions which are used to bring about a *change* in the student's capability. These we may call the *instructional conditions*. Potentially these conditions include everything that is done to or by the student from some initial point in time (when he does not possess the desired capability) to some other point in time (when he does). But more specifically, they are all the aspects of the instructional situation which can be shown to affect this change, including the events that take place in classrooms, laboratories, libraries, at his desk, or elsewhere.

Perhaps this distinction seems obvious to you—the terminal capability, on the one hand, and the instructional conditions which accomplish the change between initial and terminal capability, on the other. But this distinction has not always been carefully maintained in thinking about this problem, even by people who think profoundly about it. It is nonetheless an essential distinction, and one which will be referred to again later.

The Terminal Capability

In order to understand and specify the problem further, we need to ask again, what is the nature of this desired capability of using the approach of enquiry towards the solution of problems? Having read the authors who have written on this subject, one concludes that they have spent many more words describing what it is *not* than in describing what it *is*. What it is not, all agree, is an activity which deals with scientific concepts as things rather than abstractions, or with scientific hypotheses and theories as fixed facts rather than as convenient models subject to empirical test. I judge them to mean, that what it *is* is a set of activities characterized by a problem-solving approach, in which each newly encountered phenomenon becomes a challenge for thinking. Such thinking begins with a careful set of systematic observations, proceeds to design the measurements required, clearly distinguishes between what is observed and what is inferred, invents interpretations which are under ideal circumstances brilliant leaps, but always testable, and draws reasonable conclusions. In other words, it is the kind of activity that might be called the essence of scientific research (neglecting for the moment such clearly relevant components as obtaining research funds and writing good scientific reports, among others).

Can such inferred capabilities as these be observed as behavior? It does not seem unreasonable that this is possible, provided we accept the fact that the sample of behavior we may be able to observe is somewhat limited and therefore somewhat unreliable. This appears to be the kind of behavior the university science faculty tries to observe in its graduate students. It uses various methods of doing this, such as requiring the execution of an initial problem before the dissertation, or requiring the completion of a series of partial problems, or by asking the student to "think through" how he would approach an already reported investigation, or in some other manner. In many instances, more and better observation of this sort could actually be done, if some greater thought were given to it.

Observation of such behavior is also done with increasing frequency at the undergraduate college level. Here we find programs of independent study, honors programs, and other devices which require students to take an independent approach of enquiry towards a scientific problem. Again, the frequency and representativeness of this kind of observation of "enquiry behavior" can be improved. A number of authors suggest, for example, that the laboratory be made the setting for the practice of this approach, by designing and using the kinds of laboratory problems which are invitations to careful thought, rather than "standard exercises."

Can this kind of activity of scientific enquiry be extended downward to the secondary school and even into the primary grades? Of course it can, in some sense, since we know that even elementary students are quite capable of some pretty good thinking. But whether it should or not may involve some other considerations which we have not yet touched upon.

Conditions of Instruction

We are now ready to look more closely at the other part of the problem —how do we effect a change such that a student who doesn't initially employ the approach of enquiry toward problems will employ this approach? What are the conditions of instruction which are likely to effect this change?

PRACTICE IN ENQUIRY

One of the conditions emphasized by several writers on this question is that of *practicing strategies* in proceeding from the known to the unknown. Bruner,[2] for example, calls this "learning the heuristics of discovery," and states that although the form that such learning should take is not known in detail, it seems reasonable that improvement in the technique of enquiry should depend upon practice in enquiry. Schwab [1] points out the ways that such practice can be conducted in the laboratory and in the classroom. The import of these writings for the design of instructional conditions is clear: the student should be provided with opportunities to carry out inductive thinking; to make hypotheses and to test them, in a great variety of situations, in the laboratory, in the classroom, and by his own individual efforts.

It is impossible not to agree with this prescription in a specific sense. The student who has been given practice merely in the recall of ideas, or in their application in particular situations, will not necessarily acquire these important techniques of enquiry. In physics, for example, the setting of problems like this one is a common practice in many textbooks: "A box slides down a 30° inclined plane with an acceleration of 10 ft./sec.^{2} What is the coefficient of friction between the box and the plane?" Now the student obviously is getting practice from performing such problems, but the question is, what kind of practice? Obviously not the same kind he would get if this kind of problem were stated: "A box slides down an inclined plane. Can this event be shown to be compatible with Newton's second law of motion?" In this second case, what is being required of the student is that he relate some observed events to a general principle (or "law"), and that he himself *think out* what these relationships are. First he must identify the forces at work, specify the mass and acceleration, and then induce how these specific variables may be related to the general equation $F = ma$. And in carrying out this enquiry, he is obtaining valuable practice which will doubtless be transferable to other problems, not necessarily within the field of physics alone. A similar technique, or thinking strategy, may be useful in quite a different situation—in thinking about the reactions of chemical solutions, or about the metabolism of a cell, or even about the relation of national income to productivity.

If there are any limitations to the value of *practice in enquiry*, they are probably to be found in this fact: such practice is *not the whole story*. Establishing conditions for practice in enquiry does not by any means exhaust the requirements for the instructional conditions needed for the achievement of the desired terminal capability. And there are real dangers in thinking that such practice does constitute the entire set of requirements for this purpose.

Some scholars have perceived this danger. In a recent interview recorded in the newspapers, the noted physicist Dr. C. N. Yang [3] states his concern about the increasingly common practice of starting students on basic research early in their college careers. Students who are educated in this way, he says, will not be able to stand away from their work and see it in perspective; they will think of research as a study of a single problem rather than as a broad attack on the entire frontier of the unknown. In dealing with new problems, such students will lack the deep understanding on which to draw for help.

Dr. Yang's concern is essentially the same as that just mentioned. There is nothing wrong with practicing enquiry, and surely enquiry is the kind of capability we want students of science to attain in some terminal sense. But practicing enquiry too soon, and without a suitable background of knowledge, can have a narrowing and cramping effect on the individual's development of independent thinking. And if this is true at the level of the college sophomore, surely this danger must be all the more severe if we consider the instructional situation in the high school and the elementary school.

Is this a valid objection? If practice in enquiry can be given too soon, or too exclusively, what other parts are there to the instructional situation? What else is there to learn, if one does not practice the strategies of thinking?

Two Other Components of Instruction

There are two other major capabilities which are of importance as objectives of instruction. It is possible to think that they are at least as important as practice in enquiry, and it is possible to argue that they are even more *essential*, in the sense that they represent *prior requirements*, if the practice of enquiry is to be carried out successfully. These two other capabilities may be characterized as follows:

(1) the capability of *generalizing* the principles of knowledge to the variety of situations to which they are applicable (and have been shown to be applicable by earlier scholars); and

(2) the capability of *discriminating* the probable and improbable applicability of hypotheses to new problem situations.

In general terms, the reasons why these kinds of capability need to be fostered by the instructional situation are easy to understand. If an individual is to try to solve new problems, he must have a knowledge of a great variety of principles which can be potentially applicable to these problems. The best guarantee that these principles are available will be to insure that he has acquired generalizable knowledge, in other words, that he has *broad knowledge*. And when he does make the inductive leap that characterizes enquiry, he should be able to know that he is doing something that has a probability of being right, rather than of just being silly. He must discriminate the good ideas from the bad, in accordance with their probable consequences. One might call this *critical or incisive knowledge*. But both of these are needed *before* practice in enquiry can have the positive effects that are expected of it.

Generalizable Knowledge

Consider again the student who is asked to use the sliding of a weight down an inclined plane as an instance compatible with Newton's second law. It is obvious, isn't it, that the student must have a rather sizeable amount of broad knowledge before he can be successful at this problem? Among other things, he must know (1) what Newton's second law is, in terms which make sense to him; (2) what acceleration is, and its relation to velocity, time, and distance; (3) what mass is, and how it is related to weight; (4) how the angles of an inclined plane can lead to a conceptualization of the magnitude and direction of the forces at work. Others could undoubtedly be mentioned. It is senseless to think that these principles of knowledge are trivial, or that the student can easily have "picked them up" incidentally to some other learning, including perhaps previous practice in enquiry. It is surely wrong to believe that the student can *think* without *knowing* these principles. This would be like asking him to play chess without ever having learned what the rules are. And it is probably quite contrary to the interests of learning to ask the student to undertake "enquiry practice" without knowing these principles. As evidence for the latter statement I refer to some work of my own and my colleagues on learning in mathematics, which has shown clearly that learning to solve new problems is critically dependent upon the acquisition of previous knowledge.[4]

Broad, generalizable knowledge is a prerequisite for the successful practice of enquiry, whether as a part of the total instructional process or as a terminal capability. How does the student acquire this broad knowledge? Well, that is a question of great interest to a student of human learning. And some things are known about it, some things not yet. Here are some observations about this broad, generalizable knowledge that are relevant.

1. Such knowledge cannot all be attained by a student by the use of the method of enquiry itself. Were we to follow this suggestion, we should have to put the student back in the original situation that Newton found himself in, and ask the student to invent a solution, as Newton did. It would be difficult to achieve this situation, in the first place, and presumably not all students would achieve what Newton did, even then. But the major difficulty with this suggestion is that it would be a most terrible waste of time. Are we going to have students rediscover the laws of motion, the periodic table, the structure of the atom, the circulation of the blood, and all the other achievements of science simply in order to ensure that instructional conditions are "pure," in the sense that they demand enquiry? Surely no one seriously proposes that this method should be followed.

2. The possession of broad and generalizable knowledge is an admirable capability, and not to be equated with "knowing facts." There is quite a difference between knowing a *fact*, such as "Newton invented the laws of motion," and a *principle*, such as might be exhibited if we asked a student to describe a situation which could be used to test Newton's second law of

motion. One might call the ability to repeat verbally the statement, "If an unbalanced force acts upon a body, the body will accelerate in proportion to the magnitude, etc.," knowing a fact. But to know such a fact is not the same as knowing this law of motion as a principle, as the previous example has indicated. Knowledge of principles is generalizable; one expects a student who knows Newton's second law as a principle to be able to describe a wide variety of specific situations in which the validity of the law can be tested. Such knowledge is of tremendous value, not just in and of itself, but because it constitutes an essential basis for acquiring other knowledge. To an equal degree, it is an essential basis for the practice of the strategies of enquiry.

3. As to how knowledge is acquired, one should not assume that this has to be done, or is best accomplished, by "routine drill." Repetition does indeed appear to be one desirable condition for instruction, but only one. At least equally important, if not more so, is the condition which fosters the use of *discovery* on the part of the student. In its simplest form, this means simply that it seems to be better for learning if one can get the student to respond to a situation in his own way, and in a way which is also correct, rather than having him "copy" or "echo" something that the teacher says or that the book says.[2, 5] In other words, discovery appears to be a very fundamental principle of good instruction. It applies to *all* conceptual learning, the learning of principles and generalizations, and may even apply to the learning of a simpler sort such as the memorizing of names or facts. But discovery, as a very fundamental condition of most learning, should not be equated with enquiry, which is the exercise of all the various activities making up what we have identified as the terminal capability. The construction of a response by a learner, something that happens nearly every step of the way in the process of learning, is what usually has been called discovery. In contrast to this, enquiry is the terminal thinking process we want the student to be able to engage in, *after* he has taken all the necessary previous steps in learning.

In summary then, it appears that broad, generalizable knowledge is best conceived as knowledge of principles. As such, it may be attained in the context of instructional conditions which include "discovery" on the part of the learner. Knowledge of principles is not what is usually referred to in a deprecating manner as "knowledge of mere facts," nor is such knowledge best acquired under conditions of sheer repetition. But knowledge of principles is prerequisite to the successful practice of the techniques of enquiry.

Incisive Knowledge

The other kind of capability we have identified as prerequisite to successful enquiry is the possession of critical or incisive knowledge. In terms that the psychologist uses, this is the capability of *discriminating* between a good idea and a bad one, or between a probably successful course of action and a probably unsuccessful one.

Just for variety of illustration, let us take a new example. Suppose we set the student this problem in enquiry: "How does the picture of an object get 'into the head' in the sense of being experienced as a picture and retained from one occasion to another?" Suppose that the student has a certain amount of generalizable knowledge about the eye, and its function as a camera, so that he is able readily to recall the principles which get the picture onto the retina. But now, how does it get "into the head"? If he has no more knowledge than this, he may think of a variety of mechanisms, each of which may be brilliantly inventive, but some of which may be silly. Perhaps it is carried by a scanning mechanism similar to television. Perhaps the frequencies of various light waves are transmitted directly over nerves. Perhaps the pattern of neurones stimulated corresponds to the pattern of physical energy. Perhaps the stimulation is carried in some mechanical way. Perhaps there are differences in the strength of electrical transmission. Perhaps the pattern of brightness is transmitted as a pattern of frequencies, different from those of the light waves themselves. And so on. Any fairly bright student can probably think of quite a large number of possibilities.

Is there an instructional value to encouraging students to make such guesses? Probably so, but *only when* the means are simultaneously provided for the student to estimate that an idea is probably good or probably bad. The wildness of the guesses, or perhaps even the frequency of wild guesses, is a most doubtful criterion. (People whose guesses are extremely wild are called schizophrenics.) It seems to me that if the student is encouraged to form hypotheses, even to follow hunches, as a part of practice in enquiry, that these hunches and guesses should be *disciplined* ones. This does not mean at all that hypotheses need to be restricted in scope or simple in content. On the contrary, they can be as elaborate as his abilities and his generalizable knowledge will permit. But he should be able to estimate their consequences. Any hypothesis is subject to the discipline of ultimate verification.

What kind of knowledge is it that makes possible the discrimination of good ideas from bad? Well, it is not very different in kind, although it is different in content, from the other kind of knowledge we have described. Generally speaking, it is knowledge of principles, sprinkled here and there, perhaps, with a few facts. In the case of our example of the picture in the head, the student needs to know at least the following principles: (1) the relation between intensity of stimulation and frequency of neural response; (2) the frequency and strength of neural responses; (3) the rapidity of the nervous impulse; (4) the relation between distribution of nerve endings and distribution of frequency of nervous impulses; and a number of others. Each of these principles and facts provides him with a means of checking the compatibility of the hypotheses he generates in terms of their probability or improbability.

Here again, then, in this capability for *self-criticism of ideas*, we come upon another essential need for knowledge, prior to the exercise of enquiry. From a base of knowledge of principles, enquiry takes off. Where it comes to rest is also dependent upon the possession of knowledge. Enquiry which cannot be checked against estimates that hypotheses are probably good or probably bad will be undisciplined enquiry, possibly as satisfying as the day-dreams of Walter Mitty, but of no greater social importance. Likewise, the practice of enquiry which lacks the discipline of self-criticism may be expected to be of no positive value to the development of the individual, and could even be harmful. Which teacher of science has not encountered the student who is constantly willing to display a bubbling fountain of ideas, almost all of them worthless? Is this what we want to encourage?

THE INSTRUCTIONAL BASIS OF ENQUIRY

This analysis of the instructional conditions required to establish the capabilities for enquiry emphasizes that the major essential is the possession of a body of organized knowledge. On the whole, the more highly organized this knowledge is, the better; it will be better retained that way.

What are the implications of this line of reasoning for the science curriculum and for science instruction? It may be of greatest meaningfulness if the answer to this question is attempted by considering what science instruction might be like, not at some particular level of development, such as high school or college, but throughout the entire range of the educational sequence from kindergarten onwards. However, this might be better done "from the top down," because the interrelationships of problem-solving, knowledge, and fundamental skills are most clearly revealed by such an analysis. Accordingly, let us consider what seem to be approximately definable "levels" of science instruction. Of course these are not hard and fast distinctions, nor are they exclusive categories. Learning takes place during the entire course of an individual's lifetime, and it is only the relative priorities which can be indicated by such an analysis.

The Independent Investigator

At the highest level of development we have the student who is beginning to take all of the responsibilities of an independent scientist. He has broad knowledge, not only within his specialized field, but of others as well. Furthermore, he understands and has practiced the methods of enquiry sufficiently so that he knows what he is doing, and understands his own limitations. He is able to begin a new line of investigation in a disciplined, responsible manner, with deliberate attention to what has gone before, but with a mind unhampered by tradition. Currently, we think of this capability as being possessed by the second- or third-year graduate student. If our educational system were reasonably effective, this level could perhaps be achieved by people of the age of present college juniors.

The Scientific Enquirer

At the next lower level, we find the student who has acquired enough broad subject-matter knowledge to be able to learn to speculate, to form and test hypotheses about scientific problems which are not trivial, and which he himself can subject to the discipline of self-criticism. In other words, the emphasis at this level of instruction might profitably be upon the method of enquiry. This should be practiced in the discussion class, in the laboratory, as well as in individual study. Again, making the assumption of a reasonably efficient educational system, the student should probably be able to begin this phase of instruction at the age of present 11th graders.

But in order to do this successfully, we have argued, he must have acquired a great deal of broad and incisive knowledge. The latter kinds of knowledge are not confined to the facts and principles of content, it should be noted. They also include knowledge about methods—of observing, classifying, describing, inferring, and conceptual invention.

The Student of Knowledge

This level of instruction emphasizes the learning of broad and critical knowledge, particularly of what previous generations of scientists have found out about the world, as well as the more fundamental principles which have led to the formulation of modern scientific conceptions. At this stage, the student needs to begin to acquire large masses of previously formulated principles of knowledge. At the same time, he needs to learn to engage deliberately and systematically in the fundamental activities used by the scientist, in as wide a variety of contexts as possible. Such activities include controlled observation, classification, measurement, inference, the formulation of models. Accordingly, there is definite need for the "laboratory" at this level. But the activities resemble those of the "laboratory exercise" more than they do the "independent enquiry." If he is encouraged to do the latter, he will fail because he doesn't *know* enough to behave like a scientist. Accordingly, his activity will either be extremely narrow in scope or will tend to be ridiculous, neither of which outcomes will have salutary effects upon his learning.

Does this suggestion of an emphasis on acquiring broad knowledge carry the implication of "stifling curiosity"? Not at all. There are plenty of rewards for curiosity, in discovering new things about the world, in exploring previously unknown paths of knowledge, in trying one's hand at new kinds of classification, in finding out how indirect measurements can be made and verified, in seeing how one can best communicate scientific information, and in many other areas. Curiosity is not the special possession of the fully trained scientist. Neither is the method of discovery in learning, as has been pointed out previously.

This level of instruction could probably have its inception around the age level currently attending the 6th or 7th grade.

The Competent Performer

Acquiring broad knowledge in the way that it should be acquired, and particularly knowledge of the methods of the scientist, is in turn based upon a stage of instruction which extends downward to the kindergarten (and informally, farther than that). For what is needed first of all in science instruction are certain kinds of performance capabilities. The word *skills* should carry no negative aura, but it seems to for some people, so let us avoid it and refer to *competencies*. At this level, the question is not so much "Does the student *know* something," but "Can he *do* something." We are used to thinking of these competencies as "reading, writing, and arithmetic," but what an inadequate description that is! When one considers the competencies needed for learning about science, it is quite probable, first of all, that this set of three leaves some important ones out. Beyond this, they do not adequately convey what kinds of specific capabilities are really intended.

No one seems to have adequately faced up to the necessity for identifying and describing these fundamental competencies which underlie all of learning about science. A good list would include not only number computation, but also spatial and manipulative skills, and the capabilities of observing, classifying, measuring, describing, inferring, and model conceptualizing. In general, there should be good agreement that these competencies are important to science instruction. Shouldn't the high school student know how to *describe* an unfamiliar object seen for the first time? More than this, though, the suggestion made here is that the later acquisition of broad and incisive knowledge about science will be inadequate and unsuccessful unless the student has already acquired the capability of observing and describing what he sees. How can he acquire such knowledge unless he is able to distinguish clearly, and in terms of his own behavior, the description of an observed object or event from the description of a conceptual model?

As stated earlier, instruction in these fundamental capabilities so essential to the understanding of science carries no implication of the "routinizing of instruction" or the "deadening of curiosity." A child simply has to learn to read before he can understand printed texts. Similarly, an individual needs to know how to observe, to classify, to describe, to conceptualize, before he can understand science or the activities of scientists. All of these competencies can be acquired through his own efforts, motivated by his own curiosity, and by means of his own discoveries.

At the same time, it seems to be totally erroneous to look upon these early attainments as having anything but a specious resemblance to the activities of disciplined enquiry, or to contend that they can be acquired by "practice in enquiry." One doesn't learn to be a scientist, or to appreciate science, by pretending to be a scientist. What is the difference, in principle, between trying to "practice enquiry" in the second grade, and trying to practice "being a physician" at the same age level? Why should anyone be led, perhaps by wishful thinking, to give serious consideration to the former, while at the same time chuckling patronizingly at the latter? Engaging in enquiry of a successful, productive, and useful variety can be undertaken when the individual has acquired a store of broad and critical knowledge, and this in turn can be acquired when he has learned some prerequisite but very important fundamental capabilities. At the earliest stage of instruction, one needs to be most concerned with these latter competencies, which will remain with the student all his life.

Having described a sequence of acquired competencies from top to bottom which is based upon the best generalizations from studies of the learning process, one must be careful not to imply that there is no overlap among the kinds of capabilities to be acquired at each of these four "levels" of instruction. At the earliest stage, for example, the child is certainly acquiring some knowledge of principles, and even a little bit of the strategy of clear thinking, even though the major part of what he most needs to learn are the competencies (or skills) mentioned. And similar comments could be made about other stages. None of them is "pure." Even at the highest of these levels, as we know, the student may often have to "catch up" on some broad knowledge he somehow missed at a much earlier level. If he has missed some of the important competencies at the earliest level, the chances are very good that he has some time previously decided to major in some field other than science.

In summary then, let us consider what would happen in science instruction, this time beginning at the bottom, if it were seriously designed to establish the terminal capability of enquiry. This is not an attempt to describe what *does* happen, because we are far from that condition, but what *should* happen. At the earliest level of instruction, the individual needs to learn how to observe, how to figure, how to measure, how to orient things in space, how to describe, how to classify objects and events, how to infer, and how to make conceptual models. These capabilities he will use all of his life. If he becomes a student of science, they will make possible the acquiring of broad knowledge of principles, the incisive knowledge which makes possible the self-criticism of new ideas, and the disciplined exercise of the method of enquiry. If he chooses some other field as a career, they will provide a fundamental understanding of science which is quite independent of any particular scientific knowledge he may read about. At the next level, he needs to make a thoroughgoing start at acquiring broad knowledge and critical knowledge of the principles of science, throughout the various disciplines, and including knowledge of both content and method. This knowledge is essential if he is later going to practice making reasonable hypotheses and testing them; in other words, if he is later to practice enquiry. The practice of enquiry itself might begin at the next stage, along with a continuation of the learning of substantive knowledge, perhaps with a somewhat greater degree of specialization. This enquiry practice will, on the one hand, be soundly derived from suitably broad knowledge; and on the other, it will be carried out so as to make possible discriminations between "good" and "bad" ideas. But it will nevertheless be genuine enquiry, in which the student is encouraged to solve problems by means of unrestrained inductive thinking, and in which he is rewarded for his ingenuity. Having done all this, the student is then ready for the final stage, learning to assume the full responsibilities of the scientific investigator. At this stage, he must learn to depend upon himself, and to trust himself, to look upon problems objectively; to have new ideas; and to be able to judge them critically. In all of these activities he will be enormously aided by his previous practice in enquiry, as well as by his knowledge of scientific principles and methods, and by the fundamental capabilities he acquired early in his educational career.

It must be quite clear that "practice in enquiry" for the student of science has great value. But to be successful it must be based upon a great variety of prerequisite knowledges and competencies which themselves are learned, sometimes by "discovery," but inconceivably by what is called "enquiry."

REFERENCES

1. Schwab, J. J., "The Teaching of Science As Enquiry," *The Teaching of Science*, Harvard University Press, Cambridge, 1962.
2. Bruner, J. S., "The Act of Discovery," *Harvard Educational Review*, **31**, 21–32 (1961).
3. Yang, C. N., quoted in article in *Pittsburgh Post-Gazette*, Friday, December 28, 1962.
4. Gagné, R. M., J. R. Mayor, H. L. Garstens, and N. E. Paradise, "Factors in Acquiring Knowledge of a Mathematical Task," *Psychol. Monographs*, **76**, No. 7 (Whole No. 526) (1962).
5. Gagné, R. M., "The Acquisition of Knowledge," *Psychol. Rev.*, **69**, 355–365 (1962).

FORCES REDIRECTING SCIENCE TEACHING *

Ralph W. Tyler

Ralph W. Tyler discusses four forces redirecting science teaching today. First, the technological revolution has resulted in public recognition of the importance of the role of science in today's society. Second, there is now a closer working relationship between the university, the research scientist, and the classroom teacher. Third, the recent explosion of knowledge has changed our understanding of the nature of science, so that it is no longer considered to be the learning of basic principles and facts, but rather a process

* REPRINTED FROM *The Science Teacher*, Vol. 29, No. 6, October 1962, pp. 22–25 Copyright, 1962, by the National Science Teachers Association, Washington, D.C. Reprinted by permission of the author and the publisher. Dr. Tyler is Director of the Center for Advanced Study in the Behavioral Sciences at Stanford University.

of continuing inquiry and reconstruction of knowledge. Fourth, the wide range of pupil interests, abilities, backgrounds, and experiences calls for teaching science to meet the different needs of all pupils. Dr. Tyler describes some of the problems which have been brought into focus by these forces, and he lists some of the resources which science teachers can draw on to counter these problems.

S CIENCE teaching has taken on new life and vigor. More developments are under way in this field than in any other school subject. The National Science Foundation has spent or committed thirty million dollars to support the work of committees of scientists and teachers in developing modern courses for the high school and is beginning to work out appropriate content for the elementary school. The Federal Government has spent or committed more than two hundred million dollars to support summer institutes where science teachers can increase their training in modern science. Under the National Defense Education Act, federal funds are available to states on a matching basis, to build and modernize high school science laboratories.

The public interest in science is not only providing more moral and financial support for the efforts to improve science teaching but the public attention and concern have profoundly influenced the career choices of the ablest of high school students. Ten years ago, the most popular career choice of the ablest students was the field of medicine. At that time the American medical colleges had seven times the number of qualified applicants than they had room to admit. Last year, there were only about one and three-fourths as many qualified applicants as could be admitted. A number of the less well-known medical colleges had fewer qualified applicants than the available places. This drop in popularity of medicine among the ablest students has been paralleled by a great increase in the popularity of science. Among the National Merit Scholarship winners last year, physics and mathematics were by far the more frequent choices.

TECHNOLOGICAL REVOLUTION

The current increased interest and concern for science is commonly interpreted as the American reaction to Russian scientific achievements, and, no doubt, this is a factor. But an examination of the figures on employment and on career choices of high school and college graduates over the past fifty years makes clear that development of and interest in science and technology have been growing for a long time as a natural result of the technological revolution. Fifty years ago, scientists and engineers represented one-third of one per cent of the labor force of America. According to the 1960 census, scientists and engineers represented three per cent of the labor force. In fifty years, the proportion of people working in these fields has increased nearly tenfold. This illustrates the changing character of our economy and our society. Science, technology, and education are now the chief means by which modern industrial societies increase productivity, reduce death and illness, and provide wider opportunities for goods and services. Public recognition of this has greatly influenced science teaching.

A second major influence on science teaching is the closer working relationship between the university and research scientist and the teacher in the schools. Only a few years ago, the scientist had no first-hand contact with science teachers in the schools, and no understanding of the problems faced in teaching science to the "children of all the people." Frequently scientists blamed the teaching of science in the schools for the alleged inadequacy of college and university students, but they made no effort to help develop better courses and instructional materials, or to aid the teacher in getting a more adequate education in the sciences. In fact, most university scientists advised their good students not to go into science teaching.

The growing public concern with science led to a more comprehensive and objective appraisal of the condition of science in the schools. The shortage of qualified science teachers and the lack of authentic, up-to-date books and other instructional materials were emphasized in this survey and, in increasing numbers, highly competent scientists are responding to the need and the opportunity. The committees supported by the National Science Foundation working on new courses and teaching materials for the schools include topflight scientists as well as teachers. Summer institutes and academic year institutes for the further training of science teachers are involving an increased number of able scientists. And, although slowly, scientists are recognizing the need to encourage competent science students in the universities to go into school teaching rather than to urge them to establish careers in the research centers. This closer working relationship is redirecting science teaching by getting the best thinking of scientists into the development of the school program. The result is an expansion of the horizons of many science teachers regarding the nature of science, the kinds of educational objectives to which science can contribute, and the possibilities in new instructional materials. This relationship is also providing a new sense of confidence to the science teacher as he appreciates through this relationship his own unique and important contribution to the development of science in working with children and youth.

A third important influence on science teaching is the rapidly expanding explosion of knowledge. Although science is always advancing, the common view from 1900 to 1950 was that the basic principles and important facts of physics, chemistry, and biology had been discovered and were central to all further elaborations of these subjects. In the schools, children would learn these basic principles and important facts and they would be properly grounded in science no matter how much more research might uncover. Except for the addition from year to year of new illustrations of the applications of science, the textbook content of these subjects barely changed from 1910 to 1950. No wonder that most students and many of the teachers thought the learning of science was the memorization of the basic principles and the important facts. But new developments in science have sharply shaken this view.

The "explosion of science" is not just adding more and more details to a stable basic outline. Scientific inquiry is continually examining basic definitions, assumptions, principles, and relationships; and the results of scientific research frequently require a reconstruction of the basic ideas as well as the addition of details. If students are to understand science and contribute to its intellectual development, they need to understand it as a process of continuing inquiry and reconstruction of knowledge. As this becomes recognized by science teachers, it results in considerable influence upon their work. A science course becomes an introduction in "learning how to learn" science, an effort to start the student on a lifelong endeavor to make sense out of his experiences with the material world and the observations made of natural phenomena, as well as environment.

A fourth kind of influence which is redirecting science teaching is the increased understanding on the part of science teachers of the wide range of pupils in school—range in general and special abilities, range in interests and purposes, and range in home and community backgrounds and experiences. When science was thought to be of primary significance only to those planning to be scientists or engineers, the really basic concepts and methods of science could be developed in courses elected by senior high school students who were interested in science and well prepared to cope with the subject. Now science is conceived more broadly both as an intellectual discipline and as a means of understanding modern society, its achievements and its problems. As such, science is essential not only for those preparing for careers in science and technology but also for all citizens. Faced with this need, science teachers are realizing that the varied nature of the whole range of elementary and secondary school pupils poses problems for science teaching which have not yet been solved.

Currently, the effect of these four major forces is to bring into focus several important and difficult problems which must be solved if science teaching is to achieve its goal and carry out the responsibilities associated with this task.

TEACHING SCIENCE AS INQUIRY

There is the general problem in all science courses of ably teaching science so that it is an "introduction to learning how to learn" rather than teaching it as a collection of today's answers to questions which will be answered differently tomorrow. The tradition of teaching and learning in most school subjects is that of memorizing important facts. To change this tradition involves developing a new attitude on the part of students and teachers so that learning becomes an experience in inquiry. It must become a process in knowing how to raise questions which are relevant to science and how to carry on investigations of these questions; it must include investigations which keep broadening and deepening the student's understanding of the questions themselves and also considerations that need to be taken into account and finally the adequacy and incompleteness of possible answers. To teach science in these terms requires a change in the notion of what has to be covered, a change in the kinds of learning experiences provided, a change in instructional materials used, a change in the tests, examinations, and other evaluation procedures. This is a problem on which science teachers and educators will need to work for a long period.

A more particular problem for science teachers to solve is to provide adequate depth in the learning experiences and sufficient variety to care for individual differences in the various courses offered for the competent student who has a major interest in science. The new course-content projects supported by the National Science Foundation are developing useful materials and ideas to meet this problem.

A second particular problem is in teaching competent students whose major interests are elsewhere. Many of these boys and girls consider science as irrelevant to their purposes and as having little connection with their own lives. The teaching problem is to aid these students to perceive science as an area which is vital in their own lives and which involves intellectual efforts which are rewarding in themselves.

A third particular problem is probably the most difficult of all. It is the problem of reaching the student with more limited scholastic aptitude who has had little or no background in systematic thinking and problem solving. In the past courses have been provided for such students which did not involve inquiry, but emphasized descriptions of common and interesting applications of technology; for example, describing the operation of an electric refrigerator. Sketchy memorization was the kind of learning expected. These students rarely gained any notion of what science really is and no insight into science as an intellectual enterprise. Their notions of the marvels of science were more like beliefs in magic than in science. This approach did not prepare them to cope with the modern scientific world as citizens. Thinking, inquiry, and exercise of intelligence are possible for most if not all children and youth, but the development of intellectual potential for children with limited and inhibiting experiences in their homes and community environments requires new approaches, new materials, and new skills on the part of teachers. This is one of the important unsolved problems needing attention.

CONCLUSION

Can we expect that these difficult teaching problems can be effectively attacked? There are three kinds of resources on which science teachers may draw to counter these problems. The first of these is a more adequate knowledge of how learning takes place. Recent studies of the acquisition by children and youth of more complex mental processes provide suggestive guide lines for improved learning and teaching. The second is the number of rapidly developing devices for aiding teaching and learning; for example, new cartridge motion picture projectors for quick presentation of phenomena difficult to observe; simple laboratory equipment which can be used at home; teaching machines and programmed instructional materials which permit progress in learning at one's own rate; new printing processes which make economically feasible an individual science library; team teaching which can bring a range of teaching talents to bear on each student; cooperative work experience to extend the student's perception of meaningful science activities; and educational television which can bring additional teachers, demonstrations, etc., into the classroom or the home. Some of these devices are already being adopted and adapted by science teachers who are attacking difficult problems of teaching and learning.

To my mind, however, the one most important resource we have in improving science teaching and in solving the serious problems of this age is the science teacher. It is my opinion that we shall move forward in developing a comprehensive program of science instruction which is effective in meeting the present task because of the degree of intelligence, ingenuity, and concern among the science teachers of America.

DISCOVERY OR INVENTION? *

J. Myron Atkin and Robert Karplus

The authors maintain that it does not seem crucial to teach children to invent concepts, because they can and do invent concepts readily. The educational problem, rather, is to teach the children to carry out their creative thinking with some intellectual discipline. If the children are not able to invent the concept, it is necessary for the teacher to introduce the concept. The teacher must then follow the introduction with opportunities to discover that new observation can also be interpreted by using a concept. This

* REPRINTED FROM *The Science Teacher*, Vol. 29, No. 5, September 1962, pp. 45–51. Copyright, 1962, by the National Science Teachers Association, Washington, D.C. Reprinted by permission of the authors and the publisher. Dr. Atkin is Professor of Education at the University of Illinois. Dr. Karplus is Professor of Physics at the University of California, Berkeley.

type of discovery can be extremely valuable in solidifying learning and mo-tivating the children. Moreover, it is essential if a concept is to be used with increasing refinement and precision. As an example of this teaching approach the authors describe a thirty-minute lesson in which second-graders discovered the usefulness of the magnetic field after the teacher had invented it for them.

M ORE RECENTLY, the discussion of the role of discovery in teaching has intensified. Many authors have stressed the great educational benefits to be derived if pupils discover concepts for themselves.[1] Other authors have warned that discovery teaching is so time consuming and inefficient that it should not, in general, replace expository teaching.[2]

There is a way in which autonomous recognition of relationships by the pupils; *i.e.,* "discovery" can and should be combined with expository intro-duction of concepts in an efficient program. This will produce understanding rather than rote verbalization. The approach can be described more clearly, if a historical example[3] is given of how a particular scientific concept is developed.

In ancient times the sun and the planets were observed by man. These observations gave rise to various conceptual interpretations. There were the mythological interpretations, the interpretation as "celestial matter" with certain properties, and eventually the modern interpretation of planets orbit-ing around the sun. With the help of each of these concepts, man could attempt to understand other phenomena beside the ones that had led him to suggest the interpretation originally. These attempts, if successful, led to a reinforcement and refinement of the concept; if they failed, they revealed limits of the usefulness of the concept or even stimulated a search for a new concept. Of the three interpretations we have mentioned, the final and cur-rently accepted one has turned out to be much more powerful than its prede-cessors.

In the development of a concept, it is useful to distinguish the original introduction of a new concept, which can be called invention, from the sub-sequent verification or extension of the concept's usefulness, which can be called discovery. Of course, this distinction is not completely clear-cut, be-cause the inventor must recognize that the new concept is applicable to the phenomena he is trying to interpret; otherwise he would discard the inven-

---

[1] Jerome Bruner. *The Process of Education.* Harvard University Press, Cambridge, Mas-sachusetts, 1960.

[2] David Ausubel. *Learning by Discovery: Rationale Mystique.* Bureau of Educational Research, University of Illinois, Urbana, Illinois. 1961.

[3] The historical development and its analysis in this illustration have been greatly over-simplified. For a fuller and more profound discussion see: Thomas Kuhn, "The Nature of Scientific Revolutions," University of Chicago Press, Chicago, Illinois. (In process.)

tion immediately. Return therefore to the example for determining how the distinction can be applied. Assume that the deities, the celestial matter, and the solar system were inventions. In the mythological framework, one could then discover that the deities intervened in human affairs in certain ways and refine one's idea of the characteristics of the gods. In the framework based on the existence of celestial matter, one could discover that celestial objects move in cycles and epicycles. Finally, in the framework of the solar system, one could discover additional planets.

Undoubtedly, an invention is not complete and static, but it is the germ of a concept that is developed to greater significance by the subsequent discoveries. When an invention is made, its full significance is not evident. Still, the concept must be introduced and the invention must be made, if it is to grow in meaning.

Applying this distinction between discovery and invention to science teaching, acknowledge the fact that the pupil has experience both before he enters school and also outside the school environment during the school years. He therefore makes observations all the time, and he invents concepts that interpret the observations as well. He also makes discoveries that enable him to refine his concepts. Most of the discoveries and inventions reveal a type of natural philosophy—a "common-sense" orientation popular in the culture at a given point in history.

Yet, the objective of the science program is to teach children to look at natural phenomena from the distinctive vantage point of modern science. And in the mid-twentieth century, this vantage point differs from the culturally prevalent view. In a small way the situation is analogous to that of a Copernican teacher instructing his students that the sun is at the center of the solar system while almost everyone else in the society *knows* that the earth is at the center of the universe.

In general, no results are evident if a teaching program is based on the expectation that children can invent the modern scientific concepts, because their spontaneously invented concepts, some of which even exist at the time the child enters school, present too much of a block. After all, concepts were developed to interpret their experience; why should they change these concepts on their own? Indeed, it does not seem crucial to teach the children to invent concepts, because they can and do invent concepts readily. The educational problem, rather, is to teach the children to carry out their creative thinking with some intellectual discipline. And the development and refinement of modern scientific concepts in the light of observations would seem to be one excellent vehicle for achieving this goal.

If the children are not able to *invent* the modern scientific concepts, it is necessary for the teacher to *introduce* the modern scientific concepts. During this introduction, the teacher must make clear which previous observations of the children can be interpreted (or perhaps reinterpreted) by using a concept. Further, he must follow the introduction with opportunities for the children to discover that new observations can also be interpreted by using a concept. This type of discovery is made possible by the availability of a concept to the children, because their perception is oriented by the teacher's formulation of the new idea. This type of discovery can be extremely valuable to solidify learning and motivate the children; it is essential, if a concept is to be used with increasing refinement and precision. Categorically, the teacher must not present the concept in a complete, definitive, and authoritarian way, for concepts are never final.

As an example of this teaching approach, a thirty-minute lesson will be described in which second graders discovered the usefulness of the magnetic field concept after the teacher had invented it for them. In thirteen previous sessions, a class of fifteen pupils had discussed the selection of systems by the specification of the objects in the system, and the existence of interactions among the objects, and had been introduced to the notion of the free energy of the system.

Two new concepts were introduced to the class in the lesson: the interaction-at-a-distance, and the magnetic field. These ideas were developed through a series of experiments.

Experiment 1. Two boys pulled on a rope in opposite directions. The pupils identified the system of interest as consisting of Bruce, James, and the rope. Interactions between objects in the system included the one between James and the rope and the one between Bruce and the rope. Bruce and James were considered not to interact with each other. *Invention of interaction-at-a-distance:* Next, the teacher pointed out that Bruce and James were really the important objects in the system; that the whole class could think that there was an interaction between the two boys (at a signal, Bruce yanked James with the rope); but that it was not a *direct interaction,* it was a *distant interaction.* The new term was stressed. The rope made the distant interaction possible. The teacher further asked Bruce and James to interact strongly, then weakly, then strongly again.

Experiment 2. The teacher produced two wooden balls that were held together by a strip of rubber tacked to the balls. Five objects were identified in the system: the two balls, the rubber strip, and the two thumbtacks. The pupils identified the direct interactions ball-rubber, ball-thumbtack, and rubber-thumbtack. They identified the distant interactions ball-ball, thumbtack-thumbtack, and end of rubber-end of rubber. The pupils called the interaction weak when the balls were close together, strong when they were far apart, and medium when they were somewhat separated. The strip of rubber made the distant interaction possible.

Experiment 3. The teacher put his hand on the head of one boy. The pupils correctly identified the direct interaction, teacher-boy, and the distant acoustic interactions, teacher-all pupils.

Experiment 4. The teacher repeated Experiment 2 with a long brass spring. The distant interaction between the ends of the spring and the strength of the interaction were identified. The spring made possible the distant interaction between its own ends.

Experiment 5. The teacher produced two large U-magnets mounted to attract one another on roller skates so that they could move easily. The pupils identified the distant interaction between the two magnets in the system. They also determined that the strength of the interaction decreased as the magnets were separated. The interaction was sufficiently strong for the magnets to roll toward one another at a separation of four inches. *Invention of magnetic field:* In response to the teacher's question, "Which do you like better, direct interactions or distant interactions?" The pupils expressed a strong preference for direct interactions. The teacher now told the pupils that most people prefer to think in terms of direct interactions. In the earlier experiments there had been something between the two objects that made possible the distant interaction between them. Was there something now between the two magnets that made possible the distant interaction between them? There was nothing visible. (Curiously enough, no pupil suggested that the air was involved.) Even though the magnetic field was not yet mentioned by name, the children were given the crucial idea of a mediator (an "it") for the distant magnetic interaction. This step constituted what we have called the "invention."

Experiment 6. Discovery of the significance of the magnetic field:

a. Three children came to the demonstration table to find "it" by feeling with their fingers. They did not find "it."

b. Two children came to the demonstration table to find "it" with a wooden ruler. They did not find "it."

c. One child came to find "it" with a nail held at the end of a piece of wire. The nail responded to something!

d. All pupils wanted to explore with the nail. As others had an opportunity to do so, the teacher verbally confirmed the fact that the nail indeed seemed to have responded to something. When the teacher was going to name it, he was interrupted by one pupil who said "I know what 'it' is called. 'It' is a magnetic!" The teacher agreed to the "magnetic," because it occurred in a magnetic interaction, but proposed the name "magnetic field." Thereafter, the discussion was carried out in terms of exploring to find the magnetic field—the "it" which made possible the distant interaction between the two magnets.

e. Several more pupils explored and found the magnetic field with the nail.

f. As a final step of this experiment, the teacher invited the pupils to find the magnetic field with other objects. Screws, paper, paper clips, a screw driver, jewelry, and coins were used. Some of these objects responded to the magnetic field, some did not.

It is necessary to point out here that the appeal to the children's intuitive preference that was significant in the invention of the field concept was not at all unscientific, but was the necessary first step in the adoption of a new concept. While questions of scientific observation are decided by experiment, questions of interpretation are at first decided by preference in the light of past experience and later by the usefulness of the interpretation in generating discoveries. The magnetic field is a useful *invention,* but it is not essential to describe magnetic interactions.[4] Without the invention of the magnetic field, the subsequent explorations with the nail, etc., would have resulted in the discovery of additional distant interactions between the magnets and the nail or the other objects.

There is one feature of the preparatory Experiments 1–4 which should be emphasized. These experiments had been carried out earlier in a somewhat different way, but the distant interactions and the strength of interaction were newly introduced in this lesson. The sequence in which these experiments are carried out is not important. The pupils are not led step-by-step to the magnetic field concept. Rather, they are; "led in a circle around the magnetic field concept so they may then converge on the center of the circle from several directions." This strategy offers more promise of success.

Now, the lesson described must be placed in a science course. It is essential that the discussion of magnetic fields not be terminated and wrapped-up with the discovery described. Instead, this discovery should in itself be part of a strategy of attack on another more profound concept. In teaching the second grade, the concept of energy is the next higher order of understanding. Springs, rubber bands, dry cells, candles, and air, all these had been introduced earlier. Now magnets are seen as systems in which energy can be stored. The energy concept, in turn, is part of the strategy being developed for teaching about interactions among the objects in a system, a still higher order concept.

The pedagogical point to be stressed in conclusion is that this type of discovery teaching appears to be strongly motivating and rewarding. Yet, the teaching seems also to be reasonably efficient even when compared with a more verbal expository approach. The pupils come to the point where they know they will discover something, and they know what their discovery will mean. Hence, perhaps they did not invent the new concepts, but they did make discoveries.

[4] J. A. Wheeler and Richard P. Feynman. "Classical Electrodynamics in Terms of Direct Interparticle Action," *Reviews of Modern Physics,* 21:425. 1949.

STATEMENT OF PURPOSES AND OBJECTIVES OF SCIENCE EDUCATION IN THE ELEMENTARY SCHOOL *

William Kessen

William Kessen defines science as a structured and directed way of asking and answering questions. He believes science is best taught as procedure of enquiry. Dr. Kessen believes that the objectives in science education should include an attitude of intelligent caution and such procedures of science as the ability to state a problem, use sources of reliable information, observe, compare, classify, measure, experiment, evaluate evidence, draw conclusions, invent a model or theory, and communicate in science. Dr. Kessen also sketches an outline of the basic areas of scientific knowledge that a properly educated child should possess within the first ten years of school.

THERE IS joy in the search for knowledge; there is excitement in seeing, however partially, into the workings of the physical and biological world; there is intellectual power to be gained in learning the scientist's approach to the solution of human problems. The first task and central purpose of science education is to awaken in the child, whether or not he will become a professional scientist, a sense of the joy, the excitement, and the intellectual power of science. Education in science, like education in letters and the arts, will enlarge the child's appreciation of his world; it will also lead him to a better understanding of the range and limits of man's control over nature.

SCIENCE AS INQUIRY

Science is best taught as a procedure of enquiry. Just as reading is a fundamental instrument for exploring whatever may be written, so science is a fundamental instrument for exploring whatever may be tested by observa-

* REPRINTED FROM *Journal of Research in Science Teaching*, Vol. 2, Issue 1, 1964, pp. 4–6, by permission of the author and the editor. Dr. Kessen is Associate Professor of Psychology at Yale University.

tion and experiment. Science is more than a body of facts, a collection of principles, and a set of machines for measurement; it is a structured and directed way of asking and answering questions. It is no mean pedagogical feat to teach a child the facts of science and technology; it is a pedagogical triumph to teach him these facts in their relation to the procedures of scientific enquiry. And the intellectual gain is far greater than the child's ability to conduct a chemical experiment or to discover some of the characteristics of static electricity. The procedures of scientific enquiry, learned not as a canon of rules but as ways of finding answers, can be applied without limit. The well-taught child will approach human behavior and social structure and the claims of authority with the same spirit of alert skepticism that he adopts toward scientific theories. It is here that the future citizen who will not become a scientist will learn that science is not memory or magic but rather a disciplined form of human curiosity.

The Scientific Attitude

The willingness to wait for a conclusive answer—the skepticism that requires intellectual restraint and the maintenance of doubt—is oftentimes difficult for adult and child alike. The discipline of scientific enquiry demands respect for the work of the past together with a willingness to question the claims of authority. The attitude of intelligent caution, the restraint of commitment, the belief that difficult problems are always susceptible to scientific analysis, and the courage to maintain doubt will be learned best by the child who is given an honest opportunity to try his hand at scientific enquiry. With his successes will come an optimistic appreciation of the strength of enquiry; with his failures will come an understanding of the variety and challenge of our ignorance. For the scientist, child and adult, novelty is permanent; scientific enquiry continually builds novelty into a coherent design, full of promise, always tentative, that tames our terror and satisfies for a while the human desire for simplicity.

The Procedures of Science

Scientific problems arise in the play of children just as they arise in the guided exploration of scientists. Astonishment in the presence of natural beauty, surprise—even frustration—at the failure of a prediction, and the demand for sense in the face of confusion are the beginnings of scientific enquiry. But how do we then proceed?

Among the most demanding of scientific tasks and certainly among the most difficult to teach is the *statement* of a problem. Is there a meaningful question to be asked? What techniques should be used to answer it? How does one go about making a prediction or developing a hypothesis? As he asks these questions, the student begins to learn how active enquiry can lead to testable questions and eventually to the solution of problems. He is introduced also to the pleasures and problems of inventive thought—of considering what might be as well as what is.

There are many ways to answer a provocative question in science and the child should come to recognize that he must adapt his method to the problem in hand. As he runs against different problems, the child will learn to use several *sources of reliable information*—observation, experiment, books, museums, and informed adults.

Whatever the problem, the child's *ability to observe* should be extended so that he understands the wide range of observations possible even when simple phenomena are under study. He must learn to order the evidence of all his senses.

Attention to the complex activity of *comparison of phenomena* will introduce the child to an essential task in science—the perception of differences and similarities among events.

The child will use his ability to observe and to compare in building *systems of classification* and in recognizing their usefulness and their limitations in science.

The child should learn to use the *instruments of science*. As he studies these instruments, the teacher is given an opportunity to instruct the child in *measurement*. He will learn the need for precision in measurement, the importance of agreement among observers, and the relations among different systems of measurement.

The use of laboratory techniques—especially *the experiment*—deserves special attention. The experiment is the sharpest tool of science and in devising an experiment, the child exercises his ability to pose a question, to consider possible answers, to select appropriate instruments, to make careful measurements, and to be aware of sources of error. It is unlikely that children in the first years of school will manage well all aspects of sound laboratory procedure but the best lessons of the experiment can be taught only to the child who is actively engaged with the equipment and procedures of the laboratory. The teacher must adapt his desire for precision to the child's excitement in the search; a premature demand for exactness in experimental manipulation may blunt the student's commitment and pleasure.

After the problem is posed, a hypothesis developed, and the data gathered, the science student must *evaluate evidence and draw conclusions*. Sometimes this is a simple step; sometimes it involves the review and modification of the entire plan with renewed attention to problem, to hypothesis, and to data-protocols. The goal is to make sense of the data and the pursuit of this goal will on occasion lead to the detection of an error or to the design of another study. It may also lead to the *invention of a model or theory* through which we can comprehend data.

Throughout the course of science education, the *need to communicate* is present. Describing a bird to his class, graphing a mathematical function, writing an experimental paper—experience with each mode of report is essential to the development of the science student.

The child's ability to communicate in science will both depend upon and contribute to the achievement of this most general goal of the curriculum—accurate and effective communication.

The procedures of science described here in the context of early science education are recognizably the procedures of science at all levels of sophistication. Scientific enquiry is a seamless fabric. The content will change, the demand for precision will vary, the generality of conclusion will be different, the interrelation of studies will be understood in different ways, but the procedures and attitudes of scientific study remain remarkably the same from the time the kindergarten child wonders about color to the time the graduate physicist wonders about particle emission.

SCIENTIFIC KNOWLEDGE

The facts and principles of science change with each advance in our understanding of the world. For this reason, it is difficult to forecast with precision what scientific content the child should know. Nonetheless, it is possible to sketch in outline the scientific knowledge that the properly educated child will possess within the first ten years of school. A knowledge of the basic findings of centuries of scientific enquiry gives boundaries and direction to the child's active exploration of his world. Under the governing premise that the curriculum in science must be defined by the child's growing comprehension of nature's order and beauty more than by the conventional categories of scientific knowledge, the child should know as much as he can actively seize about

the universe, its galaxies, our solar system, the earth, and his immediate environment; the range of measurements used to describe astronomical and geological phenomena;

the structure and reactions of matter from the smallest particles to their combination in minerals and rocks; elements, compounds and mixtures, large and small molecules, atoms, protons, neutrons, and electrons;

the conservation and transformation of energy; the electro-magnetic spectrum, energy of motion and potential energy, electrical energy and chemical energy; force and work, gravitational and magnetic fields;

the interaction between living things and their environment; animal and human behavior, the relation between biological structure and function, reproduction, development, genetics, evolution, and the biological units—cell, organism, and population.

Science cannot be divided easily into labeled categories without loss. An emphasis on *scientific principles* that bridge the conventional subject-matter divisions will improve and simplify the teaching of science, making it more easily understood and more productive of meaningful problems for the child's own enquiry.

Scientific enquiry, moreover, is partner and peer of the traditional divisions of study; decisions about education in science must always be made with consideration of the relation of science to the child's other studies. Levers and poems, energy exchange and historical analysis, genetics and geography—all present to the child an opportunity to extend his reach into the world and, in their different ways, all present to the child an opportunity to see beauty.

The Child and the Teacher

Rising above any statement of objectives for education is an irreducible fact. Teaching is an exchange between people. This simple human fact is both problem and promise for education in science as it is for all education. The child can understand only what he has been prepared to understand, the teacher can teach only what he knows, and the meeting of the prepared child with skillful teacher is an unforgettable encounter for them both. In the successful educational encounter, the child will become an active searcher for knowledge and the teacher will form attitudes toward enquiry as well as offer information about the world. The related and intricate problems of teacher training and the nature of learning are closely intertwined with the goals of science education. Science, rooted in man's curiosity and love of order, is called to its full humanity by the child's desire to know.

SOME PSYCHOLOGICAL CONSIDERATIONS IN THE OBJECTIVES AND DESIGN OF AN ELEMENTARY-SCHOOL SCIENCE PROGRAM *

David P. Ausubel

David P. Ausubel believes that the discovery approach as a primary method of presenting subject matter is too time-consuming and inefficient. Another difficulty in using the discovery approach arises from the children's sub-

* REPRINTED FROM *Science Education*, Vol. 47, No. 3, April 1963, pp. 278–284, by permission of the author and the publisher. Dr. Ausubel is Professor of Educational Psychology at the University of Illinois.

jectiveness and from their tendency to jump to conclusions, to overgeneralize, and to consider only one phase of the problem at a time. Dr. Ausubel argues for breadth over depth in the content of elementary school science, allowing for an occasional introduction of atypical depth to give the student a taste of scholarship and of research inquiry. He decries probing in depth of isolated areas merely as a means of enhancing skills, and he believes this type of activity is suitable only after a degree of sophistication has been reached. Dr. Ausubel believes that the science curriculum should be concerned with the systematic presentation of an organized body of knowledge as an explicit end in itself. Furthermore, it is just as important for children to learn that science is a selectively and sequentially organized structure as it is for them to learn that science is a method of inquiry.

THE PSYCHOLOGICAL argument for teaching science in the elementary school is, in my opinion, unassailable.[1] First, it is well-known that young children spontaneously acquire many animistic and subjectivistic conceptions about the physical and biological universe.[2] These notions also tend to persist and often compete with more mature conceptions, especially when not counteracted by early scientific training. Second, without early and satisfactory instruction in science, it is difficult for children both to assimilate positive interests in and attitudes toward the scientific enterprise, and to avoid being negatively conditioned to scientific subject matter. Lastly, since elementary-school pupils can easily acquire an intuitive grasp of many scientific concepts, failure to provide suitable opportunities for them to do so not only wastes available readiness for such learning, but also wastes valuable time in junior and senior high school that could be used for more advanced instruction in science.

DEPENDENCE ON CONCRETE, EVERYDAY EXPERIENCE

The elementary-school child is completely dependent upon current or recently prior concrete-empirical experience for the meaningful understanding or manipulation of relational propositions. He tends to appreciate relationships between abstractions intuitively—as rather immediate logical extensions of his own personal experience, rather than in the truly abstract sense of relationships between general variables.[3] Hence general laws and methodological canons of science, in their own right, have little meaning and intel-

---

[1] The discussion in this paragraph is based on R. Karplus, "Beginning a Study in Elementary School Science," *American Journal of Physics*, XXX (1962).

[2] E.g., J. Piaget, *The Child's Conception of Physical Causality*. New York: Harcourt, Brace, 1932.

[3] B. Inhelder and J. Piaget, *The Growth of Logical Thinking from Childhood to Adolescence*. New York: Basic Books, 1958.

lectual appeal for him; they make sense only insofar as they are relatable to more tangible types of experience. "Utility" is a major example of this type of experience, but it's certainly not the only possible example.

As far as elementary-school children are concerned, therefore, one cannot hope to reduce science to "first principles" and basic abstract laws.[4]

At the very best one can strive for a semiabstract, intuitive grasp of these laws on a descriptive and manipulative level that is tied to particularized experience. On the methodological side, abstract principles of scientific inquiry and strategy also have much less meaning for children than a purely concrete-empirical explanation of how it is possible for mankind to know the facts and generalizations under discussion.[5]

The suggestion that sciences be studied in the order of their phenomenological complexity—i.e., that one start with "the basic concepts of physics and chemistry before tackling the complex phenomena of biology and geology" [6]—is logically sound but psychologically unfeasible. More important pedagogically than the logical structure of knowledge is the pupil's intellectual readiness to handle different kinds of subject matter; and from the standpoint of relevant experience and readiness, the phenomenologically "simple" laws of physics are far more abstract and difficult than the phenomenologically "complex" laws of biology and geology, which are so much closer to everyday experience. This is not to deny the possibility that some aspects of physics might be profitably introduced in the elementary-school curriculum. However, before this could be done in the "rigorous fashion (physics) deserves," the teaching of elementary-school mathematics would first have to be sufficiently improved to make possible a more functional intuitive understanding of the quantitative relationships that figure so prominently in the physical sciences.[7]

DEVELOPMENTAL CONSIDERATIONS: PRESENTATION OF SUBJECT-MATTER

The elementary-school child's dependence on concrete-empirical experience for the meaningful understanding of abstract propositions requires that much teaching in elementary-school science be directed toward a semi-

[4] Both Karplus, *op. cit.*, and M. H. Shamos, "Science for Citizens," *Saturday Review* (September 16, 1961), 68–69, deplore the emphasis in elementary science education upon the practical utilitarian aspects of science and the attempt "to relate science *primarily* to everyday experience." They advocate, instead, stress upon the concepts and methods of science.

[5] J. M. Atkin and S. P. Wyatt, *Astronomy: Charting the Universe*, trial edition (Urbana, Illinois: Elementary-School Science Project, University of Illinois, 1961), emphasize the "how we know" aspects of astronomy, using didactic exposition and simple exercises and demonstrations.

[6] M. H. Shamos, *op. cit.*

[7] *Ibid.*

abstract or intuitive type of learning. This does not mean, however, that all or even most teaching must necessarily be conducted on an inductive, problem-solving (discovery), and nonverbal basis. The only essential condition for learning relational concepts during this period is the availability of first-hand, nonrepresentational, and empirical experience. Didactic verbal exposition can easily be combined with such concrete-empirical props in the form of demonstrations and exercises, and usually suffices for the presentation of most subject matter that is neither excessively complex nor unfamiliar. In some instances it might be desirable to enhance verbal exposition with a semiautonomus type of problem-solving in which discovery is accelerated by the use of prompts, hints, and Socratic questioning.

Although self-discovery is by no means necessary for meaningfulness, the occasional use of inductive discovery and deductive problem-solving approaches in presenting subject-matter is clearly warranted under certain circumstances. When the new ideas to be learned are more difficult and unfamiliar, it is quite conceivable that autonomous discovery enhances intuitive understanding. It presumably does this by bringing the student into more intimate contact both with the necessary concrete experience and with the actual operations of abstracting and generalizing from empirical data. But as a primary method of transmitting subject-matter content, this approach is much too time-consuming and inefficient: simply on a time-cost basis, even secondary-school and university students would not progress much beyond the rudiments of any discipline if they were obliged to discover for themselves every fact and principle in the syllabus.[8] The desirability of occasional routine use for other purposes, however—i.e., to foster appreciation of scientific method, to test comprehension of subject matter, to develop problem-solving ability—is not denied.

Still another disadvantage in using a discovery approach for the presentation of subject-matter content inheres in the difficulties caused by children's subjectivism and by their exaggerated tendency to jump to conclusions, to overgeneralize on the basis of limited experience, and to consider only one aspect of a problem at a time.[9] It is true that one objective of the elementary science curriculum (i.e., to enhance appreciation of scientific method) implies an effort to educate them out of these tendencies. But it is one thing to do so as part of a limited laboratory program, and quite another to struggle full-time with this handicap as children are required to self-discover everything they have to learn.

Finally, one might reasonably ask how many students have the ability to discover everything they need to know. Although the ability to understand original ideas worth remembering is widely distributed, the ability to generate

---

[8] This disadvantage is admittedly less serious than it is in the case of older learners, since the time-consuming aspects of learning must take place anyway, and since a large volume of subject-matter cannot be covered in any case during the elementary-school period.

[9] J. Piaget, *op. cit.*; B. Inhelder and J. Piaget, *op. cit.*; R. Karplus, *op. cit.*

comparably original ideas autonomously is manifested by relatively few persons, that is, by gifted individuals.

BREADTH VERSUS DEPTH

Many factors counsel a choice of breadth over depth in the content of elementary-school science. First, from a logistical standpoint, the young child is not prepared for depth of subject-matter coverage. His limited attention span and his dependence on concrete-empirical props slow down greatly his rate of learning new material, thereby making it difficult for him to assimilate a wide array of information about a given topic; and the particularized, semi-abstract and relatively unprecise nature of his concepts detracts from his ability to organize and integrate this material in usable fashion. Second, because both his intellect and personality are still relatively uncrystallized and lacking in self-consistency, the elementary-school child is a "generalist." It is appropriate therefore to diversify the range of intellectual stimulation as widely as possible, because only in this way can all of the diverse potentialities both within a group of children and within a single child be brought to fruition. A broad curriculum, within the limits of pedagogic soundness, makes it possible for more pupils to experience success in the performance of school activities, and hence to develop the necessary self-confidence and motivation for continued academic striving and achievement.

Breadth, of course, inevitably implies a certain amount of superficiality. This superficiality, however, is not necessarily opprobrious. Whether it is desirable or undesirable cannot be judged in absolute terms but only in relation to the student's intellectual readiness for depth. It should also be pointed out in this connection that superficiality itself is always a relative state of affairs; the graduate school curriculum is just as superficial to the post-doctoral scholar as the elementary-school curriculum is to the college undergraduate. The spiral curriculum—the reintroduction of the same topics in progressively greater depth as intellectual readiness and maturity increase —is predicated on this assumption.

Superficiality is also not synonymous with triviality or with slipshod, unsystematic, or outdated teaching. Good teaching is as thorough as is possible at the appropriate level of breadth and depth; and even at the elementary-school level it allows for the occasional introduction of atypical depth, both substantively and methodologically, to give the student a taste of scholarship and of research inquiry. But, as will be pointed out later, the probing in depth of isolated areas, apart from the systematic presentation of subject-matter—merely as a means of enhancing inquiry skills or methodological sophistication—is indefensible at any age level, and particularly in the elementary school. It is a type of activity suitable for the scholar and research scientists—*after* he has acquired substantive and methodological sophistication in his field.

OBJECTIVES OF THE SCIENCE CURRICULUM

Many current writers [10] in the field of science education express the view that the principal objectives of science instruction are the acquisition of general inquiry skills, appropriate attitudes about science, and training in the "heuristics of discovery." Implicit or explicit in this view is the belief either that the particular choice of subject matter chosen to implement these goals is a matter of indifference (as long as it is suitable for the operations of inquiry), or that somehow in the course of performing a series of unrelated experiments in depth, the learner acquires all of the really important subject matter he needs to know. Thus, Hibbs states:

It does not matter whether the student learns any particular set of facts, but it does matter whether he learns how much fun it is to learn—to observe and experiment, to question and analyze the world without any ready-made set of answers and without any premium on the accuracy of his factual results, at least in the field of science.[11]

And Suchman contends that

. . . more basic than the attainment of concepts is the ability to inquire and discover them autonomously. . . . The schools must have a new pedagogy with a new set of goals which subordinates retention to thinking. Instead of devoting their efforts to storing information and recalling it on demand, they would be developing the cognitive functions needed to seek out and organize information in a way that would be most productive of new concepts.

In my opinion, any science curriculum worthy of the name must be concerned with the systematic presentations of an organized body of knowledge as an explicit end in itself. Even if it is relatively superficial and organized on an intuitive basis, as it must be in the elementary school, the science curriculum should make a start in this direction and give the student a feeling for science as a selectively and sequentially organized structure. This is no less important than imparting the view that science is a method of inquiry.

It is also completely unrealistic to expect that subject-matter content can be acquired incidentally as a by-product of problem-solving or discovery experience, as in the typical activity program or project method. Such incidental teaching pays too little attention to graded and systematically or-

---

[10] See, for example, J. S. Bruner, "After Dewey What?" *Saturday Review* (June 17, 1961), 58–59; 76–78; R. Karplus, *op. cit.*; J. R. Suchman, *Inquiry Training; Building Skills for Autonomous Discovery* (Urbana, Illinois: College of Education, University of Illinois, June 1961, mimeo.); A. R. Hibbs, "Science for Elementary Students," *Teachers College Record*, LXIII (1961), pp. 136–142.

[11] A. R. Hibbs, *ibid.*, p. 139.

ganized content, to substantive and programmatic aspects of presentation, and to practice and reinforcement variables.

The development of problem-solving ability is, of course, a legitimate and significant educational objective in its own right. Hence it is highly defensible to utilize a certain proportion of classroom time in developing appreciation of and facility in the use of scientific methods of inquiry and of other empirical, inductive, and deductive problem-solving procedures. But this is a far cry from advocating that the enhancement of problem-solving ability is the major function of the school. The goals of the science student and the goals of the scientist are not identical. Hence students cannot learn science most effectively by enacting the role of junior scientist.[12]

The scientist is engaged in a full-time search for new general or applied principles in his field. The student, on the other hand, is primarily engaged in an effort to learn the same basic subject matter in this field which the scientist had learned in his student days, and also to learn something of the method and spirit of scientific inquiry. Thus, while it makes perfectly good sense for the scientist to work full-time formulating and testing new hypotheses, it is quite indefensible . . . for the students to . . . [do] the same thing. . . . If he is ever to discover he must first learn; and he cannot learn adequately by pretending he is a junior scientist.[13]

To acquire facility in problem-solving and scientific method it is also unnecessary for learners to rediscover every principle in the syllabus. Since problem-solving ability is itself transferable, at least within a given subject matter field, facility gained in independently formulating and applying one generalization is transferable to other problems in the same discipline. Furthermore, over-emphasis on developing problem-solving ability would ultimately defeat its own ends. [Because of its time-consuming aspects] it would leave students with insufficient time in which to learn the content of a discipline; and hence, despite their adeptness at problem-solving they would be unable to solve simple problems involving the application of such content.[14]

Under these circumstances students would fail to acquire the minimal degree of subject-matter sophistication in a given discipline that is necessary for abstract intellectual functioning in that discipline, much less make original research contributions to science.

The proposal for training in the general "heuristics of discovery" [15] fails to take into account that research has invariably shown that grand strategies of inquiry are not generally transferable from one discipline to another. It does not seem likely that a strategy of discovery, which must necessarily be

---

[12] J. R. Suchman, op. cit., pp. 6–7, 32.

[13] D. P. Ausubel, "Learning by Discovery Rationale and Mystique," Bulletin of the National Association of Secondary School Principals, XLV (1961), pp. 38–39.

[14] D. P. Ausubel, "In Defense of Verbal Learning," Educational Theory, XI (1961), p. 23.

[15] J. R. Suchman, op. cit., p. 32; J. S. Bruner, "The Act of Discovery," Harvard Educational Review, XXXI (1961), pp. 30–32.

broad enough to be applicable to a wide range of disciplines and problems, can ever have, at the same time, sufficient particular relevance to be helpful in the solution of the problem at hand. In any case one would hardly imagine that principles of inquiry formulated at this level of abstraction would make much sense to children.

SUBSTANTIVE AND PROGRAMMATIC ASPECTS OF CURRICULUM

The substantive principles underlying the choice of subject-matter content in the Physical Science Study Committee Secondary School Physics Program hold true generally for elementary-school science as well: "(1) to plan a course of study in which the major developments of physics up to the present time are presented in a logical and integrated whole; (2) to present physics as an intellectual and cultural pursuit which is part of present-day human activity and achievement." [16] As previously suggested, however, the implementation of this latter principle in the elementary school requires greater reference to the personal, everyday world of the students, including more emphasis on such matters as utility, than is true of secondary-school physics.

In terms of providing a stable and widely transferable basis for the assimilation and integration of knowledge, the rationale of the PSSC program for its particular choice of subject matter is clear and defensible at all levels of instruction:

The Committee has chosen to select subject matter and organize it with the intent of providing as broad and powerful a base as possible for further learning—further learning both in and beyond the classroom. Through its materials the Committee seeks to convey those aspects of science which have the deepest meaning, the widest applicability. . . .

The explanatory systems of physics and how they are made have much more forward thrust as educational tools than the individual application and the discrete, unconnected explanation. Thus the PSSC has chosen for its subject matter the big over-arching ideas of physics—those that contribute most to the contemporary physicists' views of the nature of the physical world. . . . The power of the big ideas is in their wide applicability, and in the unity they bring to an understanding of what may appear superficially to be unrelated phenomena. . . . Pedagogically this choice has virtues. . . . Principal among them is the acquisition of criteria by which subject matter can be selected and organized toward the coherence the subject itself strives for.[17]

Much can also be done programmatically, by proper sequential arrangement of materials and by the use of "organizers," to enhance the learning of ele-

[16] G. C. Finlay, "Physical Science Study Committee: A Status Report," *The Science Teacher*, XXVI (1959), p. 574.
[17] G. C. Finlay, "Secondary School Physics: The Physical Science Study Committee," *American Journal of Physics*, XXVIII (1960), pp. 286–293.

mentary science. Maximum advantage is taken of the "big ideas" when they are followed by subsidiary facts, concepts, and generalizations which can be logically subsumed under them. Each new unit of learning material can also be preceded by an organizing introduction at a higher level of abstraction, generality, and inclusiveness, which seeks both to provide ideational scaffolding for the new material and to increase its discriminability from previously learned concepts.[18] The organizer makes use of established knowledge to increase the familiarity and learnability of new material, and also takes into account children's existing misconceptions about and folk lore models of physical and biological causality. Finally, the same topics can be reconsidered at progressively greater depth within the same course, as the student's level of sophistication increases. This is one of the most interesting pedagogic innovations of the PSSC program.[19]

RATIONALE OF LABORATORY WORK

Science courses at all academic levels are traditionally organized so that students waste many valuable hours in the laboratory collecting and manipulating empirical data which at the very best help them rediscover or exemplify principles that the instructor could present verbally and demonstrate visually in a matter of minutes. Hence, although laboratory work can easily be justified on the grounds of giving students some appreciation of the spirit and methods of scientific inquiry, and of promoting problem-solving, analytic, and generalizing ability, it is a very time-consuming and inefficient practice for routine purposes of teaching subject-matter content [20] or illustrating principles where didactic exposition or simple demonstration are perfectly adequate. Knowledge of the methods whereby data and principles in a particular discipline are acquired need not necessarily be gained through self-discovery in the laboratory. In many instances this purpose can be accomplished much more efficiently through didactic exposition in conjunction with demonstrations and exercises.[21]

Laboratory work in this context refers to inductive discovery experience and should not be confused with demonstrations and simple exercises. Nevertheless it involves a contrived type of discovery that is very different from the truly autonomous discovery activities of the research scholar and scientist. The immature or unsophisticated student is only confused by the natural complexities of raw, unselected, and unsystematized data. Before he can dis-

[18] See D. P. Ausubel, "The Use of Advance Organizers in the Learning and Retention of Meaningful Verbal Material," *Journal of Educational Psychology*, LI (1960), pp. 267–272; and D. P. Ausubel and D. Fitzgerald, "The Role of Discriminability in Meaningful Verbal Learning and Retention," *Journal of Educational Psychology*, LII (1961), pp. 266–274. Organizers at the elementary school level must obviously include concrete-empirical props.

[19] G. C. Finlay, *op. cit.*, 1960.

[20] Conditions under which discovery methods may be warrantedly used for transmitting subject-matter content in the elementary school have been considered above.

[21] See footnote 5 above.

cover concepts and generalizations efficiently, the problem must be structured for him, and the available procedures and methods of handling data must be skillfully "arranged" by others, that is, simplified, selectively schematized, and sequentially organized in such a way as to make ultimate discovery almost inevitable. Occasional independent design of experiments may have a salutary effect in conveying the actual spirit of scientific inquiry, but should hardly be a routine procedure.

Thus in dividing the labor of scientific instruction, the laboratory typically carries the burden of conveying the method and spirit of science, whereas the textbook and teacher assume the burden of transmitting subject-matter content.[22] The laboratory, however, should be carefully integrated with the textbook, that is, it should deal with methodology related to the subject matter of the course and not with experiments chosen solely because of their suitability for illustrating various strategies of discovery. It goes without saying, of course, that laboratory methods can only be used where the underlying methodology and substantive principles are thoroughly understood rather than followed mechanically in cookbook fashion.

[22] Exceptions to this generalization have already been noted.

SCIENCE TEACHING IN THE ELEMENTARY SCHOOL *

Paul E. Blackwood

Paul E. Blackwood presents his definition of science as "man's relentless search for verifiable patterns, concepts, descriptions, or explanations of phenomena in the universe." The recorded knowledge that results from this search, and about which people communicate, is an important part of science. Dr. Blackwood briefly discusses three basic things that scientists do: they make descriptions, explanations, and predictions. He uses a three-sided polygon to describe the necessary components of a good science education program. Side 1 represents objects, forces, and phenomena that make up the universe. Side 2 represents methods of inquiry used to study the universe. Side 3 represents the knowledge (classified as concepts, principles, laws, facts, etc.) developed about the universe.

* REPRINTED FROM *Science and Children*, Vol. 2, No. 1, September 1964, pp. 21–25. Copyright, 1964, by the National Science Teachers Association, Washington, D.C. Reprinted by permission of the author and the publisher. Dr. Blackwood is Specialist for Elementary Science at the U.S. Office of Education.

WHAT YOU see and hear in the corridor of an elementary school is often related to what goes on in classrooms. This visitor was lured into a fifth-grade classroom by a girl energetically bouncing a red rubber ball.

Inside the classroom other pupils were dropping rubber balls. They were investigating how high a ball would bounce when dropped freely from various heights. After a short period of activity, the children and teacher were confronted with 15 sets of data collected independently by 15 two-man teams. What one team recorded is shown in Chart 1.

CHART 1

HEIGHT OF DROP (INCHES)	TRIAL	REBOUND (INCHES)
24″ (2′)	1	11.00″
	2	11.50″
	3	11.75″
	Average	11.41″
48″ (4′)	1	22.50″
	2	22.75″
	3	23.25″
	Average	22.83″
72″ (6′)	1	33.00″
	2	33.75″
	3	34.00″
	Average	33.58″
96″ (8′)		?
120″ (10′)		?

How would these results look on a graph? The question by the teacher was sufficient motivation to cause the team to prepare a graph of the results similar to the one below.

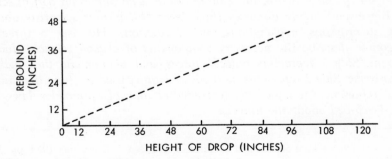

Additional questions began to emerge:

1. How far would the ball bounce if dropped from 8, 10, or 12 feet?
2. By using the graph, can one predict the height of rebound?
3. Is there a maximum height the ball will bounce, regardless of the distance it falls?
4. How does the bounce of different balls compare?
5. Do heavier balls bounce higher than lighter balls?

In another class, children were discussing the question, "How does the length of a stick's shadow change as the sun moves across the sky?" First, the children changed the question into a form which could be investigated more directly. They worded it this way: "What is the length of a stick's shadow at different times of the day?" An answer to this question could be obtained by direct measurement, and data collected to answer it would help answer the first question, so the class decided. It was not long before 15 pairs of pupils were busy in the schoolyard collecting information. Each pair was confronted with certain questions:

—How long a pole shall we use?
—Where shall we place it?
—At what intervals during the day shall we measure the shadow?

Two children decided to measure the length of the shadow of an 88-inch pole every hour from 8 a.m. to 3 p.m., just south of the school house. They measured it on June 7 and again on June 10 because the sun disappeared just after noon on the 7th. Their recorded data are illustrated in Chart 2.

CHART 2

Length of Pole: 88″ (7′4″)
Position: South of School House

TIME	LENGTH	
	JUNE 7	JUNE 10
8 a.m.	122″ (10′2″)	
9 a.m.	81″ (6′9″)	
10 a.m.	54″ (4′6″)	
11 a.m.	37″ (3′1″)	
12 m.	28″ (2′4″)	
1 p.m.	Cloudy	36″ (3′)
2 p.m.	Cloudy	53″ (4′5″)
3 p.m.	Cloudy	79″ (6′7″)

Based on these figures, the children were able to answer their questions about the changing length of shadows in relation to the position of the sun. But one youngster asked, "Does this experiment prove that the earth rotates or that the sun moves?"

The two learning experiences described above may well illustrate some characteristics of good science teaching. But a judgment can be made only in terms of what one accepts as a model of science education. Before evaluating these, or any science experiences, let us consider a model of science education which clearly recognizes two essential and perhaps interrelated features.

1. The nature of science, and
2. The purposes and methods of teaching science.

Surely a growing understanding of each of these by teachers of elementary school science is essential.

1. The Nature of Science

A working definition of science is helpful in giving clues as to what may properly be included in the study of science. The following tentative definition has the virtue of including enough ingredients to reflect the breadth and richness of science. *Science is man's relentless search for verifiable patterns, concepts, descriptions, or explanations of phenomena in the universe.*

In this definition, we see that man is in the picture. Science is an enterprise, an activity of people. Science is people searching. It is men, women, and children investigating, inquiring, and seeking verifiable knowledge. It is relentless, a continuous, never-ending attempt to find more accurate descriptions of things and events and to seek reasonable explanations of these events. The search leads to new discoveries, to new insights about unifying patterns, to concepts, to understandings, and to new knowledge. Many of these observations, descriptions, and explanations have been recorded by scientists and are available for use by other people as they attempt to extend their knowledge and understanding of the natural environment. This recorded knowledge, about which people can communicate, is an important part of science.

A definition of science like that discussed above has been eschewed by some scientists on the grounds that you can define science better in terms of what scientists do. It seems simple to say, "Science is what scientists do." But to understand this statement requires an analysis of what it is that men and women do when they are being scientists. Let us then, in our exploration of what science is, look briefly at three of the basic things that scientists do.

a. Scientists make descriptions. What is in the universe? How many? How much? How long? How frequently? Where? When? Under what circumstances? Answers to such questions are descriptions.

Astronomers use telescopes, cameras, and instruments of other kinds. They use mathematics and their minds to try to get a picture of our universe and how the bodies in space are interrelated. Geologists study rock structures, formations of the earth, and changes in its surface. The study requires careful observation and accurate reporting. Physicists attempt to find out how energy flows from one material to another and what happens to the materials.

Thus, scientists attempt to describe what is, how things are, what things are like, how they change, and how they interrelate. Improved descriptions of things and events in our universe enable scientists to discover unity within vast diversity. Methods that have proven practical in discovering the elements of unity within diversity and in getting "check-up-able" knowledge we sometimes call scientific methods. As other people use these methods, they are able to verify what someone else has observed.

b. Scientists make explanations. In a sense, scientists attempt to tell "why" certain events and phenomena occur the way they do. This usually involves observing carefully how things interact with each other. What are the interrelationships? What precedes what? What follows what? Under what conditions do certain phenomena occur? Making explanations usually involves showing the connections between events or phenomena.

In a way, an explanation is a very careful description. For example, to explain why water evaporates from an open dish requires knowledge about the physical structure of water, about the nature of molecular action, about the capacity of air to hold water molecules, the behavior of water molecules when heat energy is increased, and the like. Scientists are detectives attempting to put descriptions together in ways that help us understand events. In this way, they make explanations.

c. Scientists make predictions. In order to make knowledge more widely applicable and to extend our confidence in its validity, it must be tested in many situations. Extending our knowledge to new situations involves prediction. We have observed that water will evaporate from a dish on a window sill. We predict that it will evaporate also if placed on a warm radiator. We test to see. If it does, then our prediction is correct.

Scientists are continually testing to see if principles that apply in one situation will apply in another. Making use of a concept of generalizations or law in a situation which has not yet been tested involves prediction. Scientists have not been on the moon. Yet numerous predictions of what it is like there have been made and may be proven true. Actually, the acceptance of certain predictions as fact enables planning for the moon launch to proceed with confidence. Making predictions is an important part of what scientists do.

In making descriptions, explanations, and predictions, scientists use their minds; they use ideas of their own and ideas of others as tools for testing and gaining knowledge. They use many resources to get valid answers to their questions or solutions to their problems. They may invent new tools with which to observe or to check phenomena more accurately. Thus, scientists do many things in relation to making valid descriptions, explanations, and predictions.

Now, having considered briefly the meaning of science and what scientists do, it is appropriate to ask whether good science teaching should make provisions for children to experience science in the sense discussed. Let us postpone consideration of this question while we examine the second feature of our science education model.

2. The Purposes and Methods of Science Teaching

One way of representing a science education program is shown in the accompanying figures. It provides us with a way of describing a science education program and of questioning and constructively criticizing our efforts. In Figure 1, we see a three-sided polygon tapering off toward the bottom and flaring out at the top.[1] If this three-sided figure is opened to show its three faces, it would appear as in Figure 2.

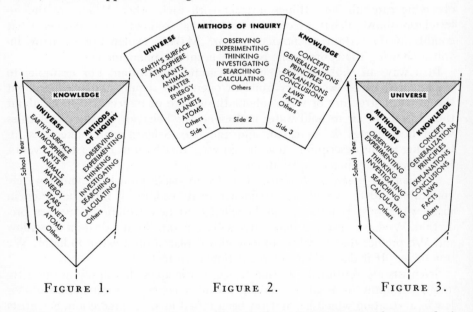

FIGURE 1.   FIGURE 2.   FIGURE 3.

Side 1 represents our universe which is the subject matter of our study in the natural sciences. It includes objects and forces and phenomena. However, the universe and things in it are *not* science. They are simply objects and forces and phenomena. These things can be grouped and organized in various ways for purposes of study.

When we begin to study, to investigate, and to inquire into things in the universe, then science appears. Side 2 of the model represents some of the ways people go about investigating their world.

[1] Adapted from an unpublished working paper produced at the American Association for the Advancement of Science Conference on Science Programs for the Elementary and Junior High School, Cornell University, Ithaca, New York. 1962.

As a result of investigating the universe, people develop knowledge about it. Some of this is scientific knowledge which we may classify as concepts, principles, laws, and facts, for example. This knowledge is represented by Side 3 of the figure.

With this model before us for purposes of discussion (no model can *be* a science curriculum) we can visualize and think about the minimum requirements of a science program in the elementary school. Most important, the model suggests that our program must thoughtfully embrace a total concept of what science is. It is a study of the universe by methods that yield valid and reproducible knowledge. Reference to our model suggests a number of more specific considerations.

a. The universe is all around but how it is organized for study and what topics, questions, or areas are selected at a particular time is a matter of choice. Since everything cannot be studied at once, choices do have to be made. Though our model does not tell us this, it seems reasonable to believe that a variety of different choices may help children equally well to gain an adequate understanding of basic laws, principles, and concepts. For example, curriculums in some schools may focus on developing the concept of *variety* through study of "plants" and "rock forms" while another school system may organize such learning around "astronomical bodies" and "animals." To help children develop an understanding of the concept of *interaction*, some schools may organize learnings around "forms of energy" and "plant growth" while another may use "atmosphere" and "geologic changes" for this purpose.

Concept Development

b. The scientific knowledge which children learn may appear in different forms—as generalizations, principles, facts, conclusions, laws. Year by year children develop a more comprehensive set of concepts which they use as intellectual tools in interpreting and understanding new phenomena or problems. Keeping the focus on concept development enables curriculum planners and the teacher, in particular, to make judicious selection of the aspects of the environment to study so that there is not a compulsion to try to "cover" all aspects of our universe each year, or indeed year after year.

c. Helping children grow from less mature to more mature "practitioners" of the methods of inquiry is an inherent part of science teaching.

It is at this point that the temptation is great to insist that children should continuously have experiences doing the kinds of things scientists do.[2] If we recognize that children are not studying science primarily to become scientists and that science teachers may use a variety of methods and materials not necessarily used by scientists, then it seems safe to say that in good science teaching children should make inquiries and investigations, should

[2] An opposite point of view is developed by Derek de S. Price in an article, "Two Cultures—and One Historian of Science." *Teachers College Record*, Columbia University, April 1963, pp. 527–535.

CLUE WORDS

Knowing

Observes	Describes	Accumulates	Looks
Identifies	Gathers	Counts	Sees

Manipulating

Measures	Selects	Computes	Weighs
Balances	instruments	Demonstrates	

Applying

Classifies	Distinguishes	Plans	Ponders
Assigns	Organizes	Compares	Groups
Defines	Estimates	Concludes	Decides
Associates	Equals	Experiments	
Arranges	Sorts	Controls	

Creating

Hypothesizes	Reflects	Incubates	Formulates
Induces	Proposes	Predicts	Interrelates
Deduces	Criticizes	Estimates	Generalizes
Speculates	Conceives	Explains	Forecasts
Analyzes	Invents	Appreciates	Extrapolates
Selects data	Guesses	Infers	Interpolates
Designs	Comprehends	Abstracts	
experiments	Doubts	Synthesizes	

Evaluating

Ponders	Pools data	Doubts	Transposes
Rejects	Recognizes errors	Verifies	Generalizes
Accepts	Equates	Decides	Controls
Believes	Distinguishes	Interprets	variables
Disbelieves	Questions	Criticizes	

Communicating

Tabulates	Explains	Debates	Questions
Graphs	Teaches	Argues	Instructs
Writes	Informs	Describes	Plots
Speaks	Charts	Demonstrates	Draws
Reports	Reads	Compares	

make descriptions and explanations, and should make predictions. It might follow that teaching which denies children a variety of opportunities to "be like scientists" is neither science nor science teaching.

In this way of thinking about science teaching, the teacher has day-to-day responsibility for involving children in behaviors that are characteristic of scientists at work. Side 2 of Figure 2 shows some of the behaviors or activities of scientists. Lest the kinds of behaviors we refer to seem few, remote, and unidentifiable, we report here a longer list [3] of clue words that suggest how rich is the array of possibilities.

d. The science curriculum must enable children at every level to build on their present experience and knowledge of science, always deepening and broadening their skills of inquiry and their understanding of concepts. The experience of each child must grow and expand as he explores new areas of the environment and deepens knowledge in old ones.

ATTITUDES AND OBJECTIVES

Let us return to our polygon again and view it from another side. (Figure 3.) Other implications for a good science program can be deduced from the model. Perhaps the reader will attempt to enumerate additional implications. Do you see a place for considering attitudes and predispositions about science? Do you see implications for statements of objectives and purposes for teaching science?

Does the model serve as a guide for evaluating specific science activities? Let us try it on the activities described earlier—the children bouncing the rubber ball and measuring shadows—and begin to make a judgment about their potential value. Answers to questions such as the following are pertinent:

1. Did the activity involve the children in describing or explaining some phenomenon?
2. Did the children collect original data from which to draw conclusions?
3. Did the children organize and communicate about the data in useful ways?
4. Did the children have opportunities to speculate and predict?
5. Did the experience relate clearly to development of a major science concept?
6. Were some questions raised that provided stimulation for further study?

If the answer to most of these questions is yes, it is probable the science experiences in question are making a positive contribution to the science education of the children engaged in it.

This article has attempted to suggest that an understanding by teachers of what science is, particularly in terms of knowing what scientists do, is essential in developing the science curriculum or course of study. A rich science program involves children in activities that encompass the entire spectrum of ways of investigating the environment used by scientists. The

---

[3] Based on an unpublished committee report of The American Association for the Advancement of Science Conference on Science for the Elementary and Junior High School, Cornell University, Ithaca, New York. 1962.

effective science curriculum is planned so that children's learning activities are focused on gaining understandings of selected concepts as intellectual tools for dealing with new problems. At every level of school, children's insights and understanding of science concepts and methods should be deepened and broadened if the science program is to make its fullest contribution to the education of children.

Section 8

RECENT CURRICULUM
DEVELOPMENTS IN
ELEMENTARY SCIENCE

INTRODUCTION

The rapid growth of the movement to stress the process approach in the teaching of science created a strong impetus for the development of new programs that would be based upon this process approach. Action came first at the secondary level, where the need was more urgent. A number of experimental curriculum study projects were created, supported for the most part by the National Science Foundation, for the purpose of producing new high school science courses.

The high school projects—and their courses as well—are known by such titles as PSSC (Physical Science Study Committee), CHEM Study (Chemical Education Material Study), CBA (Chemical Bond Approach), BSCS (Biological Sciences Curriculum Study), and ESCP (Earth Science Curriculum Project). They already have had a profound effect on the teaching of high school science.

Once the high school projects were under way, attention began to be turned to the junior high school and especially to the elementary school. Today there are a variety of curriculum study groups on elementary science in operation, sponsored by a number of agencies. All are concerned with the process approach, but they differ in the degree with which they include and structure the science content in the units and other teaching materials they are developing.

A highly significant feature of these new programs, both elementary and secondary, is the unprecedented large-scale involvement of scientists in the development of the programs. Scientists are initiating and directing almost all of the new curriculum study projects, and the impact of their philosophy and method of operation is quite noticeable. An examination of the new programs reveals strong similarities in the statements of their objectives, in the methods they use for teaching science, and in the kinds of materials they are producing.

411

Another significant feature of these new programs is the great financial support they have received. This has made it possible to employ the services of leading scientists and science teachers, maintain nationwide committees and writing teams, develop a wealth of teaching materials, test these materials in a large number of schools, and then rewrite and retest these materials as often as needed. Funds are also available for publicizing the work of the projects by the dissemination of bulletins, progress reports, and samples or illustrations of the developed teaching materials.

Since all the new programs in elementary science are in various stages of development, it is still too soon to evaluate them properly. However, enough materials have been produced to permit a preliminary evaluation of their effectiveness and to provide some prognosis as to the ultimate accomplishments of the programs.

First, their emphasis on process is a breakthrough in the teaching of elementary science. For the first time process will have been given enough publicity and stress to make the entire country very much aware that process must be an integral part of a science teaching. Second, the teaching materials seem to be enthusiastically received by both teachers and children. The materials are structured in great detail, so that the teacher can use them with little or no difficulty. Third, the programs will affect efforts to revise existing science curriculum guides in the schools, because specific provision will now have to be made for the teaching of process as well as content. Fourth, the programs will have an effect upon the kinds of in-service activities conducted for the teachers.

There are also a few criticisms of the programs, which most likely will be corrected by the time the programs are fully developed. First, many persons believe that the programs should include a structure of science content, with scope and sequence, because both content and process are equally important and mutually interdependent. Second, the teaching materials do not make enough provision for individual differences. Third, the materials are so highly structured that they hamper the distinctive style and technique of many competent teachers. Fourth, there is not enough real evaluation of the materials, with too much consideration being given to the testimonials of teachers and the displays of enthusiasm by the children.

THE PROCESS APPROACH OF THE
AAAS COMMISSION ON
SCIENCE EDUCATION *

Arthur H. Livermore

The Commission on Science Education of the American Association for the Advancement of Science is supported by the National Science Foundation. The preparation and evaluation of new science materials for the elementary school has been the purpose and major activity of the Commission since its establishment. The science materials written to date are for kindergarten through fifth grade. The subject matter is drawn from various fields in science. These science materials consist of a series of exercises designed to improve the child's skill in using the processes of science. It is the contention of the Commission that science is best taught as a procedure of inquiry and that curricular designs should be guided by this philosophy.

THE Commission on Science Education of the American Association for the Advancement of Science has accepted responsibility for stimulating improvement of science education at all academic levels. It does this in various ways. It maintains a continuous review of science education improvement programs and tries to identify the kinds of additional work that may be needed. It attempts to develop an interest in these programs within the scientific community and to recruit scientists to contribute to it. It provides for the interpretation of the new science programs to schools and assists in the selection and use of these science materials. It further encourages and stimulates course content improvement by actively engaging in the preparation and evaluation of new science materials.

The preparation and evaluation of science materials for the early grades has been a major activity of the Commission since it was established in 1962. These materials are a series of exercises published under the title, *Science—A Process Approach,* and are designed to improve the child's skills in using the processes of science. The development and tryout of this program is a major experiment in education. Three significant aspects of the experi-

---

* REPRINTED FROM *Journal of Research in Science Teaching*, Vol. 2, Issue 4, 1964, pp. 271–282, by permission of the author and the editor. Dr. Livermore is Deputy Director of Education for the American Association for the Advancement of Science.

ment are that in each exercise (1) the development of skills in using one process of science, *e.g.*, measurement, is emphasized; (2) the objectives are clearly identified; (3) provision for evaluation is built in.

Though the major thrust of the elementary science program is to develop the child's skills in using science processes, science content is not neglected. Indeed, topics rarely, if ever, included in elementary science programs are included here. For example, in the fourth and fifth grades there is a sequence of exercises from the behavioral sciences.

HISTORY OF THE PROJECT

In 1961 a feasibility study was carried out under the leadership of Dr. John R. Mayor, Director of Education, AAAS. Scientists and leaders in education were brought together to consider the need for improving science education in the elementary and junior high schools. Three conferences were held: at Berkeley, St. Louis, and Washington. The participants at these sessions agreed that there was an urgent need for new science materials for elementary and junior high schools and made suggestions concerning the nature of these materials.

To implement the recommendations that came from the feasibility study, AAAS established the Commission on Science Education in May 1962. The Commission members are scientists and leaders in education, and the chairman is Dr. Paul B. Sears, Professor of Biology, Emeritus, Conservation Program, Yale University.

The first activity of the Commission was to sponsor two eight-day conferences in the summer of 1962—at Cornell University in July and at the University of Wisconsin in August. Scientists, teachers, school administrators, and leaders in science education came together at these conferences to consider the impact of the new secondary school science curricula on science education in general, and to discuss research in science education and research in learning.

A number of possible approaches to teaching science were considered at these conferences, and drafts of possible science sequences were prepared. From the conferences came the recommendation that the Commission should sponsor the development of instructional materials beginning at the kindergarten level. It was urged that the materials stress the processes of science in the early grades—not science content alone. The work at the conferences was strongly influenced by a paper [1] on Curriculum Design presented by Dr. Robert Gagné of the American Institute for Research in the Behavioral Sciences.

Acting on the recommendations of the summer conferences, the Commission undertook the preparation of a *Statement of Purposes and Objectives of Science Education in School* [2] and of a working paper, *The Individual Basis of Scientific Inquiry*, to serve as guides for the forthcoming writing conference. The statement of purposes and objectives was prepared by Professor William Kessen of Yale University with the assistance of a panel of consultants. The attitude of the Commission toward science education is expressed well by the following excerpt from the statement:

> Science is best taught as a procedure of enquiry. Just as reading is a fundamental instrument for exploring whatever may be written, so science is a fundamental instrument for exploring whatever may be tested by observation and experiment. Science is more than a body of facts, a collection of principles, and a set of machines for measurement; it is a structured and directed way of asking and answering questions. It is no mean pedagogical feat to teach a child the facts of science and technology; it is a pedagogical triumph to teach him these facts in their relation to the procedures of scientific enquiry. And the intellectual gain is far greater than the child's ability to conduct a chemical experiment or to discover some of the characteristics of static electricity. The procedures of scientific enquiry, learned not as a canon of rules but as ways of finding answers can be applied without limit. The well-taught child will approach human behavior and social structure and the claims of authority with the same spirit of alert skepticism that he adopts toward scientific theories. It is here that the future citizen who will not become a scientist will learn that science is not memory or magic but rather a disciplined form of human curiosity.[3]

The working paper, *The Individual Basis of Scientific Inquiry*, was prepared by Dr. Robert Gagné with the assistance of several collaborators. In this paper the process approach was elaborated in detail, and the basic knowledges and skills which a child might be expected to have acquired at each grade level were identified. This paper served as a guide both to the panel which planned the writing session and later to the summer writers themselves.

SUMMER WRITING CONFERENCES

For two summers now, groups of scientists, science educators, and teachers have worked together preparing materials for *Science—A Process Approach*. The careful work of the planning panel eliminated much potential waste motion in the first writing session at Stanford in 1963. The writers quickly accepted the process approach and in eight weeks prepared in final or draft form 85 exercises for grades K through three. Many of the exercises were tried out in demonstration classes while they were still in preliminary form, and were revised if the tryout showed defects or deficiencies in them.

As we have already said, the primary aim of the program that the writers were preparing was to develop the child's skills in using science processes. Skills cannot be developed by reading about science. For this reason, the exercises were written as instructions for teachers, not as reading material for children. Each exercise described a variety of activities which the children would do, either individually or in small groups. Demonstrations by the teacher were avoided as much as possible.

The writers, with the aid of an industrial arts teacher, designed and produced a great variety of equipment—balances, spring scales, shadow boxes, wagons with wheels of various geometric shapes—and also identified many materials which the teachers would need to teach the exercises. At the end of the writing session, attention was turned not only to editing the written work, but also to the preparation of equipment in large enough amounts so that each of the children in the tryout classes would be able to enter into the activities. As it turned out, we were not completely successful in the latter effort, so a major concern of the second writing group during the summer of 1964 was to insure that individual student activity was built into the exercises.

The 1964 summer writing group had the advantage of feedback from the 1963–64 tryout program as they rewrote the exercises for grades K–3 and prepared new materials for grades 4 and 5. The group in 1964 was slightly larger than in 1963, but the composition was much the same. The first few weeks were devoted to revision of the K–3 sequence, and the remainder of the time to developing new exercises for grades 4 and 5. Again, as in 1963, the writers made good use of demonstration classes which were taught part of the time by two skilled elementary school teachers and part of the time by the writers themselves.

More attention was given in 1964 than in 1963 to the question of training teachers to use the new materials. There are two major facets to such training. First, the teacher needs to learn the philosophy of the process approach and how important it is that the children themselves are actively engaged in the activities if they are to develop skills in using science processes. Second, she needs help with science content. The teacher training group prepared a *Commentary for Teachers* to serve the first of these purposes and, in a preliminary way, to serve the second.

THE PROCESSES

In Science—A Process Approach, the processes are the warp on which the woof of content is woven. In the primary grades eight processes have been identified. They are:

Observing
Classifying
Measuring
Communicating
Inferring
Predicting
Recognizing Space/Time Relations
Recognizing Number Relations

At the level of grades 4 and 5, integrated processes are used. These are rooted in the simple processes and seem more appropriate to the aim of acquiring a scientific approach to knowledge at the intermediate grade levels. The integrated processes are:

Formulating Hypotheses
Making Operational Definitions
Controlling and Manipulating Variables
Experimenting
Interpreting Data
Formulating Models

The manner in which each of the simple processes is developed from the earliest grades is illustrated by the hierarchy of skills shown in Figure 1.

This figure summarizes the exercises in the *Observation* sequence and shows, by the arrows, how an exercise is dependent on skills that were developed in earlier exercises.

The capacity for accurate observation is present in the child, but the child's ability to use that capacity must be developed. These exercises provide experience in observing with all the senses with gradually increasing degrees of complexity.

For each of the simple processes, hierarchies of skills, similar to those illustrated for Observation, have been developed. In the *Classification* series the child begins with simple schemes for classifying common objects such as blocks, leaves, or shells. He progresses through exercises where he learns to classify objects as living or nonliving, or as solid, liquid, or gas and finally reaches the point where he develops classification codes and uses punch cards. Throughout this sequence, the purpose of classification is stressed, and the child is led to see that the sort of scheme one selects depends upon the use to which it is to be put.

Instruction in the process of *Measurement* is planned so that the child discovers that units of measurement are chosen arbitrarily and that there is more than one system of measurement units. He learns to select appropriate units for a particular measurement and to decide when to measure precisely and when to estimate. Measurement is not confined to determinations of length, area, and volume, but includes mass and weight, temperature, and rates of change. Measurements involving probability are made, and finally inaccuracies of estimation are considered in an exercise, "The Accuracy and Reliability of Perceptual Judgments."

Communication is a process important to everyone, including scientists. The purpose of the exercises on Communication is to teach children some of the basic requirements and techniques of scientific communication. This includes oral, written, and pictorial communication with emphasis on accuracy, completeness, and conciseness. The sequence includes exercises on graphing and mapping. The child learns to present data in graphs and to read

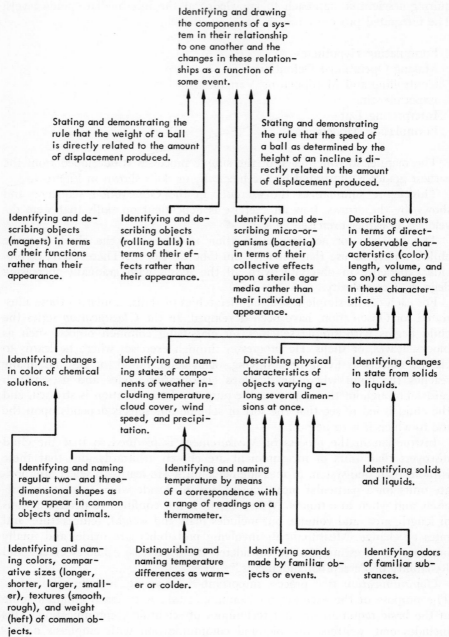

FIGURE 1.

Hierarchy of skills in the observation sequence.

the information stored in a graph. In the mapping exercises he learns how to communicate position and arrangement in space by making a map and also how to read such information from maps.

In an early exercise in the *Inference* sequence, the child is asked to make observations—shape, size, feel, sound, smell—on a wrapped package and then to infer what the contents of the package may be. In this exercise he begins to learn to distinguish clearly between an observation and an inference that is made about the observation. The other exercises in the sequence reinforce this skill. The child observes water collecting on the outside of a cold glass and infers that it comes from the air; he observes animal tracks and traces and infers the kind of animal that made them; he sees sections of three dimensional objects and infers the shape of the object. Wherever possible he makes observations which will strengthen his inference or require him to reject it and try another one.

A basic postulate of science is that nature is not capricious, but that future events may be predicted from past experiences. In several exercises in the *Prediction* sequence, the child collects data, records them on a graph, and then uses the graph to predict an event in the future. For example, he measures the length of time that a candle burns under jars of different volume. From the graphed data, he predicts when the candle will go out under a jar different in volume from any he has yet tried. Then he tests his prediction by actual trial.

Recognizing Space-Time Relations is a process that the scientist uses frequently. He visualizes the three dimensional structure of an organism from two dimensional microscopic views. He is concerned with the changes in the shape, size, and internal structure of a living thing as it grows and develops. He studies the shapes of crystals and investigates the speeds of chemical reactions. In the introductory exercises in this sequence, the child learns to name and identify two and three dimensional geometric shapes. It is expected that he will use these names to describe the shapes of objects that he observes in other exercises. Later he learns to measure time, to recognize three dimensional objects from the shadows they cast, and to look for symmetry in objects both living and nonliving. Observing change in position with time is also a part of this sequence which culminates with an exercise on "Relative Position and Motion."

Recognizing Number Relations is a process that is included in the AAAS materials because the quantitative aspects of scientific experiments require an understanding of numbers and a facility with arithmetical techniques. The mathematical exercises are introduced to insure that the children will have the requisite number skills for the exercises in other sequences. It is not intended that these numbers exercises replace or displace mathematics programs already in use in the schools. Rather, they are to be used in conjunction with the regular mathematics program whether it is traditional or modern. It is our hope that the integration of scientific process and mathematical ideas will enrich the child's understanding of the close relationship of mathematics and science.

In this series of exercises, the ideas of cardinal and ordinal numbers, as well as the concepts of sets, are introduced in kindergarten. In first grade, the child works with the number line, including both positive and negative integers, and applies the skills he learns in exercises which involve reading temperature scales and position location. He learns to add positive and negative integers at this grade level. Multiplication, division, and fractions are included in the second grade materials. In the numbers exercises in third grade, he learns to use decimals and to express large numbers as powers of ten. In grade four, from tables of data, he learns to derive sentences such as $S = F + 3$ and to graph such relations. Exercises on averaging and an introduction to the idea of probability are introduced in the fifth grade.

The process of formulating *Hypotheses* builds on previous experiences with the process of inferring. In the intermediate grades, the hypotheses that are formulated are more generalizable than the inferences that were made in earlier grades. For example, he observes the behaviors of hydra when they are subjected to various stimuli and then devises hypotheses to answer questions such as "How does the hydra realize that food is near it?" Then he makes tests to determine how good his hypothesis is.

Many terms used in science are defined on the basis of what observations and measurements must be made. One of these is density. In the first exercise in the series of exercises on *Operational Definitions*, the child not only determines the density of an object by measuring its mass and its volume, but also learns the operational definition of density. Density is the mass of the object divided by its volume. In later exercises in the sequence, he learns operational definitions of other terms from the physical and the biological sciences.

In most of the exercises in primary grades, the child makes observations and measurements but does not attempt to control conditions carefully. In the fourth and fifth grades, a series of exercises are devoted to showing the child that it is important to *Control the Variables* in an experiment. That if variables, such as light, temperature, and position, are not controlled, it may not be possible to obtain consistent results when experiments are replicated. Several exercises in the fourth and fifth grade materials emphasize the importance of controlling variables carefully in scientific investigations.

Children who have experienced the process approach in primary grades should, in the intermediate grades, enjoy planning and carrying out simple experiments. Formulating the problem in simple terms which can be approached experimentally is the first, and frequently the most difficult, step. In the series of exercises on *Experimenting* the child learns to consider a broad problem and to select variables which can be controlled for experimental study.

Interpreting Data accumulated in an experiment is an important process of science. The accuracy of observations is governed by the design of the experiment and by the skill and integrity of the investigator. The correctness of the interpretation of the data depends on the ability of the investigator to reason logically and also upon his opinions. Data interpretation may include mathematical correlations, predictions, inferences, and hypotheses. One purpose of the sequence of exercises which emphasize interpretation of data is to have the child learn to distinguish between the results obtained in an experiment by direct observation and the ideas that are obtained by interpreting data.

The most creative scientific process is *Formulating Models*—not mechanical models but the mental pictures devised to explain observed phenomena. A ball and stick model is only a crude representation of the mathematical mental model of a molecule. In this science program we do not expect the child to devise complex models. We do expect him to learn that models are devised to be used for explanation and for prediction. That if a model does not explain or predict satisfactorily, it is modified or discarded—it does not represent an immutable truth. The process of model formulation should give the child a real "feel" for the power and the satisfactions of the scientific approach to knowledge.

A SAMPLE EXERCISE

The following exercise, taken from Part Four, which is used in the third grade, illustrates the form in which the materials have been prepared for the teacher.

The exercise begins with a statement of *Objectives* in terms of what skills the child should have after the exercise has been completed. The *Rationale* tells the teacher why the exercise is included in the sequence and in many cases provides some helpful background information. The *Vocabulary* lists words that have not been used in previous exercises. The *Materials* list aids the teacher to identify the necessary supplies. In this exercise, the supplies are simple and can be obtained locally without difficulty. Where special supplies and equipment are needed, they are provided by AAAS or are prepared locally under the guidance of the center coordinator.

The section, *Originating the Problem,* is included as an aid to the teacher in arousing student interest in the subject. The *Activities* are to be done in sequence since each builds on skills developed in preceding ones.

The *Appraisal* activity at the end of the exercise is used by the teacher to determine whether the objectives of the exercise have been attained.

PREDICTION 3

Case of the Suffocating Candle

OBJECTIVES. At the end of the exercise the child should be able to:

1. State predictions given a series of observations which contain a pattern of event repetition.

2. Recognize that prediction is not based upon a single observation (or careless observations) and demonstrate this recognition by an unwillingness to state any prediction.

RATIONALE. The present exercise will illustrate the use of the term prediction in the context of a simple experiment. After sufficient data have been collected in an experiment, it is frequently reasonable to predict what the results of a future trial will be. In making such a prediction, we are reasoning from our past or present experience. We are saying that if the conditions of the experiment are the same when we try it again, then the results will be the same as they were in the past. The outcome of the event about which we are making a prediction will itself either confirm or deny that prediction.

In the activities of this exercise the class will first observe a series of demonstrations of the burning time of a candle covered by jars of several sizes. In the initial demonstrations they will observe that a candle will burn longer under a quart jar than under a half-pint jar. Prediction can occur when they are asked how long a candle will burn under a pint jar, a two-quart jar, or a gallon jar.

The idea of experimental error is introduced to the children in this exercise.

VOCABULARY. No new vocabulary.

MATERIALS.
Several small candles; food warmer type is preferred.
Wooden safety matches.
Five glass jars such as are commonly used in home canning, one each of the half-pint, pint, quart, two-quart, and gallon sizes.
Measuring cup.
One tall narrow pickle jar—about one pint.
Clock with a second hand.

ORIGINATING THE PROBLEM. This lesson may begin with a discussion of fire and burning. Ask: What do you need to keep a fire going? (Wood, paper, or some other fuel will probably be suggested.) Do you need only fuel to get a fire started or to keep it burning? (Some class member may have experience that suggests the need for an adequate draft.) Do some fires burn faster than others? What makes a fire burn faster? Get the class to recognize that the rate of burning is in common experience related to wind or ventilation. Continue by asking how fires are put out. Remind them of their experience with jack-o-lanterns. The candle in a jack-o-lantern will often burn more or less brightly depending on the wind and the size of the holes.

INSTRUCTIONAL PROCEDURE. The operations of this exercise may be done by the teacher as demonstrations. Place the four glass jars and the candle on a table in the front of the room. Be sure that no flammable material is nearby. Take this opportunity to caution children in the use of fire. Discuss how to light a match safely and how to use a match to light a candle. This exercise may, if necessary, be done as a demonstration, but it would be preferable to have it done by groups of four or five children.

Activity 1

Fasten the candle to the desk with wax. Light the candle. Tell the class you are going to put a pint jar over the burning candle. Ask: What do you expect to happen? Someone will probably suggest that the candle will go out. Ask him *why* he expects this. Has he seen the *experiment* before? Or, has he reasoned from his experience with fire in other situations? Point out that this statement of expectation is a prediction. It is a statement based on observations that he has made or has heard about in the past.

Invert the quart jar over the candle and demonstrate the extinction of the flame to the class. Draw the attention of the class to the burning time by asking them to estimate how long the flame lasted under the jar. Get them to express this time estimate in seconds. Suggest that they measure the burning time with a clock.

Thoroughly ventilate the jar by stuffing a rag into it several times. Unless the air in the jars is renewed between repetitions of a demonstration, the burning time measurements will show too much variation. Ask the class to measure the burning time by watching the wall clock as you repeat the demonstration. Record the time on the chalkboard alongside the jar volume. Ask the class what they would expect the burning time to be if the experiment were repeated. Repeat the experiment. The burning time will probably be three or four seconds different from the first value. Record this. Repeat again and ask the class to determine the mean burning time for the candle under the quart jar.

Now use the half-pint jar. Relight the candle. Ask: Will the candle burn under this smaller jar for a longer or for a shorter time than under the quart jar? The class may be in some disagreement about this. Ask those children venturing predictions to give their reasons for making them. It is likely, but not necessary at this time, that some of the class will say that the burning time will be longer in the quart jar because there is more air in the quart jar than in the half-pint. Again, ask the class to measure the length of the burning time by the clock after you cover the candle. Record this time on the chalkboard with the previous observation. Again, as in the case of the quart jar, make two more determinations and calculate the mean of the results. Typical results might be as follows (Table 1):

TABLE 1

JAR SIZE	MEAN BURNING TIME, SEC.
Half-pint	9
Quart	32

Discuss with the class the relationship of the half-pint to the quart—one quart is four half-pints. Ask them how long they would expect the candle would burn under a one pint jar. Would it burn between 9 and 32 seconds? Would it be closer to 9 than to 32 seconds? Have them explain their predictions. Do they use the relationships of the volumes in making their predictions?

Perform the test with the pint jar, recording the burning time. Discuss the list of burning times and jar sizes as they stand now. The following data were obtained with wide-mouth canning jars and a food-warmer candle (Table 2). Your own data may be quite different due to variation in the size of the flame and other factors.

In reviewing these data, it will be helpful to prepare a graph on the chalkboard. This will bring out more clearly the increase in burning time associated with each doubling of jar size.

After having discussed the relative burning times of the quart and smaller jars, ask the class to make a prediction of the burning time within the gallon jar. They should at this point be able to take into account the trend shown by their measurements on the three smaller sizes and predict times for the gallon jar. Ask for predictions expressed in seconds. List on the chalkboard as many of these as are submitted. Ask the children to explain how they arrived at their predictions. Perform the experiment; record the observed times, and compare these with the predictions. Were any of the students' estimates close? Record the data on the chalkboard and also on the graph.

The graph now might look like this (Fig. 2):

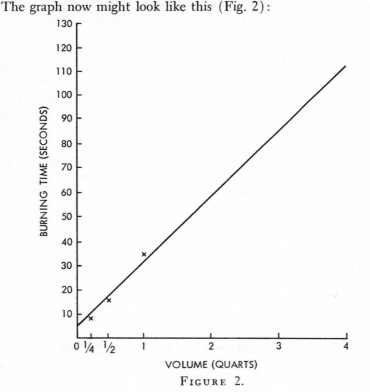

FIGURE 2.

Ask the children if they will now predict how long the candle will burn when it is placed under a two-quart jar. They may consider both the table of data on the chalkboard and the graph. Encourage them to use the graph

TABLE 2

JAR SIZE	MEAN BURNING TIME, SEC.
Half-pint	9
Pint	16
Quart	32

to make their predictions. They should select the burning time for a two-quart jar from the graph. They should predict this burning time with confidence (assuming that the candle, container shapes, and other conditions are not changed). Carry out the experiment using the two-quart jar. If it seems desirable, repeat the determination twice and determine the mean burning time. Data obtained with a food-warmer candle under wide-mouth glass jars is given below (Table 3).

TABLE 3

| JAR SIZE OZ. | BURNING TIME, SEC. | | | |
	TRIAL 1	TRIAL 2	TRIAL 3	MEAN
9	8	9	10	9
16	16	15	16	16
32	28	32	35	32
48	41	49	47	46
128	108	119	116	114

The children may determine the volumes of the jars they have been using by filling them with water and measuring the water carefully with a measuring cup.

This is a good time to introduce to the students the idea of *experimental error*. They have seen that when they repeat an experiment with the same jar and the same candle, the burning time may differ by a few seconds from the first observation. This difference may occur no matter how carefully the experimenter tries to keep the conditions exactly the same. Scientists try, by carefully controlling the conditions of an experiment, to keep experimental error to a minimum. However, they always expect to have some experimental error in their results. In the burning candle experiments, the experimental error may be ten seconds or so out of every hundred seconds. Therefore, in the case of the prediction of burning time under the two-quart jar by reading the predicted value from the graph, the experimental results may well be as much as five seconds different from the value predicted.

APPRAISAL. Show the children a tall, narrow pickle jar and ask them to predict the burning time of a candle under this jar. They should be encouraged to measure the volume of the jar and use the data obtained previously (including the graph) in making their predictions. Have them carry out the experiment to check their predictions.

TRYOUT AND EVALUATION

Science—A Process Approach is being tested in classrooms in various parts of the country by teachers having no special science skills and with children of widely varied cultural backgrounds. Over 100 teachers in grades kindergarten through three used the materials during the first tryout year: 1963–64. The teachers were in twelve centers,* each of which had a science consultant. In most cases, the consultant was a member of the summer writing team. Periodically, in most cases every two weeks, the teachers met with the consultant to discuss successes and failures, to get advice on exercises still to be taught, and to suggest changes in the materials.

After teaching each exercise the teacher completed a feedback form and returned it to AAAS. The feedback form gave the teacher an opportunity to express her opinions about the exercise, to tell whether or not the children engaged actively and enthusiastically in the activities, and to suggest modifications which would improve the exercise for classroom use. This feedback information was used by the writers who revised the exercise in the summer of 1964.

An important part of the evaluation in 1963–64 was a set of tasks, called a "Checklist of Competencies," which the teacher asked individual children to do after each exercise had been taught. The checklist was administered individually to three children who were selected at random from the class. The sample of three was changed each month so that by the end of the year most of the children in the class had been tested on one or more exercises.

The tasks in the checklist were designed to determine whether the child had achieved the skills purportedly developed in the exercises, and whether he could apply these skills in a situation different from that in any of the activities of the exercise. The following example is taken from the checklist for the exercise, Prediction 3, "The Case of the Suffocating Candle." The teacher tells the child to think about ice cubes melting in a quart jar filled with tap water. She then asks the following questions.

1. If you have observed that two ice cubes take five minutes to melt, how long would you guess it would take four ice cubes to melt? (The acceptable response is ten minutes.)

* Arizona, Tucson; California, Kern County; Florida, Tallahassee; Illinois, Chicago-Glencoe; Illinois, Monmouth (Rural Western); Maryland, Baltimore; Massachusetts, Lincoln; New York, Pelham-Manhasset; Oregon, Portland-Eugene; Pennsylvania, Philadelphia; Texas, Austin; Washington, Seattle.

TABLE 4

A Portion of the Directions to Testers from the Process Instrument for the Observation Hierarchy

PROCEDURE	INSTRUCTIONS TO THE CHILD	ADDITIONAL PROCEDURES	ACCEPTABLE RESPONSES
51. The tester removes the three objects which are color coded white, black, and red from container 0–17 and places them on the table in front of the child.	Two of these things are alike in some way. Point to the bottle which contains something different from the other two.	Do not allow the child to lift or smell the contents of the bottles.	The child should point to container coded black.
52. The tester points to the bottle selected by the child.	Why did you choose this one?		The child should indicate verbally that this is a liquid.
53. The tester points to the bottle containing the liquid.	If the thing in this bottle is called a liquid, what are the things in the other two bottles called?		The child should indicate verbally that these are solids.
54. The tester places the two vials from container 0–18 on the table in front of the child. He points to the dark blue liquid.	What color is this?		Blue or dark blue.
55. The tester points to the vial with the light blue liquid.	What color is this?		Light blue or blue. Note: The responses to question 54 and 55 may not both be blue.
56. The tester put the dark blue liquid into the bottle containing the light blue liquid and shakes the mixture.	What changes did you see?	Allow the mixture to set in front of the child for about one minute. The tester should be careful to replace the tops on the appropriate container.	Change in color from blue to black. Particles or sediment formed, or it's not clear.

2. What is the basis for your guess? (An acceptable response should indicate that since the number of ice cubes was doubled the child doubled the time necessary.)

3. If you observe in an experiment that four ice cubes take ten minutes to melt and you then guess how long it would take eight ice cubes to melt, what would you call your guess? (A prediction.)

4. From the information you have, how long would you predict it would take eight ice cubes to melt under the same conditions? (20 minutes.)

5. Now tell the child: The experiment with eight ice cubes was carried out but the melting time was found to be 40 minutes (instead of 20 minutes which is the prediction most likely to be made by a child). On the basis of this additional information, would you predict that the melting time for 16 ice cubes would be greater or less than twice 40 minutes? (More than 80 minutes.)

If the child gives a correct response he receives a "yes" check; if incorrect, a "no" check. The checklist for each of the exercises uses this binary scoring system. The child has the skill or he does not.

The tryout teachers returned the results of the Checklist of Competencies to AAAS for tabulation and analysis. The results of the 1963–64 tryout were encouraging. On the average the checklists showed that 80% of the children tested had attained 80% of the expected skills.

The tryout in 1964–65 is being carried on in fourteen centers * by more than two hundred teachers. As in 1963–64 the teachers are giving their subjective evaluation of the exercises on feedback forms and are using Checklists of Competencies as an objective measure of the skills children have achieved in using the science processes.

A pilot study is being made this year of a new process instrument. If there is indeed a hierarchy of skills for each process with each skill above the beginning level being based on earlier skills (Fig. 1), then it should be possible to devise a test which will determine how far up in the hierarchy a child has developed. Instruments have been developed to test each of the simple process hierarchies. These consist of tasks of increasing difficulty. Each level in the hierarchy is represented by three tasks in the process measure: a prototype task which appraises the behavior in the learning set, and two horizontal transfer tasks: one in which the context is changed, and the other in which the stimulus is altered from the prototype task. An example of the kinds of tasks, relating to the identification of solids and liquids in the Observation hierarchy (Fig. 1) is shown in Table 4. This Table includes tasks 51 through 56 of the process instrument for Observation.

The process tests were administered to a pilot group of children at the beginning of the 1964 school year. They will be given again at the end of the school year both to children who have had the AAAS science program and to those who have not. We expect to revise the test instrument next summer and to use the revised form in an expanded testing program in 1965–66.

---

* Arizona, Tucson; California, Kern County; California, Palo Alto-Berkeley; Florida, Tallahassee; Illinois, Chicago-Glencoe; Illinois, Monmouth (Rural Western); Maryland, Baltimore; New York, Ithaca; New York, Pelham-Manhasset; Oregon, Portland-Eugene; Pennsylvania, Philadelphia; Texas, Austin; Washington, Seattle; Wisconsin, Oshkosh.

OTHER ACTIVITIES OF THE COMMISSION ON SCIENCE ACTIVITIES

It was noted at the beginning of this article that the Commission's interests are not limited to science teaching in the early grades, but that it is concerned with science education at all academic levels.

To provide information about various curriculum improvement programs, the Commission has established a clearinghouse of information under Professor David Lockard at the Science Teaching Center of the University of Maryland. The clearinghouse has compiled reports[4] from over thirty curriculum projects including those supported by the National Science Foundation and those financed from other sources.

A review of research in science education was prepared by Professor Herbert A. Smith at the request of the Commission. This paper, which brings together information about the research which has most strongly influenced current practice in science education, was published in the *Journal of Research in Science Teaching*.[5]

Reports of developments in science education are published periodically in *Science Education News*.* Topics for the last four issues of this publication were: Science in the Kindergarten and Early Grades, Undergraduate Education in the Sciences, Course Content Development in the Social Sciences, and Science Teaching Centers.

Another concern of the Commission is teacher education. In December 1963, representatives of the college commissions on science education were brought together to consider the needs for training and recruiting teachers at all levels. From this meeting there came a number of suggestions for better training and use of teachers. The Commission is continuing to study this problem.

Related to the problem of teacher training is the problem of informing school supervisors about developments in science and science education. As a part of its activity in this area, the Commission, jointly with the American Association of School Administrators, held a three-day meeting in October 1964 where some forty school superintendents heard lectures by five leading scientists on recent developments in their fields.

The work of the Commission is carried on by a staff of four at AAAS:

These are: Dr. John R. Mayor, Director of Education; Dr. Arthur H. Livermore, Deputy Director of Education; Dr. Edwin B. Kurtz, Associate (on leave from the Department of Botany, University of Arizona); Dr. Henry H. Walbesser, Associate in Charge of Evaluation.

REFERENCES

1. Gagné, Robert M., "A Psychologist's Counsel on Curriculum Design," *J. Res. Sci. Teaching*, **1**, 27–32 (1963).

* Published quarterly by the American Association for the Advancement of Science, Washington, D. C.

2. Sears, Paul B., and William Kessen, "Statement of Purposes and Objectives of Science Education in School," *J. Res. Sci. Teaching*, **2**, 3–6 (1964).
3. Ref. 2, p. 4.
4. American Association for the Advancement of Science and the Science Teaching Center, University of Maryland, *Second Report of the Information Clearinghouse of New Science Curricula*, March 1, 1964.
5. Smith, Herbert A., "Educational Research Related to Science Instruction for the Elementary and Junior High School: A Review and Commentary," *J. Res. Sci. Teaching*, **1**, 199–225 (1963).

THE ELEMENTARY SCIENCE STUDY BRANCH OF EDUCATIONAL SERVICES INCORPORATED *

Eleanor Duckworth

This article by Dr. Duckworth and the following article by Dr. Nichols describe the Elementary Science Study (ESS) of Educational Services Incorporated, supported by the National Science Foundation. The primary objective of this project is to develop more meaningful science materials for the elementary school. These materials are designed so that they inherently allow for a flow of ideas originating from the curiosity of children. Little emphasis is given to the development of a sequential or continuing program with specific structure and assigned grade levels. The main purpose is to supply a variety of carefully thought out and tested materials which a school system may use in developing an elementary science curriculum.

THE Elementary Science Study is a branch of Educational Services, Incorporated. ESI is also the parent body of the PSSC high school physics. The elementary school science project is an interdisciplinary one, or in many cases, predisciplinary. It started about two years ago and had its initial conference in the summer of 1962 where there were close to 100 participants, most of them university scientists, with elementary school teachers, a number

* REPRINTED FROM *Journal of Research in Science Teaching*, Vol. 2, Issue 3, 1964. pp. 241–243, by permission of the author and the editor. Dr. Duckworth is associated with Educational Services Incorporated, Watertown, Massachusetts.

of psychologists, and others. Since then, a permanent staff of about 30 scientists and teachers have continued work in our Watertown, Massachusetts, office, and increasing numbers of teachers throughout the country are contributing additions and modifications on the basis of their trial teaching.

A good deal of our effort is directed toward the creation of materials which are appropriate for children's science learning. There are a number of requisites for these materials. They must be inexpensive, so that each child in a class, or at least each pair of children, can work individually. They must be simple enough so their functioning is clear, and children can raise their own questions about the materials and use them to find their own answers. They must be rich enough in possibilities so that initial questions can lead to problems of greater demand and significance.

There are always two aspects to the development of these materials. One part takes place in our laboratories. The other part takes place with children and teachers in the classroom. Anything which we produce in the way of materials or of outlines and suggestions for their use is based on trial and exploration in many different classroom situations where the children themselves have been the most important factor in the assessment.

I shall try to direct my remarks about our work to make them relevant to the topic of this conference. First of all, I will mention the extent to which there has been direct influence of cognitive research in our work, and that extent has been quite limited. There are two members whose primary academic preparation is in the field of psychology. One, Bill Hull, has been especially interested in concept formation. He has developed a set of small wooden blocks with an endless variety of games, exercises, and puzzles that range from a four-year-old level to challenges for adults. Children spend long periods of time by themselves, in small groups or with a teacher, happily passing back and forth from highly structured classification and relationship games to free and whimsical construction. Indications are that these children develop a high degree of ability in thinking about classes and relationships in general as a result of their activities with these blocks.

I am the other person, and my background is essentially psychology. I have done a few things which stem directly from this background. One was to search for activities for small children in which some constancy remained in spite of transformations since this seems to be an essential and a central notion. This led to the development of floating color tubes. They consist of two or three layers of colored immiscible liquids, and of small bits of plastic, rubber, seeds, etc., floating at the interfaces. In sealed tubes, they prove to be appreciated by small children on a number of levels: as simply something to shake, or providing beautiful bubbles and droplets to watch, or bringing the realization that they always come back to the same way they were before shaking, or that the same layer is on top, the same on the bottom, no matter which way the tube may be turned.

Happily enough, although this was not the original idea, it has turned out that older children enjoy creating such tubes for themselves, and this involves thinking about immiscibility, density, and staining, as well as demanding a highly systematic approach in order to keep all the information straight and get as many layers as possible.

These are two instances in which some sort of background in cognitive research has been relevant to development of some specific items. Apart from that, the psychologists play a general role in teaching and in evaluating the way children are learning from the materials.

Most of the other members of the staff have a different starting point rather than the psychological significance of the activities involved. Some have a particular interest in teaching some subject matter area. For instance, Ben Nichols, professor of electrical engineering at Cornell University, has been working on teaching electricity. In other instances some subject matter may seem exceedingly simple and available for children to examine; for instance, watching mold grow on foods and trying to slow down or accelerate this growth. In other cases the type of scientific investigation involved has general significance, for instance, studying the behavior of mealworms because it is a good way to become directly involved in the study of animal behavior.

In most of these, appeal is not made specifically to psychology, either for the grade level at which to try the material or for the soundest way of presenting it. But somehow the psychological basis does often turn out to be sound. This is no doubt partly because the findings in the world of psychology, like those of Piaget, have had some influence on people's ideas about what makes for good learning. At any rate, the general guidelines of most of the work done at the Elementary Science Study does prove to have characteristics of good teaching.

There are two main characteristics which we keep in mind. One is that the children use materials themselves, individually or in small groups, often raising the questions themselves, answering them in their own way, using the materials in ways the teacher had not anticipated, and coming to their own conclusions. In Piaget's terms, they are acting on things, transforming things, and learning about them by seeing the effects of these actions and transformations. The other is that we try to create situations where the children are called upon to talk to each other. One of Piaget's fundamental notions is that of egocentrism which is characteristic of small children. We might say this means not realizing that there might be some point of view different from their own. Because of this, children and even adults are often led to misread data, to assimilate it to what they think already, and then be happy with the way they read it. Several different children may see the same thing in several quite different ways. Called upon to discuss their differences and seek agreement on what really happens, they lose some of their complacency with their own first ideas.

In the time that is left, I would like to mention some of the other aspects of work at the Elementary Science Study. We are making some films for use in classrooms. Most of them are silent four-minute film loops of phenomena where children can see things in the film that they could not otherwise see. They can replay these few minutes as often as they wish, to look more closely, think about them again, and so on. Some of us are making a survey of written material for children in a specific subject matter area and are making a critical bibliography. Some are writing supplemental material for children and for teachers.

ELEMENTARY SCIENCE STUDY
—TWO YEARS LATER *

Benjamin Nichols

BY THE TIME that this paper reaches print, the Elementary Science Study (ESS) will be distributing the first five prepared units of study materials for wide testing around the country. Fifty official trial teachers will be using each unit with their classes. Some of these trial teachers have previously used ESS experimental materials or attended our summer training sessions, and others will be relying entirely upon the teacher's guides that are part of each unit.

While the testing is going on in those hundreds of classrooms, interested school systems or individuals will be able to preview the five units for themselves by ordering specially prepared Inspection Cartons. The cartons include all the written materials for the five units, and samples of supplies and equipment that have been developed for teaching each unit.

In addition, for schools that are ready to try our materials, we have prepared five hundred sets of supplies sufficient for teaching each unit to one class. Each packaged unit includes equipment for every pupil, or in some cases each pair of pupils in the class, plus teacher's guides and other printed materials. Supplementary film loops will also be available.

The ESS Inspection Carton and classroom packages represent the first general public showing of one important aspect of the work that we have been conducting for the past two years. The very titles of the units give a sense of the nature of this kind of science, for they show our emphasis upon the material physical surroundings of home and school. The list includes

* REPRINTED FROM *Journal of Research in Science Teaching*, Vol. 2, Issue 4, 1964, pp. 288–292, by permission of the author and the editor. Dr. Nichols is Professor of Electrical Engineering at Cornell University and was Director of the Elementary Science Study in 1964–1965.

Growing Seeds; Small Things; Behavior of Mealworms; Gases and "Airs"; and *Kitchen Physics: A Look at Some Properties of Liquids.*

All deal with familiar and readily available objects. From our experience in developing these units with classes at varying grade levels and in many kinds of schools, we suggest some ways to approach the investigation and a possible strategy for exploiting the questions that the children will probably raise. These suggestions are meant to be used as a helpful guide and not to provide a rigid structure.

Let me describe the production of one of the units, *Kitchen Physics*, so you can see how it differs from textbook or demonstration-taught science. As an example of the Elementary Science Study approach, a glance at the way this unit grew and changed in the process of laboratory experimentation, and then grew and changed again during classroom experimentation, illustrates the principles we are trying to incorporate into all our work.

The Kitchen Physics unit started in the fall of 1962. Dr. Malcolm Skolnick, presently a member of the MIT Department of Physics, suggested that the kitchen provides a rich laboratory for experimentation by boys and girls. He looked for experiments that could be carried out simply in classrooms or homes and that would yield macroscopic results but would suggest the need for a microscopic explanation. These involved the properties of liquids and solutions, heating and cooling, diffusion, and evaporation. The first series of experiments was centered around the properties of froths and foams as well as soap bubbles in evacuated tubes. A series of investigations using materials such as soapy water, egg white, egg yolk, milk and cream, and simple tools—the balance, the eyedropper, the capillary tube and the dishpan —would provide a basis for insight into the relations of density to volume, pressure, surface tension, and capillarity. He hoped also that children would find interest in exploring other problems such as the number of sides, vertices, and edges of soap bubbles.

With these rough ideas and materials, he began to work with a group of nine boys and nine girls in the eight and ninth grades of a junior high school in Watertown, Massachusetts. His classes were closely observed by several other staff members. After their observation, Dr. Skolnick and the ESS staff teachers working with him eliminated many of the original projects and developed new ones. Directed by the responses of the students, the work developed much more fruitfully in the areas of investigation of the cohesion, adhesion, and viscosity of liquids instead of considerations of the properties of froths, foams, and soap bubbles. The children invented their own descriptive words, such as "stickiness," "heaviness," "grabbiness," and "thickness," to describe the properties they observed. One child originated what she called a "theory of grabbitation."

The students themselves uncovered other areas for exploration. For example, blotters had been used to measure capillarity, but it was observed that different results were obtained when blotters of varying widths but cut from the same large sheet were used. These results led very naturally to the study of evaporation. Paper towels that had been used to wipe up spilled water were found to absorb five times their own weight and were thus transformed by the children into interesting experimental objects. Why were they able to soak up so much water? How fast did they dry? Did they dry more slowly when folded?

All the observers of the early trials decided that the material was suitable for younger children, and the ESS staff teachers began to trial-teach in sixth and seventh grade classes in Watertown and Cambridge. In each case, the teachers observed each other's experimental classes, and Dr. Skolnick also observed. These classes led to more new ideas, many of which were, again, suggested by the children, and they brought further refinements in the equipment.

At this point, design and production of equipment for the unit required discussions with various commercial suppliers. Arthur Vash and Wesley Perry of Macalaster Scientific Corp. made helpful suggestions and assisted in the effort to make the equipment more durable, reliable, and inexpensive. Meanwhile, preliminary teacher's guides were written and materials kits developed. During the summer of 1963, the unit was taught to fifth graders at the ESS summer school at the Peabody School in Cambridge. The teacher's guide was rewritten by Dr. Skolnick and his chief collaborators, Mrs. Margaret Pitt, a former teacher with a degree in physics, and Miguel Savage, an experienced and talented elementary school teacher.

A number of teachers from various parts of the country observed the classes at the Peabody School and worked on future additions to the unit. They took the materials back to their own schools at the end of the summer for further trial teaching during the 1963–64 academic year. Robert Gardner, a junior and senior high school science teacher, took charge of the final editing of the teacher's guide and arrangements for commercial production and packaging of the laboratory equipment during the summer and fall of 1964. A film loop to accompany the study was adapted from a film that had originally been produced to teach fluid mechanics at the college level, and a series of specially prepared film loops were begun. During the summer, teachers attending three summer science institutes (in Cambridge, Massachusetts; Webster Groves, Missouri; and Dixie School District, California) had an opportunity to work with the material. Many of those teachers will be among the official trial teachers of the Kitchen Physics unit.

Kitchen Physics is suitable for grades five through eight, and could occupy from twenty to forty class lessons. Each pair of students receives a variety of supplies, including plastic bottles, five bottle caps with different-sized openings, medicine cups, eye droppers, a balance, four different-sized plastic plates with wire spring hooks, a plastic capillary block with five different-sized holes, and some polyethylene tubing. The children may begin by comparing the time required to empty bottles filled with various liquids—tap water, soapy water, cooking oil, alcohol—through various openings. While obtaining data for the timing experiment, the students notice that the column of liquid emptying from the bottle is not uniform and that it narrows and begins to "bead." The length of the column before beading depends upon the liquid and the size of the aperture. The length of the column before beading can be measured by tearing an equivalent strip of paper; this will later serve as a basis for graphing. The same equipment has now been used for two experiments. Some order is beginning to arise out of the seemingly chaotic records. At this stage, a film loop showing the beading of a column of water, magnified and in slow motion, may be shown.

When the children attempt to explain the results of their research, they begin to isolate some of the properties of liquids such as "heaviness" (density), "thickness" (viscosity), "grabbiness" (surface tension), and "stickiness" (cohesion-adhesion). They begin to devise ways of testing their own conjectures. They assemble a simple equal-arm balance that can measure the "heaviness" of various liquids. By modifying their balances slightly, they can measure the "grabbiness." How many washers do you have to add to one arm of the balance beam to make the opposite arm lift a plastic plate off the surface of the various liquids? They begin to explore the skinlike effect that may be observed on the surface of liquids. They use the balance to check how much water a paper towel can absorb and to measure its variation with time, indicating the effect of evaporation. They use blotter strips to examine the rise of various liquids in blotters of various widths and on the capillary block. These phenomena are so interrelated that children performing experiments to seek the answers to one series of questions almost inevitably notice a new collection of effects that stimulate a new set of experiments. It is when they try to relate the results of several experiments that they gain insight into scientific principles.

Each ESS unit has its own special history and character. There are, however, certain general features that apply to all. Each has been the product of a close collaboration among scientists and elementary classroom teachers. Each is based on investigations that can be pursued by the children themselves. Each has involved children in its early development and has been tested in a large number of classrooms.

Bringing science into the elementary school requires that much more of the physical world be brought in for the child to observe, manipulate, and test. We have devoted much time to finding equipment and living things that can lead to rich and manageable experimentation by children but that are as cheap and familiar as possible. Drinking straws, dixie cups, paper clips, blotters—these are basic equipment for elementary science. But so are balances, syringe pumps, microscopes, battery holders, petri dishes, and mealworms. In many cases we have had to design the equipment ourselves. Various commercial manufacturers have worked with us and in some cases have used our prototypes to design their own inexpensive items for school use. For example, American Science and Engineering Company has constructed a sturdy and ingenious little microscope that will cost about a dollar.

Just as the equipment we have designed is not limited in its use, so have the study units and written guides been planned to provide as much help to the teacher as possible while encouraging maximum freedom in their use. All of them could be used at more than one grade level, and all provide enough activities for many more class periods than most teachers would be able to allot. Not all classes will do all the suggested experiments, and some will wish to follow original ideas that arise in their investigations. At least, that is what we hope. Real science is based upon research, not upon magic shows or demonstrations. Obviously, there will be occasions when the teacher may want to introduce the day's materials with a demonstration. But there must be many opportunities to examine the experiment from many points of view. One demonstration yields only data; it cannot be used to prove anything. In every real experiment many factors are interrelated. But to explore takes time and involvement.

Concepts such as the need for research, the need to try new things, and the need to avoid false prejudices are important by-products of elementary science. In trying various methods to make a mealworm back up or in using various sizes and kinds of wire in an electrical circuit with a battery and bulb, students become aware of the importance of careful observation and records. "Does it work?" leads to "When does it work?" and later to "How does it work?" At that stage some of the pupils will be motivated to do outside reading. To guide in separating the excellent science books from inaccurate and misleading ones, several ESS workers, whose special interests are children's literature and the history of science, are preparing critical bibliographies to accompany some of the units now being prepared for early distribution. The study areas in the second group will probably include *Butterflies, Pendulums, Frog Eggs and Tadpoles, Microgardening, Bones, Melting Ice Cubes,* and *Batteries and Bulbs.* At least fifteen or twenty other units are in varying states of readiness and are being modified on the basis of our experience with the earlier units.

The wide acceptance of the Physical Science Study Committee physics program and later curriculum reforms has broken down the barriers between the university scientists and their colleagues in the secondary schools. The collaboration has been of crucial importance in upgrading the quality of science teaching at the high-school level and has been hailed by teachers and administrators as well as by their students.

The same picture now seems to be coming into focus for the elementary grades, and the prospect that honest science study will push out memorized definitions seems very bright. But what about the elementary teacher? How are we going to retrain over a million teachers? Most of them have never seriously studied science, so how can they teach it?

Without attempting to minimize the problem, we have tried to work around it. In producing our units we have kept in mind the fact that most of the teachers who would be using the study guides knew a great deal about many other subjects but very little about the particular one at hand. Judging by our trial classes, the most capable elementary teachers quickly become the most capable elementary science teachers, regardless of their previous training. They encourage the enthusiasm and eagerness of their pupils and become eager and enthusiastic themselves. More important than knowledge of the facts of science is the experience of having been personally involved in a search for knowledge. Unfortunately, many teachers have never had this experience in the course of their own education. Changes must take place at all levels, including the colleges, if future generations are not to be similarly handicapped.

After several years of development, ESS is offering some samples of its work to a wider public. It is clear that this is only a small beginning of a much larger task that must engage the attention of more scientists, classroom teachers, psychologists, school administrators, and college faculties before it leads to significant educational results. To transform the elementary classroom into a place where individual exploration in science can take place requires experimentation in the whole classroom atmosphere and a fresh look at the relationship between teacher and pupils.

THE SCIENCE CURRICULUM
IMPROVEMENT STUDY *

Robert Karplus

The Science Curriculum Improvement Study (SCIS) is supported by a grant from the National Science Foundation. The work of the SCIS is still at an early stage, with most materials already developed intended for use in the primary grades. The study is concerned with exploring a concept of science education based on communicating scientific literacy. The large-scale organization of the curriculum is determined by the structure of science, by the maturity of the pupils, and by the pupils' preconceptions. The organization of individual lessons is determined by the discovery method of concept development and by the needs of the learners.

INTRODUCTION

Many authors have noted the winds of curriculum change which are sweeping through educational institutions at all levels.[1,2] Many of their read-

---

* REPRINTED FROM *Journal of Research in Science Teaching*, Vol. 2, Issue 4, 1964, pp. 293–303, by permission of the author and the editor. Dr. Karplus is Professor of Physics and also Director of the Science Curriculum Improvement Study at the University of California, Berkeley.

ers ask what is the reason behind these changes—what is the motivation, what is the justification? Since the Science Curriculum Improvement Study is a part of this movement of our times, a review of its work and rationale will shed some light on the answers to the more general questions raised by any innovation.

As a matter of fact, it is usually possible to present a clear identification of the social pressures, the sources of inspiration, and the educational implications involved in a period of rapid change only after it has been consummated. The instructive and comprehensive review by Herbert Smith,[3] for example, enables the reader to acquire an awareness of past periods of transition in science education. The introduction of innovations every two or three decades heralded an initial phase of enthusiasm which gradually died down as the new ideas became accepted and formed the basis of a new "tradition." Curiously enough, Smith's review, as well as the reports of other writers,[4] make it appear that research in science education has had little effect on teaching practice since Craig's study[5] in 1927 set a new direction for the profession. Smith himself suggests some reasons why this has been the case. And it is, I believe, consistent with Smith's criticisms that the current ferment in science education is in large measure due to the interests of scientists and psychologists, both newcomers to the field who are collaborating with science educators to revitalize this part of the curriculum. Of course, only the beginning of a chapter has been written; whether the current movement will come and go as have others before it, or whether it will prove more lasting, remains to be seen. It is reassuring to note, however, that many curricular features that are being emphasized today have been foreshadowed by past workers.[3]

I should really amend the previous paragraph with the observation that interest and good will of gifted individuals are not enough to mount an attack on the complex problems of modern education; the current ferment in science education is in part also due to the availability of substantial funds for the support of cohesive research efforts. The Science Curriculum Improvement Study is such an effort. It is attempting to develop a teaching program of which the objective is the increase of scientific literacy in the school and adult populations. To accomplish this aim, the Study has to formulate a view of the nature and structure of science; it has to devise learning experiences that achieve a secure connection between the pupils' intuitive attitudes and the concepts of the modern scientific point of view; and it has to find how one can determine what the children have learned. Since it appears that present knowledge is not adequate for this purpose, the Study is engaged in a research program that will eventually yield the necessary information. A science program constructed in this way will, it is hoped, have a pattern that is understandable by teachers and will not merely be a prescription to be followed blindly by them.

The general strategy of the Study is to confront the elementary school children with first-hand experience of natural phenomena and with intellectual challenges that will stimulate their further cognitive development. This strategy implies a commitment to working with a group of children over a period of several years. It was decided, therefore, that the SCIS would begin its program with children in kindergarten and first grade; each year additional material will then be made available to continue the program with the same group of children as they advance from grade to grade. This systematic longitudinal study is scheduled to start in the fall of 1966. It will be accompanied by a psychological and sociological evaluation program. Of course, one study will not be definitive. Still, it may produce tentative answers to some of the questions of curricular content and pedagogical tactics raised by Smith: [3]

The big question is which concepts are most valuable in the further intellectual development of the child and which contribute the most to the cognitive, affective, and social objectives of science instruction. . . . What procedures and techniques are most appropriately employed in merging a series of simple concepts into a larger, more comprehensive understanding? How are such insights developed and to what extent are teachers aware of the several basic understandings (simple concepts) which may be required to attain a certain generalized conception (*i.e.*, an understanding of the solar system)?

The study may also shed some light on the acceptance by school systems and their communities of an educational program designed to create inquisitiveness, mental flexibility, and intellectual independence.

For the past several years, the SCIS has been engaged in an exploratory phase to determine the most promising materials for the longitudinal study.[6-9] This exploratory phase is near conclusion for the early primary grades but will continue for some time for the intermediate and upper elementary grades. The key constructs that have been found understandable by young children and essential for further learning are the following: matter, living organism, variation within a population of similar individuals, physical system, and interaction. Trial units in which these constructs are introduced have been produced and are being tested and revised in the light of classroom experience by SCIS staff members and by regular public school teachers.

In the current exploratory phase, work is also in progress to determine ways in which the pupils' learnings can be gauged. SCIS faces several special problems in this area. First, communication with young children for evaluation or other purposes is not easy to accomplish in a standardized and reproducible fashion. Second, it is of interest to find out what the pupils have learned, not merely whether certain narrowly specified objectives have been attained. Third, the really significant long-term objectives are certainly attained only after a lengthy period of learning. But over a period of a year or two, young children mature in response to so many experiences that it is very difficult to ascribe specific changes to their activities in the school science program. Novel approaches, therefore, are called for and are being studied.

These introductory paragraphs were intended to give a brief overview of the work of the Science Curriculum Improvement Study. In the remainder of this article, two of the points that have been brought up will be treated in more detail. One of these is the relation between cognitive development and experience, a relation which strongly suggests that science should play a large role in elementary education. The second is the curriculum plan being developed by the Science Curriculum Improvement Study. Several anecdotes describing the trial teaching experience and the statement of a few significant findings conclude the article.

WHY ELEMENTARY SCHOOL SCIENCE?

In his recent book, *Intelligence and Experience*, J. McV. Hunt [10] reviews the current status of experimental work and theories concerned with the intellectual development of children. He concludes that it is high time to abandon the beliefs in a fixed intelligence and a predetermined mental development, beliefs that were dominant in the thinking of behavioral scientists until a few years ago. Together, these beliefs led to the view that intelligence was an innate characteristic of each individual and that it increased at a fixed rate to a predetermined level. These beliefs also led educators to de-emphasize intellectual stimulation and to prescribe a program that emphasized basic skills while the children's thinking abilities were thought to mature of their own accord.

In the new conception, intelligence is a hierarchy of strategies for processing information and schemata for assigning significance to information.[10-13] This hierarchy is formed and structured in accordance with the experience of the individual. Intellectual stimulation during the formative years is therefore as important as native endowment in determining adult achievement. In this view, the contribution that education can make to society is vastly greater and more vital than was previously thought possible.

The elementary school acquires a particularly deep responsibility, because the child's thinking is especially sensitive to experience as it undergoes a gradual transition from the concrete to the abstract in the age range from six to fourteen years. At the beginning of this period the child is improving control of his muscles and gaining in ability to carry out physical manipulations; in his thinking he is dependent on direct experience. At the end of the transition, the child is able to focus his thoughts consciously and to manipulate abstract relationships without constant reference to specific examples.[11, 13] As Hunt states it:

The problem for the management of child development is to find out how to govern the encounters that children have with their environments to foster both an optionally rapid rate of intellectual development and a satisfying life.[10]

What about the often heard recommendation that science instruction be postponed until the youngsters have reached the intellectual maturity of the middle teens? At this stage, unfortunately, educational efforts reach only the fraction of the student body which is favorably disposed toward science because of earlier favorable experience at home or at school.[14] For the others, many of whom form a strong dislike for science, it is too late. Their spontaneous intellectual development just does not keep pace with the expectation of the school or does not proceed in the direction of modern science.

That a science course should be a particularly effective stimulus of development is easy to understand. In the quotation above, Hunt refers to the encounters between a child and his environment. But it is just such encounters from which mankind has abstracted the concepts and relationships that constitute the present content of science. This content represents the outcome of a long, slow process. During the elementary school years, as Piaget and Hunt point out, boys and girls are engaged in precisely this kind of abstracting process with respect to their own natural environment, a process which results in the common-sense point of view characteristic of our culture. The function of education is to guide the children's development by providing them with particularly informative and suggestive experiences as a base for their abstractions. At the same time, children must be led to form a conceptual framework [12] that permits them to perceive the phenomena in a more meaningful way and to integrate their inferences into generalizations of greater value than they would form if left to their own devices.

I should like to stress the fact that I consider the conceptual framework to be an essential part of science, a part that can be developed in a properly guided substantive study of natural phenomena. A science curriculum should therefore be judged both on the opportunities it affords pupils for having stimulating experiences and on the conceptual hierarchy that these experiences nourish. The development that takes place in the absence of such instruction is haphazard and leads to many invalid generalizations that are serious obstacles to later learning. The superstitions and fears regarding natural phenomena in primitive societies and even among adults in our own advanced culture illustrate this point.

The elementary school science program has been described in terms similar to these by many educators who have concerned themselves with the general features that science courses should have.[15-17] Nevertheless, there is general agreement that current teaching practices do not meet the pupils' needs.[3] There are probably two reasons for this state of affairs. One is a conflict in goals, with science educators advocating mental flexibility and independence, while teaching practice seeks to transmit traditions of knowledge and culture, traditions that are certified by authorities and are not to be questioned. The second reason is the conflict, described above, in psychological and educational theory, with educational practice reflecting a view (fixed intelligence-predetermined development) that robs science teaching of its developmental significance.[10] It is not surprising, therefore, that one great weakness of current practice seems to be an almost exclusive reliance on textbooks and other such authoritative sources of information. These sources for science learning, however, are quite impotent compared to the direct experiences that nourish the pupil's intellectual development of "common-sense" rationality. Instead of guiding this development in the direction of modern scientific understanding, therefore, the present-day science courses create a second, separate, relatively abstract structure which is not used outside the school situation and which eventually atrophies.

What I have written must not be interpreted to mean that a pupil can learn only what he himself observes; the world is too complicated to permit that. It does mean, however, that the early years of school should provide a sufficiently diversified program based heavily on concrete experiences. The difficult part, which is often overlooked, is that the concrete experiences must be presented in a context that helps to build a conceptual framework. Then, and only then, will the early learning form a base for the assimilation of experiences that come later, experiences that may involve direct observation or the report of observations made by others. In other words, to be able to use information obtained by others, to benefit from the reading of textbooks and other references, the individual must have a conceptual structure and a means of communication that enable him to interpret the information as though he had obtained it himself. I shall call this functional understanding of science concepts "scientific literacy." It should be the principal objective of the elementary school science program.

The Curriculum Plan

In implementing a science curriculum that makes significant contributions to children's intellectual development, it is necessary to focus also on some shorter range goals. Intellectual development and scientific literacy are broad objectives which help to determine the overall curriculum strategy. They must, however, be supplemented by more specific shorter range goals to make possible spelling out of the teaching program in detail. These shorter range goals of SCIS are to acquaint pupils with specific examples of objects and organisms, to let them investigate definite examples of natural phenomena, and to help them develop skills of manipulating equipment and recording data.

To show how the long and short range goals can be combined, let me now describe the teaching program under trial by SCIS in preparation for the longitudinal study mentioned earlier. The program is characterized by two features in order to satisfy the long range objectives. First, there is extensive direct contact of the children with natural phenomena. As much *information* as possible is gathered by the children through their own observations. Little is told them by the teacher or by their books. Second, there is a slow accumulation of abstractions in a hierarchy, with broad concepts being introduced early and more sophisticated distinctions being made later. These abstractions (sometimes called conceptual inventions) are introduced by the teacher. In this dual approach, abstract relationships are pointed out by the teacher, but examples that illustrate the relationships are discovered by the pupils themselves.

The course outline of the curriculum is related to the hierarchical level of abstraction in the program. First level abstractions are the conceptions of matter, of living matter (including activity and growth), of conservation of matter (including the systems concept), and of variation in one property among similar objects. Second level abstractions are the conceptions of interaction (including causal relations or associations), and of relativity (geometrical relations or associations). Third level abstractions are the conceptions of energy (including energy transfer during interaction), of equilibrium, of steady state, and of behavior, reproduction, and speciation of living matter. The abstractions on the earlier levels have to be grasped before the ones on the later levels become meaningful. Each abstraction can be illustrated on its own level, but it is further enriched by illustrations on the succeeding levels. Thus, for example, understanding of energy transfer both depends on and enlarges the understanding of interaction, the ability to isolate a system and subsystems, and the awareness of material objects.

The details of the classroom procedure are spelled out in teacher's manuals for several units at each of the levels mentioned above. In the trial stage at present, there are five units dealing with concepts on the first and second level. Others are in preparation. The program reflects as great a breadth of natural phenomena as is consistent with the concepts being developed. The first part of the unit on *Material Objects*,[18] for example, leads the children to manipulate, describe, compare, and transform samples of metal, wood, plastic, granular materials, liquids, and gases. It presents a natural history of the objects and their composition rather than of their manufacture, of their use, or of some other aspect. A basis for this unit, of course, is a prior awareness by each child that objects in his environment have an existence separate from his own existence. Such an awareness by first graders can be taken for granted.

A second part of the unit on *Material Objects* (in preparation) introduces the notion of mentally grouping a collection of objects into a system of objects. The children will keep their attention on the system even though the objects involved may be rearranged, deformed, or broken up. In other words, the systems concept is introduced to highlight the principle of conservation of matter as a conceptual tool for dealing with all natural phenomena. In the second part of the unit, the children will also be made aware of the contrast between words that are names of material objects and words that are names of abstractions.

The next topic on the first level is treated in the unit on *Variation and Measurement*.[19] The tasks here are more difficult because understanding measurement presupposes an awareness of the constancy of the measuring instrument under the changes it undergoes (displacements, for example) as it is used to compare different specimens. The children must also be aware that some changes (*e.g.*, bending of a yardstick) may make the instrument no longer suitable for carrying out measurements. Piaget's work has shed much light on the formation of these conservation concepts, and his findings were considered in the construction of the unit. Associated with the process of measurement is the concept of variation. Here the SCIS program is again a natural history, as with *Material Objects*. This time, however, it is a natural history of sets or collections or populations of objects that are fairly similar to one another, but differ in some way, and can be grouped according to this difference. The description of the entire population is given by the children in the form of a histogram that reveals the size of each group in the population sample studied. Examples are collections of pea pods which are grouped according to the number of peas in a pod and slices of raisin bread that are grouped according to the number of raisins in each slice. A final synthesis in this unit applies the concept of variation to a set of measurements of one property made on a single object. The measurements are grouped according to their magnitude and the results displayed in the form of a histogram.

The introductory second level unit is called *Interaction and Systems*.[20] In it, the children are introduced to the idea that changes they observe can be interpreted as evidence of interaction. To find out what objects interacted, some further investigation with controlled experiments often has to be carried out.

Interaction is an interpretive concept. It is a relation among objects, not an object itself. As one makes observations, as one accumulates a natural history of objects and phenomena, one may attach significance to the phenomena in many different ways. Modern science is characterized by a certain hierarchy of interpretations. Most fundamental of these is the interpretation of change as evidence of interaction. Interaction between objects or systems is the underlying explanation for all processes or happenings. In other words, interaction causes change.

Another second level unit is entitled *Relativity of Position and Motion*.[21] Here are introduced the concept of motion as change of position relative to an observer and the concept of configuration of a system as its internal geometrical arrangement. A more extensive discussion is published elsewhere.[9]

In another unit on the second level, the concepts of systems and interaction are applied to mixtures of substances that may or may not form solutions. In early activities, the pupils make solutions of many different substances and recover the dissolved material by evaporation of the water. This technique is later used as an analytical tool for determining the concentration of material in a solution. The pupils also compare the action of water with the action of some other liquids as solvents. Finally, they investigate the changes in concentration that occur as crystals of soluble material dissolve without stirring and the solution diffuses slowly until concentration equilibrium is reached.

In the preceding review, I have purposely stressed the abstractions that are introduced by the teacher and have not enumerated explicitly the examples or illustrations that permit the children to discover the usefulness of the abstract ideas. The teacher's manuals for the units may be consulted for this information.

The pedagogical device for introducing the key concepts in each of the units is similar and follows the description given by Atkin and Karplus.[7] There is an instructional period of several class sessions in which the children are engaged in observations on a natural history level of some new or some familiar materials which they can explore quite freely. At this time, they enrich their understanding of previously formed concepts, but they also are faced with some problems with which they cannot yet deal adequately. There is then a suggestion of a new way to think about the observations. This suggestion introduces the conceptual *invention*. Finally, there is further experimentation and exploration by the children to *discover* the consequences of using the conceptual invention. Thus, *invention* is the introduction of an interpretive construct, and *discovery* is the recognition of the usefulness of the construct. Alternately, this procedure may be called guided discovery, a process of going from observation to interpretation by means of *Invention and Discovery*.

In *Interaction and Systems*, for example, the material might be magnets and nails, some dry cells and light bulbs, and so on—more or less common materials with which one can do simple experiments. The teacher then suggests to the children that they should think about the changes they observe in their experiments as being evidence of interaction. The remarkable thing is that the children do learn to think of it this way and that during a later experiment they run up to the teacher and say, "Look, there is some evidence of interaction."

An important consideration which I believe to be applicable to all future units is this: some things can be discovered by children doing experiments, but some cannot. These latter are the man-made constructs in terms of which he thinks about natural phenomena. The former are outcomes of specific experiments. To make a discovery, however, certain constructs have to be available to the observer, what Bruner [22] has called a "soft technology." The creator of a unit has to be clear in his mind what constructs are already available and what constructs must be introduced to enable the pupils to make the discoveries he would like them to make. Once he has decided, the constructs have to be "invented" for the pupils near the beginning of the unit so they may be used many times over and at the pupils' initiative before the end of the unit. In subsequent units, the previously introduced constructs serve as a starting point whose incomplete adequacy is revealed by new observations. Another cycle of growth in the pupils' conceptual structure can then commence.

CONCLUSION

This article was intended to serve as an introduction to the rationale and program of the Science Curriculum Improvement Study. Even though the work of the SCIS is only at an early stage, some qualitative but significant findings have emerged. (1) Modern science depends on numerous man-made constructs which are not inherent in natural phenomena and which usually cannot be discovered by children through their observations. (2) The content of a science curriculum must be viewed as a hierarchy of superordinate ' and subordinate elements and not as an enumeration of many equivalent elements. (3) The pupils must have a great deal of autonomy—opportunities to carry out their own manipulations, to make their own observations, and to find their own applications for conceptual inventions. (4) The views of cognitive development held by leading students of the field, Piaget, Bruner, and Hunt, to name a few, support the introduction of a strong science program in the elementary school. (5) Much current teaching practice and to an extent teacher education are not yet in tune with these views and are actually based on ideas that are incompatible with the communication of scientific literacy. These findings, I believe, can be applied to facets of experience other than experience with natural phenomena. They may, therefore, have value above and beyond the scope of the Science Curriculum Improvement Study and may suggest a challenge to all concerned about the improvement of education.

REFERENCES

1. Goodlad, John I., *School Curriculum Reform in the United States*, The Fund for the Advancement of Education, New York, 1964.
2. Gross, Ronald, "Two-Year-Olds Are Very Smart," *New York Times Magazine*, September 6, 1964, p. 10.
3. Smith, Herbert A., "Educational Research Related to Science Instruction for the Elementary and Junior High School: A Review and Commentary," *J. Res. Sci. Teaching*, 1, 199 (1963).
4. Burnett, R. Will, "On the Improvement of Research in Science Education," *J. Res. Sci. Teaching*, 1, 253 (1963).
5. Craig, Gerald S., *Certain Techniques Used in Developing a Course of Study in Science for the Horace Mann Elementary School*, Contributions to Education, No. 276, Bureau of Publications, Teachers College, Columbia University, New York, 1927.
6. Karplus, Robert, "One Physicist Looks at Science Education," *Intellectual Development: Another Look*, Association for Supervision and Curriculum Development, Washington, D. C., 1964.
7. Atkin, J. M., and Robert Karplus, "Discovery or Invention?" *The Science Teacher*, 29, 45 (1962).
8. Thier, H. D., R. Karplus, and C. A. Powell, "A Concept of Matter for the First Grade," *J. Res. Sci. Teaching*, 1, 315 (1963).
9. Karplus, Robert, "Meet Mr. O," *Science and Children*, 1, 19 (1963).
10. Hunt, J. McV., *Intelligence and Experience*, The Ronald Press Company, New York, 1961.
11. Inhelder, Bärbel, and Jean Piaget, *The Growth of Logical Thinking from Childhood to Adolescence*, Basic Books, New York, 1958.
12. Bruner, Jerome S., *The Process of Education, Harvard University Press*, Cam-

bridge, Massachusetts, 1960. See especially Chapter 2, "The Importance of Structure."

13. Piaget, Jean, *The Child's Conception of Physical Reality*, Humanities Press, New York, 1951.
14. Stendler, Celia B., "Elementary Teaching and the Piagetian Theory," *The Science Teacher*, 29, 34 (1961).
15. National Society for the Study of Education, A *Program for Teaching Science*, Thirty-First Yearbook, Part I, University of Chicago Press, Chicago, Illinois, 1932.
16. National Society for the Study of Education, *Science Education in American Schools*, Forty-Sixth Yearbook, Part I, University of Chicago Press, Chicago, Illinois, 1947.
17. National Society for the Study of Education, *Rethinking Science Education*, Fifty-Ninth Yearbook, Part I, University of Chicago Press, Chicago, Illinois, 1960.
18. Science Curriculum Improvement Study, *Material Objects*, University of California, Berkeley, California, 1963.
19. Science Curriculum Improvement Study, *Variation and Measurement*, University of California, Berkeley, California, 1964.
20. Science Curriculum Improvement Study, *Interaction and Systems*, University of California, Berkeley, California, 1963.
21. Science Curriculum Improvement Study, *Relativity of Position and Motion*, University of California, Berkeley, California, 1964.
22. Bruner, J. S., private communication.

SCIENCE IS FOR THE SENSES: UNIVERSITY OF CALIFORNIA ELEMENTARY SCHOOL SCIENCE PROJECT *

Lloyd Scott

The University of California (at Berkeley) Elementary School Science Project is supported by the National Science Foundation. Its specific purpose is to

* REPRINTED FROM *Science and Children*, Vol. 2, No. 6, March 1965, pp. 19–22. Copyright, 1965, by the National Science Teachers Association, Washington, D.C. Reprinted by permission of the author and the publisher. Dr. Scott is Associate Director of the University of California Elementary School Science Project at Berkeley.

develop and test curriculum materials on basic science for elementary schools. The teaching units are developed by the University of California faculty and tested in the University's Laboratory Schools before they are distributed to interested teachers. The units provide many opportunities for children's active involvement. The units attempt to present fundamental concepts of science and include the philosophy of experimental science in an atmosphere of challenge, interest, and excitement.

I N S O M E respects, the state of contemporary science education seems to be a projection of *Lost Horizons* where beauty abounds. It is widely known and fully appreciated that learning in science involves active participation rather than passive exposure. The recent literature in science education with its emphasis upon induction, discovery, structural configuration, and distinction between process and content has served to make activists out of all science education theorists. All classroom teachers of science have been transformed into laboratory supervisors, resource persons, and catalysts for individual experimentation. But, alas, one must leave Shangri-La to enter a school classroom.

THEORY AND REALITY

Within the realm of elementary education there is little evidence to support any of these contentions. While the observer of science instruction in elementary school classrooms may be impressed by the zeal of the teacher, and while he may sense a certain insecure willingness on the part of the teacher to conform to the "modern" expectation, he is likely to be most impressed by the extent to which science instruction continues to bear the stamp of authoritarian didactics.

In many classrooms the children, with good reason, react to science with boredom or even more negative feelings. They typically seem to resent the lack of personal participation in activities which involve their senses directly.

Jean Piaget, the renowned developmental psychologist, presented his position on classroom instruction during his recent visit to the United States. He said, "The goal in education is not to increase the amount of knowledge, but to create the possibilities for the child to invent and discover . . . Teaching means situations where structures can be discovered; it does not mean transmitting structures which may be assimilated at nothing other than the verbal level." (1) * This view is further elaborated by Lovell (2) in his discussion of thought and action. He holds that thought arises from actions, and concepts arise out of the actions which children perform with objects and not from the objects themselves.

Among those concerned with improvement of science education and for

* See references.

whom this activity-oriented instructional philosophy has appeal, at least two major courses of action come to mind. First, it would seem that the science program could be materially improved if scientists introduced teachers to the philosophy of experimental science; and the teachers, in turn, chose to transmit this philosophy to children. While such a course of action has some merit, it has three apparent weaknesses. Transmitting this philosophy to approximately one million elementary school teachers in the United States presents an apparently insurmountable obstacle. Even if such an accomplishment were feasible, it must be appreciated that experimental science has a substantial content. The philosophy probably cannot and should not be presented in the absence of a long term consideration of science content. It is doubtful that the philosophy of experimental science can be transmitted through verbal communication in any case. It is likely that the teachers must experience the philosophy and method of experimentation through active participation in science, in the same manner that it is hoped children will experience these attributes in their program.

A possible second course of action for improving science education concerns revision of the program itself. The course of study may be modified so as to include many fertile opportunities for children's active involvement. It may be modified so that it includes possibilities for children to come to grips with some of the fundamental concepts of science rather than with trivial interpretations of phenomena or the social virtues of science. It may be modified to include the philosophy of experimental science in an atmosphere of challenge, interest, and excitement.

It was upon this second course of action that the University of California Elementary School Science Project embarked in 1959. The ultimate purpose of this project is the improvement of science education at the elementary school level. Through experimentation in elementary school classrooms, answers to the following questions are sought:

1. Can the professional research scientist make a contribution to the elementary school science program which is acceptable and useful to teachers at this level?
2. Can materials be developed which emphasize fundamental science concepts and, at the same time, hold the interest of elementary school youngsters?
3. Are the methods of basic science suitable for the elementary school setting?
4. What is the grade or what are the grades at which introduction of certain science concepts produces the best result?
5. Can children be actively involved in the manipulations and procedures of experimental science?
6. Can science be made more stimulating and interesting to elementary school children and teachers?
7. What experiments and instructional procedures are most effective in promoting children's understanding of particular science concepts?

From a modest beginning involving four members of the University of California faculty, the project has included a total of twenty-one faculty participants. Each has contributed in some way to the project activity though not all have participated directly in the preparation of curriculum materials.

The curriculum research proceeds according to a general pattern, within which individual variations are common. After the scientist identifies those fundamental science concepts within his discipline which may lend themselves to treatment at the elementary school level, he begins to prepare a unit of instruction about them. In this preparation, he is usually assisted by a teaching consultant (an experienced elementary school teacher), a technical writer, and an evaluator. The scientist's working outline is expanded to include fruitful classroom activities which involve children to the maximum extent possible. In addition to suggesting some of these activities, the teaching consultant often determines their potential worth through actual trial in an elementary school classroom. She may teach a particular lesson or guide some children through a given experimental activity several times before it is finally reduced to written form. Once a series of lessons is developed to the satisfaction of the scientist, the technical writer is called upon to prepare a written unit of such form that it may be used in a trial evaluation. This preparation includes not only the suggested instructional program for children but also provides the public school teacher with a sufficient content background to maximize teaching success. The unit also includes complete descriptions of equipment to be used and detailed directions for guiding the children's experimental activity.

The first classroom trial of a unit is usually held in twelve to eighteen elementary school classrooms. This trial is commonly undertaken in the University of California Laboratory Schools. It is the purpose of this pilot test to assess all possible aspects of the interaction between the experimental program and children. Teachers are asked to comment critically on all phases of the program. They are asked to assist with decisions regarding proper grade placement of the material, whether certain activities should be included or omitted, whether the sequence of activities is reasonable, and whether the concepts covered are or can be made attractive to young children. Children's learning is evaluated through tests of various kinds, and a thorough analysis is given to the objective test data. Children's conceptual development is often observed by the scientist as well as by other members of the project staff. Both objective and subjective evaluations are synthesized into a report of the trial. This report, supplied by an evaluator, usually includes specific recommendations for the modification of the unit.

On the basis of these recommendations and the generalized impressions gained from observing children and teachers in action, the unit is revised. The revision is often drastic at this stage. Most units are subjected to two or more such trials before some broader evaluation is undertaken.

When it is felt that the local experimentation has been sufficient, the units are prepared for wider distribution. At this stage, the original unit has usually been divided into several parts, each designed for a particular grade, or grades, in the elementary school and each contributing to the total sequential, conceptual development. The materials are distributed, at cost, to approximately one thousand interested teachers beyond the range of project supervision, and these teachers are encouraged to complete summary evaluation reports regarding the use of the material in their science programs. As data from these reports are accumulated, additional revisions may be dictated.

SCIENTIFIC ACCURACY ASSURED

In all of the experimentation, the scientist plays an autonomous role. While the effort as described is clearly cooperative in all its phases, the final authority for development and change rests with the university scientist. In this manner scientific accuracy is insured, and the flavor and philosophy of experimental science are protected.

The nature of the project has permitted investigation into many science areas. While it is impossible to indicate the detail of the individual investigations, the scope of the activity is revealed by the following summary of activities of the University of California Elementary School Science Project. The list includes activities to date together with activities under way for the current year, 1964–65. Included with each activity are the names of the principal investigators responsible. (Some of these men are no longer associated with the project.)

ZOOLOGY—*Animal Coloration.* Robert Stebbins, Professor of Zoology.

The material has been extensively tested, beginning in the fall of 1960. It will be distributed in the form of four units for grades 4, 5, and 6 entitled "Animal Variation," "Principles of Concealing Coloration," "Principles of Advertising Coloration," and "Natural Selection."

BOTANY—*Plant Morphology.* Herbert Mason, Professor of Botany.

This unit is concerned with the external characteristics of seed plants. It has the additional goal of inducing the children to develop a logical classification scheme for their observations. Some extensive sequences of lessons have undergone preliminary trial on three different occasions and the preparation is continuing. The material will be submitted to formal trial during the present school year.

PHYSIOLOGY—*What Am I?* Nello Pace, Professor of Physiology; Arthur Pardee, Associate Professor of Biochemistry; and Robert Macey, Associate Professor of Physiology.

An introduction to some of the basic physiological components of the human body. The original material on human physiology and biochemistry was first tested in 1960. Revisions and trials, since the early test, have tended in the direction of reducing the material on biochemistry and partitioning the material on physiology. At the present time four different units entitled, "How I Began" (embryology), "How I Move" (skeletal and muscular systems), "How I Know" (nervous system), and "How I Keep Alive" (metabolism) are in various stages of preparation.

ECOLOGY—*Population Dynamics*. Robert Stebbins, Professor of Zoology.

The instructional program on the topic of population growth introduces children to the mechanics of population control in the animal kingdom and alerts them, through analogy, to the cruciality of the problem of uncontrolled population growth in any animal society. The unit is in the initial phase of preparation.

PALEONTOLOGY—*The Evolution of Life*. Charles Camp, Professor of Paleontology.

Through a series of historic narratives, the children are familiarized with the evidence concerning the changing life forms which have inhabited the earth and are acquainted with the discovery methods of the paleontologist. The unit is now being readied for a local trial.

ENTOMOLOGY—*Insect Life*. Harold Madsen, Associate Professor of Entomology.

Professor Madsen has expressed an interest in the preparation of material on insects but actual preparation has not begun. Various possible topics are under consideration.

GENETICS—*Heredity*. Patricia St. Lawrence, Assistant Professor of Genetics.

Predictability of animal and plant characteristics through study and genetic components. The unit is in the early stages of preparation. A teacher's background manual on genetics will be completed this year.

PHYSICS—*Force*. Robert Karplus, Professor of Physics.

A unit on force to acquaint children with Newton's Laws of Motion. (Work on this unit has been suspended.)

Gravitation and Buoyancy. Owen Chamberlain, Professor of Physics.

The work on this unit is now in suspension until adequate time and resources for its development are at hand.

Wave Motion. Roger Wallace, Research Physicist.

Properties of commonly encountered waves. Progress on the unit has continued through several revisions, and it is currently undergoing trial.

CHEMISTRY—*The Structure and Properties of Matter*. Chester O'Konski, Professor of Chemistry. Assisted by Leo Brewer, Professor of Chemistry; Charles Koch, Associate Research Chemist; and Albert English, Associate Professor of Electrical Engineering.

The molecular theory and its relationship to the composition of matter. The nature of atoms and their arrangement within substances is explored by the children. The unit has undergone extensive testing, and it is planned that another evaluation shall proceed soon.

MATHEMATICS—*Coordinates I*. Robert Karplus, Professor of Physics.

A unit on the mathematics of science. Children were taught about the Cartesian coordinate system, the use of this system in the graphing of physical behavior, and the alternative description of relationships through the use of equations. The work on this unit was suspended after the local test was completed.

Coordinates II. Stephen Diliberto, Professor of Mathematics.

This second preparation of coordinates material was designed to acquaint the children with applied mathematics. The usefulness of the Cartesian coordinate system in scientific description was exploited to the extent possible, and concrete rather than abstract expression of the mathematics was emphasized. After extensive local testing, the material was prepared in four units as follows:

Part I—The Description of Position on Lines and Planes (Grades 2–6)
Part II—The Graphical Depiction of Physical Quantities (Grades 3–6)
Part III—Equations of Straight-Line Graphs (Grades 5–6)
Part IV—Equations with Negative Slopes and Intercepts (Grade 6)

The broader evaluation of these materials is in progress. Additionally, workbooks for use by the children are being prepared.

While the above description of activities includes important information about the project, it fails to present adequately the accumulation of valuable experience and information which has been accrued by the active participants. There is no theoretical exercise or abstract formulation which can substitute for the experience of dealing with real experimental science for real children in real schools. The curriculum experimentation and the extensive experience have produced sound bases for some important, if not profound, observations:

1. The professional research scientist can and does make a substantial contribution to the improvement of elementary school science.
2. A cooperative enterprise involving scientists, educators, and writers can develop science programs which involve children and which hold their interest.
3. The methods of experimental science can usually be adapted to the elementary school setting, and children can develop an ability to use these methods.
4. An active involvement on the part of the child is necessary in most fruitful science activities.
5. The development of effective instructional outlines for the elementary school level is a difficult but absorbing enterprise.
6. Repeated trial and evaluation is a necessary component of elementary school science curriculum development, and is, of course, crucial to investigations into children's learning of science concepts.

While there are no panaceas in the task of improving elementary school science instruction, there is a principle which warrants particular attention. If science is to mean something other than a class lecture period or pages of factual material in a textbook, young children must be involved in it. To recite the virtues of the scientist in his laboratory, or to tell children that experimentation is fun and productive is grossly insufficient. Even the display of an experiment performed by the teacher falls short of the mark. To the greatest extent possible, all of the senses of the child must be involved if the flavor of science is to be known. There is no known way to obtain such involvement short of the child's direct participation. In designing a science program for the elementary school, the first and most important part of the equipment for any activity is the child himself.

REFERENCES

1. Jean Piaget. Conference at Cornell University, Ithaca, N. Y. 1964.
2. K. Lovell. *The Growth of Basic Mathematical and Scientific Concepts in Children.* Philosophical Library, New York City. 1964. p. 18.

THE SCIENCE MANPOWER PROJECT'S K–12 SCIENCE PROGRAM *

Willard J. Jacobson

A major undertaking of the Science Manpower Project has been to develop an effective K–12 science program. Five major goals of the science program for children and young people are cited and discussed: (1) to develop a better understanding of the natural, physical world, (2) to help young people gain some understanding of the methods used in the sciences, (3) to learn more about their bodies and how to take care of them, (4) to learn what it is like to work and study in science, and (5) to prepare for effective citizenship. The science program has the following seven important characteristics: (1) content from a wide range of science is included, (2) the science program is articulated, (3) a depth approach is used, (4) there is an emphasis on the broad generalizations in science, (5) science is considered as human enterprise, (6) the guidance function of science education is stressed, and (7) a variety of approaches to teaching is encouraged.

IN THE EARLY fifties several critical trends were becoming increasingly apparent to the discerning student of American science education. New information and knowledge in the sciences was accumulating at a geometric

* REPRINTED FROM *The New School Science,* American Association for the Advancement of Science, Misc. Pub. No. 63–6, 1963, pp. 63–71, by permission of the author and the publisher. Dr. Jacobson is Chairman of the Department of Science Education at Teachers College, Columbia University.

rate. In fact, new fields of science have been opened up. These developments in the sciences were not being incorporated into school science programs with sufficient rapidity. Since the thirties, there had been considerable interest in elementary school science, and increasingly effective science programs for children were being developed. But, there was little recognition of the inevitable impact of this profound development in science programs for junior and senior high schools. Although whole new sciences were being developed and the possibilities for school science programs were many and varied, many of the K–12 science programs were replete with interest-deadening repetition. Finally, a careful study of educational and population statistics yielded predictions of a sharply growing need for personnel well-educated in the sciences to man our highly sophisticated industries, shoulder the awesome responsibilities of our governmental agencies in this and other lands, staff our programs of research and development in new and exotic fields, and meet the desperate needs of our schools and colleges for teachers of science who satisfy the criterion of excellence. Such were the considerations that led to the organization of the Science Manpower Project.

A major undertaking of the Science Manpower Project has been to develop an effective K–12 science program. Undoubtedly, this is one of the most challenging tasks facing the science educator. This K–12 science program must help prepare children and young people for the world of today and tomorrow. In some way the program must deal with all aspects of science, the new as well as the traditional. It must be devoid of interest-deadening repetition, and yet it must help youngsters to build on their previous science experiences. Most importantly, the science experiences that our children and young people have must help them to grow and develop in the direction of defensible goals that have clearly defined meanings. It is little wonder that the K–12 science program is a tantalizing challenge to the science educator.

To augment the K–12 science program the Science Manpower Project has sponsored a limited amount of research and developed several teacher resource monographs. Of special importance have been Allen's studies of the attitudes toward science of high school seniors. One-tenth of the high school seniors in the public high schools of New Jersey were studied. Some of these students were restudied two years later to see what had happened to them and to see if any change in attitude had taken place. The teacher resource monographs deal with areas essential to the K–12 science program but for which there were few materials available.

The K–12 science program of the Science Manpower Project is intended for use by local school systems. It is not the "final word." Instead, this program can be used by teachers and curriculum committees as they plan the programs that will best suit the children and young people in their schools. We have suggested goals which we hope will have meaning to everyone and with which many will agree, criteria which should be considered, program characteristics which seem desirable, and a prototype program described in some detail which can be used as a reference by teachers and curriculum planners. It is hoped that these materials will improve the quality of our K–12 science programs.

Goals for a K–12 Science Program

Goals indicate directions. Teachers and curriculum planners must have some concept of the directions in which they hope that pupils and students will develop. As in science, our statements of goals should have operational meanings; i.e., they should have meanings in terms of our day-to-day work in teaching science. The following are among the goals of the Science Manpower Project K–12 science program with concrete examples to give them operational significance.

1. *To develop a better understanding of the natural, physical world.* This has always been one of the most important objectives of science teaching. We want our youngsters to develop a weltanschauung: a picture of the world in which they live, and a rational idea of their place in this world. This goal becomes critically important in this age when our knowledge of the world appears to be increasing geometrically. We are members of the animal kingdom—a recognition of this fact has led to great advances in medicine, human physiology, nutrition and other health sciences. We live in a very vast universe—a recognition of the vastness of the universe has challenged our imagination and opened new worlds for exploration. The development of a view of the world in which we live consistent with the pictures emerging from investigations in a wide range of sciences is essential for optimum intellectual growth.

All of our science activities should contribute to the achievement of this goal. One example from the Science Manpower Project's program is the study of the two leading hypotheses concerning the formation of the universe: the evolutionary or "big bang" hypothesis, and the steady state or continuous creation hypothesis. What are some of the "facts" that any theory of the formation of the universe has to explain? How do these two hypotheses deal with these "facts"? What are some of the possible ways that we might test these hypotheses? This is one example, from among many, of an area of study that will help young people to develop a more adequate picture of the universe in which they live, and begin to build a concept of the manner in which scientists deal with hypotheses.

2. *To help young people gain some understanding of the methods used in the sciences.* The methods used in the sciences are among the most powerful intellectual tools man has developed, and some of these methods can be used to deal with questions and problems that children and young people recognize. In the scientific approach, suggested answers of proposals for action are subjected to empirical, experimental tests. For example, a few years ago statements could be found in newspapers and journals to the effect that the deerfly can travel at speeds of more than 700 miles per hour, although this speed approaches the speed of sound in air. When subjected

to an empirical test, the speed of the deerfly was found to be much less than 700 miles per hour. In science, an attempt also is made to have the findings of one person checked by others. For example, when it was reported that Hahn and Strassman had found that U-235 fissioned into elements near the middle of the periodic table, American scientists did not wait for the meeting to close before they set out for their laboratories to check this report. The experiment in which all variables but one are controlled, is another important tool in the sciences. As young people engage in various kinds of science activities, it is extremely important that they understand the methods employed.

In a recent laboratory experience, some students were sprouting seeds by placing them on wet blotting paper between two pieces of glass. They were trying to find out whether or not it made any difference which end of the seed was down. After the experiment had been completed, one of the students asked, "What would happen if a full-grown plant were turned upside down?" The teacher countered with the question, "How could we find out?" Their immediate response was, "Try it!" However, the teacher hesitated and asked, "After trying it, how would you know whether or not turning a plant upside down had made a difference?" They suggested a control, i.e., growing another plant right-side-up. Also, before "trying it," the teacher asked them to suggest hypotheses as to what would happen if they tried growing a plant upside down. After carrying out the experiment, the students were asked to check textbooks, tradebooks, pamphlets and journals to see if they could find other accounts of this experiment, and to see whether or not their results were consistent with those obtained by others. What could have been only a prosaic science activity became a rather interesting demonstration of some of the methods used in the sciences.

3. *To learn more about their bodies and how to take care of them.* A great deal has been learned about the human body: how it functions, and how to achieve optimum health. This knowledge has been developed in such fields as physiology, pathology, immunology, chemotherapy, nutrition, and public health. It has helped us to increase the average life expectancy about twenty years in the last half century. However, health is more than the mere absence of disease. Instead it is a state in which each individual can operate at his optimum effectiveness. Few individuals have attained this state of optimum health. The study of the human body and how it works is especially important for the early adolescent, for he is at a stage when profound and sometimes mystifying changes are taking place in his body.

Many students have studied the effects of various kinds of diets upon growth and development. These studies are usually made with white rats. The laboratory rat has much the same nutritional requirements as humans and the effects of nutritional deprivation are seen about 30 times as fast in white rats as in human beings. The studies usually take the form of controlled experiments, in which some rats are given an adequate diet, while others are fed a diet deficient in some nutrient. Students learn how to set up a controlled experiment, make observations, secure and record data, arrange and interpret data, and discover that "what you eat makes a difference."

4. *To learn what it is like to work and study in science.* Guidance has always been seen as an important dimension of the junior high school program. Much of the basic work in guidance would be done in such areas of the curriculum as science, industrial arts, social studies, mathematics and English. Students should begin to acquire an understanding of what it is like to work in occupations and professions related to science, in preparation for the day when they will decide their life work. They should also begin to become aware of the kinds of preparation they will need for various occupations and professions. In the senior high school, they will begin to make choices among subjects in the school program. Since the basic courses in science and mathematics are often prerequisites to more advanced study, it is essential that students keep the doors to future opportunities open.

Guidance is an important feature in the Science Manpower Project's *Modern Junior High School Science*.[12] In each unit of the program some attention is devoted to the nature of the work in scientific occupations and professions related to the subject matter of the unit. Field trips to factories, laboratories, farms, and governmental agencies are encouraged, and scientists and engineers are often invited to contribute as a class studies various phases of science. In the final unit of the three-year science program there is serious consideration of science in the future, and the opportunities that young people have in the scientific enterprises.

5. *To prepare for effective citizenship.* In our democracy, citizens and their elected representatives have to make decisions concerning conservation of natural resources, agricultural policy, transportation, communication, atomic energy, public health, national defense, space exploration, industrial development, air and water pollution, and education. Science and technology are involved in almost all decisions in these areas, and, if these decisions are to be intelligent ones, citizens will have to know some basic science and technology and have the background to study and resolve these issues. For many future citizens the K–12 science program provides the last opportunity they will have for an organized study of the wide range of the sciences. The responsibility for the future effectiveness of the democratic way of life that must be shouldered by the overburdened teachers of science is indeed impressive.

Perhaps one of the best ways to prepare for effective citizenship is to have experience in studying, analyzing and suggesting solutions for current community, regional, state, national, and international problems related to science and technology. In the Science Manpower Project's program for example, problems of the conservation of biological resources are considered

12 Fischler, Abraham S., *Modern Junior High School Science*. New York: Bureau of Publications, Teachers College, Columbia University, 1961.

at the community level, problems relating to energy sources are among the regional problems studied, and the control of nuclear energy is considered as an example of a national and international problem. In the study of these problems, the methods of study and analysis are emphasized, for as time goes on, the nature of the problems will change, but it will always be helpful to seek all pertinent information, to know how to use expert judgment, and to consider with respect differing and often controversial opinions.

THE SCIENCE MANPOWER PROJECT'S K–12 PROGRAM

It is clear that a variety of approaches to effective science programs are possible. Communities, student groups, and teachers vary in a multitude of ways. This is why the program sponsored by the Science Manpower Project is primarily a guide to the development of the programs at the local level. At the same time, however, it is believed to have several important characteristics which should be represented in any local program modeled upon it. These characteristics are as follows:

1. *Content from a wide range of sciences is included.* Biology, chemistry, and physics are the traditional sciences of the schools. But, today, it becomes virtually impossible to ignore the potential contributions of astronomy, geology, astronautics, oceanography, and meteorology, or the subsciences of physiology, biochemistry, biophysics, genetics and nutrition. The range of our scientific knowledge is being extended, and it is high time that we recognize the fact in the design of science education programs.

2. *The science program is articulated.* One of the faults of too many K–12 science programs is that there is too much obvious repetition. At the same time, important areas of science are ignored. The Science Manpower Project's K–12 science program is an example of the broad spiral approach to curriculum planning. Similar areas of science are considered every third or fourth year rather than every year, and each time an area is included in the program an attempt is made to use a fresh, new approach at a more sophisticated level.

3. *A depth approach is used.* Areas of science are developed in greater depth than in most previous courses of study so that students can obtain a better understanding of the subject matter. The depth approach also makes it possible to give greater attention to method. Many of the areas of science should be developed through the use of the problem approach with emphasis on problem solving methods used in science.

4. *There is an emphasis on the broad generalizations of science.* Areas of science have been analyzed to identify the most important ideas or generalizations. Science activities are planned to help students develop clearer and more sophisticated concepts of these important generalizations.

5. *Science is considered as a human enterprise.* Scientific enterprise is not a separate entity devoid of relationships with other activities, nor are the various sciences unrelated to one another. Instead, the sciences represent an

important kind of human activity, and there are many interrelationships among them. In the Science Manpower Project's Programs for the junior and senior high school, the year's work in science is developed around a unifying theme or a small number of unifying concepts that serve to emphasize these interrelationships. The emphasis upon ways of working and methods of investigation also help students to develop a concept of science as a human enterprise.

6. *The guidance function of science education is stressed.* In this age of science and technology, all students should learn something about studying and working in the area of the sciences. Many of them may find their life occupations in the scientific enterprise. Basic to any school's guidance program is the instruction in subject-matter fields. The Science Manpower Project's program, and especially the junior high school segment, is designed to provide the kinds of experiences that provide essential background for an effective guidance program.

7. *A variety of approaches to teaching is encouraged.* There is no one best way of teaching science. In fact, good teachers will use a variety of approaches: laboratory experimentation, demonstrations, field work, project work, library research, lectures, and class discussions. They will also use a variety of teaching and learning materials: tradebooks and textbooks, films and filmstrips, radio and television, magazines, and mimeographed materials. The question is not, "What methods and materials are best for teaching science?" Instead, *the basic question* is: "What methods and materials are best to achieve a particular objective at a particular time with a particular group of young people?" In teaching the Science Manpower Project's K–12 science program the enterprising teacher will be able to utilize the wide variety of teaching methods and materials that are now available. *Science for the elementary school.* A two-dimensional program of elementary school science is suggested in *Modern Elementary School Science.*[13] In the flexible dimension of the program, children have a wide variety of experiences related to the questions they ask, to other subjects in the curriculum, to timely concerns in the community, and to special science projects that they may undertake. In the planned dimension of the program, high quality experiences developed in depth are planned in each of six major areas of science. This elementary school science program can be taught by the classroom teacher. However, it is suggested that more effective experiences can be developed by a classroom teacher—science consultant teaching team.

THE FLEXIBLE DIMENSION OF THE ELEMENTARY SCHOOL SCIENCE PROGRAM

In this phase of the program we are primarily concerned with the needs and interests of children as expressed through their questions and interests.

[13] Jacobson, Willard J. and Tannenbaum, Harold E., *Modern Elementary School Science*, New York: Bureau of Publications, Teachers College, Columbia University, 1961.

Since the purpose of the elementary school is to help children achieve optimum intellectual, social, and physical growth and development, this phase of the science program will almost always be closely related to work in non-science areas of the curriculum. Excellent science experiences are often developed as part of a broader study. The flexible dimension also makes it possible to meet the wide range of individual differences in ability and interest among children in most elementary schools.

The following are approaches to the flexible dimension of elementary school science:

1. Science experiences developed from children's questions.
2. Science experiences developed as a part of a broad area of study.
3. Science experiences related to other subjects.
4. Science experiences to meet individual differences.

See Jacobson and Tannenbaum [14] for a distribution of materials from six areas of science:—The Earth on Which We Live; Healthy Living Through Science; The Earth in Space; Machines, Materials, and Energy; The Physical Environment; and The Biological Environment.

[14] *Ibid.*, p. 43.

ASTRONOMY FOR GRADES FIVE
THROUGH EIGHT:
UNIVERSITY OF ILLINOIS
ELEMENTARY SCHOOL
SCIENCE PROJECT *

Joann M. Stecher

The University of Illinois Elementary School Science Project is supported by the National Science Foundation. Its specific purpose is to produce astronomy materials that are sound astronomically, that reflect the structure of the sub-

* REPRINTED FROM *Science and Children*, Vol. 2, No. 5, February 1965, pp. 23–24. Copyright, 1965, by the National Science Teachers Association, Washington, D.C. Reprinted by permission of the author and the publisher. Miss Stecher is Research Associate at the University of Illinois.

ject as it is viewed by astronomers of stature, and that can be handled by teachers and children in actual classrooms. The prepared materials are designed for use in grades five through eight.

THE University of Illinois Elementary School Science Project is an astronomy sequence for grades five through eight that delineates certain major concepts intended to assist the student to perceive the basic structure of the subject. By concentrating on the intellectual power of a few pervasive ideas in astronomy, a cogent entity is developed, rather than a description of loosely connected facts and phenomena. "Process" goals that characterize certain elementary-school science programs are also emphasized. In particular, project books stress the development of a rational argument for a scientific idea, rather than assertion.

During the summer of 1964, nineteen astronomers, science education specialists, and teachers participated in the fourth summer writing conference of the Project. A brief description of the six books written during these conferences illustrates the topics by which the unifying ideas of the astronomy sequence are presented.

Book 1, *Charting the Universe,* covers such topics as measurement, distances in the solar system and beyond, the size and shape of the earth, and the inverse square law applied to light as a tool for determining great distances. Book 2, *The Universe in Motion,* outlines conceptual models to account for observed motion. The student is introduced to geocentric and heliocentric perspectives. Book 3, *Gravitation,* deals with such concepts as velocity, acceleration, mass, and force. The focus of Book 4, *The Message of Starlight,* is on methods astronomers use in analyzing starlight to obtain information about the composition of stars. The emphasis in Book 5, *The Life Story of a Star,* is stellar evolution. Book 6, *Galaxies and the Universe,* introduces the student to our galaxy, other galaxies, and cosmology. Astronomy is an outstanding instance of an interdisciplinary field in the physical sciences. Concepts of physics, mathematics, physical chemistry, and geophysics are essential features of each book.

The first three books have had extensive trial in schools all over the country. The classroom situations were in public and private schools; suburban and urban schools; segregated and nonsegregated classes. The teachers varied widely in science background. Science consultants, principals, or teachers served as local project coordinators and also gave assistance to individual teachers as needed.

Book revision has been based on the reactions solicited from cooperating teachers both in writing and through interviews. Members of the Project staff observe extensively in classes where the materials are being tried to supplement written teacher reactions. Numerous conferences are held with participating teachers. Judgments are also invited from scientists who have not participated in the summer writing conference.

The testing phase of Book 1, *Charting the Universe,* and Book 2, *The Universe in Motion,* and their teacher's guides have terminated. Enough data from teachers and consultants were accumulated to develop an edition of these books that will stand for the present. Book 3, *Gravitation,* was revised in 1964 on the basis of reactions from over 300 teachers who tested the materials during the 1963–64 school year. The teacher's guide for *Gravitation;* Book 4, *The Message of Starlight* and its guide, are now in trial edition form and are being tested in classrooms during 1964–65. Substantial preliminary writing has been completed on the remaining books in the series, but Books 5 and 6 will not be submitted for extensive classroom trial until 1965–66.

Certain evaluation activities have been initiated that extend beyond book revision. The Project is interested in certain long-range effects of the books on children—how their viewpoint of science and scientists may have been modified, for example.

The Project has been supported since 1960 by the National Science Foundation. Co-directors are J. Myron Atkin, Professor of Science Education, University of Illinois and Stanley P. Wyatt, Jr., Professor of Astronomy, University of Illinois. Senior authors for the series are Henry Albers, Astronomy Department, Vassar College (Book 1); Karlis Kaufmanis, Astronomy Department, University of Minnesota (Book 5); Benjamin F. Peery, Astronomy Department, Indiana University (Book 4); Gibson Reaves, Astronomy Department, University of Southern California (Book 6); and Stanley P. Wyatt, Jr. (Books 2 and 3).

THE SCHOOL SCIENCE CURRICULUM
PROJECT *

Richard F. P. Salinger

The School Science Curriculum Project (SSCP) at the University of Illinois is supported by the National Science Foundation. Its specific purpose is to develop improved science materials for the elementary and junior high school via instructional materials for students and teachers. This project is committed to a philosophy described by the term "humanistic efficiency." Such

* REPRINTED FROM *The Science Teacher,* Vol. 33, No. 1, January 1966, pp. 37–39. Copyright, 1966 by the National Science Teachers Association, Washington, D.C. Reprinted by permission of the author and the publisher. Dr. Salinger is Project Director of the School Science Curriculum Project at the University of Illinois.

efficiency would enable children and adults to recognize the nature of our times and that of the future; to recognize the interdependence of the total range of man's intellectual endeavor and the rate at which things are changing; and to recognize the many opportunities that can lead to the development of functional, literate human beings.

THE SCHOOL Science Curriculum Project at the University of Illinois began its work early in 1963 to direct efforts toward the improvement of science programs in the elementary through junior high school levels. Originated under the College of Education by the late Gilbert C. Finlay, Professor of Education, and funded by the National Science Foundation, SSCP operates under the principles laid down in the early planning stages. These are to search for and to develop the most effective teaching methods and to make selections of science content best suited to serve current and future needs.

Activities are focused to provide a judicious selection of topics and an efficient teaching strategy in materials developed for elementary through junior high school science programs. Periodic meetings include summer study sessions of scientists, educators, and consultants in various fields; workshops for teachers and children; liaison and exchange of personnel in related curriculum projects; attendance at professional conferences of science and education groups; and frequent consultation of staff members with interested school groups, professional organizations, academic institutions, industry, and government.

Prepared mainly for teachers, materials are selected from a variety of discipline areas, such as the physical and biological sciences, earth sciences, anthropology, mathematics, linguistics, and design. In addition, inexpensively constructed apparatus models, as well as films, are developed to accompany some of the lesson demonstrations. As the materials take form, initial testing is done with small local classes. Later such materials are revised and developed for broader testing and use at the SSCP Trial Centers, currently consisting of 21 and located throughout the nation. After evaluation procedures are completed on feedback data from the Trial Centers, materials are released for more extensive use under direction of the Project.

The SSCP is one curriculum project, among several, whose efforts are directed primarily toward content course improvement in the levels from kindergarten through junior high school. It recognizes that curriculum development is a complex activity that defies a simple, clear description; and also that one unique solution does not exist or ever will. Nevertheless, its objectives will follow basically the development of a curriculum capable of formulating habits that are applicable beyond the educational structures in which they are required. Within this framework, the SSCP believes that a child or student learns best—when he is given an opportunity to be involved in science himself; when he sees the rationale and structure of the problems to be solved; and when he can make his own analysis of such problems. Thus, by a strong emphasis on personal involvement, the teaching units of SSCP aim at helping the student form and use rational, yet creative thought patterns. The challenge is to sort from the myriad possibilities open, those experiences of sufficient generalizing potential to make them worth developing on the child's part, as opposed to those which add to the storehouse of factual knowledge.

PHILOSOPHY OF THE PROJECT

The SSCP is committed to a philosophy more aptly described by the term of *humanistic efficiency*. In definition, the purport of the term conveys an urgent need to be *efficient*—not an efficiency in the cold sense, but one which recognizes we are working with people—children and adults. Such efficiency must be stratified to enable us to recognize the nature of our times and that of the rapidly approaching future; to recognize the interdependence of the total range of man's intellectual endeavor and the rate at which things are changing; and to recognize the many opportunities that can lead to the development of functional, literate human beings.

Following are the major points of an interpretative summary in terms of humanistic efficiency as related to SSCP objectives.

Fundamentally, and most important in a democratic society, a subject—whether it be science or any other study—should be taught for its own sake in any curriculum for general education. Satisfaction of learning in any area should be reason enough for its study. Although this view is less popular than many of the existing arguments for teaching science, it constitutes a potent wedge for shaping new norms in a curriculum program.

Recognizing the force of such a wedge, the School Science Curriculum Project directs its early development stages around the question: "What should an adult know about science?" The Project then works backward, in effect, to find out what can be inserted in the traditional sense, and where or at what levels material with implicit values can best be introduced to meet the needs of future citizens.

A number of questions immediately come to mind. Which adults are we concerned about—living in what time? In effect, who are we educating and why? Actually, we are concerned about the education of the general public for the time in which they live and the time into which they are rapidly moving; an education that encourages and contributes to scientific literacy. More importantly, the view is to understand the nature of the scientific enterprise, as well as to stress some of its practical aspects. It is what Robert Karplus has described as providing students with sufficient knowledge and experience so they will have some understanding of the scientific work being carried on by others, even though they, themselves, do not become scientists.

On the purely intellectual level, science is as honest, creative, and challenging an intellectual activity as any to which one could devote his energy.

We want to emphasize further that there is nothing new in suggesting that people find out about the nature of the world around them, or study natural law, or attempt to understand something of science, or "sciencing." After all, science is a part of Western history, culture, and tradition. Western man has devoted intellectual energy to the pursuit of this activity for centuries. It is disturbing when a value judgment is made by some as to whether science is good or bad, or better or worse than the humanities; and whether one subject should be studied as opposed to another. An individual in today's age cannot function effectively unless he is knowledgeable in both science and the humanities. To function effectively, one must be a part of the decision-making process. People cannot afford to go through life in an enforced passive role, unable to participate in any active way, either in supporting or criticizing important actions taken in "their behalf" because of ignorance of the underlying rationale for the idea in question.

Furthermore, the role of science in today's life is beyond value judgment. The role played by science and technology in our daily activities is a reality, not a question of *like* or *dislike*. Moreover, its role increases daily. Although a functional adult in our times should know something about science, this does not mean that he *must* be a scientist. It does mean that he *must* know enough about the scientific enterprise to understand something of its nature, its limitations, its capacity for change, the implications of scientific things in our daily lives, and, even more important, the relationship of science to the other fields. Specifically, we need to avoid what David B. Truman, Dean of Columbia College, has described as "cultural incompetence."

People need to be aware of the "inter-connectedness" of knowledge in *all* fields. Without such knowledge, it is difficult for man to manage such complex problems as, for example, urban chaos and the possibilities of nuclear war. Unless we learn to handle the complex problems of society involving many fields of knowledge, our incompetence will result in destroying the fabric of society and extinguishing the values that have made our technical achievements possible. The greatest danger lying ahead in the unfamiliar, revolutionary future, as pointed out by Elting Morison, is that men with obsolete learnings and modes of learning will lose the power to understand their environments or themselves in the midst of their novel surroundings.

What we need are profound changes in the process of education. We need somehow, in the development of our materials, to make provision for exchange of information and activities between teachers and schools, to overcome the lack of lateral and vertical communication between teachers within a school, and the lack of articulation between schools of different levels.

Humanistic efficiency dictates economy of effort in our own work. Our stand is strong in this direction. Rather than put our energy into development of materials while removed from children, hoping the materials will be suitable when tried and perhaps learning otherwise after the expenditure of much effort, we insist on working with children from the outset.

We select an idea from our accumulated pool (a choice governed by the talents of our staff, consistent with our reasoning that a person should work only in his area of competence), and start to prepare an outline representing, at the adult level, the steps we believe must be followed to achieve a reasonable understanding of the idea. At this point, having made only a modest investment of time, we invite children representing several grade levels and different cultural backgrounds to visit the Project and work with us. Through conversation and/or manipulation of materials and apparatus, information is gathered about how far and how fast we can go with a particular idea. In other words, with a small intellectual and time investment, we can begin to judge the suitability and feasibility of the ideas in our lesson outlines.

It must be clearly understood in what sense we seek the aid of children. As adults we earnestly try to avoid making *a priori* assumptions about what is right and good for children. Rather, we decide on the areas to which they might be exposed. Only the children, with their different perception of the world, can help us make intelligent modifications of our adult outlines. In effect, the child's role is to moderate our work, providing the key to guide us in determining how much, and at approximately what age level, we can insert certain topics to begin building competence in a particular area. One contingency for which we must be prepared as a result of this approach is the possibility that our research may lead to inclusion of new topics and abandonment of dearly held ones that generally have been included at the elementary level. For example, work to date might cast doubt on including, with young children, such sophisticated subjects as atomicity, electricity, and the nature of light—in spite of their power as scientific models.

Having made the first trial for feasibility and the adjustments which seem indicated in our original outline, we next try the material from the modified outline in a classroom. A member of the Project staff acts as "teacher" in this step, usually under observation by another staff member. The classroom trial yields information about the interaction of students with one another, the teacher, and the material, which cannot be obtained by working with a few selected students. We begin to discover the logistic problems: How the students can be supplied with apparatus if required; how we can work in the time allotted; some of the questions that will be raised; the answers students give to questions posed by other students; the kinds of discussion which can be generated; the aspects of our outline which are worthy of more expansion than we had anticipated; and those aspects which should be dropped.

At the conclusion of this second level in the development of material, we are ready to write for teachers on how a similar set of lessons could be conducted. To this point, the investment of time is relatively modest. We think it represents better intellectual economy to begin serious writing only after these first steps have been taken.

CONCLUSION

We firmly believe that to produce a group of materials which are *humanistically efficient*, we must abandon the notion that one starts, with a clearly stated set of enumerated objectives, grade by grade. We are firmly convinced that the major task of curriculum developers is to search for feasible subject matter and efficient techniques for teaching it. Only when a set of such material has been accumulated should energy be directed toward consideration of possible curricular patterns of development.

We want our materials to be flexible for use in a variety of existing situations. We would like to suggest some alternative curricular patterns for materials, but we do not want to say that this is *the curriculum*. What is more, we know that our materials, in time, will become obsolete and be superseded by other materials in the future. Our real function is to provide a model that can be used successfully as the times change. In parallel with the development of materials for the classroom, more and more of our efforts need to be directed toward improvement of teacher-education programs.

Thus, we hope that our own enthusiasm may be successfully transmitted to the teacher. Enthusiasm is contagious; surely the teacher's own eagerness closely correlates with the successful use of our materials. Our intention is to foster lively classroom discussion, intelligently led, in which the teacher becomes a moderator and listens, and the child acts as the chief participant.

In the midst of a knowledge explosion, however, we must guard against overcrowding the curriculum. Data do not last long. We are beginning to see that learning can take place faster and earlier than we thought possible. We hope to generate not only a storehouse of knowledge, but also competence in individuals to make reasonable decisions and choices, to be aware of the possibility of change, and to be able to operate under present and future world conditions.

We believe an accumulation of learning and data, by themselves, has little meaning, and that it is unlikely that youngsters can be led to have a "real feeling" for the scientific enterprise by discussing the elements of something called the "scientific method." They need experience in working scientifically on a significant problem. In our trial teaching we allow the children to confront the data as developed and let them derive their own "answers." The materials are structured to let a child deal with natural phenomena that can be observed, measured, questioned, and classified by use of his own senses. We find it useful to avoid saying things like "we want to work like a scientist." The word "science" need not even enter the lessons as such. One learns by doing, not by being told what to do, or by applying labels to everything that is done. Many children are alienated from science by a continuous pitch for "a scientific method" that at times assaults them from every side.

We are mindful of the two kinds of behavior described by Jerome Bruner —the left-handed, and the right-handed ways of knowing and acting: the right-handed being clear, purposeful, and straightforward; the left-handed tentative, playful, witty, imaginative, or, sometimes, just "plain wrong." Our materials attempt to reflect opportunities for children to examine both ways. David Hawkins (previously with Educational Services, Inc.) has said: ". . . when the mind is evolving the abstractions leading to physical comprehension, all of us must cross the lines between ignorance and insight; many times before we truly understand."

The Project is addressing itself to an audience of more than 30 million children and one million teachers, representing an enormous plurality of situations, backgrounds, and aspirations. We are arguing for changes in a social structure governed by many fixed and binding conventionalities, some of which are about forty-five centuries old. The Project accepts the challenge underlining the involvements of the task to be done and has no illusions of the formidable obstacles to overcome.

MINNEMAST: THE COORDINATED SCIENCE AND MATHEMATICS PROGRAM *

Robert B. Ahrens

MINNEMAST, the Minneapolis Mathematics and Science Teaching Project, is a National Science Foundation supported curriculum project for mathematics and science in the elementary school. In this program, children are encouraged to examine the intimate relationship between science and mathematics. The emphasis is placed upon the activities of the scientist. Sequential units have been developed in mathematics and science based upon the key operations of science. The MINNEMAST science curriculum has a spiral structure that is based on these key operations of science rather than on the customary science topics.

"BUT SEED coats don't have zippers," cried the young botanist, with a hurt look in his eyes. He was discussing a question about a story of the germination of a bean seed with the story's author, a professional children's story writer. The writer was visibly disturbed that young children would gain a misconception about bean seeds. The problem was resolved to both parties' satisfaction by changing the terminology.

---

* REPRINTED FROM *Science and Children*, Vol. 2, No. 5, February 1965, pp. 16–18. Copyright, 1965, by the National Science Teachers Association, Washington, D.C. Reprinted by permission of the author and the publisher. Mr. Ahrens is a Science Teacher at the Vogel Elementary School in Evansville, Indiana.

The above was one of many similar incidents that occurred during the 1964 MINNEMAST Summer Writing Conference held at the University of Minnesota. MINNEMAST, Minnesota Mathematics and Science Teaching Project, is a National Science Foundation sponsored curriculum project for mathematics and science in the elementary school. During the 1964 summer writing conference, a composite group of eighty educators, scientists, mathematicians, psychologists, children's writers, science writers, artists, librarians, a musician, a historian, and college elementary education majors pooled their ideas, talents, and efforts to lay the groundwork for a coordinated science and mathematics program for kindergarten through ninth grade.

COORDINATED PROGRAM

A science program which makes use of mathematics skills will add to the child's capacity to gain a quantitative and deeper understanding of his physical and biological environment. In reciprocal fashion, the science program can serve to initiate and develop concepts of mathematics. This type of science program can provide the opportunities and emphasize the necessity of using mathematical skills. If young children are encouraged to examine critically the intimate relationship between science and mathematics, it should be possible to teach these children both mathematics and science in greater depth and understanding. Thus, the principle of a coordinated science and mathematics program for kindergarten through grade nine appears not only to be logical and practical, but mandatory. The National Science Teachers Association (NSTA) position on this subject is as follows: "Efforts in science curriculum development should be accompanied by corresponding developments in mathematics, and the two must be closely correlated at all levels."[1]

The emphasis of the MINNEMAST science program is placed upon the activities of scientists—what they do; how they think; how problems are approached and solved; and how these activities lead to prediction, new problems, and new experiments. The MINNEMAST program does not have as one of its objectives the teaching of the "scientific method" in the all too familiar way. Instead, the program is keyed to the operations of science.

OPERATIONS OF SCIENCE

Recent studies by psychologists and learning theorists have shown the importance of personal observation of objects in his environment and experimentation by the child. While results appear favorable, they also indicate that additional studies should and must be considered. It would seem only logical then, to extend observation and experimentation by encouraging active

[1] "The NSTA Position on Curriculum Development in Science." *The Science Teacher*, 29:32–5. December 1962.

student participation into other fundamental processes of science as much as possible.

The MINNEMAST Science Program has conveniently classified the operations of science into the following: Observation, Measurement, Experimentation, Description, Generalization, and Deduction. While other processes may be equally suitable, these seem useful as a point of departure. The operations of science, as listed above, are clearly interrelated and interwoven. It then becomes evident that an activity in such a program will involve not one, but several of the operations of science.

The problem of developing for the child the operations of science in appropriate teaching units is by no means a simple one. In fact, the success of the program is dependent upon the manner in which this is done. There is more to the operation of *Observation* than just training children to be observers. The operation of *Description* implies more than teaching children to give reports of their observations. The operation of *Experimentation* is much more than the duplication of some scientific experiment. It is therefore evident that if the operations of science framework are to be developed into a sound science program, a logical, complete, and sequential series of teaching units must be achieved.

SEQUENTIAL UNITS

The MINNEMAST sequential teaching units may be best illustrated by tracing the development of the operations of science through several units. A kindergarten unit encourages the child to disregard most of his physical and biological surroundings and to focus his attention upon simple objects one at a time. The children actually collect their own objects while participating in an "object hunt" activity either on the playground or on a walk through the neighborhood. Examination of the collected objects provides an observational technique that permits full use of the child's sensory equipment in a productive way. The child is then asked to sort the objects into groups called sets (mathematics program reinforcement). This forces the child to focus his attention on the properties of objects. He may place the objects into sets according to size, color, function, etc. A description of the object is then made in terms of its properties.

This type of *Observation* and *Description* approach is extended much more fully a year later in a first-grade unit emphasizing the properties of objects. A later first-grade unit places two or more objects into a system. Again the child is encouraged to ignore the objects outside the system. Here the child is confronted with the problem of the function that each object performs in the system. Experimentation begins when the child changes the initial state of a system in another first-grade unit and observes corresponding changes in its final state. A second-grade unit on variation of objects requires the child to employ basic techniques of *Measurement*. A later second-grade unit requires the child to employ data gained from measurement to predict the height of plants at a given future time.

As briefly indicated, various scientific operations are developed into sequential units that make clear some of the more detailed aspects of these operations and, in addition, exhibit some of their interrelationships.

SPIRAL STRUCTURE

The MINNEMAST science curriculum is based on a spiral structure. The structure is not based on the familiar repetition of subject-matter topics that one finds in the usual curriculum of this type. The MINNEMAST spiral is based on the operations of science as mentioned earlier: Observation, Measurement, Experimentation, Description, Generalization, and Deduction. The first "loop" of the spiral would include grades kindergarten through grade two. In this loop, the child will gain some experience in all of the listed scientific operations. The child's objective in this loop is to gain a modest overview and limited experiences in the entire structure of scientific activity. As a result, sequential activities in the next loop will have more meaning when they can be related to the overall structure.

Although the kindergarten-second grade loop contains all the operations, its greater emphasis will be with *Observation* and *Description*. As new units of the succeeding loop for grades three and four are developed, the emphasis will perhaps shift to *Measurement* and *Experimentation*. If this trend continues, the fifth-sixth grade loop would conceivably emphasize *Generalization* and *Deduction*. The reader should be reminded again that all loops will be represented by experiences in each of the six operations of science. The emphasis will change according to the needs of the child and the sequence of the program.

The objective of the MINNEMAST science program is to provide the child with a way of getting at information he seeks. The intellectual tools needed by the child can be compared to those needed by the scientist. The tools are really step-by-step schemes that the child can use discovering relationships and developing understandings.

The MINNEMAST science program has attempted to incorporate the findings of the Swiss child psychologist, Jean Piaget,[2] into the curriculum. The brevity of this article prevents a just discussion; but, briefly, Piaget's findings indicate the sequence in the manner concepts are constructed by the child.

It is expected that children involved in the program will actually obtain more information in an incidental way than those exposed to an information-oriented curriculum. Children will acquire knowledge only for the purpose

[2] F. H. Flavell. *The Development of Psychology of Jean Piaget.* D. Van Nostrand, Inc., Princeton, New Jersey, 1963, p. 85–237.

of winning new knowledge. Factual information unrelated to the purpose has little value. Children will instead learn fundamental operations common to all science.

MINNEMAST'S FUTURE?

The MINNEMAST program is just one of perhaps a half dozen major science curriculum studies being conducted in the elementary school today. Its strategies of learning appear to be on a solid foundation when compared to the criteria set down by a recent Conference on Science Concepts called by NSTA.[3] Its program is now being tested by fifteen college test centers and 8200 children throughout the United States. Its worth must still be proven, but the future of this coordinated science and mathematics program appears bright.

[3] Paul DeHart Hurd. "Toward a Theory of Science Education Consistent with Modern Science." *Theory Into Action . . . in Science Curriculum Development.* National Science Teachers Association, Washington, D.C. 1964, p. 9.

A SCIENCE PROGRAM FOR THE ELEMENTARY GRADES: THE UTAH ELEMENTARY SCHOOL SCIENCE PROJECT *

John K. Wood

The Elementary School Science Project at the Utah State University is supported by the National Science Foundation. Its purpose is to provide lessons in basic science for elementary school children in grades one and two, stressing methods of observing changes in the characteristics of interacting objects. This program is in the form of a manual for first and second grade teachers. The children are given relatively simple puzzles to solve in order to develop observational skills. Problems are then introduced which are more complex. Attention, however, is still focused on single attributes of objects. After

* REPRINTED FROM *Journal of Research in Science Teaching*, Vol. 2, Issue 4, 1964, pp. 323–327, by permission of the author and the editor. Dr. Wood is Chairman of the Department of Physics at Utah State University, Logan.

children have had experience recognizing various properties of objects, they are brought to situations where the description of an object may change as a result of its interaction with another object. This science program attempts to reinforce the child's own experience of observation and classification, and proposes to teach him a systematic approach to new problems.

SCIENCE, including mathematics, should be a basic part of the primary curriculum along with communication skills. This conclusion is based on the need of children for rather simple, clear cut steps in concept formation. It is easier, for example, for a child to understand the concept of force well enough to express himself by actions or words than to understand the concept of government or good health. The implication is not that one should avoid teaching ideas about government and good health, but that the examples leading to a concept of force are less complicated, and the conditions are more sharply defined and therefore easier for a child to grasp. He has had far more personal experience with forces than he has had with government or the need for good health. A concept is a word or phrase which represents a generalization of experience.[1] The concept, for example, tree, is a generalization based on visual and tactile experience, and a child can express this generalization on command, by drawing a recognizable object.

The child learns, in his first four or five years, to observe trees and classify them in such a way that he does not mistake a tree for a telephone pole or a weed. He can learn to classify objects in many different ways if the occasion is provided, and this experience can be used to develop an understanding of many scientific concepts. The purpose of the study described here was to develop observational awareness in first grade children and to provide experiences that would give them an understanding of the procedures used in science and some of the concepts which arise.

Much material has been written for the first grade teacher to use, but in far too many cases, the material provides a great heap of ready-made observations rather than experiences in how these observations are obtained and how they are related. For example, a child may read or observe that a magnet picks up iron nails or that a plant requires light to grow, but he is not made aware that these are both instances of the interaction of objects, and a careful study of interactions of objects makes up the concept we call science. The child is thus deprived of an understanding of science in favor of a catalog of the facts of science.

The writers of science teaching material cannot be indicted as a group for presenting a picture of science which does not approximate more closely the science being practiced. The writers are not, for the most part, practicing scientists but have obtained their knowledge of the subject, second-hand at best. The indictment remains for the scientists, only some of whom have realized recently that they must contribute to elementary science teaching and avoid misrepresentation. The problem of communication with non-scientists arises, and it is even more acute when one tries to communicate with children. This is, however, a surmountable problem.

Many methods have been chosen as ways to teach science to young people. The seasons, weather, rocks, and machines have been used as science units. A number of facts are presented and experiments are described in these units which the student is expected to accept because the title on the cover of the book is "Science" and we live in an age of science. This is not the way that scientific ideas are developed nor is it the way in which scientists get the information.

Problems in science do not just materialize with full-blown answers, complete with a list of pertinent observations. Problems arise because of the curiosity of some person, that is, how and why does this phenomenon occur? The only prior information one has about this phenomenon is all the pertinent knowledge he has gained up to the present, and even the usefulness of this information may be doubtful. How does one go about solving a problem? Can this procedure be taught to first grade children? The first question can be answered, since these are the procedures used in science. The second question is under investigation by several groups, and only qualitative subjective answers can be given at present.

Since all information in science is obtained through the senses, the observer is an important factor in the procedure of collecting information. The observer [2] must note carefully all that happens and report what he sees without making any comment. The properties of objects, such as size, color, shape, weight, or temperature are noted because the interesting phenomena of nature occur when objects interact with resultant changes in their properties. New interactions and new properties of objects are discovered in the process of making careful observations. Gathering information in this way is not new to six-year-old children. These are the methods they have always used and they are delighted to know that these procedures are approved.

THE PROGRAM FOR THE FIRST GRADE

The ideas expressed above, have been incorporated into a first grade science program by the Elementary School Science Project * at Utah State University. This program is in the form of a manual for teachers and will be followed by a similar manual for the second grade. The children are given some relatively simple puzzles to solve in order to develop their observational skills. They practice planning a course of action to solve the puzzles. The puzzles are based on two sets of blocks and follow a proposal of Vygotsky [1] which was developed into games by the K-3 section of the 1963 Elementary Science Conference of the Educational Services, Inc.[3] The children identify patterns formed with the blocks in several simple games. The blocks of the

* Supported by the National Science Foundation.

second set have three properties or attributes, *viz.*, color, shape, and size (four colors, four shapes, two sizes). These blocks provide for somewhat more complicated games in which the child must conceive a plan encompassing several steps to solve the problem. The general type of problem requires that the child describe a block which is missing from a pre-established matrix. This identification is based upon the pupil's discernment of the pattern or sequence of the remaining blocks, or through his asking questions about the attributes of the missing or displaced block.

The next step is to introduce the children to problems that are more complex than the block puzzles; however, attention is focused on single attributes of the object in succession. The attributes of some objects are compared, such as weight, temperature, size, color, position, or pitch. The children are then given many examples where they must decide on the similarity or difference between object A and object B. Only a comparison is given with no explanation of why a difference or similarity exists. Objects are then classified according to many different criteria. Two objectives are gained with these experiments. The children develop an awareness that (1) observations can be made with all the senses, and (2) that objects can be classified according to the different attributes of the objects. One child, for example, brought a collection of different kinds of objects which cover containers. These were lids and stoppers of many kinds, and the collection was made with no suggestion or help from either teacher or parents. The children are shown visually and aurally, the relationship between the volume and pitch of an air stream blown over the open edge of a bottle. They can then guess the relative volumes of unseen containers by hearing the sounds produced by the air stream.

The classification of objects can be extended as far as the manipulative and communicative skills of the child are capable. Teaching time does not allow extensive development of this objective in any one year, but the basic foundation can be built upon with more complicated problems as the child progresses through school. The classification of biological specimens presents an excellent example of this type of problem. It is interesting to note that the historical development of biological science starts with classification.

After the children have had some experience recognizing the various properties of objects, they are shown some situations where the description of the object may change as a result of its interaction with another object. The length of a spring changes when it is pulled by some other object such as a hand or a weight. A chair changes its position in the room when it is pushed with a finger. The tips of fingers change shape and color when they are against tables or windows or other finger tips. Many of the experiments which are used to describe the attributes of objects are repeated to show the changes in properties when objects interact with each other. The attention of the child is focused, not on the properties of the objects but on the changes in these properties. The child is well aware that something caused the interaction and may be aware of a causal chain of events, but he is usually satisfied to rest his attention on the interacting objects at a particular time and position.

One can draw on the child's experience as a starting point to illustrate the interaction of objects and to center the attention of the child on the system of interacting objects. A sentence such as "Tom kicks the ball" is a description of an interaction between two objects. The direct interaction between the ball and Tom's foot implies that a better description of the interaction might be "Tom's foot kicks the ball." The children have learned to describe what they see, and this description turns out to be an enumeration of the objects of a system and their interaction. Other kinds of interacting systems of objects can be demonstrated where the children participate in the experiment. The children can connect wires, batteries, and lamps to produce an electrical interaction with very little guidance. They can produce acoustical interactions with resonant tuning forks and elastic interactions when springs are stretched, when sticks are bent, or when finger tips are pressed against window panes.

The strength of an interaction is demonstrated by comparing a large change in an object with a small change. The interaction between a spring and a finger is larger when the spring is stretched a great deal than when it its only stretched a small amount. The effect of one magnet on another is greater at short distances than at large distances. An attempt is made to measure the strength of interaction between a spring and a weight by successively adding equal sized weights to the end of the spring. The children measure the increasing length of the spring with paper tapes or marks on the chalkboard. No distinction is made between mass and weight. Weight, for the purposes of the manual is just the "heft" of an object as the child compares one object with another. Since the manipulative skill of a first grade pupil is limited, no special attempt is made to introduce quantitative measurement beyond using a length scale. Qualitative measurement is used extensively, however.

Although a reasonable amount of time was devoted to science in the first trial year of the first grade material, the teachers did not go beyond the introduction of interactions between objects and the suggestion that the strength of an interaction could be measured. The word, force, was introduced to represent the strength of an interaction, and the children appeared to have some understanding of the word judging from playground conversation.

THE SECOND GRADE TEACHER'S GUIDE

A second grade teacher's manual is under development, and a number of lessons are under preliminary test. The block games are re-introduced to the children in the form of more complex puzzles requiring a synthesis of several steps, and the interactions of objects are reviewed. The strength of an interaction is presented in greater detail using many of the examples already discussed in the first grade work. Elastic interactions, using for examples, finger tips, springs, rubber balls, or balloons, are close to the experience of the child and form a good base for illustration. Each child feels the repulsion and attraction of one magnet on another. They pull on springs, push chairs, pull each other at the end of a rope, and bounce balls. Thus, the concept of force arises as a way of describing the observation of the interaction of objects rather than being considered an object itself.

Energy is also presented as an interaction strength of a system of objects. An interaction between two objects is demonstrated which is detectable by the sense of touch in a different way than was used to detect "forces." A heated block of metal is placed in contact with a cold block of metal. A very noticeable change occurs, sensed by touching both after a few minutes of contact. There are no changes in shape or position but there is a change in temperature. Other illustrations of this kind can be shown, such as, the interaction between the sun and a piece of lead, a heater and a radiometer, or a beaker of water and a burner. Examples of "energy" changes are not difficult to find.

The problems which can be investigated using the concepts developed in the manner given above are numberless. The child has a framework of ideas which will be used in each new problem. There are, however, other aspects of science which a child should learn so that the quantitative understanding of interactions can be developed. They need to be able to tabulate and graph the data of experiments. A few such experiments were tried at the first grade level with moderate success. The children were provided with pictures of objects of different color and shape and were required to sort some similar objects and record the number of each kind beside the corresponding picture. The second grade children are introduced to graphical procedure through the used of peg boards. The position of a peg is located from a number pair, and simple designs are constructed from a set of number pairs, and an elastic band outlines the shape of the resulting figure.

An extension of the utility of the graphical procedure introduces a time scale through the number line method of arithmetic. The children can then perform a number of experiments which are dependent on time. The time-temperature graph of heating water appears to be within the grasp of second grade children since they have had experience in reading a thermometer and a clock. The heating rate is varied in a subsequent experiment. They plot the recorded information with some assistance and get an overall view of the effect of temperature on water.

The extension of science teaching to interactions other than the ones mentioned here seems to be unlimited. The interaction approach has meaning for the first grade child and the teachers are able to pick up the ideas with very little outside help. Limited experience with teachers who are new to the program indicates that they are somewhat apprehensive of starting, but after seeing a lesson or two presented by another teacher, they are eager to try. An elementary school supervisor who has taught or studied the program can apparently lead a group of teachers through the first grade manual.

It is evident from the description that this project contains little biology.

This is not due to any reluctance to use the method in biology. A biology supplement has been prepared for trial use. Biology at the first or second grade level involves classification of plants and animals and fits very well into the program described here. The introduction of interactions will follow the same general outline that is used for any system of objects, but one must remember that the environment is somewhat more extensive and more difficult to control for a biological experiment than for a purely physical one; nevertheless, the problems are similar. Biology is not a branch of physical science, and distinctive methods and procedures have developed in its growth. However, the basic structure of any science follows the general steps proposed for children in this science program.

The science program described here reinforces the child's own experience of observation and classification and proposes to teach him a systematic approach to new problems. The causal explanations of the studied phenomena are given by the teacher or are suggested by an experiment within the framework of the observation of interacting objects. As the children become more proficient in handling both ideas and objects, the problems can become more complex, and more detailed observations can be made. Special training for the teacher does not appear to be necessary, at least at the first and second grades; however, a trained supervisor gives the teacher the confidence necessary to undertake the program.

REFERENCES

1. Vygotsky, L. S. *Thought and Language*, Wiley, New York, 1962, pp. 56, 82.
2. Karplus, R., "Meet Mr. O," *Science and Children*, 1, 19–24 (1963).
3. Armitage, D., W. Hull, and A. Kattet, *Progress Report of the K–3 Section— Explorations with Five-Year-Olds*, Elementary School Science Conference, Peabody School, Cambridge, Massachusetts, Educational Services, Inc., Watertown, Massachusetts, 1963.

DISADVANTAGED CHILDREN AND THEIR PARENTS: THE HOWARD UNIVERSITY ELEMENTARY SCIENCE PROJECT *

Joseph C. Paige

The Howard University Elementary Science Project is supported by a grant from the Cooperative Research Branch, U.S. Office of Education. The program attempts to involve disadvantaged children and their parents in a program of compensatory science experiences. The project hopes to measure its success in positive behavior changes both in children and in their parents, as reflected in improved reading and verbal skills, development of scientific attitudes and reasonable competencies, improved human relation practices, and a willingness to share community leadership and work for the solution of community problems.

THE Howard University Elementary Science Project (ESP) has been designed to fill some educational gaps of children and their parents that have resulted from economic deprivation. The purposes of ESP are (1) to develop a program of compensatory science experiences for disadvantaged children (K–6) and their parents; (2) to determine whether or not the participation in these experiences by disadvantaged children and their parents can help, in a significant way, to overcome social and personal handicaps which usually attend such privation; and (3) to discover what changes in behavior in both children and parents may result from participation in the project.

The Project, supported by a grant from the Cooperative Research Branch, U. S. Office of Education, grew out of the need to provide innovations to conventional efforts in education that schools in deprived areas either could not or have failed to provide for their students. The program attempts to involve children and their parents simultaneously. Children from kindergarten through sixth grade are given simple instructions for participation in science

---

* REPRINTED FROM *Science and Children*, Vol. 2, No. 6, March 1965, pp. 11–13. Copyright, 1965, by the National Science Teachers Association, Washington, D.C. Reprinted by permission of the author and the publisher. Dr. Paige is an Assistant Professor in the Department of Education and of Physics, and also Director of the Elementary Science Project, at Howard University.

experiences, to be performed jointly with their parents at school or in their homes.

Project investigation has suggested an urgent need for some drastic reforms in the teaching of science in slum area public schools. ESP research also suggests some basic weaknesses in the teaching of some nonscience subjects. Hence, the Project has many implications for school systems which have not found adequate means of dealing with these disadvantaged children.

COOPERATING CENTERS

Cooperating centers have been established in Washington, D. C., North Carolina, and New York City. (In Washington, D. C., the Katie C. Lewis School and the New Samaritan Baptist Church serve as centers. In North Carolina, four rural groups comprise one center. In New York, The East River Children's Center of Mills College of Education serves as the center.) Discussions are also under way to use the Project materials in some of the programs of the Howard University Community Service Center and the Model School System of the District of Columbia. More than 300 children and their parents have used the materials in cooperating centers of the Project.

SELECTION OF PARTICIPANTS

When selecting participants for the Project, special consideration is given to persons in the lowest socioeconomic categories. Criteria for family participation in the program includes the following:

1. Residence within the area of a cooperating center;
2. Agreement to attend Saturday sessions by all siblings in grades K–6, and at least one parent or adult member of the household;
3. Free of any physical disability that might impede reasonable participation in program activities;
4. Free of serious behavior problems which the project staff considered undesirable from the point of view of classroom control or teacher effectiveness;
5. Reasonable facility with the English language; and
6. Socioeconomic status of the family within the range generally described as representative of "deprived" or "disadvantaged" circumstances, except in special cases.

PROCEDURE

The operation is divided into four phases. Phase I covered the period of March 1–September 30, 1964; this phase consisted of the development and testing of some materials with respect to their utility. A Summer Writing Conference comprised Phase II. Phase III (still in process) consists of expanded development and testing of materials produced during the Summer Writing Conference of the 1964–65 school year. Phase IV will deal with evaluation of the 1964–65 trial materials, a writing conference, and Project expansion.

Each Project center works with twenty families. Coordinators and interviewers are assigned to explain the Project to the families in home visits. This prepares families for the science experiences to be conducted at home and group meetings, and to establish liaison between the families and the center group. All ESP personnel are readied for this work by an orientation program which includes the following topics: (1) assumptions and aims of the Project, (2) social problems and resources in the local area, (3) problems of communication, (4) methods for approaching, interviewing, and working with disadvantaged persons, (5) group dynamics, and (6) use of the science materials.

VOLUNTEER ASSISTANTS

Nonprofessionals comprise the corps of volunteer assistants for the Project. The volunteers are, for the most part, undergraduate college students, high school graduates, and some school dropouts. All volunteers are trained by the Project staff. A volunteer worker has a threefold role. He serves as interviewer, tutor, and aide. As interviewer, he has the responsibility of visiting the homes of a specified number of families to establish necessary rapport, and to collect pertinent data. The volunteer also participates in scheduled periodic interviews usually held by a Project staff member on Saturdays following the science participation session.

As tutor, he visits homes and assists children and their parents in performing their home science experiences. His responsibility as an aide is to assist the teacher-coordinator in all aspects of the science participation program.

Individual histories, reports from interviews, observations of classroom teachers, and other reports of the participating families are made available to the volunteer assistants. This background information enables the assistant to evaluate the progress the entire family is making during their participation in the program.

HOME VISITS

Home visits by coordinators, interviewers, and volunteer assistants help to effect cooperation among family members in performing the experiences and to prepare them for sharing as families in the programs at the center. Several inter-family projects have been established at the centers.

SUPPLEMENTARY MEETINGS

Additional sessions for children and adults are scheduled at various homes. These sessions may center around one of the science experiences, a related area, a new science topic, or any area of interest to the group. These sessions are aimed at raising questions of personal and community health and welfare, suggesting relations between science and other areas, and broadening general experiences. In performing the science experiences at home, participants are encouraged to cope with problems in their own way and to follow-up whatever new problems develop.

SMALL GROUP ORGANIZATION

The organization of the centers into small groups has several advantages. It facilitates the coordination of Project operations and observations. Participants seem to develop (1) a sense of individual pride through increased general literacy and scientific literacy in particular, (2) a sense of family pride and harmony through successful interactions in a common experience, (3) the power of articulating needs through science experiences, and (4) a new awareness of the world in which they live.

DESIGN OF EXPERIENCES

1. *Materials:* Materials for the experiences include science packets, kits, and simple items adapted to the disadvantaged persons. The Project also draws materials from other national science programs, adapting them when necessary to fit into the aims of ESP. To date, the Project has used modifications of material developed by the Elementary Science Study, Educational Services, Inc.; Science Service, Inc.; Science Materials Center, Inc.; and Ward's Natural Science Establishment.

2. *Plan:* The assumption is made that the attention span of our participants is short; discouragement is easy. Hence, the science experiences are designed to be short and simple, yet probing enough to arouse and hold the interest of children and adults. Each experience is designed to allow the participant to make his own discoveries.

3. *Format:* Elementary Science Project kits present wide flexibility with respect to the interests and abilities of family groups. Each kit consists of some simple materials and a work booklet which takes into account the limitations of the participants.

The organizational format of the work booklet provides a minimum set of directions, guiding the children and their parents through the experience by raising questions. Observation and our experience has shown that questions raised by the child- or parent-manipulator and the "trial" and "error" follow-ups, are far more significant than the questions suggested by the materials. The answers to these questions have taken a variety of forms, some have required thought, others have required careful experimentation, and detailed observations.

The design of the science experiences are basically open-ended. Materials have been designed to help the experimenter to develop a logical consistency in his explanation, rather than seeking a correct answer. Understanding of a particular concept or generality is emphasized. "Yes" or "no" answers to questions are discouraged in all Elementary Science Project experiences. Instead, discussions are encouraged whenever questions are raised. In fact, a major provision of the Project plan is that discussion will develop concurrently with the experimentation.

Fifty experience packets have been tested by the Project staff. These materials were the products of the 1964 Summer Writing Conference and cover such diverse topics as: light, color, heat, pressure, friction, nutrition, sensual perception, crystals, metals, magnets, suction cups, and taste. The selection of these topics was somewhat arbitrary, but the staff thought that they would serve to encourage discovery, inference, exploration, observation, and other competencies, attitudes, and skills.

The design of the science experience is to help participants learn (1) how to observe and to keep accurate records of their observations, (2) how to follow directions, (3) how to make accurate measurements, and (4) how to apply some of what they learn to daily living.

One other objective of the Project is the hope that through home and group activities, the subjects might gain experience in (1) meeting unexpected situations, (2) making initial contact with people, (3) arousing interest in problems of mutual concern, and (4) soliciting and utilizing the opinions of others for constructive individual and group action.

EVALUATION

At this time, the real value of the Project is difficult to appraise. Parent participants in the Project, rarely, if ever, attended the meetings of the parent-teacher associations, neighborhood clubs, or community civic groups. The children had occasionally attended after-school programs at school, church, or a movie, but seldom, if ever, with their parents. After they had been helped individually in their own homes and at the Saturday sessions, many of these family groups began to relate to each other, to their neighbors, to the community, and to the school. The success of ESP will have to be measured in the positive behavior changes of the children and their parents, as reflected in improved reading and verbal skills, development of scientific attitudes and reasonable competencies, improved human relations practices, and more specifically, in the willingness to share community leadership and work for the solution of community problems.

SCIENCE TEACHER'S ADAPTABLE CURRICULUM: THE PORTLAND STAC PROJECT *

John S. Hutchinson

The Portland, Oregon, Science Teachers Adaptable Curriculum (STAC) is supported by Ford Foundation, Portland Public School, and Oregon State Curriculum funds. The Adaptable Curriculum involves the use of Keysort cards, on which are printed a marginal program and curriculum ideas. As such, the curriculum can be continuously revised rather than sporadically. The curriculum is designed to make use of the "discovery approach," in which the teacher attempts to stimulate the spirit of inquiry by conducting his class in a manner similar to the operation of a scientific research laboratory. The curriculum design also attempts to be consistent with the revisionary nature of science.

TWO TERMS which might be used to describe the science curriculum in Portland are flexibility and involvement. Its flexibility allows teachers to use a wide variety of curricular patterns in their classrooms. Involvement is an important aspect of the Portland program, accomplished by involving many teachers in committee work directed toward the improvement of the curriculum.

Flexibility and involvement are particularly applicable to a curriculum innovation which was initiated during the 1962–63 school year. This program is known as the Science Teacher's Adaptable Curriculum project and locally is referred to as STAC. This project incorporates a variety of teaching ideas placed on Keysort cards and used in a way similar to a teacher's handbook. In addition to the Keysort cards, reference books and other visual and audio resources are available. The reference materials are in the classrooms and are immediately available to the student and the teacher for continued research information.

---

* REPRINTED FROM *Journal of Research in Science Teaching*, Vol. 2, Issue 4, 1964, pp. 356–363, by permission of the author and the editor. Dr. Hutchinson is Assistant Supervisor of Science for the Portland, Oregon, Public Schools.

HISTORY OF STAC

Two committees of teachers met periodically during the 1961–62 school year for the purpose of preparing for a summer writing session. The committees were organized to study ways of improving general science, a ninth grade course, and applied science, an eleventh grade course. The general science course in Portland had traditionally been offered to heterogeneous groups of ninth graders as a survey course and taught for the most part from a single textbook. The applied science course was established locally to fill a void created when a new physical science course was written for college-capable, non-science oriented students. Applied science was to be taught to 11th and 12th grade underachievers who had not yet completed one year of science required by law for graduation. The course was to be oriented around laboratory work with no reading assignments being made. Classroom work was to be initiated from films, discussions, demonstrations, and other audio-visual stimuli.

In the summer of 1962, a writing session was held at Madison High School in Portland for the purpose of developing curriculum material. A wide variety of ideas was developed by the writing participants. Those participating in this writing conference were: Mrs. Hazel F. Karr, chairman from Wilson High School, Portland; Mr. Ralph Ennis of Madison High School, Portland; Mr. Frank Hutchison, Cleveland High School, Portland; Mr. James Karle, Lewis and Clark College, Portland; Miss Helen Koopman, Jefferson High School, Portland; Mr. John Sheehy, Roosevelt High School, Portland; Dr. Donald W. Stotler, Science Supervisor, Portland; Mr. Robert Van Atta, Portland State College, Portland; and Mr. Thomas Witty, Wilson High School, Portland. The writing session was one phase of a total curriculum study which is officially known as the Portland High School Curriculum Study.[1] The entire study touched most areas of the curriculum and was financed through a grant from the Ford Foundation. The writing session was conducted during one of the final years of the support for the total study.

The results of the first writing session amounted to a set of Keysort cards numbering in excess of 175. The specific ideas for these cards were organized around the three conceptual themes of *Physical-Chemical, Space Study,* and *Living Things.* The ideas were printed on the cards, and the marginal program of the cards was punched out corresponding to the conceptual theme and the specific ideas with which it dealt. The design of these materials was intended to include ideas which could be used in two and possibly all three of the approaches in the margin. In the finished product, it was found that regardless of which of the three approaches was selected, approximately 70% of the instructional programs overlapped.

Experimentation with the cards was carried out during the 1962–63 school year. Most of the general science teachers and applied science teachers used the STAC cards as the skeleton for their curriculum during that year. In addition, there were four elementary teachers officially experimenting with the materials at the 7th and 8th grade levels. Science in the seventh and eighth grades was taught in the homeroom. The major difficulties with the STAC program during the first year centered around insufficiencies of quickly available reference materials, and necessary equipment and supplies.

In-service plans for implementing the program extensively at the elementary level were made during the 1962–63 school year. Teachers from each of the ten comprehensive high schools in the city were called together during the winter term, 1963, for the purpose of instruction in the new approaches to elementary science both locally and nationally. The major emphasis in this class was on the Science Teacher's Adaptable Curriculum project. The selection of these in-service instructors was based on their prior experience with the STAC program in their own classrooms. These teachers conducted in-service classes in the spring term in their own high schools with one elementary teacher from each of the feeder schools to that high school. The teachers who attended from each of the elementary schools were then given a set of STAC cards for instructional purposes with students and other teachers in their own building. The STAC program at that time was still geared to the 7th, 8th, and 9th grades and to the 11th grade applied science course.

Committees of elementary teachers were established from the primary, intermediate, and upper grades during the 1963–64 school year. It was the intent for these committees to develop STAC decks for use by teachers at those three levels and also to act as feedback committees to screen any materials which came in from teachers who were using the card system in their classrooms. This work was financed by curriculum development funds from the Oregon State Department of Education. A limited number of cards was prepared and printed during 1963–64. Additional cards were printed during the summer of 1964 and sent to schools having teachers using these materials in their classrooms.

Two different types of in-service courses were taught during the 1963–64 school year. The first was a year-long, three-term course which started teachers in the fall in the intermediate and upper grade levels and walked them through individual teaching programs using the STAC cards as the skeleton outline. A second was taught as a single term course repeated for three terms. This course was primarily for people who already had a feeling for the philosophy of this approach but wanted to get some contact with the mechanics of using the cards.

The plans for the 1964–65 school year include a continuation of in-service courses in the use of these materials. These courses will include a year-long, walk-through for teachers at the primary, intermediate, and upper levels and also single term courses for teachers of the same grade levels. Furthermore, an evaluation of this program is now under way and should be completed in the spring of 1965. This evaluation will be described in a later section of this report.

Philosophy of STAC

A great deal has been written in recent years about the necessity for stimulating a spirit of inquiry in the student, particularly in science classes.[2,3] Indeed, a common ingredient of the NSF-financed science curricula is attention to ways of promoting student inquiry. The STAC program is designed to be most useful to that teacher who is attempting to stimulate his students to inquire into the nature of the universe and their place in that universe. In such a situation the teacher's role changes considerably. The teacher's role in the traditional science classroom has been one of a "fountain of knowledge." The teacher lectures about the facts of science, and the laboratory is a place where the student goes to prove that what the teacher has just stated is true. Instead of the natural reward of discovery on his own, he is rewarded artificially when he verifies the answer which the teacher has just given him in the lecture.

In promoting true inquiry on the part of the student, it is the responsibility of the teacher to establish an environment in which natural discovery can take place. This has been referred to in the literature [4] as the "Discovery Approach" in which the classroom-laboratory organization is a replication of a scientific research laboratory. The teacher is the director of research, and the researchers are the students in the class. All avenues of discovery are placed at the disposal of the students. Responsibility for this kind of organization falls jointly into the hands of the teacher and the student working together in cooperative planning sessions. The teacher is now more than a technician carrying out the instructions of a textbook author. He becomes a truly professional person directing the educational program which he, in his professional judgment, considers appropriate for the kind of student he has in class.

Additional support for this approach has been published recently in *School Science and Mathematics*.[5] This report clearly establishes that there has been little, if any, data supporting the premise that the most permanent learning comes from textbook-dominated courses. Indeed, these data support the hypothesis that a more effective learning environment is established with a room library of reference materials and a planned curriculum. A recent issue of *NEA Journal* spotlights an article which describes [6] how an entire school system adopted a research approach to science learning.

The STAC program is designed to be consistent with the revisionary nature of science. It has been estimated that half the scientific knowledge today will be revised to some extent within ten years. This kind of revision demands a curriculum which is evolutionary in the same way that an organism is evolutionary, with old tissue being discarded and replaced while at the same time new tissue is produced. The STAC program can carry out just such a self-renewing pattern. As old ideas become replaced by new, the old card containing these ideas can be discarded and improved materials can be added to the program. In fact one of the most important sources of revision is the teacher himself. As he tries these materials in the classroom, he can submit possible improvements to a screening board of teachers and scholars for incorporation in the program. In this way, the entire curriculum becomes a concerted effort of all teachers.

Feedback committees have been established at the primary (K–3), intermediate (4–6), and upper (7–9) grade levels to screen suggested improvements in the program. These feedback committees consisting of Portland teachers have a membership which is replaced each year. One person is retained to assure continuity. Scholars from the community act as consultants and help to avoid a curriculum which otherwise could become ingrained. This involvement taps a creative resource previously untouched. Such feedback provides an immediate test of theory in classroom practice, a situation which has existed all too little in the field of education in the past.

A program based on continuous feedback and revision, which places the teacher in the role of director of learning activities, can promote the realistic attainment of educational goals. Four goals or objectives have been established as those of foremost importance for the science instructional program in the Portland Public Schools. These are:

1. Stimulation and release of natural curiosity, initiative, and love of exploration.
2. The development of self-learning skills such as problem recognition, accurate observation and classification of those observations, appropriate hypotheses selection, and ability to design appropriate experiments.
3. Development of appropriate insights into the environment and self through selecting learning experiences from the various disciplines of science.
4. The development of values that are essential to successful inquiry such as integrity, humaneness, and faith in scientific procedures.

In order for these objectives to be realistic they must be bolstered with specific student behaviors which relate directly to those objectives and which are subject to immediate evaluation in the classroom. Such specifics have been written into the Portland program.

MECHANICS OF STAC

A teacher's handbook is generally organized in a manner logical to the person who has put it together. This handbook is intended to provide a variety of ideas for teaching and learning for both the instructor and student in a classroom. An important difference of the STAC program from the conventional handbook is that the ideas can be arranged in a pattern which is logical to the person organizing the learning.

The first step one takes in using the STAC deck is to consider the three approaches on the margin of the card (*Physical-Chemical, Space Study, Liv-*

ing Things) and decide which is most appropriate to his own background and the background and abilities of the students in his class. He selects from these three approaches or conceptual themes by pushing the needle sorter through the hole directly above the area which he has selected.

Let us assume that we have selected *Space Study* as our conceptual theme for the year's study in science at the 6th grade level. By inserting the needle through the hole directly above *Space Study* and raising the needle, the cards related to that conceptual theme will fall out. Once the desired cards have been separated, the remainder of the deck can be put away for the year. The cards which have been sorted from the deck represent the skeleton of our science curriculum for the year. These cards should be sorted and arranged by specific ideas into a sequence which seems most logical to the person who is conducting the course for the year. Once this is done he is ready to look at some things he can do to get the class started. Under each of the three approaches is a space labeled Starter. He should now place the needle through this hole and sort out those cards which will help him to get his study under way.

The directions and ground rules for using the STAC program are also included in the deck on specific cards and can be sorted out for the teacher who is unfamiliar with this program. Also, the objectives, basic ideas, and book lists are included for helping the teacher begin the program.

The specific ideas listed under *Space Study* may be used as guideposts for the year's study. The teacher should have done sufficient preplanning before introducing each topic to have reference materials and supplies on hand which will make it possible for students to pursue topics of their own selection within the area of study. These guideposts are tied together by the interconnecting thread of *Space Study*. In this way the program can maintain reasonable continuity throughout the year.

It becomes apparent that specific ideas from other approaches are also punched along the margin in addition to those in the conceptual theme selected for the year. This emphasizes the fact that the areas of science are interrelated and that study down a single narrow path for the year would be difficult. It indicates that the students also have the opportunity to broaden their base of scientific knowledge as they gain facility with the important processes of science.

Evaluation of STAC

The evaluation of an innovation in curriculum will form a base from which the program can be improved. The feedback obtained from this evaluation should be used to make judgments on future directions and thus the program continues to evolve and become more useful to those for whom it is designed.

Initial evaluation of the STAC program was done in terms of the enthusiasm with which the program was received by teachers. The approach used in requesting experimentation with this program was quite the reverse of that used with a traditional handbook for teachers. Traditionally, the materials of a handbook are developed by one person or a group of persons, bound into an inflexible book, and distributed among those for whom it was written. In requesting experimentation with this type of handbook, it becomes necessary that one build up all the strengths of such a handbook and play down any weaknesses which it may have. After the teacher has had an opportunity to examine it carefully, he can reject the entire package on the basis of a few weak spots.

The opposite approach has been used with the STAC program. As these cards were distributed among teachers, they were told that the program had weaknesses which they surely would discover and that their help was being sought in working out these weaknesses. They were requested to submit recommended activities for those which they found weak. Those activities which passed the feedback committee were printed and carried the names of the teachers who submitted them. The value of placing the name on the card is two-fold. First, it gives recognition to the person who has submitted it, and second, if another teacher has a question about any part of an activity, he can go directly to the originator of the material.

The major evaluation of STAC therefore has been based on the amount of use which the cards get in the classroom and the amount of feedback which is obtained from the teachers themselves. The response at the elementary level has been most encouraging. At least one set of materials has gone out to each of the grade level divisions (K–3, 4–6, 7–8) in each of the 76 eight-grade elementary schools of the district, and to many of the remaining 22 schools having fewer than eight grades. Most of the STAC decks were assigned to a school on the basis of teacher participation in the in-service classes which were offered. Thus, the interest has become widespread and use of the program is being rapidly extended. This observation offers positive evidence of the value and usefulness of the STAC program to teachers.

A statistical evaluation has been planned for the program. This evaluation involves comparing the mean scores of a group of students who were with the teachers one year when they were not using the program with the mean scores of a second group who were with the same teachers the following year when they were using the STAC program. The mean differences will be subjected to the t-test at the 1% level of confidence to determine whether or not the differences are significant. This evaluation is scheduled for completion sometime in the spring of 1965. The testing instrument to be used for this evaluation is a locally-designed test called the Portland Science Test. This test is now in its fifth year of development and has been subjected to the usual tests for validity and reliability. The format consists of a picture associated with a group of questions to focus attention and reduce the wording. Two columns of test items are on each page, one for measuring knowledge of the products of science, and the other for measuring knowledge of science processes.

FUTURE OF STAC

The world of business and industry is rapidly extending the techniques of computer analysis to greater efficiency of operation. There is no doubt that the computer will play an increasingly important role in the lives of all people. If educators are reluctant to examine the possibility of applying computer techniques to the problem areas of education, the day will surely come when the community pressures will force the application with great haste and little thought. It is immensely important that educators face the computer age with confidence and curiosity rather than reluctance and fear of replacement.

When Orville Wright first became airborne at Kittyhawk, N. C. in 1903, only the most daring thinkers considered that this flimsy craft would evolve into the powerful interplanetary space vehicles so familiar to us today. Yet the dynamics were set into motion when this flight took place. The dynamics are present and a similar evolution is possible for the STAC program. At the present rate of change, time is greatly compressed, however, and the evolution of STAC to computer techniques is already being considered.

A variety of clerical minutia captures the valuable instructional time of all teachers. Included in this minutia are several critical tasks which increase the effectiveness with which teachers can plan the learning experiences for the students. One of these tasks is the collection of information about the backgrounds and abilities of the 25 to 35 students in the class. Another is the collection of the appropriate learning experiences for these students in the light of their interests and abilities. With this information, the teacher must then match his own abilities and interests to those of the students and to the available curriculum. This triple matching process is accomplished only crudely, if at all, with present manual retrieval methods.

The STAC program is the first step in providing automatic retrieval of curricular ideas to the teacher. It may well be considered the "poor man's" computer! The next step is to devise a way to program the curriculum for a computer. Many high schools are already using computer techniques for storing and processing student data such as test scores and attendance. Others, such as Marshall High School in Portland, Oregon, are using computers experimentally to program students and thereby devise flexible class schedules.

The teacher may soon have all the elements necessary to set the stage for effective learning, literally at his very fingertips. He can maintain his position as generalist with all the specialist's advantages computerized for his use. A triple matching of student learning readiness with appropriate curriculum and instructor will complete the first step in the modern scheduling. The instructor would maintain final judgment for the selection of the actual learning experiences offered. A monitor screen would be located in his classroom on which he could request a preview of the available curriculum content and hints for teaching. His selection could then be requested and would be typed for him on a remote typewriter in his classroom. The appropriate equipment, supplies, and reference materials would be retrievable via computer and available immediately upon request.

If this sounds far-fetched, one should remember that the devices for such a pattern are already in existence. The creative genius of man is just starting to scratch the surface of the myriad possibilities. A step in this direction has already been taken in the Portland Public Schools. A grant of $12,500 has been made by the Board of Directors of the Louis W. and Maud Hill Family Foundation to this school system to aid in the initiation of a pilot project designed to use a Computer Center to program educational services.

The fascinating aspect of the computerized system is that it can be programed to do the unhuman chores, thereby liberating the teacher to do the human professional job for which he is hired. Thus, the teaching profession need not fear the future with computers but instead put its creative shoulder to the wheel and join in helping to go in directions which are concerned with better education for children.

REFERENCES

1. Kitzhaber, Albert R., Robert M. Gorrell, and Paul Roberts, *Portland High School Curriculum Study*, Ronald Press, New York, 1961.
2. Suchman, J. Richard, *The Elementary School Training Program in Scientific Inquiry*, University of Illinois, Urbana, Illinois, 1964.
3. Slesnick, Irwin L., "Inquiry and Critical Thinking in Science," *The Instructor*, **73**, 63 (1964).
4. Stotler, Donald W., "Elementary School Science in Portland, Oregon," *The Science Teacher*, **30**, 33–39 (1963).
5. Barrilleaux, Louis E., "A Comparison of Textbooks and Multiple Library Reference—A Report on the Initial Phases of an Experimental Study," *School Science and Mathematics*, **63**, 245–249 (1963).
6. Schulz, Richard W., "Building a Science Curriculum," *NEA Journal*, **53**, 21–23 (1964).

EVALUATING NEW PROGRAMS IN
ELEMENTARY SCIENCE *

Alphoretta S. Fish

Alphoretta S. Fish cautions against the use of teachers as mere adjuncts to the materials they teach when new programs are instituted. Dr. Fish considers it imperative that teachers play a more prominent role in the (1) examination of the system within which programs are conceived, (2) evaluation of the relationships between goals and methods, and (3) reconstruction of the program.

THERE IS much competition at this time to describe and prescribe for science instruction at the elementary school level. Scientists, psychologists, and educators are making concerted efforts to develop various curricula. Since scientists, psychologists, and educators represent different frames of reference, widely divergent kinds of curriculum designs are emerging. For example, there is a notion, on the one hand, that any effort to guide pupils to develop an understanding of the processes of inquiry should not be undertaken at the elementary school level. The psychologist, Gagné,[1] has stated:

"There is nothing wrong with practicing enquiry, and surely enquiry is the kind of capability we want students of science to attain in some terminal sense. But practicing enquiry too soon, and without a suitable background of knowledge, can have a narrowing and cramping effect on the individual's development of independent thinking."

On the other hand is the conviction that an important function of elementary school science instruction is to develop both the skills and understandings attending inquiry. Suchman [2] has stated his rationale as follows:

[1] Gagné, Robert M. "The Learning Requirements for Enquiry," *Journal of Research in Science Teaching*, I (1963), 147.
[2] Suchman, J. Richard, *The Elementary School Program in Scientific Inquiry*. Urbana, Illinois: University of Illinois, 1962.

---

* REPRINTED FROM *School Science and Mathematics*, Vol. 65, No. 6, June 1965, pp. 531–533, by permission of the author and the publisher. Dr. Fish is Assistant Professor of Education at the University of Arizona.

"(a) Learning through inquiry transcends learning which is directed wholly by the teacher or the textbook; the autonomous inquirer assimilates his experience more independently. He is free to pursue knowledge and understanding in accordance with his cognitive needs and his individual level and rate of assimilation.

(b) Inquiry is highly motivated because children enjoy autonomous activity particularly when it produces conceptual growth.

(c) Concepts that result from inquiry are likely to have greater significance to the child because they have come from his own acts of searching and data processing. They are formed by the learner himself from the data he has collected and processed himself; and for that reason should be more meaningful to him, and hence more stable and functional."

Obviously, curricula resulting from such opposing viewpoints are bound to be quite different. Who then is to make judgments and select from among alternative curricula?

THE FRAME OF REFERENCE FOR EVALUATION

As a matter of fact, the first order of business once a new program has been conceived and developed is to have classroom teachers test it. Unfortunately, classroom teachers too often are introduced to the means—that is, the materials and activities—of the program and to the stated goals, or the end-in-view, of the program without being thoroughly grounded in what Walbesser calls "the character of what is to be learned." [3] Walbesser, who is in charge of the evaluation study of the new curriculum materials for elementary school science being developed by the Commission on Science Education of AAAS, has stated:

"If any hope of success for a given set of activities is to be sustained, then the individuals attempting to use the materials must know the character of what is to be learned." [4]

The character of what is to be learned is to be located in the system within which it was conceived and cannot be discerned from the materials alone. As a matter of fact, teachers are more than mere adjuncts to the materials they teach; and little that is significant can be determined about the effectiveness of a curriculum by merely providing opportunity for teachers to "live through" a set of activities with a group of pupils.

CRITERIA FOR SELECTING CURRICULUM

Selection of a curriculum should be based on a set of criteria for judging that is consistent with the philosophy underlying the curriculum. Otherwise, inconsistencies exist between the criteria for judging valued by the teachers

[3] Walbesser, Henry H., "Curriculum Evaluation by Means of Behavioral Objectives," *Journal of Research in Science*, I (1963), 297.

[4] *Loc. cit.*

and the criteria for judging valued by the curriculum designers. For example, one of the criteria often valued by teachers with regard to new curriculum designs is: Is it different from what I do regularly? Comments such as, "These are the same kinds of activities we do in arithmetic," represent the teacher's lack of understanding of how the materials, the objectives, and the methods are related. Such comments may indicate also that teachers fail to recognize the importance of being involved in the evaluation of the new curriculum.

To effectively judge a new curriculum, teachers must be encouraged to inquire into the very system in which the rationale of the curriculum is grounded. Initially, teachers should be concerned with:

1. The stated goals of the curriculum and should inquire: Are these the goals we want?
2. The means for achieving the goals and should inquire: Are the means selected appropriate to reach the goals?
3. The methods for achieving the goals and should inquire: Are the methods consistent with the stated goals?

Hence it is that materials and methods are judged according to their relevancy to the desired outcomes.

Consistency of Evaluative Measures

Another, even more crucial concern in judging the consistency of new curricula should be the validity of the methods to be employed in the programs for evaluating the stated goals. This concern should lead the teacher to inquire: Are the means and methods of evaluating the program consistent with the stated goals? The practice of using evaluative instruments which are subject matter oriented to judge goals stated in behavioral terms cannot be defended on the basis that the results are more easily quantified. For example, any new curriculum which purports to develop behavioral outcomes which in any way reflect inquiry should have an evaluative instrument designed *not to test subject matter and manipulative skill competencies* but to answer such questions as:

1. As a result of the new curriculum design, do pupils who formerly asked questions only about subject matter now ask questions about the processes as well?
2. As a result of the new curriculum design, do pupils who formerly failed to question science meanings now build criteria for examining and judging meanings and demand precision in language, logic in argument, and responsibility in judgment making?

ROLE OF THE TEACHER IN CURRICULUM DESIGN

It seems reasonable to suggest, at this point, that in order to judge a new curriculum effectively, teachers should be provided with ample opportunity to inquire into the relationships among the activities, the goals, and the methods in order to develop an understanding of the system within which the program was conceived. It is not enough that curriculum designers state in the preface of a curriculum guide that the activities contained therein promote particular behaviors. For as long as the question, "How do these means promote these ends?" remains unanswered in the mind of the teacher, she cannot even be expected to perceive the relationships between the activities to be tested and the behaviors which supposedly will be evoked. With the question unanswered, neither can the teacher be expected to transmit the significance of the activities of the pupil.

Therefore, if the practice of asking teachers to "test" new curricula is to be continued, it would seem to be imperative that teachers play a more prominent role in the (1) examination of the system within which the programs are conceived, (2) evaluation of the relationships between goals and method, and (3) reconstruction of the program.

IN THE FUTURE *

Philip G. Johnson

This forecast is an excerpt from Philip G. Johnson's article "Emerging Curriculum Studies in Elementary and Junior High School Science." Dr. Johnson predicts science curricular changes in the future. He believes that the amount of subject matter taught in each grade will be reduced. There will be a shift from the use of one book in a science series to the use of many books. Many relatively unstructured methods of inquiry will be used instead of just one problem-solving method. Future emphasis will be on how to find and create knowledge rather than on the accumulation of knowledge. Skills in inquiry will become a major goal in science education at the expense of science content, and concepts will be learned only as they develop from the use of the process of inquiry. Dr. Johnson also sees a greater emphasis on the relationship between mathematics and science.

---

* REPRINTED FROM *Supervision for Quality Education in Science*, U.S. Office of Education, Document OE-29039, Bulletin 1963, No. 3, pp. 132–140. Dr. Johnson is Chairman of the Division of Science Education at Cornell University.

W HAT ARE the changes that are likely to become more noticeable in the years ahead? In what directions are our science curricular changes heading? Let me put my vision of these changes into a few bold statements.

CHANGE FROM MUCH SUBJECT MATTER TO RELATIVELY LESS SUB-JECT MATTER. Some general science teachers attempt to cover as many as 20 or 24 topics in a year. Others settle for as few as eight or ten. The change from a 4-year senior high school with 1 year for general science to a 3-year junior high school followed by a 3-year senior high school has meant that general science could be scheduled for a 3-year interval. Some science teachers took the 24-or-so topics and spread them over the 3 years, arriving at about 8 topics per year. Since in many schools general science is taught for only a single term in the seventh and eighth grades, some assigned 12 of the topics to the seventh and eighth grades, leaving 12 for the ninth grade. Again some other schools adopted some type of a spiral plan in which topics studied in the seventh and eighth grades were studied again at a higher level, in the ninth grade or later. This meant that the number of topics could be reduced substantially from the number of 20 or 24. The high school physics course often having from 6 to 12 topics has been reduced to 4 topics. Some leaders propose that the elementary school teacher at a certain grade level should not be expected to teach a multitude of 6 to 20-or-so subject matter areas, but should be encouraged to prepare for effective work in but 1 or 2 areas. Just how this problem will be resolved is yet to be determined, because some leaders propose that an elementary or junior high school teacher should not teach topics at all.

CHANGE FROM ONE PROBLEM-SOLVING METHOD TO MANY RELA-TIVELY UNSTRUCTURED METHODS OF INQUIRY. Problem solving in science has, to many persons, been a clear set of steps leading from problem to evidence and then to conclusions. Some insisted on adding a phase called application. Some had very clear ideas about just how the gathering of evidence should be done. All in all it was a problem-solving method and many teachers went through the motions thinking that they were con-tributing to a pupil's understanding of the scientific process. Most of the persons who encouraged this view of problem solving had had little experi-ence with scientific research and knew very little about how scientists went about finding and solving problems. In recent years some very competent scientists have given their time and talents to helping young people under-stand science and scientists. Teachers who study their efforts are a bit confused because they do not recognize what they had come to regard as problem solving. Furthermore, in studying how scientists find and solve problems it has become evident that they do not follow a series of steps that one can find in the work of different kinds of scientists. They do find problems in many ways. They do approach answers in many ways. It is coming to be recognized that the best way to help young people to understand the scientific process is to help them find problems and to seek answers rather than to tell them how scientists do it.

CHANGE FROM USE OF A BOOK IN A SERIES TO THE USE OF MANY BOOKS. The great majority of science teachers, especially the teachers in junior high school and in elementary schools, have relatively little preparation in the sciences. They are often expected to teach science areas where they have had no college studies or even high school studies. Furthermore, they may be expected to teach several different subjects with a day full of school responsibilities. They have come to accept the adopted textbook as their guide to organization and content. Library facilities are often limited and there is little time or help to learn about the materials. The school librarians often do not know what books to buy, and they select books from some science list in order to have materials for the few students who ask about books in the area of science. Recently scientists have given their judgments concerning good science reference books for the precollege levels. Such books have been assembled in sets and circulated in schools; the results of their availability have been studied. Books on these progressively improved lists have been purchased by many schools, while other schools have made a beginning and plan to continue purchasing such reference books. With such reference materials available and an encouragement to stimulate wider reading both by school and by home influences, there is more and more use of reference books. With this growth many students find the reference books to be interesting and helpful in gathering information for topics and projects. In recent years the growth of science exhibits and fairs has caused students and teachers to look to reference books as aids, and they are beginning to use more and more books rather than depending on the one textbook. The influence of scientists who continually use many reference materials, both books and periodicals, has caused teachers to catch the idea that it is rewarding to the student as well as the teacher to use a number of books. This change is likely to continue.

CHANGE FROM AN EMPHASIS ON ACCUMULATING KNOWLEDGE TO AN EMPHASIS ON HOW TO FIND OUT AND CREATE KNOWLEDGE. One needs only to study the kinds of tests that teachers over the years have been using to note that there used to be an attempt to determine only the subject matter that pupils had learned. Pupils were expected to mark statements as true or false, to match a statement with a word, to select a proper completion, or to answer a question in some expected form. The answer was the important thing and the way the student progressed toward an answer was of no avail unless it led to the correct answer. The answer determined the grade, and an error in one operation was just too bad. Gradually there has come to be concern for the student who can carry through the question, but in so doing makes an error which results in an incorrect final answer. Partial credit for the correct method has become acceptable in many situations. More recently, tests have been constructed that are built on known information, or the needed information is made a part of the question, and the student is tested to note whether or not he can interpret or use the information properly. Tests of the ability to apply what has been learned to novel situations have followed, until now there are tests available that are considered to have little recall base and much need for thinking and reasoning. Recently tests on understanding science have become available in experimental form. We can expect to see more and better tests that measure the students' ability to think like scientists think.

CHANGE FROM FACTS AND FACTUAL CONCEPTS AS INSTRUCTIONAL GOAL TO SKILLS IN INQUIRY AS THE TEACHING GOALS. Most courses of study in use today give the impression that concepts have been accepted as the teaching goal, but one need not look very far below the surface to note that information related to a topic is given even more stress than are concepts. In many cases even the concepts are statements of fact and little more. There is a clear topical organization in many instructional guides developed by committees of teachers. The guide for a particular grade is divided into a number of topics. Each topic in turn is outlined so as to show the sub-topics. In a number of instances such an outline forms the major left-hand column of the guide. The second column may be devoted to the concepts to be achieved and, farther to the right, there are columns for activities and references.

There appears to be an increasing number of instructional guides that begin with approach activities which are designed to create questions or problems in the minds of students. One such problem is made the subject of investigation. Students are encouraged to propose hypotheses and then to gather evidence to support or refute the hypotheses. Evidence is to be obtained from experiments, most of which are suggested, but there is more and more encouragement for students to design experiments that may produce significant evidence. Students are also encouraged to consult reference books and to interview people who are thought to know something about the problem under study. Later students are encouraged to select and to restate, with proper caution, what appears to be their best hypothesis and to use it in attempts to explain phenomena. Very recently expert scientists have taken an interest in developing guides for the study of their area of specialization with the spirit of inquiry uppermost in mind. Concepts still rank high as the objective to be sought, but they are not listed and therefore not likely to be taught as such. They are to come quite naturally from the process of inquiry. This change seems to be in its initial stage of development.

CHANGE FROM TEACHER-SELECTED CONCEPTS AS INSTRUCTIONAL GOALS TO CONCEPTS AS THEY MAY ARISE IN THE PROCESS OF CONFIRMING OR REJECTING HYPOTHESES. We must admit that most instructional guides and most textbooks indicate rather clearly the statement of the concepts that students should acquire. There is not much encouragement for allowing students to state their own hypotheses and, following a time devoted to seeking confirmation or rejection, to come to their own concepts. However, this seems to be the direction that some leaders are encouraging teachers to take. Stress on the processes of inquiry would seem to promise that there will be more and more encouragement for this type of teaching. It is one thing for an expert scientist to guide students in this process and quite another for a rather poorly prepared teacher to do so. Will it be possible to develop manuals for the great number of mediocre teachers who will need much guidance in order to feel any significant sense of security in this type of teaching? How can teachers be developed for the inquiry type of teaching? While the change seems to be pointing in the direction indicated, it is doubtful that we have enough evidence of this change to think of it as a present trend, but it seems to be indicative of a future trend.

CHANGE FROM RELIANCE ON QUALITATIVE OBSERVATIONS TO MORE AND MORE STRESS ON SECURING AND RECORDING QUANTITATIVE OBSERVATIONS. Many leaders in education have stressed the values to be derived from personal firsthand observations. Observations concerning shape, color, and texture, together with changes in such qualities, have been encouraged by teachers. Students have been asked to represent these and other qualities on paper, with clay, and in words. Scientists who are working at the forefront of scientific developments see in the precollege science studies a great and seemingly deliberate avoidance of the quantitative observations, which are the very heart of science as practiced by scientists. Their influence and the growth of movements to make mathematics more meaningful to the students have brought a resurgence of stress on quantitative measurements. Using conventional units, as well as creating units which are later related to conventional units, has come into rather common use. Along with this change has come the use of models, graphs, tables, and new symbols for presenting and representing what has been observed. These help students to sense relationships. Use of available measuring devices has been encouraged while scientists have put their minds and hands to work in search of inexpensive and simple ways to make relatively accurate measurements. The search for similarities and differences calls for accurate observations, and such observations require measurements to be noted and reported. We can expect this change to continue.

CHANGE FROM SCIENCE EXPERIENCES AS PREPARATION FOR SECONDARY SCHOOL SCIENCE TO EXPERIENCES FOR BASIC EDUCATION OF ALL STUDENTS. Developments in recent years and the massive attempts to develop a science program for elementary and junior high school students indicate that this change is being accelerated. Leaders for more than a century have been pointing out the values of actual studies of the environment. The object study methods gave this a strong impetus, and the change from mere object study to the scientific study of nature hastened the development of science studies for all youth. While the senior high school sciences in the early part of the century were for the relatively few students who continued in school beyond the early grades, the development of general science opened the area of science to a large number of youth. Few people question the need to develop a scientifically literate citizenry, and school leaders who have no organized science program are actively seeking ways to develop a program to help their teachers include science in the program of studies. The change is clearly a definite one, but how best to guide the change is still an area where there are many disagreements. The efforts of competent scientists working with other knowledgeable people in the spirit of mutual respect and good will are certain to arrive at several acceptable answers. As a result, this change will bring good science experiences for all youth. Many persons think this change will also result in the best science experiences for those who will continue in the study of science.

CHANGE FROM SCIENCE AS SOMETHING TO BE LEARNED FROM BOOKS TO SCIENCE AS SOMETHING THAT GROWS OUT OF A SERIES OF EXPERIMENTS. Some active leaders, who provide college work for elementary school teachers in the area of science, are deploring the purchase of boxes or kits of science equipment, since these are placed in the schools without the teachers' knowing what to do with the materials. The boxes or kits usually contain some type of a guide giving the teacher instructions for performing a large number of experiments. Once a teacher develops confidence in using items to show an experiment and notes the delight of the pupils, there is a desire for ideas concerning additional experiments. Teachers who take courses to prepare them for better work in the area of science usually give high praise for their work on such experiments. Often such courses have a number of teachers who serve at different grade levels, and when they first try their experiments with their pupils they find high interest. If they try these same experiments a year later, they find a few students who remark that they saw or tried them last year. Each year, unless there is some plan for grade placing the experiments, the problem of duplication becomes greater and more annoying. While science experiments seem to be possible for teachers and of high interest to pupils, something other than experiments seems necessary to a science program in the schools. The change toward some grade placement of experiments within a larger framework promises to continue.

CHANGE FROM A SCIENCE PROGRAM BASED ON TOPICS TO A SCIENCE PROGRAM BASED ON A MORE FUNDAMENTAL FRAME OF REFERENCE. Many of the outstanding scientists who have interested themselves in the science programs for elementary and junior high school have become unhappy with what they have found. They do not consider the covering of science topics and the doing of experiments as representative of what science really is. Some of them seem to feel that the covering of topics and the doing of demonstrations may be worse than not doing anything at all. They speak of discovering science concepts, helping youth to interpret natural phenomena, developing understanding of science, learning the ways of scientists, and becoming effective inquirers. Some of them have been giving much time and thought to developing materials and trying them out with children. While they often state that there must be a planned scope and sequence to the science work, they are not at all clear concerning the nature of this scope and sequence as it pertains to grades 1, 2, 3, and so forth. While they are amazed at the number of diverse topics that teachers often have been trying to include for their grade, they are not definite in suggesting the much more limited scope that they seem to favor. While they are disturbed by a program based on different topics, sometimes in a spiral plan, from grade to grade, they have no suggestions concerning the way a sequence should be planned. While they deplore teaching "topics," in their own courses where most of our teachers receive their education they themselves teach topic after topic. The massive efforts being planned for the study of ways to formulate strong science programs for the elementary and junior high schools will give rise to different frames of reference that will present improved views of the scope and sequence of science for the grades prior to the senior high school.

CHANGE FROM EMPHASIS ON TECHNOLOGY TO EMPHASIS ON SCIENCE. One of the aspects of our current elementary and junior high school science courses which has bothered scientists has been the great attention to uses of science, including technology. In the new senior high school science courses there has been a deliberate attempt to omit technology and to stress science. Some leaders in science education have expressed their judgment that the study of high school physics as science, with little or no attention to technology, fails to challenge the capable science-interested student whose orientation is in the direction of the applications of science to problems of engineering and industrial production. They feel that some inclusion of technology would challenge and hold the interests of these students and would help direct a larger number of capable students into the study of engineering. Furthermore, they feel that technology is a part of our way of life, and to reduce attention to this area of applications is to fail to inform youth of an important area of everyday living.

The courses in general science have given much, many would say far too much, attention to technology in the various topics or units. Often the topic or unit would center around a product which resulted from utilizing the principles of science in meeting a human need. Perhaps it was the study of a home refrigerator or the automobile or musical instruments. The principles of science were given little attention, while the construction and operation of the device was given much stress. Applications or uses were often the focus

of attention in many of the general science courses. The seeking of fundamental principles of science and coming to understand them through
demonstration experiments and individual experiments were set aside in
favor of reading the book about various technological developments. Many
leaders would agree that general science courses have given too much stress
to technology. Just how these courses can be made to reveal science and
scientists in proper balance to engineers and technology remains to be
developed. Just what attention can and should be given to the role of
technicians and the developments in which they participate also remains to
be clarified. The major studies currently in the formative stage promise to
give searching attention to such problems.

CHANGE FROM SCIENCE THAT MUST BE DEVELOPED FROM A
LIMITED UNDERSTANDING OF MATHEMATICS TO SCIENCE THAT IS
BUILT ON MATHEMATICS. Some teachers of mathematics have in their
own preparation given much attention to the sciences, especially the physical
sciences. Undoubtedly many of them make use of real problems that must be
solved in the sciences when they consider the related concepts and operations
in mathematics. However, a very large number of teachers of mathematics
have avoided the sciences in favor of more and more mathematics. For them
the important outcome in the study of mathematics is to become prepared to
understand further mathematics and to think creatively in mathematical
terms. If we may judge from similar teachers in the colleges, we can note a
very real resistance to the inclusion of problems from the sciences and
engineering when related mathematical concepts are considered. There is
even greater resistance to the inclusion of problems related to economics
and finance.

Is any progress being made in relating mathematics and science? Dr.
Irving Adler, who spoke to the State Supervisors of Mathematics at an Office
of Education conference last year, stated that "the greatest mathematicians
have always combined dedication to pure mathematics with a strong interest
in its applications." In another statement, he remarked, "Now, more than
ever, it is true that mathematics is the handmaiden of the sciences."

Are mathematics and science moving ahead hand in hand? While we see
the inclusion of a type of laboratory work in mathematics classes and the
use of mathematics in science classes, these seem to be the results of
individual or departmental interests rather than the product of much inter-
departmental planning. When one talks with science teachers and hears
their remarks about the inability of students to handle the needed mathematical operations, one finds more evidence for a rather cool handmaiden
relationship. Just how closely should mathematics and science be related?
How can mathematics be truly a handmaiden to science and still be good
mathematics? How can science teachers and science supervisors develop good
working relationships with mathematics teachers and mathematics supervisors with the goal of improving both science and the mathematics instruc-

tion? Many leaders sense a growing kinship between those who serve in science and those who serve in mathematics. They sense that persons in each discipline have the important responsibility to advance the frontiers of their field. They also sense that advancement in one discipline conditions to a large extent the possible advances in the other. They believe that working relationships would be developed and extended, not only between these two disciplines, but also with leaders in the liberal and fine arts. Some would also include leaders in the vocational areas to the end that future citizens may be sensitive to and informed about the wide spectrum of human endeavors. Perhaps the change is becoming less and less invisible if it is not more and more visible.

Date Due
